Products

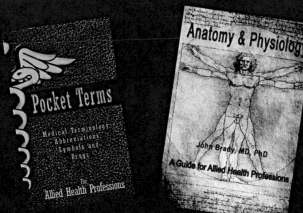

Proven, Experienced, & Trusted!
for 24 years

101 W. Buckingham Rd.
Richardson, Tx. 75081
(800) 443-7397
www.medbooks.com

Since
MedBooks
1985

2012 MEDBOOKS

MEDBOOKS SERVICES

Serving the Medical, Academic & Professional fields for 25 years!

Retroactive Billing Services

Place MedBooks' years of experience to practical use. Let us re-bill and re-file your unpaid claims, thus giving you the money that you have worked for (and not received).

Coding & Reimbursement Seminars

Wide in scope and comprehensive in coverage, our how-to coding seminars uncover the mysteries of:

1. Why physicians lose money,
2. How to help patients pay lower balances,
3. How to obtain payment for supplies and drugs,
4. How to use the fifth digit, and
5. What are the perils of mismatching diagnoses/procedures?

Coding & Reimbursement Audits

MedBooks offers a rare opportunity to sneak an objective and expert peek into what the insurance carriers and Medicare will look for once you have filed your claims. By looking at a broad sampling of your practice's submissions, we evaluate, grade and report back to you how to get paid for the services that you provide, what you may be doing wrong, AND how to stay clear (and safe) in an insurance audit.

Expert Witnessing/Testimony

When you need expert testimony delivered in a way that can be easily understood - MedBooks is your source. Put 23+ years of coding experience on your side.

Superbill/Fee Slip Review

Are you working with an outdated Fee Slip or Superbill? Let MedBooks review what you are currently using, and make the necessary changes.

Physician Fee Analysis Service

Are you billing the correct amount? Let MedBooks review your codes and compare them with the current RBRVS.

101 W. Buckingham Rd.
Richardson, Tx. 75081
(800) 443-7397
www.medbooks.com

Since MedBooks 1985

cpTeach

Expert Medical Coding Made Easy!

Workbook

Now with CPT, ICD, HCPCS,
Anatomy and Physiology and Medical Terminology

MedBooks, Incorporated
101 West Buckingham Road
Richardson, Tx. 75081

Copyright 2012 by MedBooks, Inc.©
All rights reserved. Published 2012
Printed in the United States of America
11 10 09 08 07 06 05 04 03 02 01 00 99 98 97 96 95 94 93 92 91 90 89

ISBN: 978-1-937816-04-9

CPT CODES

The 2012 cpTeach® series includes some of the American Medical Association's Physician's Current Procedural Terminology descriptive terms, numeric identifying codes, and modifiers for reporting medical services and procedures that were identified by the author, MedBooks, for inclusion in this book. Physician's Current Procedural Terminology® is copyrighted (from 1966 through 2011) by the American Medical Association. Any use of the CPT® outside cpTeach® should refer to the CPT® book as it contains the most current listings of the descriptive terms, numeric services, and procedures. The AMA assumes no liability for information contained or not contained within this book. CPT® is a registered trademark of the American Medical Association (AMA). Suggestions on code additions or deletions in the CPT® book should be directed to the American Medical Association at the following address:

Information and Education Services
CPT®
American Medical Association
515 North State Street
Chicago, Illinois 60610
800-634-6922

DEDICATION

Last year, when we dedicated cp "Teach," we mentioned all of the students and teachers who had helped us make some significant revisions to our book for 2011 and 2012. Thanks to your input, we are proud to report that cp "Teach" is a winner of the distinguished McGuffey Award through the Text and Academic Author's Association. To our knowledge, it is the only how-to version of a medical coding and billing book to ever win such an award.

In addition to all of you listed above, Randy and I would like to give special thanks to:

Marge McQuade for her chapters on Insurance Basics and ICD. Marge, your contribution to cp "Teach" with these two chapters significantly help us round out the book and make it better than any one of its kind. Not only can students get the full spectrum of coding with both CPT and ICD as well as the basics of insurance, they can learn it in a way that is easy to understand. Thank you!

Mark Lerner for his creativity and dedication to making our new cover, and for keeping the interior of the book easy to read and interesting. For those of you who don't know Mark, he has single handedly made cp "Teach" the user friendly guide that it is and he did it all while designing and managing several other books, creating his own, and holding down the fort. We could not make it without Mark. Thank you!

Heather Alling for her artistic skills and amazing turn around time. Heather, you are so accommodating to all of us who ask for what we want and expect it to be done in a flash. You always exceed our expectations. Thank you!

John Brady, M.D., Ph.D., for the patience you have with all of us in explaining the difficult medical procedures and concepts in ways that we can understand as well as your support and positive words of encouragement that are so crucial to keep us going. You are such an incredible asset to our team! Thank you!

Finally, to both Amy Burt and Calla Spatz for allowing us the extra at home time we needed to produce the first award winning version of cp "Teach" ever made. We love both of you dearly and in case we haven't mentioned it today, we really do think that you are the best! Thank you!

cpTeach® 2012 Workbook

TABLE OF CONTENTS

PREFACE

The cp "Teach"® was written with one single objective: to teach coders how to properly code "according to the book" (the CPT® codebook). It is our experience, in years of dealing with thousands of coders nationwide, that proper coding results in many benefits to the physician's office. Among them are optimum reimbursement, which increases revenues, the recovery of "lost" (previously unbilled) dollars, and increased staff efficiency, because coding properly decreases time spent dealing with receivables and claim filing.

For best results, we recommend that you follow each chapter along with the current edition of the CPT® manual at your fingertips. This will allow you to learn by doing. Look up the examples given in cp "Teach" in the CPT® manual and digest them before moving on to the next example.

CONTRIBUTING EDITORS

MedBooks would personally like to thank the following individual who contributed their time, energy, and vast knowledge to help make this 2012 24th edition of cpTeach® our best ever.

Jeanne Yoder, CPC, RHIA, CCS-P is the billing director for a health care chain with more than 50 hospitals/ medical centers and 100 clinics in more than 25 states and 5 foreign countries. She has presented at the AAPC and AHIMA national conferences. She is an approved Professional Medical Coding Curriculum (PMCC) instructor. Ms. Yoder formerly worked with the Department of Defense at the Pentagon, where she held the rank of Lt. Colonel, USAF, MSC. She was previously the Program Manager UBO, TMA-OCFO for Tricare. Ms. Yoder provided the Anesthesia chapter for cpTeach®.

Marge McQuade, CMSCS, CMM is a certified medical manager and a certified multi-specialty coding specialist who has over 35 years experience in the medical field. She has been an office manager in several different specialties and has taught coding and practice management at the community college level. At present, Marge is the Director of Education for PAHCS (Professional Association of Healthcare Coding Specialists). She is an active member of PAHCOM for over 20 years. Marge is a past Advisory Board member for several HCPro publications and currently is a contributing editor for BC Advantage. Contact her at margepahcs@gmail.com

CPT Basics

CPT®, or Current Procedural Terminology, is a book used to code the procedures and services performed by physicians. This book contains a listing of all current and FDA (Food and Drug Administration) approved physicians' procedures and services. Individual code numbers have been assigned to identify all procedures and services.

An example of a CPT® code and its corresponding services is:

> 99201   *Office and other outpatient visit for the evaluation and management of a new patient, which requires these 3 key components:*
>
> - *A problem focused history;*
>
> - *A problem focused examination;*
>
> - *Straightforward medical decision making.*
>
> *Counseling and /or coordination of care with other providers or agencies are provided consistent with the nature of the problem(s) and the patient's and/or family's needs.*
>
> *Usually, the presenting problem(s) are self-limited or minor. Physicians typically spend 10 minutes face-to-face with the patient and/or family.*

As you can see, the number 99201 identifies a certain service, in this case, an office or outpatient visit for a new patient. The service identified in the code 99201 is the history, exam and medical decision making that includes focusing on one and only one problem of the patient.

No two procedures share the same number. That is, code number 99201 will always mean, to the computer and the coder, a problem focused history and exam with straightforward decision making for an office/outpatient visit on a new patient.

A different code is assigned to every service and every procedure that a physician performs. In this way, a number, instead of a lengthy written description can identify each procedure or service.

By having a code for each individual procedure provided by a doctor to a patient, insurance carriers across the country are able to:

1.   More effectively communicate with each other;
2.   Compare reimbursable amounts for services and supplies;
3.   Speed the processing of claims.

Because the codes on the claims are easily read, interpreted, and reimbursed by computer rather than by people (e.g., individual data processors, although these processors may "input" the data), carriers are able to reduce the manpower needed for claims processing. Soon we will see that electronic filing of all insurance claims will be required.

Although CPT® described physician's procedures and services, it did not include some other items, which needed to be reported to Medicare, such as ambulance services, wheelchairs, or an extensive list of drugs used for individual injections. Because of CPT's limitations in this area, the Health Care Financing Administration (HCFA), now called CMS, invented a common coding system. This system worked out to be a tri-level coding system that employed CPT® as its first level (Level I) and then adds two other levels (Level II or National codes and Level III or Local codes). As of October 2002, it was mandated that Level III Local codes would be eliminated. National codes are not found in the CPT® codebook and must be obtained separately. (National codes are commonly called HCPCS, pronounced HICPICS). These can be obtained by calling **1-800-443-7397** or by logging on to **www.medbooks.com**.

WORKBOOK

cpTeach
Expert Medical Coding Made Easy!

2012

Name:_____

Class/Section:_____

Date:_____

EXERCISE 1.1

1. Incision and drainage of an ankle abscess

   _____

2. Injection of an antibiotic into the muscle

   _____

3. Keller procedure

   _____

4. Bone density study - axial skeleton

   _____

5. Family psychotherapy

   _____

6. Rabies vaccine

   _____

7. Incision of the retina

   _____

8. Transurethral bladder neck resection

   _____

9. Catheterization of the fallopian tube

   _____

10. Electrolysis

   _____

Before You Begin:
Read Chapter 1 in the cpTeach® book on "CPT® Basics."

Purpose of this Lesson:
To familiarize the student with the different CPT® codes and how the book has a CPT® code number for each procedure that a physician can provide.

Instructions:
1. Using your CPT® codebook, locate the codes or code ranges for the services below.

2. Write either the CPT® code itself in the space provided or list the range of codes given in the CPT® Index.

Before You Begin:

Read Chapter 1 in cpTeach® on "CPT Basics." Follow along in CPT® with the points illustrated in cpTeach®.

Purpose of this Lesson:

To familiarize the student with the different CPT® codes and the corresponding unique sections of the codebook that they describe.

Instructions:

1. Look up the following CPT® code numbers in CPT®.

2. Match each set of numbers to the corresponding sections, subsection or sub-subsection where the code numbers can be found.

Example:

A. 99201 through 99215
   <u>Office or Other
   Outpatient Services</u>

EXERCISE 1.2

1.   99221 through 99223

   _____

2.   99281 through 99288

   _____

3.   99241 through 99245

   _____

4.   00100 through 01999

   _____

5.   12001 through 12021

   _____

6.   29000 through 29799

   _____

7.   10021 through 69990

   _____

8.   70010 through 79999

   _____

9.   80047 through 89398

   _____

10.   90476 through 90749

   _____

EXERCISE 1.3

1. 29999_____

2. 28140_____

3. 19316_____

4. 94375_____

5. 84260_____

6. 68200_____

7. 70355_____

8. 84252_____

9. 99238_____

10. 11011_____

11. 0058T_____

12. 58356_____

Before You Begin:
Read Chapter 1 in cpTeach® on "CPT Basics." Follow along in CPT® with the points illustrated in cpTeach®.

Purpose of this Lesson:
To familiarize the student with the idea that each CPT® code is different, and each CPT® code has its own unique descriptions.

Instructions:
1. Look up the following CPT® code numbers in CPT®.

2. Write the corresponding description for each CPT® code.

Example:
A. 30220 Insertion, nasal septal prosthesis (button)

Name:_____

Class/Section:_____

cpTeach

Date:_____

2012

Before You Begin:

Read Chapter 1 in cpTeach® on "CPT Basics." Follow along in CPT® with the points illustrated in cpTeach®.

Purpose of this Lesson:

To familiarize the student with the different CPT® codes and their corresponding unique descriptions and/or different coding categories (subsections).

Instructions:

1. Look up the following CPT® code numbers or range of numbers in CPT®.

2. Match the different codes to the appropriate section or description.

Example:

A. 99201 through 99215
   Office or Other
   Outpatient Services

EXERCISE 1.4

_____	99211	**a.** Office or other outpatient visit for the evaluation and management of an established patient, that may not require the presence of a physician, etc.
_____	99288	**b.** Exploration of penetrating wound (separate procedure)
_____	99429	**c.** Application of a modality to 1 or more areas; hot or cold packs
_____	20100	**d.** Radiology section
_____	10040	**e.** Physician direction of emergency medical systems (EMS) emergency care, advanced life support
_____	97010	**f.** Evisceration of ocular contents; without implant
_____	40490	**g.** Pathology and Laboratory section
_____	70010 - 79999	**h.** Copper
_____	80047 - 89398	**i.** Acne surgery (e.g., marsupialization, opening or removal of multiple milia, comedones, cysts, pustules)
_____	65091	**j.** Biopsy of lip
_____	82525	**k.** Unlisted preventive medicine service
_____	78000	**l.** Thyroid uptake; single determination

What is HCPCS?

HCPCS is a system used by Medicare for the coding of procedures, services, and supplies for Medicare patients.

HCPCS currently is composed of two separate coding systems. These include CPT® codes (Level I) and National Codes (Level II). Since the larger carriers (who have the government contracts to process Medicare claims) also have private insurance plans, many of them recognize both the CPT® and National Code portions of HCPCS.

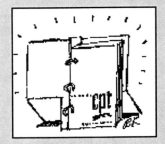

Prior to 2004 HCPCS also included the Local Codes (Level III). These were unique codes that were used by local Medicare carriers within each state, and they were deleted due to efforts by the federal government to simplify the insurance process and make it more uniform.

For the most part, CPT® codes are five-digit numeric codes beginning with the numbers 0 through 9. The Category II codes were new to the codebook in 2004. These codes are alphanumeric codes that start with a number and end with an alpha character (e.g., 1002F). The Category II codes are supplemental codes to be used in conjunction with other non-alphanumeric CPT® codes and are not reimbursable by themselves. The Category III codes are alphanumeric codes that start with a number and end with an alpha-character (e.g., 0019T). The sections in CPT® have the following coding structure:

National Codes are also five-digit alphanumeric codes beginning with the letters A through V.

CPT® best describes physicians' procedures and services, but is expanding to include services by other providers (e.g., home health agencies, physical therapists, etc.). It is updated once per year and is generally released in November/December of the preceding year.

National codes describe physicians' procedures and services done by other kinds of providers and also include codes for supplies, materials and drugs for injections. These codes are found in the HCPCS National Coding Manual.

H   C   P   C   S

Healthcare   Common   Procedure   Coding   System

A lot of revenue is lost in the physician's office from a failure to use the National Coding Manual. This loss could be avoided if more coders were knowledgeable about the book and how to use it. The National Coding Manual, commonly called HCPCS (pronounced HICPICS), may be obtained by calling **1-800-443-7397** or by logging on to **www.medbooks.com**.

SECTION	FIRST DIGIT
EVALUATION AND MANAGEMENT	9
ANESTHESIA	0
SURGERY	1 THROUGH 6
RADIOLOGY	7
PATHOLOGY AND LABORATORY	8
MEDICINE	9
CATEGORY II CODES	0 THROUGH 7
CATEGORY III CODES	0

EXERCISE 2.1

1. Ifosfamide, 1gm

   _____

2. Slings

   _____

3. Echocardiography transmission

   _____

4. Surgical Tray

   _____

5. Underarm pad, crutch, replacement, ea.

   _____

6. Electrodesiccation

   _____

7. Amygdalin

   _____

8. Adjust partial denture

   _____

9. Ambulance service, emergency, water, special transportation services

   _____

10. Immune globulin (Ig), human, for intramuscular use

    _____

Before You Begin:
Read Chapter 2 in cpTeach® on "What is HCPCS?" Follow along in your CPT® and HCPCS National Coding Manual with the points illustrated in cpTeach®.

Purpose of this Lesson:
To familiarize the student with the different CPT® and HCPCS National Codes, and their corresponding unique subsections.

Instructions:
1. Read each of the statements below and state where you would be able to find each of the following items or procedures (i.e., in the CPT® or National Coding Manual).

WORKBOOK

cpTeach

2012

Name:_____

Class/Section:_____

Date:_____

Before You Begin:
Read Chapter 2 in cpTeach® on "What is HCPCS?" Follow along in your CPT® codebook and HCPCS National Coding Manual and with the points illustrated in cpTeach®.

Purpose of this Lesson:
To familiarize the student with HCPCS and its meaning.

Instructions:
1. Read about the definition of HCPCS, and what it stands for, in cpTeach® in Chapter 2.

2. Write the corresponding definition for HCPCS below.

EXERCISE 2.2

H _____

C _____

P _____

C _____

S _____

Name: _____

Class/Section: _____

Date: _____

EXERCISE 2.3

	FOUND IN CPT	ALSO FOUND IN HCPCS
Ambulance Services		
Chemotherapeutic Drugs		
Consultations		
Dental		
Durable Medical Equipment		
Hospital Visits		
Injections		
Office Visits		
Ophthalmologic Visits		
Orthotics/Prosthetics		
Pathology/Lab Services		
Rehabilitation Services		
Supplies		
Surgery		
Vision Services		

Before You Begin:
Read Chapter 2 in cpTeach® on "What is HCPCS?" Follow along in your CPT® codebook and HCPCS National Coding Manual with the points illustrated in cpTeach®.

Purpose of this Lesson:
To familiarize the student with the difference between CPT® Codes and National Codes, their unique descriptions, as well as the differences between the two coding systems.

Instructions:
1. Using both the index in CPT® and HCPCS, look at the following kinds of codes that are described below.

2. Complete the diagram by indicating where you would be most likely to find a particular kind of code.

Before You Begin:

Read Chapter 2 in cpTeach® on "What is HCPCS?" Follow along in your CPT® and National Coding books with the points illustrated in cpTeach®.

Purpose of this Lesson:

To familiarize the student with the differences between CPT® codes and their unique first digits, and National Codes with their unique first digits.

Instructions:

1. Look up the following code numbers in the CPT® or HCPCS National Coding Manual.

2. Place each of the numbers under the correct category where you would be able to find that code number.

EXERCISE 2.4

43020	A4550	P7001
99282	92311	21182
V2500	21139	J0800
J0300	10040	78190
90935	E2311	D4321
00147	86977	L2430

CPT®	NATIONAL

WORKBOOK

cpTeach

2012

Name:_____

Class/Section:_____

Date:_____

EXERCISE 2.5

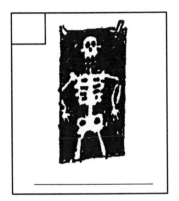

Before You Begin:
Read Chapter 2 in cpTeach® on "What is HCPCS?" Follow along in CPT® with the points illustrated in cpTeach®.

Purpose of this Lesson:
To familiarize the student with the way the CPT® book is arranged.

Instructions:
1. Look at the following pictures.

2. Identify which sections of the CPT® book they describe.

3. Place the pictures in order by numbering them from one through six in the upper left hand boxes of each. The first section found in CPT® would begin with the number one, the second number two and so on.

4. Place the range of codes under each picture indicating what codes would be found in that particular section.

Name:_____

Class/Section:_____

Date:_____

cpTeach

2012

Before You Begin:
Read Chapter 2 in cpTeach®
on "What is HCPCS?"
Follow along in your CPT®
and HCPCS National Coding
Manual with the points
illustrated in cpTeach®.

Purpose of this Lesson:
To familiarize the student
with the different CPT® codes
and HCPCS National Codes
and their corresponding
unique subsections.

Instructions:
1. Look at the code headers
    (number that the code
    begins with) below.

2. Match each header to the
    corresponding sections
    that it represents.

    NOTE: Some sections
    may share the same
    header.

EXERCISE 2.6

0
_____

1
_____

2
_____

3
_____

4
_____

5
_____

6
_____

7
_____

8
_____

9
_____

J
_____

D
_____

PATHOLOGY

RADIOLOGY

MEDICINE

SURGERY

ANESTHESIA

INJECTIONS

DENTAL CODES

E/M CODES

EXERCISE 2.7

Across
2 Formerly CMS _____
5 Known as Level II _____
6 Governmental body for Medicare _____
7 Local Codes were also known as _____
9 CPT Codes are also known as _____
11 "D" Codes describe _____

Down
1 Were also known as Level III _____
2 Medicare's name for Level I & II Codes _____
3 Organization that determines CPT Codes _____
4 Number of digits in each CPT code _____
8 National Codes are also known as _____
10 "J" Codes represent _____

Before You Begin:
Read Chapter 2 in cpTeach® on "What is HCPCS?" Follow along in your CPT® and HCPCS National Coding Manual with the points illustrated in cpTeach®.

Purpose of this Lesson:
To familiarize the student with the different terminology used in HCPCS.

Instructions:
1. Determine the correct answer to solve the crossword puzzle.

HCPCS: *Editorial Notations*

The purpose of this chapter is to explain some of the peculiarities found in the HCPCS National Coding Manual. If you don't already have a copy, you must obtain one as soon as possible. The official Medicare version of the HCPCS National Coding Manual is available from both MedBooks and from the U.S. Government Printing Office.

HCPCS National Codes are five-digit, alphanumeric codes (e.g., A4550) used mainly for the coding of supplies, prosthetics, and drugs usually *not* found in CPT®.

The HCPCS National Coding Manual is not hard to use. As we already discussed, the proper use of the HCPCS National Coding Manual is critical for full and accurate coding.

There are many fields (or explanations/further information given) that Medicare has made available to you in this book. See example below.

HCPCS Code	Long Description	Coverage	Action Code	PI	MPI	CIM	MCM	Statute	Lab Cert	X-Ref	ASC PayGroup	ASC Pay Group Eff. Date	Proc. Notes	BETOS	TOS	Anesthesia Units	Code Add Date	Code Eff. Date	Code Delete Date
J0895	INJECTION, DEFEROXAMINE MESYLATE, 500 MG	D	N	51	A		2049			Q0087				01E	1,P	0	19920101	20010101	

Most of these fields in the regular Medicare version of the HCPCS National Codes do not have any application for the regular coder who codes on a daily basis. In the HCPCS Manual published by MedBooks (see **www.medbooks.com**, or call 1-800-443-7397), we have taken away most of the "fluff" (removing fields that will have nothing to do with your coding) and given you the information that you need to make coding selections as easily and effectively as possible and those that give you the needed information to complete the CMS-1500 claim form or the UB 04 (CMS-1450). That being said, there are several "fields" that you need to be made aware of. These include, but are not limited to the following:

1. THE **HCPCS** FIELD: This is the area where you will find a particular alphanumeric code *or* a HCPCS National Coding Manual modifier. "HCPCS" is an acronym (a word made out of the first letters of other words) that stands for *H*ealthcare *C*ommon *P*rocedure *C*oding *S*ystem. You will see that the codes here mostly describe supplies used by medical providers (e.g., durable medical equipment, drugs for injections, surgical trays), but they also can *and do* describe some procedures or services (e.g., administration of influenza virus vaccine, G0008).

2. ACTION CODE FIELD: You can see that this field actually uses the words "Action Code" to describe itself. It is here that Medicare tells you what they have done (if anything) to the code. More information about the Action Code field will be discussed later in this chapter.

   A. *Add procedure or modifier code.* To you, knowing that the code has been added should clue you into the fact that there may not be a lot of charge history on the procedure, service or supply and you need to be careful about the charges that you are submitting as they will help in establishing the worth of the code.

   B. *Change in both the administrative data field (which includes information on reimbursement, payment groups, cross references, etc.) and long description of procedure or modifier code.* To you, knowing that there was a change in the description of a code and/or possibly the administrative data field could mean that the reimbursement has also been affected.

   C. *Change in the long description of the procedure or modifier code.* Under the C designation, supposedly only the description of the code has changed. As was mentioned under the B action code, however, this is important to you because it could mean that the reimbursement has also been affected.

   D. *Discontinued procedure or modifier code.* The impact of seeing this in the action code field is that it tells you not to use the code any longer, as you simply will not be paid for it.

   F. *Change in the administrative data field of procedure or modifier code.* This means that some of the information about payment or other items may have been changed.

   N. *No maintenance for this code.* This means that Medicare does not consider itself responsible for updating this code and it also usually means that because they are not responsible for it, they will not pay on it either.

P.　　*Payment change (MOG, pricing indicator codes, anesthesia base units, Ambulatory Surgical Centers).* A payment change notation is self-explanatory but gives the heads up to find out what the change has been.

R.　　*Re-activate discontinued/deleted procedure or modifier code.*

S.　　*Change in the short description of the procedure.* This usually does not impact you as you should be reading the long description anyway, but it does tell you that the description of the code is different than it was in prior versions of HCPCS. Short descriptions do not give you enough detailed information. Remember: When a description has changed, very often the reimbursement for that service or supply may also be different.

T.　　*Miscellaneous change (BETOS, type of service change).* When you see this notation, try to figure out what the change has been.

3. **COVERAGE FIELD:** This field describes whether or not a code is "covered" by Medicare. More information about this field will be discussed later in this chapter.

　C　=　**Carrier Judgment**

　D　=　**Special Coverage Instructions Apply**

　I　=　**Not Valid for Medicare (No Grace Period)**

　M　=　**Not Covered by Medicare**

　S　=　**Not Covered by Medicare Statute**

4. **STATUTE FIELD:** This field tells you whether or not a procedure, service or supply is covered by Medicare statute. More information about this field will be discussed later in this chapter.

5. **X-REF:** This field stands for the cross-reference field. It is here that you will find out if there is a code other than the one you are looking at that

can be cross-referenced. This field will be important to you if you are looking at a newer version of the HCPCS National Coding Manual and comparing it to an older one where there may have been some deletion of codes which could be cross-referenced to new or different codes.

6. **PI:** This acronym stands for the *P*ricing *I*ndicator field. It is here that Medicare tells you what methodology they used to come up with the price for the service, supply or procedure for the Part B portion of the Medicare program.

  00   Services are not separately priced by Medicare Part B (e.g., services not covered, bundled, used by Part A only, etc.)

LINKED TO PHYSICIAN FEE SCHEDULE

  11   Price established using national relative value units
  12   Price established using national anesthesia base units
  13   Price established by carriers (e.g., not otherwise classified, individual determination, carrier discretion)

CLINICAL LAB FEE SCHEDULE

  21   Price subject to national limitation amount
  22   Price established by carriers (e.g., gap-fills, carrier established panels)

DURABLE MEDICAL EQUIPMENT, PROSTHETICS, ORTHOTICS, SUPPLIES AND SURGICAL DRESSINGS

  31   Frequently serviced durable medical equipment (DME) (price subject to floors and ceilings)
  32   Inexpensive and routinely purchased DME (price subject to floors and ceilings)
  33   Oxygen and oxygen equipment (price subject to floors and ceilings)
  34   DME supplies (price subject to floors and ceilings)
  35   Surgical dressings (price subject to floors and ceilings)
  36   Capped rental DME (price subject to floors and ceilings)
  37   Ostomy, tracheostomy and urological supplies (price subject to floors and ceilings)
  38   Orthotics, prosthetics, prosthetic devices, and vision services (price subject to floors and ceilings)

39	Parenteral and Enteral Nutrition
45	Customized DME items
46	Carrier priced (e.g., not otherwise classified, individual determination, carrier discretion, gap-filled amounts)

OTHER

51	Drugs
52	Reasonable charge
53	Statute
54	Vaccinations
55	Priced by carriers under clinical psychologist fee schedule (not applicable as of January 1, 1998)
56	Priced by carriers under clinical social worker fee schedule (not applicable as of January 1, 1998)
57	Other carrier priced
99	Value not established

7. **ASC (Ambulatory Surgical Center) Payment Classification Groups**
Not all providers of health services are paid in the same way. For instance, emergency room facilities are paid on the services that are similar in time and on the resources it takes physicians to perform these services. Medicare originally grouped those services which were clinically similar or which involved similar resource use into different groups known as ASC payment groups. In order to come up with these groupings, Medicare took most of the CPT codes (that could be used in an ambulatory setting) and classified them into different payment classification groups. The current ASC Payment System consists of about 3400 procedures divided into several hundred payment groups. The payments for these procedures can be found by looking at addendums that the government prepared and which can be found in the HCPCS Book produced by MedBooks. You can obtain a copy of this book by calling 1-800-443-7397.

When you look at this column for ASC payment groups in HCPCS, you will see that there is the YY notation. This means that when you access the addendums that we spoke about in the earlier paragraph, you will see each CPT or HCPCS code outlined there as well as the payments for each.

Note that the payment for ASC's is generally at a rate of 65% what is paid to the hospital under the Outpatient Prospective Payment

System which covers the cost of the facilities, equipment, supplies and hospital staff only.

Below you will see an example of an ASC Payment Group code. There are other examples in your HCPCS book of codes that are in the ASC Payment Group "YY." The "YY" designation is the only ASC Payment Group code you will find throughout the government's version of the HCPCS 2012.

HCPCS Code	Long Description	Coverage	Action Code	PI	MPI	CIM	MCM	Statute	Lab Cert	X-Ref	ASC PayGroup	ASC Pay Group Eff. Date	Proc. Notes	BETOS	TOS	Anesthesia Units	Code Add Date	Code Eff. Date	Code Delete Date
G0105	COLORECTAL CANCER SCREENING COLONOSCOPY ON INDIVIDUAL AT HIGH RISK	D	N	11	A						YY	19980101	0064	P8D	2	0	19980101	19980101	

McGUFFEY	Name:_____
WORKBOOK cpTeach 2012	Class/Section:_____
	Date:_____

Exercise 3.1

D

_____

_____

_____

I

_____

_____

_____

M

_____

_____

_____

S

_____

_____

_____

C

_____

_____

_____

Before You Begin:
Read Chapter 3 in cpTeach® on "HCPCS Editorial Notations." Follow along in your National Coding Manual with the points illustrated in cpTeach®.

Purpose of this Lesson:
To familiarize the student with the Notations found in the National Code book and to enable the student to recognize these notations and their significance from a payment standpoint.

Instructions:
1. Define the following Coverage Field Notations. Give three examples of each, using codes that begin with codes found at the beginning of the HCPCS National Coding Manual.

Before You Begin:

Read Chapter 3 in cpTeach® on "HCPCS: Editorial Notations." Follow along in your National Coding Manual with the points illustrated in cpTeach®.

Purpose of this Lesson:

To familiarize the student with the HCPCS editorial notations and coverage issues.

Instructions:

1. Look up the following procedures in the HCPCS National Coding Manual.

2. Write the notation(s) that appear for each code.

3. Describe what action has taken place by Medicare by indicating the action in the first column.

4. If information on coverage is supplied, list it in the second column.

EXERCISE 3.2

Code		Action Code	Coverage
1. A4215	Needle, sterile, any size, each	_____	_____
2. D7991	Coronoidectomy	_____	_____
3. B4083	Stomach Tube - Levine Type	_____	_____
4. A4259	Lancets, per box of 100	_____	_____
5. C9224	Injection, Galsulface, per 5mg	_____	_____
6. D7972	Surgical Reduction of Fibrous Tuberosity	_____	_____
7. B4081	Nasogastric tubing with stylet	_____	_____
8. J7300	Intrauterine Copper Contrceptive	_____	_____
9. A4421	Ostomy supply, miscellaneous	_____	_____
10. L8010	Breast Prothesis, Mastectomy Sleeve	_____	_____
11. M0301	Fabric wrapping of abdominal aneurysm	_____	_____
12. L3465	Heel, Thomas with wedge	_____	_____

* These codes were taken from 2012 HCPCS National Coding Manual.

> McGUFFEY
> WORKBOOK
> cpTeach
> 2012
>
> *Name:*_____
>
> *Class/Section:*_____
>
> *Date:*_____

Exercise 3.3

Action Code	**Long description**
Alphanumeric codes	**Multiple Pricing (Indicators)**
ASC Eff Date	**Pricing Indicators**
ASC Pay Group	**Short description**
Cross Reference	**Statute**
Editorial Notation	**Supplies**
HCPCS	

Before You Begin:
Read Chapter 3 in cpTeach® on "HCPCS: Editorial Notations." Follow along in your HCPCS National Coding Manual with the points illustrated in cpTeach®.

Purpose of this Lesson:
To familiarize the student with the HCPCS editorial notations and coverage issues.

Instructions:
1. Find the following fields located on the next page.

2. Circle the field(s) that appear for each word.

Workbook

cpTeach
2012

Name:_____

Class/Section:_____

Date:_____

H	P	R	I	C	I	N	G	I	N	D	I	C	A	T	O	R	S
A	A	A	I	T	S	A	E	D	N	T	A	R	S	T	E	A	F
L	R	T	S	S	G	P	O	K	E	C	L	I	F	C	V	M	K
P	O	I	E	C	R	O	S	S	R	E	F	E	R	E	N	C	E
H	S	N	D	T	P	I	W	A	B	T	E	N	I	F	O	P	T
A	P	H	G	O	Z	A	S	S	U	P	P	L	I	E	S	V
N	K	E	V	D	A	G	Y	Y	I	F	E	B	A	S	A	L	B
U	C	I	T	N	E	S	F	G	T	A	N	S	C	T	S	I	S
M	A	T	G	C	N	S	P	O	R	X	O	P	E	O	C	D	B
E	V	H	A	I	W	A	C	T	I	O	N	C	O	D	E	M	C
R	F	C	W	V	E	T	C	R	W	F	U	O	B	H	F	S	A
I	S	P	P	O	R	A	T	D	I	E	Z	P	O	S	F	F	E
C	N	C	I	T	C	H	S	V	M	P	V	O	T	A	D	F	K
C	A	S	M	A	B	S	T	A	T	U	T	E	G	S	A	A	M
O	T	N	P	S	L	R	W	C	D	T	K	I	E	R	T	G	H
D	O	I	A	F	G	S	D	A	S	Q	S	T	O	A	E	F	I
E	M	U	L	T	I	P	L	E	P	R	I	C	I	N	G	T	E
S	H	O	R	T	D	E	S	C	R	I	P	T	I	O	N	E	D
S	N	O	I	T	A	T	O	N	L	A	I	R	O	T	I	D	E

CPT© : Format of the Book

CPT is a coding system that uses, for the most part and with the exception of Category II and III codes, five-digit numeric codes. It is updated annually and is usually released in November of the year preceding its date (e.g., the 2012 version was released in October of 2011). Because of the many changes made to the CPT codebook each year, it is important to buy a new book each and every year to insure that you can keep abreast of any revisions, additions or deletions that have been made during the preceding year. There are six major sections in CPT. These are: Evaluation & Management, Anesthesia, Surgery, Radiology, Pathology & Laboratory, and Medicine.

Code:	9	9	2	0	1
Digits:	1	2	3	4	5

Category II and III codes can be found following the Medicine Section. They begin with a number, and end with the letters "F & T" respectively. These letters indicate to the user that they are either Facilitators of data collection ("F") or Temporary codes ("T"). While Category II and III codes are located in a specific section of the CPT codebook, they describe various different types of services (e.g., portions of histories, exams, and different kinds of surgeries, X-rays) that are placed altogether in this portion of the CPT codebook.

Knowing the numeric headers to each section of the book can help you identify a mistake on your claim form, master sheet or superbill. You can identify these mistakes by simply looking at the beginning number of the code and its corresponding description and seeing if the description of the codes makes sense with the header. For example, a code starting off with the number 7 would indicate that the service should be a Radiology code. If the description next to the code said something about a cesarean delivery, you would know that the code number is incorrect.

Use of incorrect codes will lead to incorrect reimbursement. Please check your code usage, and when you are in doubt about which code to use, ask your doctor to look at the codes you have narrowed it down to and then have her pick the correct one.

The Introduction to the CPT® codebook is very important. It outlines for you some of the important ground rules that you will need for proper coding. Some of the things you will learn about in the Introduction include:

1. The different editorial notations found in the CPT® codebook;

2. Special reports;

3. Unlisted procedures or services;

4. Requests to update the CPT® codebook;

5. The electronic formats of CPT®.

Guidelines preceding a section give the "ground rules" for that section and tell you about how the codes in that particular section should be handled.

Category II codes facilitate insurance companies and the like in being able to understand and track parts of what physicians may typically include as inherent parts of standard services. For example, the code 2000F stands for "blood pressure, measured" and is normally an inherent part of a standard office visit. Using these codes will allow the carriers to monitor what you feel are normal parts of the services that you provide to your patients. The Category II codes have no reimbursement associated with them.

Category III codes are temporary codes that allow insurance companies and the like to collect data on the usage and performance of the procedures described by these codes. Coders can and should use Category III codes in place of Unlisted Procedure Codes whenever possible.

There are several appendices found in the CPT® codebook. Appendix A is a complete list of all of the modifiers that you will find throughout the CPT® codebook. Appendix B is a summary of the additions, deletions, and revisions that have been made to the book in the past year. Appendix C cites examples of the different kinds of Evaluation and Management services, while Appendix D lists the

No two codes are alike...

"add-on" codes (those that can go in addition to other codes and which do not require the use of the modifier -51 for Multiple Procedures). Appendix E lists all of the codes that do not require the use of the modifier –51 (for multiple services) when these procedures are done in conjunction with one another. Likewise, Appendix F addresses those codes that are exempt for the modifier –63, procedures performed on infants less than 4 kg. If you need to have a summary of the codes that already include conscious sedation, look to Appendix G. Appendix H will help you with the use of the Category II codes in that you will find additional information about what is included in the Category II codes. If you are providing any genetic testing, you can find an entire list of modifiers that will support the codes you use by looking to Appendix I. Some of the codes in CPT® (e.g., 95900) involve the nerves that you will find in Appendix J. Be sure to look there if you are providing any services from the Medicine section that deal with the nerves. Appendix K was a new addition to the CPT® codebook for 2006 and includes a listing of all of the CPT® codes that are pending FDA approval. Last but not least, you will see Appendixes L and M. Appendix L can be very helpful to you in understanding the different routes that the vascular system takes starting from the aorta. Appendix M, new to the CPT® book in 2007, is a crosswalk of the deleted CPT® codes to other codes you can use.

In order to find a code, the coder needs to be as resourceful as possible in looking it up in the index. Sometimes a code is listed under the procedure or service itself (e.g., cardioversion) or kind of procedure or service (e.g., catheterization); other times by the name of the person who invented the procedure (e.g., Marshall-Marchetti-Krantz); and at still other times, it may be listed under the body part (e.g., mastoid). Do not be discouraged if you cannot find a code in the index after the first try. Look up synonyms, abbreviations or the like to assist you in code localization.

Name:_____

Class/Section:_____

Date:_____

2012

Before You Begin:

Read Chapter 4 in cpTeach® on "CPT®: Format of the Book." Follow along in CPT® with the points illustrated in cpTeach®.

Purpose of this Lesson:

To familiarize you with the CPT® codebook and its arrangement.

Instructions:

1. Use your CPT® codebook as a guide to fill in the following sentences.

Exercise 4.1

1.   The codes found in the Radiology section begin with the number _____

2.   The codes found in the Pathology section begin with the number _____

3.   The codes found in the Medicine section begin with the number _____

4.   The codes found in the Surgery section begin with the number _____

5.   The Evaluation and Management codes begin with the number _____

6.   The codes found in the Anesthesia section begin with the number _____

7.   The codes found in Category II end with the letter _____

8.   The codes found in Category III end with the letter _____

WORKBOOK	McGUFFEY	Name:_____
		Class/Section:_____
	cpTeach 2012	Date:_____

EXERCISE 4.2

1. _____

2. _____

3. _____

4. _____

5. _____

6. _____

7. _____

8. _____

Before You Begin:
Read Chapter 4 in cpTeach® on "CPT®: Format of the Book." Follow along in CPT® with the points illustrated in cpTeach®.

Purpose of this Lesson:
To familiarize you with the CPT® codebook and its arrangement.

Instructions:
1. Use your CPT® as a guide to fill in the following. Excluding the introduction to the CPT® book and the appendices, but including the Category II and III codes, list the sections in the order in which they appear in CPT®.

WORKBOOK

cpTeach

2012

Name:_____

Class/Section:_____

Date:_____

Before You Begin:
Read Chapter 4 in cpTeach® on "CPT®: Format of the Book." Follow along in your CPT® with the points illustrated in cpTeach®.

Purpose of this Lesson:
To familiarize you with the CPT® codebook and the codes in it. To get you to see that by knowing the first digit of the code, you can identify which section of CPT® the code number came from and what set of rules to apply to those numbers.

Instructions:
1. Look up the following procedures in your CPT® codebook.

2. Indicate which section the code can be found in by writing the first letter describing each section. (Medicine = M, Anesthesia = A, E/M = E, Surgery = S, Radiology = R, etc.)

EXERCISE 4.3

36415	_____	58740	_____	78607	_____
67875	_____	58270	_____	78808	_____
53449	_____	44310	_____	81000	_____
32110	_____	56405	_____	40702	_____
31830	_____	65771	_____	92567	_____
29881	_____	78596	_____	84135	_____
29800	_____	90696	_____	00147	_____
86602	_____	90650	_____	99291	_____
28292	_____	86978	_____	10061	_____
76000	_____	77431	_____	83615	_____
99058	_____	77403	_____	21127	_____
70552	_____	67028	_____	83625	_____
88304	_____	99253	_____	33530	_____
99201	_____	96913	_____	76587	_____
99000	_____	27025	_____	26070	_____
92002	_____	00873	_____	99334	_____
01990	_____	17108	_____	76705	_____
01780	_____	20693	_____	78428	_____
12001	_____	90951	_____	86215	_____
14000	_____	92060	_____	00400	_____

EXERCISE 4.4

MEDICINE _____	a. describes lab tests
ANESTHESIA _____	b. the "invasive" section
SURGERY _____	c. section whose codes begin with 7
RADIOLOGY _____	d. the "non-invasive" section
PATHOLOGY _____	e. section whose codes begin with "0"
E/M _____	f. lists codes for histories, exams and medical decision making

Before You Begin:
Read Chapter 4 in **cpTeach®** on "CPT®: Format of the Book." Follow along in CPT® with the points illustrated in **cpTeach®**.

Purpose of this Lesson:
To familiarize the student with the CPT® codebook and its arrangement.

Instructions:
1. Match the following CPT® sections to their corresponding descriptions.

Before You Begin:

Read Chapter 4 in **cpTeach**® on "CPT®: Format of the Book." Follow along in your CPT® with the points illustrated in **cpTeach**®.

Purpose of this Lesson:

To familiarize the student with the CPT® codebook and its arrangement.

Instructions:

1. **WITHOUT** using your CPT®, decide if the following CPT® codes and descriptions are, *IN ALL LIKELIHOOD*, correct. (Hint: you will be able to tell by knowing what kind of codes (and the corresponding first digits) should be found in each section.)

2. If the CPT® codes are correct for the corresponding description, mark a "✓" in front of the code. If the code is incorrect, mark an "**X**" in front of the description.

Example:

1. _____
   80000   Anesthesia for all procedures on esophagus

EXERCISE 4.5

1. _____   99441   Telephone evaluation and management services provided by a physician to an established patient, parent, or guardian not originating from a related E/M service provided within the previous 7 days nor leading to an E/M service or procedure within the next 24 hours or soonest available appointment; 5-10 minutes of medical discussion

2. _____   79058   Office services provided on an emergency basis

3. _____   22849   Reinsertion of spinal fixation device

4. _____   33233   Removal of permanent pacemaker pulse generator

5. _____   90010   Renal exploration, not necessitating other specific procedures

6. _____   73825   Mercury, quantitative

7. _____   75801   Lymphangiography, extremity only, unilateral, radiological supervision and interpretation

8. _____   71100   Radiologic examination, ribs, unilateral; two views

9. _____   86602   Antibody; actinomyces

10. _____   66588   Streptococcus, screen, direct

11. _____   68000   Necropsy (autopsy), gross examination only; without Central Nervous System

EXERCISE 4.5

12. _____   84285   Silica

13. _____   90100   Anesthesia for procedure on salivary glands, includ-
                          ing biopsy

14. _____   99000   Handling and/or conveyance of specimen for
                          transfer from the physician's office to a laboratory

Before You Begin:

Read Chapter 4 in **cp**Teach® on "CPT®: Format of the Book." In particular, read the portion on the index. Follow along in CPT® with the points illustrated in **cp**Teach®.

Purpose of this Lesson:

To familiarize the student with CPT® and its "Index" and to show you that sometimes you need to be resourceful in finding a code in the CPT "Index."

Instructions:

1. Look up the following procedures in the CPT® Index by finding the key word in each descriptor.

2. Next to each procedure list the range of codes (if a "range" exists), that is listed in the Index for the procedure.

3. Identify the correct procedure by placing the CPT® code on the second line.

Example:

44361, 44377 S m a l l intestinal endoscopy, enteroscopy beyond second portion.

44361 of duodenum, not including the ileum with a single biopsy.

EXERCISE 4.6

_____ 1. Gammaglobulin (immunoglobulin); IgA, IgD, IgG, IgM, each.

_____ 2. Insertion of ocular implant, secondary; after evisceration,
_____   in scleral shell

_____ 3. Removal of foreign body external eye; conjunctival
_____   superficia

_____ 4. Drainage abscess or hematoma, nasal, internal
_____   approach

_____ 5. Cytopathology, slides, cervical or vaginal, definitive
_____   hormonal evaluation (e.g., maturation index,
                 karyopyknotic index, estrogenic index)

_____ 6. Photochemotherapy; psoralens and ultraviolet
                 A (PUVA)

_____ 7. Hearing aid examination and selection; monoaural

_____ 8. Ligation or transection of fallopian tube(s), abdominal
_____   or vaginal approach, unilateral or bilateral

_____ 9. Hypophysectomy or excision of pituitary tumor, trans
_____   nasal or transseptal approach, nonstereotactic

_____ 10. Evisceration of ocular contents; without implant
_____

WORKBOOK *cpTeach* 2012	*Name:*_____
	*Class/Section:*_____
	*Date:*_____

EXERCISE 4.7

CPT CODE	INDEX KEY WORD
28008	_____
29894	_____
31505	_____
15852	_____
67715	_____
82286	_____
82525	_____
20931	_____
82003	_____
84146	_____

A	I	D	R	V	E	C	B	R	A	D	Y	K	I	N	I	N
N	O	S	N	E	R	O	S	J	Y	L	I	M	E	G	C	E
V	A	R	T	H	R	O	S	C	O	P	Y	N	Y	T	S	X
U	V	X	E	Q	P	K	M	Y	D	X	C	M	L	V	W	Q
L	B	X	R	V	O	I	U	J	B	P	O	X	W	K	O	C
C	T	L	H	C	A	N	T	H	O	T	O	M	Y	D	E	X
P	I	N	E	F	O	R	H	V	O	J	U	N	E	O	N	M
C	O	P	P	E	R	W	N	I	K	I	S	S	V	D	O	I
M	Y	R	C	X	W	E	C	V	Y	T	O	N	C	W	R	T
V	Y	D	R	E	S	S	I	N	G	C	H	A	N	G	E	R
B	O	X	E	R	A	L	L	O	G	R	A	F	T	B	U	F
Z	R	E	M	F	K	U	T	M	B	C	K	G	T	R	E	W
A	C	E	T	A	M	I	N	O	P	H	E	N	M	I	H	G
Y	P	O	C	S	O	G	N	Y	R	A	L	R	A	L	N	Y
W	O	T	I	P	D	O	L	P	B	R	E	D	P	M	B	T
F	X	T	R	C	P	R	O	L	A	C	T	I	N	I	N	L

Before You Begin:

Read Chapter 4 in **cpT**each® on "CPT®: Format of the Book." In particular, read the section on the "Index." Follow along in CPT® with the points illustrated in **cpT**each®.

Purpose of this Lesson:

To familiarize the student with the different CPT® codes and their corresponding unique descriptions as well as with the use of the CPT® index and text.

Instructions:

1. Look up each of the following procedure codes in CPT®.

2. Identify which word in the description would probably be used to find the code in the "Index."

3. Find the word in the anagram below. Remember the word or words can be listed horizontally, vertically, backwards or any which way.

CPT©: Editorial Notations

There are seven editorial notations found in the CPT® codebook that could impact your coding practices. These are:

1. ●   the bullet = new code;
2. ▲   the triangle = revised code;
3. ✚   the plus sign = add-on code;
4. ⊘   the circle with a line drawn through it = modifier -51exempt code;
5. ►◄   the inverted triangles = text change;
6. ⊙   the bull's-eye = conscious sedation;
7. ⚡   the lightning bolt = pending FDA approval;
8. O   the empty circle = the code has been re-instated or recycled;
9. #   the pound sign = out of the numeric sequence.

The **bullet** (●) tells the coder that the procedure that it identifies is a new one. All bullets will be found in front of a code and are only found on a particular code for one year. The practical application of the bullet for the coder is that it tells you that you need to come up with a price for the new procedure or service and that some carriers will not yet have any charge data on it. Once you select a fee for that procedure or service, it will be important to use that fee (and not to keep moving it up or down) in order for your office to establish some sort of history of charges for that particular code.

The **triangle** (▲) is also found in front of a code and it appears for one year. The **triangle** tells the coder that the description of the service has changed. This could also impact your reimbursement in that if the description of a code has changed, some part of the procedure may have been deleted or added to.

Tip

Bullet (●) = new code.

Tip

Triangle (▲) = revised code.

At any rate, if part of the description of the code has been deleted, the chances of your reimbursement going down for that service are pretty high. If something has been added to the code, then you may expect an increase in the reimbursement for the procedure. If the change made to the description neither takes away from nor adds to the service, but rather makes it more specific, no change in the reimbursement amount is likely.

The **plus sign** (✚) indicates "add-on" codes. Add-on codes are those that may go together with a larger service. An example would be removal of skin tags. Suppose that you remove 20 skin tags. As you can see from looking up the code(s), you will need two CPT® codes to completely describe your services.

> 11200   *Removal of skin tags, multiple fibrocutaneous tags, any area; up to and including 15 lesions*
>
> ✚11201   *each additional ten lesions or part thereof (List separately in addition to code for primary procedure)*
>
> Copyright AMA, 2011

Tip

The Plus Sign (✚) = additional work associated with the main service.

The first code, the 11200, only describes the first 15 lesions. Because you removed 20, you would need both the 11200 and the 11201 codes (you would need to "add-on" the 11201 to the 11200 - hence the name "add-on" codes). You do **not** need to use the modifier -51 for multiple procedures on any add-on codes. The plus sign is important to the coder as it tells him/her that the services (where the plus sign is present) can be added to others (usually in the same series) without having to also append a modifier to indicate that multiple services were performed at the same time. Make sure to check in Appendix D of your CPT® codebook to find a list of the add-on codes.

The **exempt sign** (⊘) is used to designate services found in CPT® that do not require the use of the modifier -51 for Multiple Services, but which do not have the add-on (plus sign) notation. This is important to the coder as the use of the modifier -51 has been known to reduce payments on the secondary, additional and lesser procedures.

Tip

Inverted Triangles (▶◀) = change in text around the CPT code.

Inverted triangles (▶◀), like the regular triangles discussed above, mean that something has changed. The difference between inverted triangles and regular triangles is that inverted triangles signify that the verbiage, or text, (in and around the code) has changed. You will see inverted triangles around the text portion of the CPT® codebook, and you can bet that the changes they denote are important to your coding. Make it a point to read the text of your CPT® codebook always, but especially when you see inverted triangles in and around the codes you are about to use. You will find some very important information listed there.

Conscious sedation (⊙) You will find the conscious sedation notation on codes that already include conscious sedation as an inherent part of the overall service.

The **lightning bolt** (⚡) tells the coder that the code is awaiting FDA approval.

The **empty cirle** (O) signifies that the code has been re-instated or recycled.

The **pound sign** (#) tells the coder that a code they are using is part of a grouping of other codes but that it is out of the numeric sequence.

Key

The ⚡ notation indicates that the code and description are awaiting FDA approval.

WORKBOOK

McGUFFEY

cpTeach
Expert Medical Coding Made Easy!

2012

Name:_____

Class/Section:_____

Date:_____

Before You Begin:

Read Chapter 5 in cpTeach® on "CPT®: Editorial Notations." Follow along in your CPT® with the points illustrated in cpTeach®.

Purpose of this Lesson:

To familiarize the student with the different CPT® editorial notations.

Instructions:

1. Look at the following definitions of the editorial notations.

2. Draw the appropriate notation for each definition.

EXERCISE 5.1

1. _____   new code

2. _____   revised code/revised description

3. _____   new and revised text (not including procedure descriptors)

4. _____   code can be added to others without use of modifier -51

5. _____   denotes codes that do not require the use of modifier-51, but which do not have "add-on" status

6. _____   tells the coder that the procedure is pending FDA approval

7. _____   the sedative used was an inherent part of the global service

8. _____   tells the coder that the code is out of numreic sequence

9. _____   a reinstated or recycled code

*Name:*_____

*Class/Section:*_____

*Date:*_____

EXERCISE 5.2

1. _____ 19295
2. _____ 22633
3. _____ 99359
4. _____ 22610
5. _____ 93530
6. _____ 16036
7. _____ 20974
8. _____ 95905
9. _____ 93312
10. _____ 22527

11. _____ 20982
12. _____ 49411
13. _____ 75946
14. _____ 50382
15. _____ 37185
16. _____ 31632
17. _____ 32501
18. _____ 36620
19. _____ 33225
20. _____ 31500

Before You Begin:
Read Chapter 5 in cpTeach® on "CPT®: Editorial Notations." Follow along in CPT® with the points illustrated in cpTeach®.

Purpose of this Lesson:
To familiarize the student with the different CPT® editorial notations and where they may be found.

Instructions:
1. Find each code in your CPT®.

2. List the appropriate notation of each code. Some of the codes may have more than one notation.

Name:_____

Class/Section:_____

Date:_____

Before You Begin:
Read Chapter 5 in cpTeach® on "CPT®: Editorial Notations." Follow along in CPT® with the points illustrated in cpTeach®.

Purpose of this Lesson:
To familiarize the student with the different CPT® editorial notations and where they may be found.

Instructions:
1. Starting with the Surgery section (with the exception of the lightning bolt (⚡) which you should find in Medicine), find a code (or text) with the following notations.

2. Fill in the code number next to the notation. Some of the codes may have more than one notation.

EXERCISE 5.3

1.   ▲   _____

2.   ●   _____

3.   ►◄   _____

4.   ✚   _____

5.   ⊘   _____

6.   ⚡   _____

7.   ⊙   _____

WORKBOOK

cpTeach
Expert Medical Coding Made Easy!

2012

Name:_____

Class/Section:_____

Date:_____

EXERCISE 5.4

1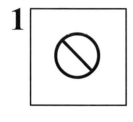
_____

2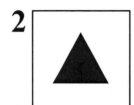
_____

3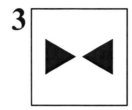
_____

4
_____

5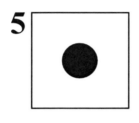
_____

6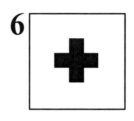
_____

7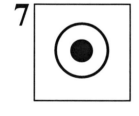
_____

8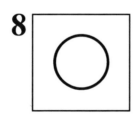
_____

9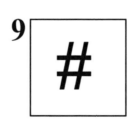
_____

Before You Begin:
Read Chapter 5 in cpTeach® on "CPT®: Editorial Notations." Follow along in your CPT® with the points illustrated in cpTeach®.

Purpose of this Lesson:
To familiarize the student with the different CPT® notations.

Instructions:
1. Look at the following signs.

2. List the appropriate definition of each notation.

_____   _____   _____

Name:_____

Class/Section:_____

cpTeach Date:_____
2012

SUMMARY: CHAPTERS 1 THROUGH 5

EXERCISE 5.5

Before You Begin:
Read Chapters 1 through 5 in cpTeach®. Follow along in CPT® and the HCPCS National Coding Manual with the points illustrated in cpTeach®.

Purpose of this Lesson:
To help the student summarize and put together the different concepts learned up to this point.

Instructions:
1. Complete the following crossword puzzle.

ACROSS

2. The section that contains codes beginning with the numbers 1 through 6.
4/5. The bullet indicates a _____.
7. The Medicine section begins with this number.
8. A code that does not require the use of a modifier -51 is called an _____.
9. The section in CPT® that contains lab procedures.
11. Contains new or revised text (_____ triangles)
12. What kind of code is 0041T?

DOWN

1. New procedure notation is symbolized by this.
3. The common name for CMS.
5. Triangle denotes a _____ procedure.
6. The section that begins with the number 7 is:
10.   Symbol indicating a revised code description is _____.

Evaluation & Management

The Evaluation and Management section is the first section in the CPT® codebook. All of the codes in the Evaluation and Management section begin with the number 9 and are five-digit, numeric codes. Services found in the Evaluation and Management section include histories, examinations, and decisions that must be made regarding the patient's diagnosis and treatment. Additionally, you will find codes for telephone calls, critical care services, transport of pediatric/neonatal patients, etc.

The CPT® codebook defines two different kinds of patients for the Evaluation and Management section. These are:

- New Patient, and
- Established Patient

A new patient is one who has not received any professional services (defined by CPT® as "face-to-face" services) from a physician or, if within the same group practice, professional services from another doctor of the same specialty within the past three years. This definition also holds true for Medicare reporting. Likewise, an established patient is one who has received professional services from a given physician (or another in the same group practice who is also of the same specialty) within the past three years.

In order to code well, it is important to understand the four different kinds of histories, the four different kinds of examinations, and the variety of decisions that can be made before you try to use the Evaluation and Management codes.

HISTORIES
Histories fall into the following categories:

- **Problem focused;**
- **Expanded problem focused;**

Key

All codes in the Evaluation and Management section begin with the number "9."

Key

The major difference between the two lower levels of history (problem focused and expanded problem focused) and the detailed one is that in a detailed history the physician obtains information about the patient's past history, the patient's family history, and/or the patient's social history. None of these kinds of histories were required as part of the problem focused and expanded problem focused histories.

  • **Detailed;**   • **Comprehensive.**

To describe the different kinds of histories it seems easier if you go in reverse and look at the largest, most global kind of history first, see what's included in it and then compare it to the others.

A *comprehensive* history contains the chief complaint, an extended history of the present illness, a review of the systems involved which are directly related to the patient's problem(s), as well as a review of all additional systems and a complete past, family and social history.

A *detailed* history includes the chief complaint and the extended history of the present illness, but only includes a limited review of systems which are pertinent to what problem(s) was (were) discovered in the history and a pertinent past family and/or social history.

As you can see, the *comprehensive* history takes into account the patient's entire past family and social history, whereas a detailed does not.

Like the others, *expanded problem focused* histories take into account the chief complaint, but only require a brief history of the present illness and a problem pertinent system review.

Finally, the *problem focused* history concentrates on the chief complaint and the brief history of the present illness or problem.

EXAMS

Like histories, exams have the same names. Again, we will start from the highest level and work backwards.

A *comprehensive* exam includes a complete examination of a single organ system or a general multi-system exam. Physicians must be careful to document each organ system that they cover and make sure that the appropriate notes are made that show the findings for each system.

A *detailed* examination is one in which the physician performs an extended exam of the affected body area(s) and other symptomatic or related organ system(s). Notice that words like "extended" and "complete" are subjective and really depend upon the physician to distinguish between them. Although under consideration by Medicare to come up with a system that would be more definitive and objective than the current one, nothing has been adopted as of the writing of this book.

It is important not to confuse the words your physician may use with those in the CPT® codebook. For example, a physician may think that he has provided a very thorough exam and history for a patient on a particular

Tip

Problem focused histories are the simplest form of histories that can be taken.

Comprehensive exam

Detailed exam

body part (e.g., let's just say the knee). By the definitions used in the CPT® codebook, however, a thorough exam and history on the knee area would not be considered "complete," unless the physician provided a review of the entire musculo-skeletal system (i.e., complete single system review) or a complete multi-system review (which as you can see, was not provided in this example). A sound understanding of how the CPT® codebook defines these words and what is or is not included with these definitions will assist you as you code for different scenarios.

Expanded problem focused exam

Expanded problem focused exams are those that are limited to the affected body area or organ system and which may also include examining other affected areas or organ systems.

Finally in a ***problem focused exam***, the physician simply performs a limited examination of the affected body area or organ system.

Problem focused exam

Once you have decided which kind of history you have provided and which kind of exam, you need to select the kind of medical decision making that was done. Medical decision making takes three things into account. These are:

1. **Number of diagnoses or management options;**

2. **Amount and/or the complexity of the data to review;**

3. **Risk of complications and/or morbidity or mortality.**

Each of these is selected from a decision making chart like the one you see on the next page.

The rule of thumb in selecting a type of decision making is to consider each of the columns (i.e., number of diagnoses, amount of data to review, etc.) individually. In other words, ask yourself if the number of diagnoses was minimal, limited, multiple or extensive. (Once again, these words are subjective, but use your best guess.) For example, suppose a patient comes into your office needing a complete history and exam before she can go on a special college trip overseas. This is a new patient for you who is normal, healthy and 19 years old. You ask the patient all about her past and get a complete past history, finding out about past surgeries (none were done), past sicknesses (none) and past family and social history (nothing too exciting to report in these areas either). All in all, the patient seems like a good old-fashioned type girl with sound morals and good judgment. Your exam reveals nothing out of the ordinary as you provide this patient with a complete multi-system exam. Okay, now it is time to look at this medical decision making tree. Looking at the three areas that you must consider in coming up with the kind of medical decision making, you will probably agree that the number of diagnoses or management options for this patient was minimal (so circle that on the chart).

Key

Always look at the history and exam independently of one another. This would be the same as when you make a cake. You would measure the eggs independently of the oil. It is the combination of all of the ingredients that make the cake. Likewise, it is the combination of the key components (history, exam, and medical decision making) that make up the E/M service.

You will also probably agree that the amount of data reviewed (e.g., past x-rays, lab tests, etc.) was also minimal to none (so circle that on the chart above) and finally, the risk of complications and/or morbidity or mortality was minimal (we all doubt very seriously that anything will "happen" to this patient based upon her present condition), so you will circle that also. If you were to go across the page and match the words that you just circled with what the words are that appear under the type of decision making column on the far right hand side of the chart, you will see that they all match up to the word "straightforward," which is then the type of decision making that was made in this case.

1	2	3	4
AMT. OF DX	**AMT. OF DATA TO REVIEW**	**RISK**	**TYPE OF DECISION**
minimal	minimal to none	minimal	straightforward
limited	limited	low	low complexity
multiple	moderate	moderate	moderate complexity
extensive	extensive	high	high complexity

When you have selected each of the types of decision making for each of the three areas (number of diagnoses, amount of data, and risk of complications) and mapped them out on the chart above, you will see that there will be words (straightforward, low, moderate or high) that you will meet with your charting or exceed at least two of the three times. This will be the kind of decision making that you will select for the Evaluation and Management code.

Let's take another example:

A "key component" is to a visit what an "important ingredient" is to a recipe.

Suppose, the number of diagnoses were minimal and when you went across to the right on the first chart it was equal to "straightforward" under the heading of Type of Decision Making. Likewise, if the amount of data to review is limited, then the type of decision making selected would be "low complexity." If you were to place the words "straightforward" next to the # of diagnoses on the chart below as well as the words "low complexity" next to the title data to review and finally, pretend that the risk of complication to the patient and/or morbidity or mortality is minimal, you would see that you have two straightforward types of decisions (one for number of diagnoses and one for risk), and one for low complexity. Using the two out of three rule, you would select straightforward decision making for this service.

Remember that the "key" components to any Evaluation and Management visit are the history, exam and medical decision making and to qualify for a new patient visit, all three key components must be considered. In an established patient visit, this is not the case and only two of the three components need to be met or exceeded. The use of the **DOC FORM** found later in this workbook will help you extensively in selecting a particular Evaluation and Management level.

You will see average time frames listed as a part of many of the Evaluation and Management services. These time frames are only averages and should not be used in selecting a level of service unless the counseling and/or coordination of care portion of the visit exceeds (is more than) the time it takes you to perform the history, exam and medical decision making.

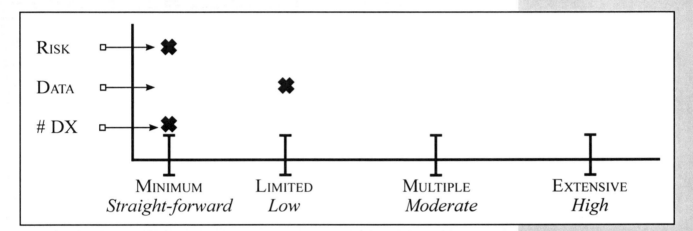

Let's say the history, exam and decision making take ten minutes. Suppose the patient ends up being with you for extra counseling and/or coordination of care due to being new to the area or nervous about their condition or having you explain the case to a spouse a second time, and you end up spending 30 minutes with the patient. You would see that the counseling portion (about 20 minutes) was at least 50% of the total face-to-face time you spent with the patient, and you would code with relationship to time, picking a code that corresponds to the 30-minute visit that transpired.

KINDS OF EVALUATION AND MANAGEMENT SERVICES
There are several different kinds of Evaluation and Management services. It will only be the scope of this workbook to describe the ones of special significance.

Hospital Observation Services are used to report histories, exams and medical decisions that are made on patients in an observation area of the hospital. This location could be a specialized observation unit or even a section of the hospital designated for that purpose (e.g., part of the emergency room). Observation services are used for patients who receive services in the hospital, but who have not been "admitted" to the hospital. There are two subsections in the CPT® codebook that address hospital observation. The first section, codes 99217 through 99220, includes codes that account for the hospital observation and discharge done on *different* dates. The second set of codes includes hospital admission and discharge done on the *same date* of service (see codes 99234 through 99236).

"Initial" Hospital Care codes can be used only by the *admitting* physician. All other physicians who provide initial hospital care must use either the Consultation codes (if appropriate) or the "Subsequent" Hospital Care codes.

Consultations are defined as services in which the consulting physician renders his/her opinion or gives advice. The purpose of the consultation is not to treat the patient although this does sometimes happen. Remember, in a consultation, the patient plans on going back to the primary care doctor for the treatment of his/her condition. The consultant is simply trying to give an opinion on how that condition should be treated. If a physician treats a patient during a consultation, any "subsequent" service rendered by the consulting physician to that patient will be considered another type of Evaluation and Management service *other than* a consultation (e.g., office/outpatient visit, hospital visit, etc.) and should be coded accordingly. (The visit that started out as a consultation can still remain a consultation.)

Emergency Department Service codes are to be used only when the facility is an organized, hospital- based facility, open 24 hours a day for the provision of unscheduled, episodic services. The Emergency Department Service codes do not include surgeries and many other procedures, but do include the history, exam and medical decision making required to get to the decision of surgery.

Critical Care codes describe services rendered by the hour to stabilize the critically ill or injured patient who is experiencing a life-threatening situation. These codes include the interpretation of cardiac output measurements, chest x-rays, pulse oximetry, blood gases, and information data stored in computers (e.g., ECG's, blood pressures, hematologic data), gastric intubation, temporary transcutaneous pacing, ventilator management and vascular access procedures. Services that are not part of this list (e.g., CPR) should be coded separately.

Prolonged Services are those in which "treatment" of the patient and/or the coordination of care involves at least a 30-minute period beyond the usual service. These codes can be used in addition to the other service codes including E/M services.

Care Plan Oversight Services are those procedures in which a physician is integrally involved in overseeing and monitoring the care of patients for at least 30 days under the direct care of nursing homes or home health organizations. This may include physician development of a course of treatment/action, review of lab results, telephone calls, integration of new information into a plan of action, adjustment of therapy, etc.

The **Preventive Medicine** codes describe services provided to patients who desire to "nip their problems in the bud" and who in many cases have no specific complaints, problems or established illnesses. These codes are based on whether or not the patient is new or established and also on the age of the patient. If an abnormality is encountered during a preventive medicine visit, and if the problem is significant enough to require the extra work found in the regular Evaluation and Management services, then the coder can code for both the regular Evaluation and Management visit AND the Preventive Medicine code.

Finally, **Special Evaluation and Management Services** include examinations used to evaluate the health of a patient and get some sort of baseline idea of the patient's physical status so that a disability or life insurance policy can be issued.

USING THE DOC FORM

The greatest challenge that a coder faces is to accurately code the E/M section. This is difficult, because it requires a judgment on the part of the coder or physician.

It is of critical importance to note that not all of your encounters with patients will fit neatly into the prepackaged descriptions listed in the CPT® codebook. You won't always have, for example, a problem focused history, problem focused exam and straightforward medical decision as described in the 99201 code.

You will see that you may provide a problem focused history on a person and an expanded problem focused exam, and there would be no exact code description given in CPT® to describe this scenario. Because of this, let's talk about an easy way to implement these ideas in a manner that will help you select accurate visit codes for all patient/physician encounters. You can do this by using the following form, called the **DOC Form**. The **DOC** stands for "Doctor's Office Checklist."

The DOC form allows the physician to easily take an active part in the E/M coding decision, and allows the coder to work with greater speed (rather than having to constantly ask the doctor - what exactly did you do, what body parts did you examine, what kind of decision did you make, what was/were the diagnosis (es) how long did it take you to reach your decision, and so on).

The other side of the DOC form includes Evaluation and Management services that occur in the hospital setting. These include:

1. **Hospital inpatient visits (for both initial and subsequent visits);**

2. **Observation services (for same or different dates of discharge); and**

3. **Emergency services (for both new and established patients).**

Let's begin our study of the DOC form by looking at the first side, the office/outpatient side.

As you scan the DOC form (from left to right), you can see that both Office/Outpatient Visits and Consultations are listed at the top. As was previously stated, these two kinds of services have been placed together on this particular DOC form, because both are rendered in the office/outpatient setting.

DOC Form®
(Doctor's Office Checklist)

	OFFICE/OUTPATIENT		CONSULTATION	
	New (3)	Established (2)	Office/O.P. (3)	Inpatient (3)
Minimal Service		99211		

HISTORY
Problem Focused	99201	99212	99241	99251
Exp/Prob Focused	99202	99213	99242	99252
Detail	99203	99214	99243	99253
Comprehensive	99204/05	99215	99244/45	99254/55

EXAMINATION
Problem Focused	99201	99212	99241	99251
Exp/Prob Focused	99202	99213	99242	99252
Detail	99203	99214	99243	99253
Comprehensive	99204/05	99215	99244/45	99254/55

MEDICAL DECISION MAKING
Straight Forward	99201/2	99212	99241/42	99251/52
Low Complexity	99203	99213	99243	99253
Mod Complexity	99204	99214	99244	99254
High Complexity	99205	99215	99245	99255

TIME:_____   Counsel/Coordination of Care:_____
10 Minutes	99201	99212		
15 Minutes		99213	99241	
20 Minutes	99202			99251
25 Minutes		99214		
30 Minutes	99203		99242	
40 Minutes		99215	99243	99252
45 Minutes	99204			
55 Minutes				99253
60 Minutes	99205		99244	
80 Minutes			99245	99254
110 Minutes				99255

Patient Name:_____

Date:_____Physician Signature:_____

MedBooks, Inc.
101 W. Buckingham Road, Richardson, Tx. 75081 (800) 443-7397
Warning: This product is copyrighted and is not to be duplicated in any manner without the express written permission of MedBooks.

Beneath each of these services is a further explanation of the encounter. For example, the words "New (3)" and "Established (2)" under the bold heading of **Office/Outpatient Visits** tell whether the patient is new to the physician or established. Additionally, it tells us that either three (see the parenthesis next to the word "new") or two (see the parenthesis next to the word "established") key components will be required to code and bill for these services. In the exact same way, the words "Office/O.P. (Outpatient)" with the parenthesis and the number 3,

DOC Form®
(Doctor's Office Checklist)

	HOSPITAL		OBSERVATION		ER
	Initial (3)	Sub (2)	Discharge Date		New/Estab (3)
			Different (3)	Same (3)	

HISTORY					
Problem Focused		99231			99281
Exp/Prob Focused		99232			99282/83
Detail	99221	99233	99218	99234	99284
Comprehensive	99221/2/3		99218/19/20	99234/35/36	99285

EXAMINATION					
Problem Focused		99231			99281
Exp/Prob Focused		99232			99282/83
Detail	99221	99233	99218	99234	99284
Comprehensive	99221/2/3		99218/19/20	99234/35/36	99285

MEDICAL DECISION MAKING					
Straight Forward	99221	99231	99218	99234	99281
Low Complexity	99221	99231	99218	99234	99282
Mod Complexity	99222	99232	99219	99235	99283/84
High Complexity	99223	99233	99220	99236	99285

DISCHARGE		99217			
≤ 30 Minutes		99238			
> 30 Minutes		99239			

TIME					
15 Minutes		99231			
20 Minutes					
25 Minutes		99232			
30 Minutes	99221				
35 Minutes		99233			
45 Minutes					
50 Minutes	99222				
60 Minutes					
70 Minutes	99223				

Patient Name:_____

Date:_____Physician Signature:_____

MedBooks, Inc.
101 W. Buckingham Road, Richardson, Tx. 75081 (800) 443-7397
Warning: This product is copyrighted and is not to be duplicated in any manner without the express
written permission of MedBooks.

and the word "Inpatient" with the parenthesis and the number 3 under the bold heading of **Consultation** tell us about these services, explaining different kinds of consultations and how many key components are required in order to code for each.

Going from the top of the page to the bottom, you can see the key components of the visits (e.g., history, exam, and medical decision making).

Although time is not considered a key component, it does influence the code selected when the portion of the visit concerning counseling or coordination of care takes more than 50% of the total encounter.

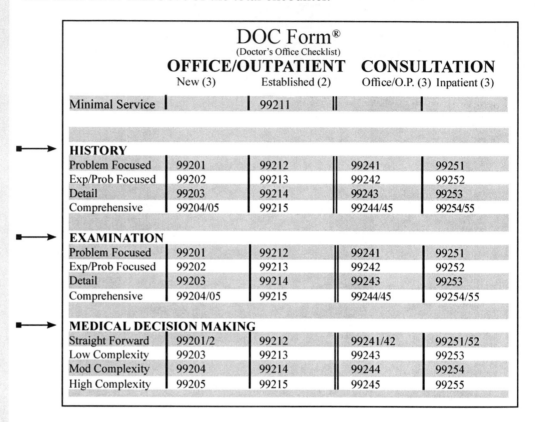

DOC Form® (Doctor's Office Checklist)				
	OFFICE/OUTPATIENT		**CONSULTATION**	
	New (3)	Established (2)	Office/O.P. (3)	Inpatient (3)
Minimal Service		99211		
HISTORY				
Problem Focused	99201	99212	99241	99251
Exp/Prob Focused	99202	99213	99242	99252
Detail	99203	99214	99243	99253
Comprehensive	99204/05	99215	99244/45	99254/55
EXAMINATION				
Problem Focused	99201	99212	99241	99251
Exp/Prob Focused	99202	99213	99242	99252
Detail	99203	99214	99243	99253
Comprehensive	99204/05	99215	99244/45	99254/55
MEDICAL DECISION MAKING				
Straight Forward	99201/2	99212	99241/42	99251/52
Low Complexity	99203	99213	99243	99253
Mod Complexity	99204	99214	99244	99254
High Complexity	99205	99215	99245	99255

When you look at the DOC form, you will see that time is listed at the bottom following the three key components.

TIME:_____   **Counsel/Coordination of Care:_____**

10 Minutes	99201	99212		
15 Minutes		99213	99241	
20 Minutes	99202			99251
25 Minutes		99214		
30 Minutes	99203		99242	
40 Minutes		99215	99243	99252
45 Minutes	99204			
55 Minutes				99253
60 Minutes	99205		99244	
80 Minutes			99245	99254
110 Minutes				99255

Patient Name:_____

Date:_____Physician Signature:_____

MedBooks, Inc.
101 W. Buckingham Road, Richardson, Tx. 75081 (800) 443-7397
Warning: This product is copyrighted and is not to be duplicated in any manner without the express written permission of MedBooks.

As you can see by looking at the form, a space follows the word "time." In this space, your physician should mark the amount of time spent with the patient. In most circumstances, the number of minutes will be consistent with the average length of time listed for the service in the code description. Your physician can also circle the amount of time spent as it is listed under the **Time** heading. Listing the amount of time on the form is a good habit, even if counseling or coordination of care is not the dominant factor controlling the visit. If you consistently list it, you can be sure it will be there when you need it.

DOC Form®
(Doctor's Office Checklist)
OFFICE/OUTPATIENT   CONSULTATION

	New (3)	Established (2)	Office/O.P. (3)	Inpatient (3)
Minimal Service		99211		

HISTORY

	New (3)	Established (2)	Office/O.P. (3)	Inpatient (3)
Problem Focused	99201	99212	99241	99251
Exp/Prob Focused	99202	99213	99242	99252
Detail	99203	99214	99243	99253
Comprehensive	99204/05	99215	99244/45	99254/55

EXAMINATION

Problem Focused	99201	99212	99241	99251
Exp/Prob Focused	99202	99213	99242	99252
Detail	99203	99214	99243	99253
Comprehensive	99204/05	99215	99244/45	99254/55

MEDICAL DECISION MAKING

Straight Forward	99201/2	99212	99241/42	99251/52
Low Complexity	99203	99213	99243	99253
Mod Complexity	99204	99214	99244	99254
High Complexity	99205	99215	99245	99255

TIME: (10)   **Counsel/Coordination of Care:**_____

	New	Established	Consult O.P.	Consult Inpatient
10 Minutes	99201	99212		
15 Minutes		99213	99241	
20 Minutes	99202			99251
25 Minutes		99214		
30 Minutes	99203		99242	
40 Minutes		99215	99243	99252
45 Minutes	99204			
55 Minutes				99253
60 Minutes	99205		99244	
80 Minutes			99245	99254
110 Minutes				99255

Patient Name:_____

Date:_____Physician Signature:_____

MedBooks, Inc.
101 W. Buckingham Road, Richardson, Tx. 75081 (800) 443-7397
Warning: This product is copyrighted and is not to be duplicated in any manner without the express written permission of MedBooks.

EXAMPLE 6.1

Using The DOC Form In The Office/Outpatient Environment

Let's do an exercise to show how you can piece this whole thing together.

Suppose a 10-year-old new patient comes into your office complaining of itching on his leg. Your physician takes a problem focused history (records the patient's name and age, finds out how he got the rash, determines whether he has any allergies) and completes a problem focused examination (looks at the rash, notices how red it is, notices if it is inflamed). Your physician decides that the patient has poison oak and that he needs a certain lotion (straightforward decision making). The physician writes down the name of the lotion for the patient, tells him how to use it, and thanks him for coming in. The entire visit takes about 10 minutes.

As you look at the DOC form, you will circle the following:
- Problem Focused History
- Problem Focused Examination
- Straightforward Medical Decision Making

You will also indicate 10 minutes in the space provided for the total time.

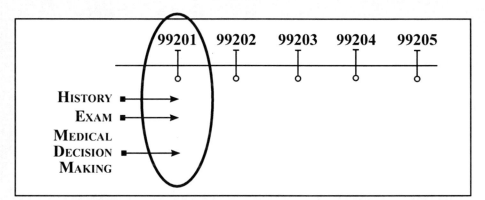

As you can see from the DOC Form on the previous page, under **New Patient**, you should choose the 99201 code because you circled 99201 at least three times (see *Example 6.1*). This means your physician met or exceeded the required number in at least three cases. The reason this number must be met (indicated by the same code number) or exceeded (indicated by a greater number) in at least three cases is that three key components are required for this visit. You were reminded that you needed three key components when you saw "New (3)" under Office/Outpatient Visits. On a lineal scale this example would appear as follows:

Notice that you met the number 99201 three out of the three required times for this new patient.

Let's take another example (see *Example 6.2*).

Suppose a second new patient comes into your office with the same complaint (poison oak). This time, your physician provides exactly the same services she provided for the first patient (problem focused history and examination with straightforward decision making). At the end of the visit, however, the mother of this boy goes on to explain that her son has had problems concentrating in school and asks for some advice on what to do. In other words, this "10-minute visit" has taken 30 minutes!

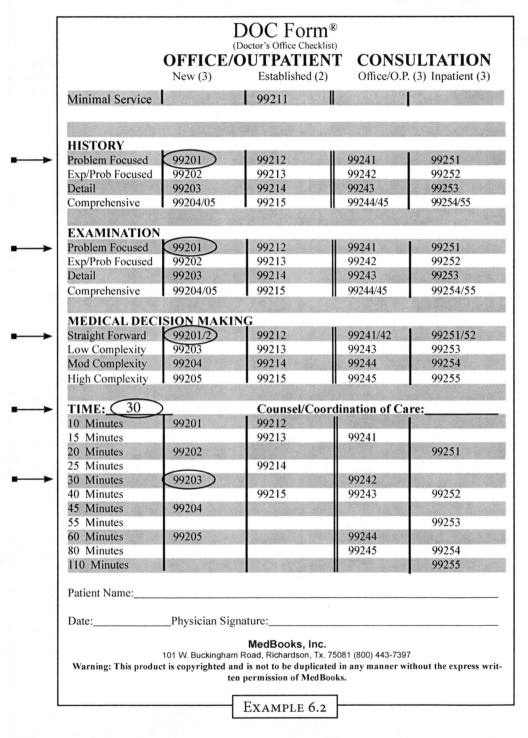

DOC Form®
(Doctor's Office Checklist)

OFFICE/OUTPATIENT　　　**CONSULTATION**

	New (3)	Established (2)	Office/O.P. (3)	Inpatient (3)
Minimal Service		99211		

HISTORY

Problem Focused	(99201)	99212	99241	99251
Exp/Prob Focused	99202	99213	99242	99252
Detail	99203	99214	99243	99253
Comprehensive	99204/05	99215	99244/45	99254/55

EXAMINATION

Problem Focused	(99201)	99212	99241	99251
Exp/Prob Focused	99202	99213	99242	99252
Detail	99203	99214	99243	99253
Comprehensive	99204/05	99215	99244/45	99254/55

MEDICAL DECISION MAKING

Straight Forward	(99201/2)	99212	99241/42	99251/52
Low Complexity	99203	99213	99243	99253
Mod Complexity	99204	99214	99244	99254
High Complexity	99205	99215	99245	99255

TIME: (30)　　　　　　**Counsel/Coordination of Care:** _____

10 Minutes	99201	99212		
15 Minutes		99213	99241	
20 Minutes	99202			99251
25 Minutes		99214		
30 Minutes	(99203)		99242	
40 Minutes		99215	99243	99252
45 Minutes	99204			
55 Minutes				99253
60 Minutes	99205		99244	
80 Minutes			99245	99254
110 Minutes				99255

Patient Name:_____

Date:_____Physician Signature:_____

MedBooks, Inc.
101 W. Buckingham Road, Richardson, Tx. 75081 (800) 443-7397
Warning: This product is copyrighted and is not to be duplicated in any manner without the express written permission of MedBooks.

EXAMPLE 6.2

By looking at the circles on your DOC Form, you can see that the correct code to use is 99203 because of the additional time spent in counseling.

The reason 99203 is the correct code for the second example is that the counseling was greater than 50% of the total time. Notice that the code associated with the 30-minute time frame was the code 99203.

Let's take one final example (*Example 6.3*).

Suppose an established patient who seems very ill comes into the office. Your physician performs an expanded problem focused history and an expanded problem focused examination. Because of the number of

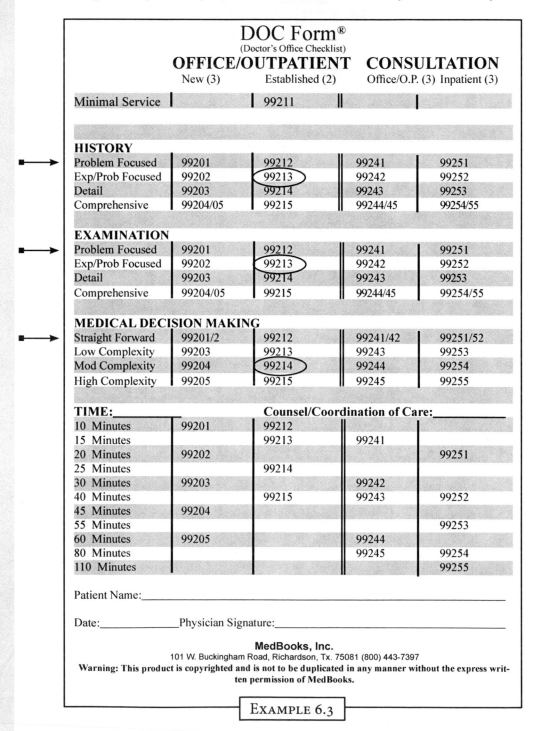

EXAMPLE 6.3

management options he has to consider, the amount and complexity of the data he has to review, and the risk of complications associated with various treatments, your physician makes a treatment decision that is moderately complex.

The DOC form (see *Example 6.3*) illustrates this.

As you can see, the circled codes are 99213 for the history, 99213 for the examination, and 99214 for the decision making. Because this is an established patient, two key components must be met or exceeded to qualify for the visit (see *Example 6.3*).

Looking at this on the lineal scale you can see that 99213 has been met twice and exceeded once (by 99214). Because 99213 has been exceeded only once (and **two** key components have to be met or exceeded), you must choose 99213.

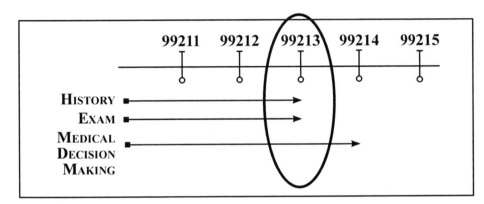

There are many systems available for choosing the appropriate E/M code. The DOC form is only one of them. Check with your supplier for either the DOC Form or another system.

On a final note, many people will tell you that it is better for you (if you can) to code and bill for a new patient visit because it pays more. This is not necessarily true. Because of the three-out-of-three rule for new patients and two-out-of-three rule for established ones, you may find that the exact same kind of visit may render two very different levels of service.

To illustrate this, let's say you saw a normal, healthy, 24-year-old patient for her yearly physical. If she were a new patient and your decision making were straightforward – even though you may have done a head to toe check with a pap smear and obtained a comprehensive history – you would need to code that visit as a 99202. This would be because of the fact that three of the three key components (i.e., history, exam and medical decision making) must be met, and the medical decision making portion brought you down to a straightforward or low complexity level (see DOC form). This same patient on an established level might be coded as a 99215, because only two of the three key components are required – which you qualify for under your history and exam (i.e., you met the 99215 under history and 99215 under exam, because both of them are comprehensive).

See *Example 6.4*. It's probably good for you to work this example out using the DOC form tools contained herein. Once you can "see" this example of the DOC form and once you go through the "process" of having to figure out the medical decision making, all of this will really make sense to you.

DOC Form®
(Doctor's Office Checklist)

OFFICE/OUTPATIENT   CONSULTATION

	New (3)	Established (2)	Office/O.P. (3)	Inpatient (3)
Minimal Service		99211		

HISTORY

Problem Focused	99201	99212	99241	99251
Exp/Prob Focused	99202	99213	99242	99252
Detail	99203	99214	99243	99253
Comprehensive	(99204/05)	(99215)	99244/45	99254/55

EXAMINATION

Problem Focused	99201	99212	99241	99251
Exp/Prob Focused	99202	99213	99242	99252
Detail	99203	99214	99243	99253
Comprehensive	(99204/05)	(99215)	99244/45	99254/55

MEDICAL DECISION MAKING

Straight Forward	(99201/2)	(99212)	99241/42	99251/52
Low Complexity	99203	99213	99243	99253
Mod Complexity	99204	99214	99244	99254
High Complexity	99205	99215	99245	99255

TIME:_____   Counsel/Coordination of Care:_____

10 Minutes	99201	99212		
15 Minutes		99213	99241	
20 Minutes	99202			99251
25 Minutes		99214		
30 Minutes	99203		99242	
40 Minutes		99215	99243	99252
45 Minutes	99204			
55 Minutes				99253
60 Minutes	99205		99244	
80 Minutes			99245	99254
110 Minutes				99255

Patient Name:_____

Date:_____Physician Signature:_____

MedBooks, Inc.
101 W. Buckingham Road, Richardson, Tx. 75081 (800) 443-7397
Warning: This product is copyrighted and is not to be duplicated in any manner without the express written permission of MedBooks.

EXAMPLE 6.4

Now let's move on to a discussion of the nuances in each subsection.

Office Or Other Outpatient Services

The Office/Outpatient subsection is divided into two parts: visits for new patients (those who have not received any professional services from the physician in the past three years) and visits for established patients (those who **have** received professional services in the past three years). (See exact definitions of new and established patients at the beginning of this chapter.) Once you have determined whether the patient is new or established, you must determine the degree of history, physical examination, and medical decision making performed in the visit.

It is important for you to understand that your "office" may be located in a stand-alone facility or in a hospital. **Where** it is located doesn't matter. As long as it's your office, you qualify to use these office visit codes.

An outpatient facility is one where the patient may be seen before being admitted to a hospital, nursing facility, or observation unit. These sites may include your office or some other ambulatory facility. If your physician is seeing patients in these environments, you can appropriately code for histories, examinations, and medical decisions rendered by using the Office/Outpatient Evaluation and Management codes.

If during the course of the patient encounter, your physician decides that the patient needs to be admitted to a hospital or nursing facility, you will have to use the codes from one of those sections and **not** the Office/Outpatient codes. Likewise, if your physician decides that the patient needs to be observed and followed until a decision to admit the patient is made, you would use the Hospital Observation service codes.

As you can see by looking at the Evaluation and Management codes described earlier, each time frame listed is the average length of time a particular visit takes among many different specialties. Don't get hung up on these time frames. What we said before bears repeating: An Evaluation and Management service deals with what the physician does during the time he or she spends with the patient, **not** with the amount of time itself. The exception is when the physician spends more than 50% of the total time in counseling and coordination of care.

As we also said earlier, remembering that time is not a "key ingredient" is one of the best things you can do for your office. Many billers cause a considerable loss of time and money for their physicians by not paying attention to the definitions and uses of key components. Insurance carriers have had many problems in the past with physicians who misused the "levels of service" in prior versions of CPT®. As a result, implementation and use of the Evaluation and Management codes is monitored very closely.

Although it is not a substitute for written documentation, use of the DOC form (in conjunction with patient progress notes) may protect the practice in an insurance audit. With the DOC form and your physician's complete notes in the medical record, you can easily show how you've followed the rules for CPT® Evaluation and Management codes in your billing practices.

Many a coder has made the grim mistake of choosing codes for one of the following reasons:

1. We need to code it that way to get the money our office requires for this type of examination.

2. The Evaluation and Management codes just don't pay correctly.

Using either of these reasons can cause your office trouble if you are audited by an insurance carrier.

Medicare (like the IRS) has the authority to audit each and every physician's office for misuse of codes. If a physician's office is found in violation of the coding rules, that physician may be required to repay all overcharges to the Medicare program or even be barred from participating in the program.

Medicare, like the IRS,
has the authority to audit.

Medicare carriers can often tell by their internal computers which codes your office uses most often. They track the charges submitted by your office and the codes you have used to submit those charges. For example, if your office only uses the Evaluation and Management code that describes a comprehensive history and examination (99204) for every new patient, the carrier's computer will show only this number on your office's history of charges for new patients.

Keep in mind that to carriers, not all patients fall into the same category. The old days of charging all new patients the same fee for the first visit, regardless of what the physician does, are gone. You must now code each patient visit according to the specific levels of judgment exercised by your physician during the visits.

The point of coding according to the level of expertise exercised in the patient/ physician encounter cannot be overstressed! A little care on the front end could save your office hours of work and headaches on the back end during an audit.

EXERCISE 6.1

1. A new patient is:_____

   _____

2. An established patient is:_____

   _____

3. The KEY components to a visit in the "Evaluation and Management" section are:

   a. _____

   b. _____

   c. _____

4. Face-To-Face Time:_____

   _____

5. HISTORY(IES) obtained by the physician fall into four types. Name each kind of history and give the description found in CPT®.

   a. _____

   b. _____

   c. _____

   d. _____

Before You Begin:
Read Chapter 6 in cpTeach® on "Evaluation and Management" and follow along in CPT®.

Purpose of this Lesson:
To familiarize the student with the Evaluation and Management codes found in the first chapter of CPT®.

Instructions:
1. Complete the following definitions.

WORKBOOK

cpTeach
2012

Name:_____

Class/Section:_____

Date:_____

Exercise 6.1

6. EXAMINATION(S) of the patient by the physician fall into four types. List the types and give the description from CPT®.

    a. _____

    b. _____

    c. _____

    d. _____

7. List the four types of medical decision making categories that are recognized. What three elements must be considered?

    a. _____

    b. _____

    c. _____

    d. _____

    Must consider:

    a. _____

    b. _____

    c. _____

Name:_____

Class/Section:_____

Date:_____

cpTeach
2012

EXERCISE 6.1

8. In general, all three key components for E/M codes should be **met or exceeded** in which of the following cases:

    _____　　a.　　When the patient is established.

    _____　　b.　　When the patient is new.

    _____　　c.　　When the patient is having an initial visit (i.e., initial hospital visit).

    _____　　d.　　None of the above.

    _____　　e.　　A and B are true.

    _____　　f.　　B and C are true.

9. Two of the three key components must be met or exceeded when:

    _____　　a.　　The patient is established.

    _____　　b.　　The patient is new.

    _____　　c.　　When the patient is having an initial visit (i.e., initial hospital visit).

    _____　　d.　　None of the above.

10. In order for you to be able to code using the Emergency Department codes, the facility must meet some very specific requirements. What are they?

    a.　_____

    b.　_____

WORKBOOK

cpTeach

2012

Name:_____

Class/Section:_____

Date:_____

Before You Begin:
Read the chapter in cpTeach®
that outlines the Evaluation
and Management codes.
Follow along in CPT® with
the points illustrated.

Purpose of this Lesson:
To familiarize the student
with the Evaluation and
Management codes.

Instructions:
1. Match the given range
   of codes to the correct
   description.

EXERCISE 6.2

99201 - 99205   _____   **a.** Inpatient Consultations

99221 - 99226   _____   **c.** Domiciliary, Rest Home (e.g.
                                     Boarding Home), or Custodial Care
                                     Services, New Patient

99231 - 99239   _____   **e.** Office or Other Outpatient
                                     Consultations

99238 - 99239   _____   **i.** Critical Care Services

99241 - 99245   _____   **o.** Initial Hospital Care

99251 - 99255   _____   **p.** Delivery/Birthing Room
                                     Attendance and Resuscitation
                                     Services

99324 - 99328   _____   **r.** Hospital Discharge Services

99464 - 99465   _____   **t.** Emergency Department Services

99281 - 99288   _____   **u.** Subsequent Hospital Care

99288   _____   **w.** Other Emergency Services

EXERCISE 6.2

99291 - 99292   _____   **y.**   Office or Other Outpatient Services; New Patient

99363 - 99368   _____   **z.**   Case Management Services

Before You Begin:

Read Chapter 6 in **cp**Teach® on "Evaluation and Management."

Purpose of this Lesson:

To familiarize the student with the different categories of E/M for both new and established patients as well as for subsequent and follow-up visits, and to instruct in the proper completion of the DOC form.

Instructions:

1. Using the DOC form, decide which category of E/M code to use for each patient in the following case studies. Complete the CPT® coding portion of the CM-1500 Claim form on the back of each page.

EXERCISE 6.3

Mrs. Hunter comes to Dr. A. B. Domen's office for advice at the request of her family practitioner, Dr. Landry. Mrs. Hunter is complaining of stomach pain. Dr. Domen records Mrs. Hunter's chief complaint, completes a past, family and social history and reviews systems directly related to her stomach problems. Performing a complete single system specialty exam of her stomach, he makes a decision of moderate complexity and prepares a report with his recommendations for Dr. Landry.

Notes: _____

_____

_____

_____

_____

_____

_____

_____

_____

_____

_____

_____

_____

_____

_____

_____

_____

_____

_____

_____

_____

_____

_____

_____

DOC Form®
(Doctor's Office Checklist)

| | OFFICE/OUTPATIENT | | CONSULTATION | |
	New (3)	Established (2)	Office/O.P. (3)	Inpatient (3)
Minimal Service		99211		
HISTORY				
Problem Focused	99201	99212	99241	99251
Exp/Prob Focused	99202	99213	99242	99252
Detail	99203	99214	99243	99253
Comprehensive	99204/05	99215	99244/45	99254/55
EXAMINATION				
Problem Focused	99201	99212	99241	99251
Exp/Prob Focused	99202	99213	99242	99252
Detail	99203	99214	99243	99253
Comprehensive	99204/05	99215	99244/45	99254/55
MEDICAL DECISION MAKING				
Straight Forward	99201/2	99212	99241/42	99251/52
Low Complexity	99203	99213	99243	99253
Mod Complexity	99204	99214	99244	99254
High Complexity	99205	99215	99245	99255

TIME:_____		Counsel/Coordination of Care:_____		
10 Minutes	99201	99212		
15 Minutes		99213	99241	
20 Minutes	99202			99251
25 Minutes		99214		
30 Minutes	99203		99242	
40 Minutes		99215	99243	99252
45 Minutes	99204			
55 Minutes				99253
60 Minutes	99205		99244	
80 Minutes			99245	99254
110 Minutes				99255

EXERCISE 6.3

WORKBOOK

cpTeach
2012

Name:_____

Class/Section:_____

Date:_____

1500
HEALTH INSURANCE CLAIM FORM

APPROVED BY NATIONAL UNIFORM CLAIM COMMITTEE 08/05

PICA		PICA

1. MEDICARE MEDICAID TRICARE CHAMPUS CHAMPVA GROUP HEALTH PLAN FECA BLK LUNG OTHER	1a. INSURED'S I.D. NUMBER (For Program in Item 1)
(Medicare #) (Medicaid #) (Sponsor's SSN) (Member ID#) (SSN or ID) (SSN) (ID)	

2. PATIENT'S NAME (Last Name, First Name, Middle Initial)	3. PATIENT'S BIRTH DATE MM DD YY SEX M F	4. INSURED'S NAME (Last Name, First Name, Middle Initial)
5. PATIENT'S ADDRESS (No., Street)	6. PATIENT RELATIONSHIP TO INSURED Self Spouse Child Other	7. INSURED'S ADDRESS (No., Street)
CITY STATE	8. PATIENT STATUS Single Married Other	CITY STATE
ZIP CODE TELEPHONE (Include Area Code) ( )	Employed Full-Time Student Part-Time Student	ZIP CODE TELEPHONE (Include Area Code) ( )

9. OTHER INSURED'S NAME (Last Name, First Name, Middle Initial)	10. IS PATIENT'S CONDITION RELATED TO:	11. INSURED'S POLICY GROUP OR FECA NUMBER
a. OTHER INSURED'S POLICY OR GROUP NUMBER	a. EMPLOYMENT? (Current or Previous) YES NO	a. INSURED'S DATE OF BIRTH MM DD YY SEX M F
b. OTHER INSURED'S DATE OF BIRTH MM DD YY SEX M F	b. AUTO ACCIDENT? PLACE (State) YES NO	b. EMPLOYER'S NAME OR SCHOOL NAME
c. EMPLOYER'S NAME OR SCHOOL NAME	c. OTHER ACCIDENT? YES NO	c. INSURANCE PLAN NAME OR PROGRAM NAME
d. INSURANCE PLAN NAME OR PROGRAM NAME	10d. RESERVED FOR LOCAL USE	d. IS THERE ANOTHER HEALTH BENEFIT PLAN? YES NO If yes, return to and complete item 9 a-d.

READ BACK OF FORM BEFORE COMPLETING & SIGNING THIS FORM.

12. PATIENT'S OR AUTHORIZED PERSON'S SIGNATURE I authorize the release of any medical or other information necessary to process this claim. I also request payment of government benefits either to myself or to the party who accepts assignment below.	13. INSURED'S OR AUTHORIZED PERSON'S SIGNATURE I authorize payment of medical benefits to the undersigned physician or supplier for services described below.
SIGNED_____ DATE_____	SIGNED_____

14. DATE OF CURRENT: MM DD YY ILLNESS (First symptom) OR INJURY (Accident) OR PREGNANCY(LMP)	15. IF PATIENT HAS HAD SAME OR SIMILAR ILLNESS. GIVE FIRST DATE MM DD YY	16. DATES PATIENT UNABLE TO WORK IN CURRENT OCCUPATION MM DD YY MM DD YY FROM TO
17. NAME OF REFERRING PROVIDER OR OTHER SOURCE	17a. \ 17b. NPI	18. HOSPITALIZATION DATES RELATED TO CURRENT SERVICES MM DD YY MM DD YY FROM TO
19. RESERVED FOR LOCAL USE		20. OUTSIDE LAB? YES NO $ CHARGES

21. DIAGNOSIS OR NATURE OF ILLNESS OR INJURY (Relate Items 1, 2, 3 or 4 to Item 24E by Line)	22. MEDICAID RESUBMISSION CODE ORIGINAL REF. NO.
1. |___.___| 3. |___.___|	
2. |___.___| 4. |___.___|	23. PRIOR AUTHORIZATION NUMBER

24. A. DATE(S) OF SERVICE From To MM DD YY MM DD YY	B. PLACE OF SERVICE	C. EMG	D. PROCEDURES, SERVICES, OR SUPPLIES (Explain Unusual Circumstances) CPT/HCPCS MODIFIER	E. DIAGNOSIS POINTER	F. $ CHARGES	G. DAYS OR UNITS	H. EPSDT Family Plan	I. ID. QUAL.	J. RENDERING PROVIDER ID. #
1								NPI	
2								NPI	
3								NPI	
4								NPI	
5								NPI	
6								NPI	

25. FEDERAL TAX I.D. NUMBER SSN EIN	26. PATIENT'S ACCOUNT NO.	27. ACCEPT ASSIGNMENT? (For govt. claims, see back) YES NO	28. TOTAL CHARGE $	29. AMOUNT PAID $	30. BALANCE DUE $
31. SIGNATURE OF PHYSICIAN OR SUPPLIER INCLUDING DEGREES OR CREDENTIALS (I certify that the statements on the reverse apply to this bill and are made a part thereof.) SIGNED_____ DATE_____	32. SERVICE FACILITY LOCATION INFORMATION a. b.	33. BILLING PROVIDER INFO & PH # ( ) a. b.			

NUCC Instruction Manual available at: www.nucc.org   OMB APPROVAL PENDING

PATIENT AND INSURED INFORMATION

PHYSICIAN OR SUPPLIER INFORMATION

EXERCISE 6.4

Dee Pression, a 16-year-old female patient, is referred to your office from the Emergency Room after overdosing on a bunch of Tylenol, sleeping pills and leftover cortisone that her mother had taken for poison ivy. You complete a family history and a personal history including finding out about her social habits. During your history taking you discover that this patient has had two abortions and that she abuses alcohol. You also learn that she has had multiple sexual partners, that her parents are divorced and that she hasn't seen her biological mother for 6 years. Additionally, she discusses her reasons for her suicide attempt relating that her boyfriend is seeing another girl.

Notes: _____

_____

_____

_____

_____

_____

_____

_____

_____

_____

_____

_____

_____

_____

_____

_____

_____

_____

_____

DOC Form®
(Doctor's Office Checklist)

OFFICE/OUTPATIENT　　　**CONSULTATION**

	New (3)	Established (2)	Office/O.P. (3)	Inpatient (3)
Minimal Service		99211		

HISTORY

	New (3)	Established (2)	Office/O.P. (3)	Inpatient (3)
Problem Focused	99201	99212	99241	99251
Exp/Prob Focused	99202	99213	99242	99252
Detail	99203	99214	99243	99253
Comprehensive	99204/05	99215	99244/45	99254/55

EXAMINATION

	New (3)	Established (2)	Office/O.P. (3)	Inpatient (3)
Problem Focused	99201	99212	99241	99251
Exp/Prob Focused	99202	99213	99242	99252
Detail	99203	99214	99243	99253
Comprehensive	99204/05	99215	99244/45	99254/55

MEDICAL DECISION MAKING

	New (3)	Established (2)	Office/O.P. (3)	Inpatient (3)
Straight Forward	99201/2	99212	99241/42	99251/52
Low Complexity	99203	99213	99243	99253
Mod Complexity	99204	99214	99244	99254
High Complexity	99205	99215	99245	99255

TIME:_____　　　　　**Counsel/Coordination of Care:_____**

	New (3)	Established (2)	Office/O.P. (3)	Inpatient (3)
10 Minutes	99201	99212		
15 Minutes		99213	99241	
20 Minutes	99202			99251
25 Minutes		99214		
30 Minutes	99203		99242	
40 Minutes		99215	99243	99252
45 Minutes	99204			
55 Minutes				99253
60 Minutes	99205		99244	
80 Minutes			99245	99254
110 Minutes				99255

EXERCISE 6.4

Name:_____

Class/Section:_____

Date:_____

WORKBOOK

cpTeach
2012

1500

HEALTH INSURANCE CLAIM FORM

APPROVED BY NATIONAL UNIFORM CLAIM COMMITTEE 08/05

	PICA								PICA	

1. MEDICARE	MEDICAID	TRICARE CHAMPUS	CHAMPVA	GROUP HEALTH PLAN	FECA BLK LUNG	OTHER	1a. INSURED'S I.D. NUMBER	(For Program in Item 1)
(Medicare #)	(Medicaid #)	(Sponsor's SSN)	(Member ID#)	(SSN or ID)	(SSN)	(ID)		

2. PATIENT'S NAME (Last Name, First Name, Middle Initial)

3. PATIENT'S BIRTH DATE MM DD YY   SEX   M   F

4. INSURED'S NAME (Last Name, First Name, Middle Initial)

5. PATIENT'S ADDRESS (No., Street)

6. PATIENT RELATIONSHIP TO INSURED   Self   Spouse   Child   Other

7. INSURED'S ADDRESS (No., Street)

CITY   STATE

8. PATIENT STATUS   Single   Married   Other

CITY   STATE

ZIP CODE   TELEPHONE (Include Area Code) (   )

Employed   Full-Time Student   Part-Time Student

ZIP CODE   TELEPHONE (Include Area Code) (   )

9. OTHER INSURED'S NAME (Last Name, First Name, Middle Initial)

10. IS PATIENT'S CONDITION RELATED TO:

11. INSURED'S POLICY GROUP OR FECA NUMBER

a. OTHER INSURED'S POLICY OR GROUP NUMBER

a. EMPLOYMENT? (Current or Previous)   YES   NO

a. INSURED'S DATE OF BIRTH MM DD YY   SEX   M   F

b. OTHER INSURED'S DATE OF BIRTH MM DD YY   SEX   M   F

b. AUTO ACCIDENT?   PLACE (State)   YES   NO

b. EMPLOYER'S NAME OR SCHOOL NAME

c. EMPLOYER'S NAME OR SCHOOL NAME

c. OTHER ACCIDENT?   YES   NO

c. INSURANCE PLAN NAME OR PROGRAM NAME

d. INSURANCE PLAN NAME OR PROGRAM NAME

10d. RESERVED FOR LOCAL USE

d. IS THERE ANOTHER HEALTH BENEFIT PLAN?   YES   NO   If yes, return to and complete item 9 a-d.

READ BACK OF FORM BEFORE COMPLETING & SIGNING THIS FORM.

12. PATIENT'S OR AUTHORIZED PERSON'S SIGNATURE I authorize the release of any medical or other information necessary to process this claim. I also request payment of government benefits either to myself or to the party who accepts assignment below.

SIGNED_____   DATE_____

13. INSURED'S OR AUTHORIZED PERSON'S SIGNATURE I authorize payment of medical benefits to the undersigned physician or supplier for services described below.

SIGNED_____

14. DATE OF CURRENT: MM DD YY   ILLNESS (First symptom) OR INJURY (Accident) OR PREGNANCY(LMP)

15. IF PATIENT HAS HAD SAME OR SIMILAR ILLNESS. GIVE FIRST DATE MM DD YY

16. DATES PATIENT UNABLE TO WORK IN CURRENT OCCUPATION MM DD YY   FROM   TO   MM DD YY

17. NAME OF REFERRING PROVIDER OR OTHER SOURCE   17a.   17b. NPI

18. HOSPITALIZATION DATES RELATED TO CURRENT SERVICES MM DD YY   FROM   TO   MM DD YY

19. RESERVED FOR LOCAL USE

20. OUTSIDE LAB?   YES   NO $ CHARGES

21. DIAGNOSIS OR NATURE OF ILLNESS OR INJURY (Relate Items 1, 2, 3 or 4 to Item 24E by Line)

1. |___.___   3. |___.___

2. |___.___   4. |___.___

22. MEDICAID RESUBMISSION CODE   ORIGINAL REF. NO.

23. PRIOR AUTHORIZATION NUMBER

24. A DATE(S) OF SERVICE						B. PLACE OF SERVICE	C. EMG	D. PROCEDURES, SERVICES, OR SUPPLIES (Explain Unusual Circumstances)		E. DIAGNOSIS POINTER	F. $ CHARGES	G. DAYS OR UNITS	H. EPSDT Family Plan	I. ID. QUAL.	J. RENDERING PROVIDER ID. #
From MM DD YY			To MM DD YY					CPT/HCPCS	MODIFIER						
1														NPI	
2														NPI	
3														NPI	
4														NPI	
5														NPI	
6														NPI	

25. FEDERAL TAX I.D. NUMBER   SSN   EIN

26. PATIENT'S ACCOUNT NO.

27. ACCEPT ASSIGNMENT? (For govt. claims, see back)   YES   NO

28. TOTAL CHARGE $

29. AMOUNT PAID $

30. BALANCE DUE $

31. SIGNATURE OF PHYSICIAN OR SUPPLIER INCLUDING DEGREES OR CREDENTIALS (I certify that the statements on the reverse apply to this bill and are made a part thereof.)

SIGNED_____   DATE_____

32. SERVICE FACILITY LOCATION INFORMATION

a. NPI   b.

33. BILLING PROVIDER INFO & PH # (   )

a. NPI   b.

NUCC Instruction Manual available at: www.nucc.org

OMB APPROVAL PENDING

PATIENT AND INSURED INFORMATION

PHYSICIAN OR SUPPLIER INFORMATION

X

WORKBOOK	*Name:* _____	
cpTeach 2012	*Class/Section:* _____	
	Date: _____	

EXERCISE 6.5

Thor Asic, a 75-year-old male patient, presents himself to your office at the request of his internist. He explains to you that he has been urinating a lot (has frequent episodes of having to get up in the middle of the night to go to the bathroom) and that it is painful for him to ride his bike for any period of time. He also tells you that his primary care physician had ordered a PSA level on him and that his results were elevated. Additionally, when you review the past medical history and medical chart, you learn that he has had a biopsy of his prostate and that the biopsy showed cancer. This patient is very active (as you learn about during the social history) and in addition to being full of life, he has maintained his body quite well and has kept his cholesterol low. You complete a physical exam checking all body systems including chest, eyes, lungs, heart, cardiovascular and urinary system and you perform a rectal exam to check the prostate. At the conclusion of the visit, you discuss with the patient possible treatment options including surgery to remove his prostate and you send a letter explaining your findings to the internist. The patient chooses surgery and you schedule the operation for the following week. Code for the E/M service only.

Notes: _____

_____

_____

_____

_____

_____

_____

DOC Form®
(Doctor's Office Checklist)

	OFFICE/OUTPATIENT		CONSULTATION	
	New (3)	Established (2)	Office/O.P. (3)	Inpatient (3)
Minimal Service		99211		

HISTORY				
Problem Focused	99201	99212	99241	99251
Exp/Prob Focused	99202	99213	99242	99252
Detail	99203	99214	99243	99253
Comprehensive	99204/05	99215	99244/45	99254/55

EXAMINATION				
Problem Focused	99201	99212	99241	99251
Exp/Prob Focused	99202	99213	99242	99252
Detail	99203	99214	99243	99253
Comprehensive	99204/05	99215	99244/45	99254/55

MEDICAL DECISION MAKING				
Straight Forward	99201/2	99212	99241/42	99251/52
Low Complexity	99203	99213	99243	99253
Mod Complexity	99204	99214	99244	99254
High Complexity	99205	99215	99245	99255

TIME: _____		**Counsel/Coordination of Care:** _____		
10 Minutes	99201	99212		
15 Minutes		99213	99241	
20 Minutes	99202			99251
25 Minutes		99214		
30 Minutes	99203		99242	
40 Minutes		99215	99243	99252
45 Minutes	99204			
55 Minutes				99253
60 Minutes	99205		99244	
80 Minutes			99245	99254
110 Minutes				99255

MedBooks, Inc.
101 W. Buckingham Road, Richardson, Tx. 75081 (800) 443-7397
Warning: This product is copyrighted and is not to be duplicated in any manner without the express written permission of MedBooks.

EXERCISE 6.5

Name:_____

Class/Section:_____

cpTeach 2012   Date:_____

[1500]

HEALTH INSURANCE CLAIM FORM
APPROVED BY NATIONAL UNIFORM CLAIM COMMITTEE 08/05

☐☐☐ PICA

PICA ☐☐☐

1. MEDICARE	MEDICAID	TRICARE CHAMPUS	CHAMPVA	GROUP HEALTH PLAN	FECA BLK LUNG	OTHER	1a. INSURED'S I.D. NUMBER	(For Program in Item 1)
☐ (Medicare #)	☐ (Medicaid #)	☐ (Sponsor's SSN)	☐ (Member ID#)	☐ (SSN or ID)	☐ (SSN)	☐ (ID)		

2. PATIENT'S NAME (Last Name, First Name, Middle Initial)

3. PATIENT'S BIRTH DATE MM DD YY   SEX M ☐ F ☐

4. INSURED'S NAME (Last Name, First Name, Middle Initial)

5. PATIENT'S ADDRESS (No., Street)

6. PATIENT RELATIONSHIP TO INSURED   Self ☐ Spouse ☐ Child ☐ Other ☐

7. INSURED'S ADDRESS (No., Street)

CITY   STATE

8. PATIENT STATUS   Single ☐ Married ☐ Other ☐   Employed ☐ Full-Time Student ☐ Part-Time Student ☐

CITY   STATE

ZIP CODE   TELEPHONE (Include Area Code) (   )

ZIP CODE   TELEPHONE (Include Area Code) (   )

9. OTHER INSURED'S NAME (Last Name, First Name, Middle Initial)

10. IS PATIENT'S CONDITION RELATED TO:

11. INSURED'S POLICY GROUP OR FECA NUMBER

a. OTHER INSURED'S POLICY OR GROUP NUMBER

a. EMPLOYMENT? (Current or Previous)   YES ☐ NO ☐

a. INSURED'S DATE OF BIRTH MM DD YY   SEX M ☐ F ☐

b. OTHER INSURED'S DATE OF BIRTH MM DD YY   SEX M ☐ F ☐

b. AUTO ACCIDENT?   YES ☐ NO ☐   PLACE (State)

b. EMPLOYER'S NAME OR SCHOOL NAME

c. EMPLOYER'S NAME OR SCHOOL NAME

c. OTHER ACCIDENT?   YES ☐ NO ☐

c. INSURANCE PLAN NAME OR PROGRAM NAME

d. INSURANCE PLAN NAME OR PROGRAM NAME

10d. RESERVED FOR LOCAL USE

d. IS THERE ANOTHER HEALTH BENEFIT PLAN?   YES ☐ NO ☐ If yes, return to and complete item 9 a-d.

READ BACK OF FORM BEFORE COMPLETING & SIGNING THIS FORM.
12. PATIENT'S OR AUTHORIZED PERSON'S SIGNATURE I authorize the release of any medical or other information necessary to process this claim. I also request payment of government benefits either to myself or to the party who accepts assignment below.

SIGNED_____   DATE_____

13. INSURED'S OR AUTHORIZED PERSON'S SIGNATURE I authorize payment of medical benefits to the undersigned physician or supplier for services described below.

SIGNED_____

14. DATE OF CURRENT: MM DD YY ◄ ILLNESS (First symptom) OR INJURY (Accident) OR PREGNANCY(LMP)

15. IF PATIENT HAS HAD SAME OR SIMILAR ILLNESS. GIVE FIRST DATE MM DD YY

16. DATES PATIENT UNABLE TO WORK IN CURRENT OCCUPATION MM DD YY FROM   TO MM DD YY

17. NAME OF REFERRING PROVIDER OR OTHER SOURCE

17a.

17b. NPI

18. HOSPITALIZATION DATES RELATED TO CURRENT SERVICES MM DD YY FROM   TO MM DD YY

19. RESERVED FOR LOCAL USE

20. OUTSIDE LAB?   YES ☐ NO ☐ $ CHARGES

21. DIAGNOSIS OR NATURE OF ILLNESS OR INJURY (Relate Items 1, 2, 3 or 4 to Item 24E by Line)

1. |___.___| 3. |___.___|

2. |___.___| 4. |___.___|

22. MEDICAID RESUBMISSION CODE   ORIGINAL REF. NO.

23. PRIOR AUTHORIZATION NUMBER

24. A. DATE(S) OF SERVICE From MM DD YY To MM DD YY	B. PLACE OF SERVICE	C. EMG	D. PROCEDURES, SERVICES, OR SUPPLIES (Explain Unusual Circumstances) CPT/HCPCS MODIFIER	E. DIAGNOSIS POINTER	F. $ CHARGES	G. DAYS OR UNITS	H. EPSDT Family Plan	I. ID. QUAL.	J. RENDERING PROVIDER ID. #
1								NPI	
2								NPI	
3								NPI	
4								NPI	
5								NPI	
6								NPI	

25. FEDERAL TAX I.D. NUMBER   SSN ☐ EIN ☐

26. PATIENT'S ACCOUNT NO.

27. ACCEPT ASSIGNMENT? (For govt. claims, see back)   YES ☐ NO ☐

28. TOTAL CHARGE $

29. AMOUNT PAID $

30. BALANCE DUE $

31. SIGNATURE OF PHYSICIAN OR SUPPLIER INCLUDING DEGREES OR CREDENTIALS (I certify that the statements on the reverse apply to this bill and are made a part thereof.)

SIGNED_____   DATE_____

32. SERVICE FACILITY LOCATION INFORMATION

33. BILLING PROVIDER INFO & PH # (   )

a.   b.

a.   b.

Name:_____

Class/Section:_____

cpTeach Date:_____

2012

EXERCISE 6.6

Young Billy Rubin, a four-year-old established patient of yours, presents himself to your office for a check up of ear tubes that were placed 8 months ago. You question both the mother and the patient about hearing problems or concerns, and find that there are none. You examine the ears and conclude that the patient is proceeding along beautifully and does not need any additional follow-up unless there are any problems.

Notes: _____

_____

_____

_____

_____

_____

_____

_____

_____

_____

_____

_____

_____

_____

_____

_____

_____

_____

_____

_____

_____

_____

_____

_____

_____

DOC Form®
(Doctor's Office Checklist)

OFFICE/OUTPATIENT — CONSULTATION

	New (3)	Established (2)	Office/O.P. (3)	Inpatient (3)
Minimal Service		99211		

HISTORY

	New (3)	Established (2)	Office/O.P. (3)	Inpatient (3)
Problem Focused	99201	99212	99241	99251
Exp/Prob Focused	99202	99213	99242	99252
Detail	99203	99214	99243	99253
Comprehensive	99204/05	99215	99244/45	99254/55

EXAMINATION

	New (3)	Established (2)	Office/O.P. (3)	Inpatient (3)
Problem Focused	99201	99212	99241	99251
Exp/Prob Focused	99202	99213	99242	99252
Detail	99203	99214	99243	99253
Comprehensive	99204/05	99215	99244/45	99254/55

MEDICAL DECISION MAKING

	New (3)	Established (2)	Office/O.P. (3)	Inpatient (3)
Straight Forward	99201/2	99212	99241/42	99251/52
Low Complexity	99203	99213	99243	99253
Mod Complexity	99204	99214	99244	99254
High Complexity	99205	99215	99245	99255

TIME:_____   Counsel/Coordination of Care:_____

	New (3)	Established (2)	Office/O.P. (3)	Inpatient (3)
10 Minutes	99201	99212		
15 Minutes		99213	99241	
20 Minutes	99202			99251
25 Minutes		99214		
30 Minutes	99203		99242	
40 Minutes		99215	99243	99252
45 Minutes	99204			
55 Minutes				99253
60 Minutes	99205		99244	
80 Minutes			99245	99254
110 Minutes				99255

MedBooks, Inc.
101 W. Buckingham Road, Richardson, Tx. 75081 (800) 443-7397
Warning: This product is copyrighted and is not to be duplicated in any manner without the express written permission of MedBooks.

EXERCISE 6.6

1500
HEALTH INSURANCE CLAIM FORM
APPROVED BY NATIONAL UNIFORM CLAIM COMMITTEE 08/05

☐☐☐ PICA

| | | | | | | | | PICA ☐☐☐ |

1. MEDICARE (Medicare #) ☐   **MEDICAID** (Medicaid #) ☐   **TRICARE CHAMPUS** (Sponsor's SSN) ☐   **CHAMPVA** (Member ID#) ☐   **GROUP HEALTH PLAN** (SSN or ID) ☐   **FECA BLK LUNG** (SSN) ☐   **OTHER** (ID) ☐   **1a. INSURED'S I.D. NUMBER** (For Program in Item 1)

2. PATIENT'S NAME (Last Name, First Name, Middle Initial)

3. PATIENT'S BIRTH DATE MM | DD | YY   **SEX** M ☐ F ☐

4. INSURED'S NAME (Last Name, First Name, Middle Initial)

5. PATIENT'S ADDRESS (No., Street)

6. PATIENT RELATIONSHIP TO INSURED Self ☐ Spouse ☐ Child ☐ Other ☐

7. INSURED'S ADDRESS (No., Street)

CITY | **STATE**

9. PATIENT STATUS Single ☐ Married ☐ Other ☐

CITY | **STATE**

ZIP CODE | **TELEPHONE** (Include Area Code) ( )

Employed ☐ Full-Time Student ☐ Part-Time Student ☐

ZIP CODE | **TELEPHONE** (Include Area Code) ( )

9. OTHER INSURED'S NAME (Last Name, First Name, Middle Initial)

10. IS PATIENT'S CONDITION RELATED TO:

11. INSURED'S POLICY GROUP OR FECA NUMBER

a. OTHER INSURED'S POLICY OR GROUP NUMBER

a. EMPLOYMENT? (Current or Previous) YES ☐ NO ☐

a. INSURED'S DATE OF BIRTH MM | DD | YY   **SEX** M ☐ F ☐

b. OTHER INSURED'S DATE OF BIRTH MM | DD | YY   **SEX** M ☐ F ☐

b. AUTO ACCIDENT? PLACE (State) YES ☐ NO ☐

b. EMPLOYER'S NAME OR SCHOOL NAME

c. EMPLOYER'S NAME OR SCHOOL NAME

c. OTHER ACCIDENT? YES ☐ NO ☐

c. INSURANCE PLAN NAME OR PROGRAM NAME

d. INSURANCE PLAN NAME OR PROGRAM NAME

10d. RESERVED FOR LOCAL USE

d. IS THERE ANOTHER HEALTH BENEFIT PLAN? YES ☐ NO ☐ If yes, return to and complete item 9 a-d.

READ BACK OF FORM BEFORE COMPLETING & SIGNING THIS FORM.
12. PATIENT'S OR AUTHORIZED PERSON'S SIGNATURE I authorize the release of any medical or other information necessary to process this claim. I also request payment of government benefits either to myself or to the party who accepts assignment below.

SIGNED_____ DATE_____

13. INSURED'S OR AUTHORIZED PERSON'S SIGNATURE I authorize payment of medical benefits to the undersigned physician or supplier for services described below.

SIGNED_____

14. DATE OF CURRENT: MM | DD | YY ◄ ILLNESS (First symptom) OR INJURY (Accident) OR PREGNANCY(LMP)

15. IF PATIENT HAS HAD SAME OR SIMILAR ILLNESS. GIVE FIRST DATE MM | DD | YY

16. DATES PATIENT UNABLE TO WORK IN CURRENT OCCUPATION FROM MM | DD | YY TO MM | DD | YY

17. NAME OF REFERRING PROVIDER OR OTHER SOURCE

17a.
17b. NPI

18. HOSPITALIZATION DATES RELATED TO CURRENT SERVICES FROM MM | DD | YY TO MM | DD | YY

19. RESERVED FOR LOCAL USE

20. OUTSIDE LAB? YES ☐ NO ☐   **$ CHARGES**

21. DIAGNOSIS OR NATURE OF ILLNESS OR INJURY (Relate Items 1, 2, 3 or 4 to Item 24E by Line)

1. |___.___   3. |___.___

2. |___.___   4. |___.___

22. MEDICAID RESUBMISSION CODE   ORIGINAL REF. NO.

23. PRIOR AUTHORIZATION NUMBER

24. A. DATE(S) OF SERVICE						B. PLACE OF SERVICE	C. EMG	D. PROCEDURES, SERVICES, OR SUPPLIES (Explain Unusual Circumstances)		E. DIAGNOSIS POINTER	F. $ CHARGES	G. DAYS OR UNITS	H. EPSDT Family Plan	I. ID. QUAL.	J. RENDERING PROVIDER ID. #
From MM	DD	YY	To MM	DD	YY			CPT/HCPCS	MODIFIER						
1														NPI	
2														NPI	
3														NPI	
4														NPI	
5														NPI	
6														NPI	

25. FEDERAL TAX I.D. NUMBER SSN ☐ EIN ☐

26. PATIENT'S ACCOUNT NO.

27. ACCEPT ASSIGNMENT? (For govt. claims, see back) YES ☐ NO ☐

28. TOTAL CHARGE $

29. AMOUNT PAID $

30. BALANCE DUE $

31. SIGNATURE OF PHYSICIAN OR SUPPLIER INCLUDING DEGREES OR CREDENTIALS (I certify that the statements on the reverse apply to this bill and are made a part thereof.)

SIGNED_____ DATE_____

32. SERVICE FACILITY LOCATION INFORMATION

a. NPI   b.

33. BILLING PROVIDER INFO & PH # ( )

a. NPI   b.

NUCC Instruction Manual available at: www.nucc.org

OMB APPROVAL PENDING

Name:_____

Class/Section:_____

Date:_____

EXERCISE 6.7

Sarah Bellum, an established patient of yours, comes to your office today because she was tested for different allergies yesterday. Your nurse has been instructed to observe her to see if there have been any follow-up reactions. No reactions to any of the antigens are noted and the patient is released until the physician can order further tests.

Notes: _____
_____
_____
_____
_____
_____
_____
_____
_____
_____
_____
_____
_____
_____
_____
_____
_____
_____
_____
_____
_____
_____
_____
_____

DOC Form®
(Doctor's Office Checklist)

	OFFICE/OUTPATIENT		CONSULTATION	
	New (3)	Established (2)	Office/O.P. (3)	Inpatient (3)
Minimal Service		99211		

HISTORY

	New (3)	Established (2)	Office/O.P. (3)	Inpatient (3)
Problem Focused	99201	99212	99241	99251
Exp/Prob Focused	99202	99213	99242	99252
Detail	99203	99214	99243	99253
Comprehensive	99204/05	99215	99244/45	99254/55

EXAMINATION

	New (3)	Established (2)	Office/O.P. (3)	Inpatient (3)
Problem Focused	99201	99212	99241	99251
Exp/Prob Focused	99202	99213	99242	99252
Detail	99203	99214	99243	99253
Comprehensive	99204/05	99215	99244/45	99254/55

MEDICAL DECISION MAKING

	New (3)	Established (2)	Office/O.P. (3)	Inpatient (3)
Straight Forward	99201/2	99212	99241/42	99251/52
Low Complexity	99203	99213	99243	99253
Mod Complexity	99204	99214	99244	99254
High Complexity	99205	99215	99245	99255

TIME: **Counsel/Coordination of Care:**

	New (3)	Established (2)	Office/O.P. (3)	Inpatient (3)
10 Minutes	99201	99212		
15 Minutes		99213	99241	
20 Minutes	99202			99251
25 Minutes		99214		
30 Minutes	99203		99242	
40 Minutes		99215	99243	99252
45 Minutes	99204			
55 Minutes				99253
60 Minutes	99205		99244	
80 Minutes			99245	99254
110 Minutes				99255

MedBooks, Inc.
101 W. Buckingham Road, Richardson, Tx. 75081 (800) 443-7397
Warning: This product is copyrighted and is not to be duplicated in any manner without the express written permission of MedBooks.

EXERCISE 6.7

Name:_____

Class/Section:_____

cpTeach 2012

Date:_____

1500
HEALTH INSURANCE CLAIM FORM
APPROVED BY NATIONAL UNIFORM CLAIM COMMITTEE 08/05

PICA

PICA

PATIENT AND INSURED INFORMATION

1. MEDICARE	MEDICAID	TRICARE CHAMPUS	CHAMPVA	GROUP HEALTH PLAN	FECA BLK LUNG	OTHER	1a. INSURED'S I.D. NUMBER (For Program in Item 1)
(Medicare #)	(Medicaid #)	(Sponsor's SSN)	(Member ID#)	(SSN or ID)	(SSN)	(ID)	

2. PATIENT'S NAME (Last Name, First Name, Middle Initial)

3. PATIENT'S BIRTH DATE MM DD YY   SEX M F

4. INSURED'S NAME (Last Name, First Name, Middle Initial)

5. PATIENT'S ADDRESS (No., Street)

6. PATIENT RELATIONSHIP TO INSURED Self Spouse Child Other

7. INSURED'S ADDRESS (No., Street)

CITY   STATE

8. PATIENT STATUS Single Married Other

Employed Full-Time Student Part-Time Student

CITY   STATE

ZIP CODE   TELEPHONE (Include Area Code) ( )

ZIP CODE   TELEPHONE (Include Area Code) ( )

9. OTHER INSURED'S NAME (Last Name, First Name, Middle Initial)

10. IS PATIENT'S CONDITION RELATED TO:

11. INSURED'S POLICY GROUP OR FECA NUMBER

a. OTHER INSURED'S POLICY OR GROUP NUMBER

a. EMPLOYMENT? (Current or Previous) YES NO

a. INSURED'S DATE OF BIRTH MM DD YY   SEX M F

b. OTHER INSURED'S DATE OF BIRTH MM DD YY   SEX M F

b. AUTO ACCIDENT? PLACE (State) YES NO

b. EMPLOYER'S NAME OR SCHOOL NAME

c. EMPLOYER'S NAME OR SCHOOL NAME

c. OTHER ACCIDENT? YES NO

c. INSURANCE PLAN NAME OR PROGRAM NAME

d. INSURANCE PLAN NAME OR PROGRAM NAME

10d. RESERVED FOR LOCAL USE

d. IS THERE ANOTHER HEALTH BENEFIT PLAN? YES NO If yes, return to and complete item 9 a-d.

READ BACK OF FORM BEFORE COMPLETING & SIGNING THIS FORM.
12. PATIENT'S OR AUTHORIZED PERSON'S SIGNATURE I authorize the release of any medical or other information necessary to process this claim. I also request payment of government benefits either to myself or to the party who accepts assignment below.

SIGNED_____ DATE_____

13. INSURED'S OR AUTHORIZED PERSON'S SIGNATURE I authorize payment of medical benefits to the undersigned physician or supplier for services described below.

SIGNED_____

PHYSICIAN OR SUPPLIER INFORMATION

14. DATE OF CURRENT: MM DD YY ILLNESS (First symptom) OR INJURY (Accident) OR PREGNANCY(LMP)

15. IF PATIENT HAS HAD SAME OR SIMILAR ILLNESS. GIVE FIRST DATE MM DD YY

16. DATES PATIENT UNABLE TO WORK IN CURRENT OCCUPATION MM DD YY   MM DD YY FROM   TO

17. NAME OF REFERRING PROVIDER OR OTHER SOURCE

17a.
17b. NPI

18. HOSPITALIZATION DATES RELATED TO CURRENT SERVICES MM DD YY   MM DD YY FROM   TO

19. RESERVED FOR LOCAL USE

20. OUTSIDE LAB? YES NO $ CHARGES

21. DIAGNOSIS OR NATURE OF ILLNESS OR INJURY (Relate Items 1, 2, 3 or 4 to Item 24E by Line)

1. |___.___
2. |___.___
3. |___.___
4. |___.___

22. MEDICAID RESUBMISSION CODE   ORIGINAL REF. NO.

23. PRIOR AUTHORIZATION NUMBER

24. A. DATE(S) OF SERVICE From MM DD YY To MM DD YY	B. PLACE OF SERVICE	C. EMG	D. PROCEDURES, SERVICES, OR SUPPLIES (Explain Unusual Circumstances) CPT/HCPCS MODIFIER	E. DIAGNOSIS POINTER	F. $ CHARGES	G. DAYS OR UNITS	H. EPSDT Family Plan	I. ID. QUAL.	J. RENDERING PROVIDER ID. #
1								NPI	
2								NPI	
3								NPI	
4								NPI	
5								NPI	
6								NPI	

25. FEDERAL TAX I.D. NUMBER   SSN EIN

26. PATIENT'S ACCOUNT NO.

27. ACCEPT ASSIGNMENT? (For govt. claims, see back) YES NO

28. TOTAL CHARGE $

29. AMOUNT PAID $

30. BALANCE DUE $

31. SIGNATURE OF PHYSICIAN OR SUPPLIER INCLUDING DEGREES OR CREDENTIALS (I certify that the statements on the reverse apply to this bill and are made a part thereof.)

SIGNED_____ DATE_____

32. SERVICE FACILITY LOCATION INFORMATION

a.   b.

33. BILLING PROVIDER INFO & PH # ( )

a.   b.

NUCC Instruction Manual available at: www.nucc.org

OMB APPROVAL PENDING

Name: _____	
Class/Section: _____	
Date: _____	
2012	

Exercise 6.8

Kathy Ter, an established patient of yours, calls you today demanding to be seen. She says that she is itching all over her body and that she can't stand it anymore. Once at your office, she relates to you that she had been gardening the day before and had pulled some major vincs (one inch diameter) off of the shed outside. Upon examination of her entire body, you notice that your patient has a very serious case of poison ivy that has impacted about 80 percent of her body. You check her for any signs of shock or allergy, but at this point she seems okay although the risk of morbidity or mortality in a case like this is high. Since she is so severely infected, you prescribe some cortisone and some oatmeal baths and ask that she return in a few days and to call you if anything gets any worse. You also suggest that a dip in the local public pool would be very soothing for the itching.

Notes: _____

_____

_____

_____

_____

_____

_____

_____

_____

_____

_____

_____

_____

_____

_____

DOC Form®
(Doctor's Office Checklist)

OFFICE/OUTPATIENT　　CONSULTATION

	New (3)	Established (2)	Office/O.P. (3)	Inpatient (3)
Minimal Service		99211		

HISTORY

Problem Focused	99201	99212	99241	99251
Exp/Prob Focused	99202	99213	99242	99252
Detail	99203	99214	99243	99253
Comprehensive	99204/05	99215	99244/45	99254/55

EXAMINATION

Problem Focused	99201	99212	99241	99251
Exp/Prob Focused	99202	99213	99242	99252
Detail	99203	99214	99243	99253
Comprehensive	99204/05	99215	99244/45	99254/55

MEDICAL DECISION MAKING

Straight Forward	99201/2	99212	99241/42	99251/52
Low Complexity	99203	99213	99243	99253
Mod Complexity	99204	99214	99244	99254
High Complexity	99205	99215	99245	99255

TIME:_____　　Counsel/Coordination of Care:_____

10 Minutes	99201	99212		
15 Minutes		99213	99241	
20 Minutes	99202			99251
25 Minutes		99214		
30 Minutes	99203		99242	
40 Minutes		99215	99243	99252
45 Minutes	99204			
55 Minutes				99253
60 Minutes	99205		99244	
80 Minutes			99245	99254
110 Minutes				99255

MedBooks, Inc.
101 W. Buckingham Road, Richardson, Tx. 75081 (800) 443-7397
Warning: This product is copyrighted and is not to be duplicated in any manner without the express written permission of MedBooks.

EXERCISE 6.8

Name: _____

Class/Section: _____

Date: _____

1500

HEALTH INSURANCE CLAIM FORM

APPROVED BY NATIONAL UNIFORM CLAIM COMMITTEE 08/05

| | PICA | | | | | | | | PICA | |

1. MEDICARE	MEDICAID	TRICARE CHAMPUS	CHAMPVA	GROUP HEALTH PLAN	FECA BLK LUNG	OTHER	1a. INSURED'S I.D. NUMBER	(For Program in Item 1)
(Medicare #)	(Medicaid #)	(Sponsor's SSN)	(Member ID#)	(SSN or ID)	(SSN)	(ID)		

2. PATIENT'S NAME (Last Name, First Name, Middle Initial)

3. PATIENT'S BIRTH DATE MM DD YY   SEX M F

4. INSURED'S NAME (Last Name, First Name, Middle Initial)

5. PATIENT'S ADDRESS (No., Street)

6. PATIENT RELATIONSHIP TO INSURED   Self Spouse Child Other

7. INSURED'S ADDRESS (No., Street)

CITY   STATE

8. PATIENT STATUS   Single Married Other

CITY   STATE

ZIP CODE   TELEPHONE (Include Area Code) ( )

Employed Full-Time Student Part-Time Student

ZIP CODE   TELEPHONE (Include Area Code) ( )

9. OTHER INSURED'S NAME (Last Name, First Name, Middle Initial)

10. IS PATIENT'S CONDITION RELATED TO:

11. INSURED'S POLICY GROUP OR FECA NUMBER

a. OTHER INSURED'S POLICY OR GROUP NUMBER

a. EMPLOYMENT? (Current or Previous) YES NO

a. INSURED'S DATE OF BIRTH MM DD YY   SEX M F

b. OTHER INSURED'S DATE OF BIRTH MM DD YY   SEX M F

b. AUTO ACCIDENT?   PLACE (State) YES NO

b. EMPLOYER'S NAME OR SCHOOL NAME

c. EMPLOYER'S NAME OR SCHOOL NAME

c. OTHER ACCIDENT? YES NO

c. INSURANCE PLAN NAME OR PROGRAM NAME

d. INSURANCE PLAN NAME OR PROGRAM NAME

10d. RESERVED FOR LOCAL USE

d. IS THERE ANOTHER HEALTH BENEFIT PLAN? YES NO   If yes, return to and complete item 9 a-d.

READ BACK OF FORM BEFORE COMPLETING & SIGNING THIS FORM.

12. PATIENT'S OR AUTHORIZED PERSON'S SIGNATURE I authorize the release of any medical or other information necessary to process this claim. I also request payment of government benefits either to myself or to the party who accepts assignment below.

SIGNED_____ DATE_____

13. INSURED'S OR AUTHORIZED PERSON'S SIGNATURE I authorize payment of medical benefits to the undersigned physician or supplier for services described below.

SIGNED_____

14. DATE OF CURRENT: MM DD YY   ILLNESS (First symptom) OR INJURY (Accident) OR PREGNANCY(LMP)

15. IF PATIENT HAS HAD SAME OR SIMILAR ILLNESS. GIVE FIRST DATE MM DD YY

16. DATES PATIENT UNABLE TO WORK IN CURRENT OCCUPATION MM DD YY FROM TO MM DD YY

17. NAME OF REFERRING PROVIDER OR OTHER SOURCE

17a. 17b. NPI

18. HOSPITALIZATION DATES RELATED TO CURRENT SERVICES MM DD YY FROM TO MM DD YY

19. RESERVED FOR LOCAL USE

20. OUTSIDE LAB? YES NO $ CHARGES

21. DIAGNOSIS OR NATURE OF ILLNESS OR INJURY (Relate Items 1, 2, 3 or 4 to Item 24E by Line)

1. |___.___   3. |___.___

2. |___.___   4. |___.___

22. MEDICAID RESUBMISSION CODE   ORIGINAL REF. NO.

23. PRIOR AUTHORIZATION NUMBER

24. A. DATE(S) OF SERVICE		B. PLACE OF SERVICE	C. EMG	D. PROCEDURES, SERVICES, OR SUPPLIES (Explain Unusual Circumstances)		E. DIAGNOSIS POINTER	F. $ CHARGES	G. DAYS OR UNITS	H. EPSDT Family Plan	I. ID. QUAL.	J. RENDERING PROVIDER ID. #
From MM DD YY	To MM DD YY			CPT/HCPCS	MODIFIER						
1										NPI	
2										NPI	
3										NPI	
4										NPI	
5										NPI	
6										NPI	

25. FEDERAL TAX I.D. NUMBER   SSN EIN

26. PATIENT'S ACCOUNT NO.

27. ACCEPT ASSIGNMENT? (For govt. claims, see back) YES NO

28. TOTAL CHARGE $

29. AMOUNT PAID $

30. BALANCE DUE $

31. SIGNATURE OF PHYSICIAN OR SUPPLIER INCLUDING DEGREES OR CREDENTIALS (I certify that the statements on the reverse apply to this bill and are made a part thereof.)

SIGNED_____ DATE_____

32. SERVICE FACILITY LOCATION INFORMATION

a. NPI   b.

33. BILLING PROVIDER INFO & PH # ( )

a. NPI   b.

NUCC Instruction Manual available at: www.nucc.org

OMB APPROVAL PENDING

EXERCISE 6.9

As an internal medicine physician you see some interesting cases. In this example, you make an initial hospital visit to a young high school aged patient named Arthur Ectomy admitted through ER (but for whom you are the primary care physician) for severe fever, dehydration and a diagnosis of mononucleosis. You examine the patient's throat, checking the adenoids, ears, nose and lungs as well as the entire body in general, ask the patient a few questions, talk with the parents about how long the patient has been ill, and write some orders to the nursing staff about prescribed antibiotics and IV therapy.

Notes: _____

_____

_____

_____

_____

_____

_____

_____

_____

_____

_____

_____

_____

_____

_____

_____

_____

_____

_____

DOC Form®
(Doctor's Office Checklist)

	HOSPITAL		OBSERVATION		ER
	Initial (3) Sub (2)		Discharge Date		New/Estab (3)
			Different (3) Same (3)		

HISTORY

	HOSPITAL Initial (3)	Sub (2)	OBSERVATION	Discharge Date	ER New/Estab (3)
Problem Focused		99231			99281
Exp/Prob Focused		99232			99282/83
Detail	99221	99233	99218	99234	99284
Comprehensive	99221/2/3		99218/19/20	99234/35/36	99285

EXAMINATION

	HOSPITAL Initial (3)	Sub (2)	OBSERVATION	Discharge Date	ER New/Estab (3)
Problem Focused		99231			99281
Exp/Prob Focused		99232			99282/83
Detail	99221	99233	99218	99234	99284
Comprehensive	99221/2/3		99218/19/20	99234/35/36	99285

MEDICAL DECISION MAKING

	HOSPITAL Initial (3)	Sub (2)	OBSERVATION	Discharge Date	ER New/Estab (3)
Straight Forward	99221	99231	99218	99234	99281
Low Complexity	99221	99231	99218	99234	99282
Mod Complexity	99222	99232	99219	99235	99283/84
High Complexity	99223	99233	99220	99236	99285

DISCHARGE 99217

	HOSPITAL	Sub			
≤ 30 Minutes		99238			
> 30 Minutes		99239			

TIME

	HOSPITAL	Sub			
15 Minutes		99231			
20 Minutes					
25 Minutes		99232			
30 Minutes	99221				
35 Minutes		99233			
45 Minutes					
50 Minutes	99222				
60 Minutes					
70 Minutes	99223				

Patient Name:_____

Date:_____Physician Signature:_____

EXERCISE 6.9

WORKBOOK

Name:_____

Class/Section:_____

cpTeach

Date:_____

2012

1500

HEALTH INSURANCE CLAIM FORM

APPROVED BY NATIONAL UNIFORM CLAIM COMMITTEE 08/05

	PICA										PICA	

1. MEDICARE   MEDICAID   TRICARE CHAMPUS   CHAMPVA   GROUP HEALTH PLAN   FECA BLK LUNG   OTHER   1a. INSURED'S I.D. NUMBER   (For Program in Item 1)

(Medicare #)   (Medicaid #)   (Sponsor's SSN)   (Member ID#)   (SSN or ID)   (SSN)   (ID)

2. PATIENT'S NAME (Last Name, First Name, Middle Initial)   3. PATIENT'S BIRTH DATE   SEX   4. INSURED'S NAME (Last Name, First Name, Middle Initial)
MM   DD   YY   M   F

5. PATIENT'S ADDRESS (No., Street)   6. PATIENT RELATIONSHIP TO INSURED   7. INSURED'S ADDRESS (No., Street)

Self   Spouse   Child   Other

CITY   STATE   9. PATIENT STATUS   CITY   STATE

Single   Married   Other

ZIP CODE   TELEPHONE (Include Area Code)   ZIP CODE   TELEPHONE (Include Area Code)

Employed   Full-Time Student   Part-Time Student

( )   ( )

9. OTHER INSURED'S NAME (Last Name, First Name, Middle Initial)   10. IS PATIENT'S CONDITION RELATED TO: 11. INSURED'S POLICY GROUP OR FECA NUMBER

a. OTHER INSURED'S POLICY OR GROUP NUMBER   a. EMPLOYMENT? (Current or Previous)   a. INSURED'S DATE OF BIRTH   SEX
                                                YES   NO   MM   DD   YY   M   F

b. OTHER INSURED'S DATE OF BIRTH   SEX   b. AUTO ACCIDENT?   PLACE (State)   b. EMPLOYER'S NAME OR SCHOOL NAME
MM   DD   YY   M   F   YES   NO

c. EMPLOYER'S NAME OR SCHOOL NAME   c. OTHER ACCIDENT?   c. INSURANCE PLAN NAME OR PROGRAM NAME
                                                YES   NO

d. INSURANCE PLAN NAME OR PROGRAM NAME   10d. RESERVED FOR LOCAL USE   d. IS THERE ANOTHER HEALTH BENEFIT PLAN?
                                                YES   NO   If yes, return to and complete item 9 a-d.

READ BACK OF FORM BEFORE COMPLETING & SIGNING THIS FORM.
12. PATIENT'S OR AUTHORIZED PERSON'S SIGNATURE I authorize the release of any medical or other information necessary to process this claim. I also request payment of government benefits either to myself or to the party who accepts assignment below.

13. INSURED'S OR AUTHORIZED PERSON'S SIGNATURE I authorize payment of medical benefits to the undersigned physician or supplier for services described below.

SIGNED   DATE   SIGNED

14. DATE OF CURRENT: ILLNESS (First symptom) OR INJURY (Accident) OR PREGNANCY(LMP)   15. IF PATIENT HAS HAD SAME OR SIMILAR ILLNESS. GIVE FIRST DATE   MM   DD   YY   16. DATES PATIENT UNABLE TO WORK IN CURRENT OCCUPATION
MM   DD   YY   MM   DD   YY   MM   DD   YY
                                                FROM   TO

17. NAME OF REFERRING PROVIDER OR OTHER SOURCE   17a.   18. HOSPITALIZATION DATES RELATED TO CURRENT SERVICES
                                        17b. NPI   MM   DD   YY   MM   DD   YY
                                                FROM   TO

19. RESERVED FOR LOCAL USE   20. OUTSIDE LAB? $ CHARGES
                                                YES   NO

21. DIAGNOSIS OR NATURE OF ILLNESS OR INJURY (Relate Items 1, 2, 3 or 4 to Item 24E by Line)   22. MEDICAID RESUBMISSION CODE   ORIGINAL REF. NO.

1. |____.____   3. |____.____   23. PRIOR AUTHORIZATION NUMBER

2. |____.____   4. |____.____

24. A. DATE(S) OF SERVICE						B. PLACE OF SERVICE	C. EMG	D. PROCEDURES, SERVICES, OR SUPPLIES (Explain Unusual Circumstances)		E. DIAGNOSIS POINTER	F. $ CHARGES	G. DAYS OR UNITS	H. EPSDT Family Plan	I. ID. QUAL.	J. RENDERING PROVIDER ID. #
From MM	DD	YY	To MM	DD	YY			CPT/HCPCS	MODIFIER						
1														NPI	
2														NPI	
3														NPI	
4														NPI	
5														NPI	
6														NPI	

25. FEDERAL TAX I.D. NUMBER   SSN   EIN   26. PATIENT'S ACCOUNT NO.   27. ACCEPT ASSIGNMENT? (For govt. claims, see back)   YES   NO   28. TOTAL CHARGE $ 29. AMOUNT PAID $ 30. BALANCE DUE $

31. SIGNATURE OF PHYSICIAN OR SUPPLIER INCLUDING DEGREES OR CREDENTIALS (I certify that the statements on the reverse apply to this bill and are made a part thereof.)   32. SERVICE FACILITY LOCATION INFORMATION   33. BILLING PROVIDER INFO & PH # ( )

SIGNED   DATE   a.   b.   a.   b.

NUCC Instruction Manual available at: www.nucc.org   OMB APPROVAL PENDING

EXERCISE 6.10

Later the same day, you admit another patient to the hospital because they are having a severe acute asthmatic attack. (They had previously been on therapy for the asthma that did not work.) In addition to completing a comprehensive history and comprehensive examination your decision making is of moderate complexity.r the same day, you admit another patient to the hospital because they are having a severe acute asthmatic attack. (They had previously been on therapy for the asthma that did not work.) In addition to completing a comprehensive history and comprehensive examination your decision making is of moderate complexity.

Notes: _____

_____

_____

_____

_____

_____

_____

_____

_____

_____

_____

_____

_____

_____

_____

_____

_____

DOC Form®
(Doctor's Office Checklist)

	HOSPITAL		OBSERVATION		ER
	Initial (3) Sub (2)		Discharge Date Different (3) Same (3)		New/Estab (3)
HISTORY					
Problem Focused		99231			99281
Exp/Prob Focused		99232			99282/83
Detail	99221	99233	99218	99234	99284
Comprehensive	99221/2/3		99218/19/20	99234/35/36	99285
EXAMINATION					
Problem Focused		99231			99281
Exp/Prob Focused		99232			99282/83
Detail	99221	99233	99218	99234	99284
Comprehensive	99221/2/3		99218/19/20	99234/35/36	99285
MEDICAL DECISION MAKING					
Straight Forward	99221	99231	99218	99234	99281
Low Complexity	99221	99231	99218	99234	99282
Mod Complexity	99222	99232	99219	99235	99283/84
High Complexity	99223	99233	99220	99236	99285
DISCHARGE			99217		
≤ 30 Minutes		99238			
> 30 Minutes		99239			
TIME					
15 Minutes		99231			
20 Minutes					
25 Minutes		99232			
30 Minutes	99221				
35 Minutes		99233			
45 Minutes					
50 Minutes	99222				
60 Minutes					
70 Minutes	99223				

Patient Name:_____

Date:_____ Physician Signature:_____

EXERCISE 6.10

Name:_____

Class/Section:_____

cpTeach
2012
Date:_____

1500

HEALTH INSURANCE CLAIM FORM

APPROVED BY NATIONAL UNIFORM CLAIM COMMITTEE 08/05

EXERCISE 6.11

Rick Tum, one of your favorite patients, is seen in the hospital for review of the effectiveness of medication you prescribed a day or two ago to treat his uncomplicated pneumonia. He seems to be in great spirits. During your exam, you check the eyes, ears, nose, throat and lungs and find that the patient is really progressing very nicely. You ask his parents if they have noticed that your patient is sleeping any better. The parents respond positively. You review the notes made by all nurses and tell the parents that their son will be discharged tomorrow.

Notes: _____
_____
_____
_____
_____
_____
_____
_____
_____
_____
_____
_____
_____
_____
_____
_____
_____
_____
_____
_____

DOC Form®
(Doctor's Office Checklist)

	HOSPITAL		OBSERVATION		ER
	Initial (3) Sub (2)		Discharge Date Different (3) Same (3)		New/Estab (3)

HISTORY

Problem Focused		99231			99281
Exp/Prob Focused		99232			99282/83
Detail	99221	99233	99218	99234	99284
Comprehensive	99221/2/3		99218/19/20	99234/35/36	99285

EXAMINATION

Problem Focused		99231			99281
Exp/Prob Focused		99232			99282/83
Detail	99221	99233	99218	99234	99284
Comprehensive	99221/2/3		99218/19/20	99234/35/36	99285

MEDICAL DECISION MAKING

Straight Forward	99221	99231	99218	99234	99281
Low Complexity	99221	99231	99218	99234	99282
Mod Complexity	99222	99232	99219	99235	99283/84
High Complexity	99223	99233	99220	99236	99285

DISCHARGE　　　　　　　　　　　99217

≤ 30 Minutes		99238			
> 30 Minutes		99239			

TIME

15 Minutes		99231			
20 Minutes					
25 Minutes		99232			
30 Minutes	99221				
35 Minutes		99233			
45 Minutes					
50 Minutes	99222				
60 Minutes					
70 Minutes	99223				

Patient Name:_____

Date:_____ Physician Signature:_____

EXERCISE 6.11

Name:_____

Class/Section:_____

Date:_____

2012

1500

HEALTH INSURANCE CLAIM FORM

APPROVED BY NATIONAL UNIFORM CLAIM COMMITTEE 08/05

| | PICA | | | | | | | | PICA | |

1. MEDICARE MEDICAID TRICARE CHAMPUS CHAMPVA GROUP HEALTH PLAN FECA BLK LUNG OTHER	1a. INSURED'S I.D. NUMBER (For Program in Item 1)

(Medicare #) (Medicaid #) (Sponsor's SSN) (Member ID#) (SSN or ID) (SSN) (ID)

2. PATIENT'S NAME (Last Name, First Name, Middle Initial)	3. PATIENT'S BIRTH DATE SEX MM DD YY M F	4. INSURED'S NAME (Last Name, First Name, Middle Initial)

5. PATIENT'S ADDRESS (No., Street)	6. PATIENT RELATIONSHIP TO INSURED Self Spouse Child Other	7. INSURED'S ADDRESS (No., Street)

CITY STATE	8. PATIENT STATUS Single Married Other	CITY STATE

ZIP CODE TELEPHONE (Include Area Code) ( )	Employed Full-Time Student Part-Time Student	ZIP CODE TELEPHONE (Include Area Code) ( )

9. OTHER INSURED'S NAME (Last Name, First Name, Middle Initial)	10. IS PATIENT'S CONDITION RELATED TO:	11. INSURED'S POLICY GROUP OR FECA NUMBER

a. OTHER INSURED'S POLICY OR GROUP NUMBER	a. EMPLOYMENT? (Current or Previous) YES NO	a. INSURED'S DATE OF BIRTH SEX MM DD YY M F

b. OTHER INSURED'S DATE OF BIRTH SEX MM DD YY M F	b. AUTO ACCIDENT? PLACE (State) YES NO	b. EMPLOYER'S NAME OR SCHOOL NAME

c. EMPLOYER'S NAME OR SCHOOL NAME	c. OTHER ACCIDENT? YES NO	c. INSURANCE PLAN NAME OR PROGRAM NAME

d. INSURANCE PLAN NAME OR PROGRAM NAME	10d. RESERVED FOR LOCAL USE	d. IS THERE ANOTHER HEALTH BENEFIT PLAN? YES NO If yes, return to and complete item 9 a-d.

READ BACK OF FORM BEFORE COMPLETING & SIGNING THIS FORM.

12. PATIENT'S OR AUTHORIZED PERSON'S SIGNATURE I authorize the release of any medical or other information necessary to process this claim. I also request payment of government benefits either to myself or to the party who accepts assignment below. SIGNED_____ DATE_____	13. INSURED'S OR AUTHORIZED PERSON'S SIGNATURE I authorize payment of medical benefits to the undersigned physician or supplier for services described below. SIGNED_____

14. DATE OF CURRENT: MM DD YY ILLNESS (First symptom) OR INJURY (Accident) OR PREGNANCY(LMP)	15. IF PATIENT HAS HAD SAME OR SIMILAR ILLNESS. GIVE FIRST DATE MM DD YY	16. DATES PATIENT UNABLE TO WORK IN CURRENT OCCUPATION MM DD YY MM DD YY FROM TO

17. NAME OF REFERRING PROVIDER OR OTHER SOURCE	17a. 17b. NPI	18. HOSPITALIZATION DATES RELATED TO CURRENT SERVICES MM DD YY MM DD YY FROM TO

19. RESERVED FOR LOCAL USE		20. OUTSIDE LAB? $ CHARGES YES NO

21. DIAGNOSIS OR NATURE OF ILLNESS OR INJURY (Relate Items 1, 2, 3 or 4 to Item 24E by Line) 1. |___.___ 3. |___.___ 2. |___.___ 4. |___.___	22. MEDICAID RESUBMISSION CODE ORIGINAL REF. NO. 23. PRIOR AUTHORIZATION NUMBER

24. A. DATE(S) OF SERVICE From To MM DD YY MM DD YY	B. PLACE OF SERVICE	C. EMG	D. PROCEDURES, SERVICES, OR SUPPLIES (Explain Unusual Circumstances) CPT/HCPCS MODIFIER	E. DIAGNOSIS POINTER	F. $ CHARGES	G. DAYS OR UNITS	H. EPSDT Family Plan	I. ID. QUAL.	J. RENDERING PROVIDER ID. #
1									NPI
2									NPI
3									NPI
4									NPI
5									NPI
6									NPI

25. FEDERAL TAX I.D. NUMBER SSN EIN	26. PATIENT'S ACCOUNT NO.	27. ACCEPT ASSIGNMENT? (For govt. claims, see back) YES NO	28. TOTAL CHARGE $	29. AMOUNT PAID $	30. BALANCE DUE $

31. SIGNATURE OF PHYSICIAN OR SUPPLIER INCLUDING DEGREES OR CREDENTIALS (I certify that the statements on the reverse apply to this bill and are made a part thereof.) SIGNED_____ DATE_____	32. SERVICE FACILITY LOCATION INFORMATION a. b.	33. BILLING PROVIDER INFO & PH # ( ) a. b.

NUCC Instruction Manual available at: www.nucc.org

OMB APPROVAL PENDING

PATIENT AND INSURED INFORMATION

PHYSICIAN OR SUPPLIER INFORMATION

EXERCISE 6.12

Constance Pation has been referred to you by her OB/GYN. She is 25 years old and has recently given birth to an 11-pound baby boy. Unbelievable! During the visit, she tells you that she is really having some severe rectal pain and that it is so bad that she has great difficulty sitting down. You learn during her history that the baby was born six weeks ago and that Ms. Pation has a history of constipation. When you check into her diet, you also learn that she had been anemic during the pregnancy and that her physician had prescribed some heavy-duty iron pills. The patient tells you that these episodes of constipation seem to come and go. When you perform your exam, you see that the patient has some pronounced hemorrhoids, but nothing that will not go away after she loses some weight and "gets over" the pregnancy. Your rectal exam proves that these hemorrhoids are located both internally and externally. You explain all treatment options and even list surgery as a possible option. You write a letter to her OB/GYN explaining your action plan.

Notes: _____

_____

_____

_____

_____

_____

_____

_____

_____

_____

_____

_____

_____

DOC Form®
(Doctor's Office Checklist)

	OFFICE/OUTPATIENT		CONSULTATION	
	New (3)	Established (2)	Office/O.P. (3)	Inpatient (3)
Minimal Service		99211		

HISTORY

Problem Focused	99201	99212	99241	99251
Exp/Prob Focused	99202	99213	99242	99252
Detail	99203	99214	99243	99253
Comprehensive	99204/05	99215	99244/45	99254/55

EXAMINATION

Problem Focused	99201	99212	99241	99251
Exp/Prob Focused	99202	99213	99242	99252
Detail	99203	99214	99243	99253
Comprehensive	99204/05	99215	99244/45	99254/55

MEDICAL DECISION MAKING

Straight Forward	99201/2	99212	99241/42	99251/52
Low Complexity	99203	99213	99243	99253
Mod Complexity	99204	99214	99244	99254
High Complexity	99205	99215	99245	99255

TIME:_____   Counsel/Coordination of Care:_____

10 Minutes	99201	99212		
15 Minutes		99213	99241	
20 Minutes	99202			99251
25 Minutes		99214		
30 Minutes	99203		99242	
40 Minutes		99215	99243	99252
45 Minutes	99204			
55 Minutes				99253
60 Minutes	99205		99244	
80 Minutes			99245	99254
110 Minutes				99255

EXERCISE 6.12

Name:_____

Class/Section:_____

cpTeach Date:_____

2012

```
[1500]
HEALTH INSURANCE CLAIM FORM
APPROVED BY NATIONAL UNIFORM CLAIM COMMITTEE 08/05
```

PICA | | | | | | PICA | |

1. MEDICARE	MEDICAID	TRICARE CHAMPUS	CHAMPVA	GROUP HEALTH PLAN	FECA BLK LUNG	OTHER	1a. INSURED'S I.D. NUMBER (For Program in Item 1)
(Medicare #)	(Medicaid #)	(Sponsor's SSN)	(Member ID#)	(SSN or ID)	(SSN)	(ID)	

2. PATIENT'S NAME (Last Name, First Name, Middle Initial)

3. PATIENT'S BIRTH DATE MM DD YY   SEX M F

4. INSURED'S NAME (Last Name, First Name, Middle Initial)

5. PATIENT'S ADDRESS (No., Street)

6. PATIENT RELATIONSHIP TO INSURED   Self Spouse Child Other

7. INSURED'S ADDRESS (No., Street)

CITY   STATE

8. PATIENT STATUS   Single Married Other

Employed Full-Time Student Part-Time Student

CITY   STATE

ZIP CODE   TELEPHONE (Include Area Code) (   )

ZIP CODE   TELEPHONE (Include Area Code) (   )

9. OTHER INSURED'S NAME (Last Name, First Name, Middle Initial)

10. IS PATIENT'S CONDITION RELATED TO:

11. INSURED'S POLICY GROUP OR FECA NUMBER

a. OTHER INSURED'S POLICY OR GROUP NUMBER

a. EMPLOYMENT? (Current or Previous) YES NO

a. INSURED'S DATE OF BIRTH MM DD YY   SEX M F

b. OTHER INSURED'S DATE OF BIRTH MM DD YY   SEX M F

b. AUTO ACCIDENT? YES NO   PLACE (State)

b. EMPLOYER'S NAME OR SCHOOL NAME

c. EMPLOYER'S NAME OR SCHOOL NAME

c. OTHER ACCIDENT? YES NO

c. INSURANCE PLAN NAME OR PROGRAM NAME

d. INSURANCE PLAN NAME OR PROGRAM NAME

10d. RESERVED FOR LOCAL USE

d. IS THERE ANOTHER HEALTH BENEFIT PLAN? YES NO   If yes, return to and complete item 9 a-d.

READ BACK OF FORM BEFORE COMPLETING & SIGNING THIS FORM.

12. PATIENT'S OR AUTHORIZED PERSON'S SIGNATURE I authorize the release of any medical or other information necessary to process this claim. I also request payment of government benefits either to myself or to the party who accepts assignment below.

SIGNED_____ DATE_____

13. INSURED'S OR AUTHORIZED PERSON'S SIGNATURE I authorize payment of medical benefits to the undersigned physician or supplier for services described below.

SIGNED_____

14. DATE OF CURRENT: MM DD YY ILLNESS (First symptom) OR INJURY (Accident) OR PREGNANCY(LMP)

15. IF PATIENT HAS HAD SAME OR SIMILAR ILLNESS. GIVE FIRST DATE MM DD YY

16. DATES PATIENT UNABLE TO WORK IN CURRENT OCCUPATION MM DD YY FROM TO MM DD YY

17. NAME OF REFERRING PROVIDER OR OTHER SOURCE

17a.
17b. NPI

18. HOSPITALIZATION DATES RELATED TO CURRENT SERVICES MM DD YY FROM TO MM DD YY

19. RESERVED FOR LOCAL USE

20. OUTSIDE LAB? YES NO $ CHARGES

21. DIAGNOSIS OR NATURE OF ILLNESS OR INJURY (Relate Items 1, 2, 3 or 4 to Item 24E by Line)

1. |___.___   3. |___.___
2. |___.___   4. |___.___

22. MEDICAID RESUBMISSION CODE   ORIGINAL REF. NO.

23. PRIOR AUTHORIZATION NUMBER

24. A. DATE(S) OF SERVICE						B. PLACE OF SERVICE	C. EMG	D. PROCEDURES, SERVICES, OR SUPPLIES (Explain Unusual Circumstances)		E. DIAGNOSIS POINTER	F. $ CHARGES	G. DAYS OR UNITS	H. EPSDT Family Plan	I. ID. QUAL.	J. RENDERING PROVIDER ID. #
From MM DD YY			To MM DD YY					CPT/HCPCS	MODIFIER						
1														NPI	
2														NPI	
3														NPI	
4														NPI	
5														NPI	
6														NPI	

25. FEDERAL TAX I.D. NUMBER   SSN EIN

26. PATIENT'S ACCOUNT NO.

27. ACCEPT ASSIGNMENT? (For govt. claims, see back) YES NO

28. TOTAL CHARGE $

29. AMOUNT PAID $

30. BALANCE DUE $

31. SIGNATURE OF PHYSICIAN OR SUPPLIER INCLUDING DEGREES OR CREDENTIALS (I certify that the statements on the reverse apply to this bill and are made a part thereof.)

SIGNED_____ DATE_____

32. SERVICE FACILITY LOCATION INFORMATION

a.   b.

33. BILLING PROVIDER INFO & PH # (   )

a.   b.

NUCC Instruction Manual available at: www.nucc.org

OMB APPROVAL PENDING

EXERCISE 6.13

You are called in, as the internal medicine physician on call, to see a patient who has recently undergone a liposuction with an abdominoplasty and who is now presenting with a severe fever. The patient was admitted to the hospital by the plastic surgeon who noticed that the patient did not seem to be recovering well from the surgery. You examine the chart, see that the patient is an otherwise healthy 33-year-old patient who had no previous surgeries and no pregnancies. There are no known allergies and the fever is currently 103 degrees. Motrin had been prescribed which brought the fever down about 3 degrees and you are being asked your opinion as to how the surgeon should proceed. You recommend that the patient should continue on the Motrin and on fluids and that she should be checked again tomorrow as long as the fever does not spike later that evening.

Notes: _____

_____

_____

_____

_____

_____

_____

_____

_____

_____

_____

_____

_____

_____

_____

_____

DOC Form®
(Doctor's Office Checklist)

	OFFICE/OUTPATIENT		CONSULTATION	
	New (3)	Established (2)	Office/O.P. (3)	Inpatient (3)
Minimal Service		99211		

HISTORY

Problem Focused	99201	99212	99241	99251
Exp/Prob Focused	99202	99213	99242	99252
Detail	99203	99214	99243	99253
Comprehensive	99204/05	99215	99244/45	99254/55

EXAMINATION

Problem Focused	99201	99212	99241	99251
Exp/Prob Focused	99202	99213	99242	99252
Detail	99203	99214	99243	99253
Comprehensive	99204/05	99215	99244/45	99254/55

MEDICAL DECISION MAKING

Straight Forward	99201/2	99212	99241/42	99251/52
Low Complexity	99203	99213	99243	99253
Mod Complexity	99204	99214	99244	99254
High Complexity	99205	99215	99245	99255

TIME:_____   Counsel/Coordination of Care:_____

10 Minutes	99201	99212		
15 Minutes		99213	99241	
20 Minutes	99202			99251
25 Minutes		99214		
30 Minutes	99203		99242	
40 Minutes		99215	99243	99252
45 Minutes	99204			
55 Minutes				99253
60 Minutes	99205		99244	
80 Minutes			99245	99254
110 Minutes				99255

EXERCISE 6.13

Name:_____

Class/Section:_____

Date:_____

2012

1500

HEALTH INSURANCE CLAIM FORM

APPROVED BY NATIONAL UNIFORM CLAIM COMMITTEE 08/05

| PICA | | | | | | | | | PICA |

| 1. MEDICARE (Medicare #) | MEDICAID (Medicaid #) | TRICARE CHAMPUS (Sponsor's SSN) | CHAMPVA (Member ID#) | GROUP HEALTH PLAN (SSN or ID) | FECA BLK LUNG (SSN) | OTHER (ID) | 1a. INSURED'S I.D. NUMBER (For Program in Item 1) |

2. PATIENT'S NAME (Last Name, First Name, Middle Initial)

3. PATIENT'S BIRTH DATE MM DD YY   SEX M   F

4. INSURED'S NAME (Last Name, First Name, Middle Initial)

5. PATIENT'S ADDRESS (No., Street)

6. PATIENT RELATIONSHIP TO INSURED Self Spouse Child Other

7. INSURED'S ADDRESS (No., Street)

CITY   STATE

8. PATIENT STATUS Single Married Other Employed Full-Time Student Part-Time Student

CITY   STATE

ZIP CODE   TELEPHONE (Include Area Code) ( )

ZIP CODE   TELEPHONE (Include Area Code) ( )

9. OTHER INSURED'S NAME (Last Name, First Name, Middle Initial)

10. IS PATIENT'S CONDITION RELATED TO:

11. INSURED'S POLICY GROUP OR FECA NUMBER

a. OTHER INSURED'S POLICY OR GROUP NUMBER

a. EMPLOYMENT? (Current or Previous) YES NO

a. INSURED'S DATE OF BIRTH MM DD YY   SEX M   F

b. OTHER INSURED'S DATE OF BIRTH MM DD YY   SEX M   F

b. AUTO ACCIDENT?   PLACE (State) YES NO

b. EMPLOYER'S NAME OR SCHOOL NAME

c. EMPLOYER'S NAME OR SCHOOL NAME

c. OTHER ACCIDENT? YES NO

c. INSURANCE PLAN NAME OR PROGRAM NAME

d. INSURANCE PLAN NAME OR PROGRAM NAME

10d. RESERVED FOR LOCAL USE

d. IS THERE ANOTHER HEALTH BENEFIT PLAN? YES NO   If yes, return to and complete item 9 a-d.

READ BACK OF FORM BEFORE COMPLETING & SIGNING THIS FORM.

12. PATIENT'S OR AUTHORIZED PERSON'S SIGNATURE I authorize the release of any medical or other information necessary to process this claim. I also request payment of government benefits either to myself or to the party who accepts assignment below.

SIGNED_____ DATE_____

13. INSURED'S OR AUTHORIZED PERSON'S SIGNATURE I authorize payment of medical benefits to the undersigned physician or supplier for services described below.

SIGNED_____

14. DATE OF CURRENT: MM DD YY ILLNESS (First symptom) OR INJURY (Accident) OR PREGNANCY(LMP)

15. IF PATIENT HAS HAD SAME OR SIMILAR ILLNESS. GIVE FIRST DATE MM DD YY

16. DATES PATIENT UNABLE TO WORK IN CURRENT OCCUPATION MM DD YY   TO   MM DD YY

17. NAME OF REFERRING PROVIDER OR OTHER SOURCE

17a.

17b. NPI

18. HOSPITALIZATION DATES RELATED TO CURRENT SERVICES MM DD YY   FROM   TO   MM DD YY

19. RESERVED FOR LOCAL USE

20. OUTSIDE LAB? YES NO $ CHARGES

21. DIAGNOSIS OR NATURE OF ILLNESS OR INJURY (Relate Items 1, 2, 3 or 4 to Item 24E by Line)

1. |___.___   3. |___.___

2. |___.___   4. |___.___

22. MEDICAID RESUBMISSION CODE   ORIGINAL REF. NO.

23. PRIOR AUTHORIZATION NUMBER

24. A. DATE(S) OF SERVICE						B. PLACE OF SERVICE	C. EMG	D. PROCEDURES, SERVICES, OR SUPPLIES (Explain Unusual Circumstances) CPT/HCPCS MODIFIER	E. DIAGNOSIS POINTER	F. $ CHARGES	G. DAYS OR UNITS	H. EPSDT Family Plan	I. ID. QUAL.	J. RENDERING PROVIDER ID. #
From			To											
MM	DD	YY	MM	DD	YY									
1														NPI
2														NPI
3														NPI
4														NPI
5														NPI
6														NPI

25. FEDERAL TAX I.D. NUMBER   SSN EIN

26. PATIENT'S ACCOUNT NO.

27. ACCEPT ASSIGNMENT? (For govt. claims, see back) YES NO

28. TOTAL CHARGE $

29. AMOUNT PAID $

30. BALANCE DUE $

31. SIGNATURE OF PHYSICIAN OR SUPPLIER INCLUDING DEGREES OR CREDENTIALS (I certify that the statements on the reverse apply to this bill and are made a part thereof.)

SIGNED_____ DATE_____

32. SERVICE FACILITY LOCATION INFORMATION

a.   b.

33. BILLING PROVIDER INFO & PH # ( )

a.   b.

NUCC Instruction Manual available at: www.nucc.org   OMB APPROVAL PENDING

PATIENT AND INSURED INFORMATION

PHYSICIAN OR SUPPLIER INFORMATION

EXERCISE 6.14

The next day, the surgeon calls on you to check on the patient once again. The fever has not spiked but is remaining steady. You look at the chart and feel that the patient was just slow at recovering from the surgery. Code for your service.

Notes: _____

_____

_____

_____

_____

_____

_____

_____

_____

_____

_____

_____

_____

_____

_____

_____

_____

_____

_____

_____

_____

_____

_____

_____

_____

_____

_____

_____

_____

_____

DOC Form®
(Doctor's Office Checklist)

	HOSPITAL		OBSERVATION		ER
	Initial (3) Sub (2)		Discharge Date Different (3) Same (3)		New/Estab (3)

HISTORY

Problem Focused		99231			99281
Exp/Prob Focused		99232			99282/83
Detail	99221	99233	99218	99234	99284
Comprehensive	99221/2/3		99218/19/20	99234/35/36	99285

EXAMINATION

Problem Focused		99231			99281
Exp/Prob Focused		99232			99282/83
Detail	99221	99233	99218	99234	99284
Comprehensive	99221/2/3		99218/19/20	99234/35/36	99285

MEDICAL DECISION MAKING

Straight Forward	99221	99231	99218	99234	99281
Low Complexity	99221	99231	99218	99234	99282
Mod Complexity	99222	99232	99219	99235	99283/84
High Complexity	99223	99233	99220	99236	99285

DISCHARGE   99217

≤ 30 Minutes		99238			
> 30 Minutes		99239			

TIME

15 Minutes		99231			
20 Minutes					
25 Minutes		99232			
30 Minutes	99221				
35 Minutes		99233			
45 Minutes					
50 Minutes	99222				
60 Minutes					
70 Minutes	99223				

Patient Name:_____

Date:_____Physician Signature:_____

EXERCISE 6.14

1500

HEALTH INSURANCE CLAIM FORM

APPROVED BY NATIONAL UNIFORM CLAIM COMMITTEE 08/05

| | PICA | | | | | | | PICA | |

1. MEDICARE   MEDICAID   TRICARE CHAMPUS   CHAMPVA   GROUP HEALTH PLAN   FECA BLK LUNG   OTHER

(Medicare #)   (Medicaid #)   (Sponsor's SSN)   (Member ID#)   (SSN or ID)   (SSN)   (ID)

1a. INSURED'S I.D. NUMBER   (For Program in Item 1)

2. PATIENT'S NAME (Last Name, First Name, Middle Initial)

3. PATIENT'S BIRTH DATE   MM   DD   YY   SEX   M   F

4. INSURED'S NAME (Last Name, First Name, Middle Initial)

5. PATIENT'S ADDRESS (No., Street)

6. PATIENT RELATIONSHIP TO INSURED   Self   Spouse   Child   Other

7. INSURED'S ADDRESS (No., Street)

CITY   STATE

8. PATIENT STATUS   Single   Married   Other

Employed   Full-Time Student   Part-Time Student

CITY   STATE

ZIP CODE   TELEPHONE (Include Area Code)   (   )

ZIP CODE   TELEPHONE (Include Area Code)   (   )

9. OTHER INSURED'S NAME (Last Name, First Name, Middle Initial)

10. IS PATIENT'S CONDITION RELATED TO:

11. INSURED'S POLICY GROUP OR FECA NUMBER

a. OTHER INSURED'S POLICY OR GROUP NUMBER

a. EMPLOYMENT? (Current or Previous)   YES   NO

a. INSURED'S DATE OF BIRTH   MM   DD   YY   SEX   M   F

b. OTHER INSURED'S DATE OF BIRTH   MM   DD   YY   SEX   M   F

b. AUTO ACCIDENT?   PLACE (State)   YES   NO

b. EMPLOYER'S NAME OR SCHOOL NAME

c. EMPLOYER'S NAME OR SCHOOL NAME

c. OTHER ACCIDENT?   YES   NO

c. INSURANCE PLAN NAME OR PROGRAM NAME

d. INSURANCE PLAN NAME OR PROGRAM NAME

10d. RESERVED FOR LOCAL USE

d. IS THERE ANOTHER HEALTH BENEFIT PLAN?   YES   NO   If yes, return to and complete item 9 a-d.

READ BACK OF FORM BEFORE COMPLETING & SIGNING THIS FORM.

12. PATIENT'S OR AUTHORIZED PERSON'S SIGNATURE I authorize the release of any medical or other information necessary to process this claim. I also request payment of government benefits either to myself or to the party who accepts assignment below.

SIGNED_____   DATE_____

13. INSURED'S OR AUTHORIZED PERSON'S SIGNATURE I authorize payment of medical benefits to the undersigned physician or supplier for services described below.

SIGNED_____

14. DATE OF CURRENT: MM   DD   YY   ILLNESS (First symptom) OR INJURY (Accident) OR PREGNANCY(LMP)

15. IF PATIENT HAS HAD SAME OR SIMILAR ILLNESS. GIVE FIRST DATE   MM   DD   YY

16. DATES PATIENT UNABLE TO WORK IN CURRENT OCCUPATION   MM   DD   YY   FROM   TO   MM   DD   YY

17. NAME OF REFERRING PROVIDER OR OTHER SOURCE

17a.

17b. NPI

18. HOSPITALIZATION DATES RELATED TO CURRENT SERVICES   MM   DD   YY   FROM   TO   MM   DD   YY

19. RESERVED FOR LOCAL USE

20. OUTSIDE LAB?   YES   NO $ CHARGES

21. DIAGNOSIS OR NATURE OF ILLNESS OR INJURY (Relate Items 1, 2, 3 or 4 to Item 24E by Line)

1. |___.___   3. |___.___

2. |___.___   4. |___.___

22. MEDICAID RESUBMISSION CODE   ORIGINAL REF. NO.

23. PRIOR AUTHORIZATION NUMBER

24. A. DATE(S) OF SERVICE						B. PLACE OF SERVICE	C. EMG	D. PROCEDURES, SERVICES, OR SUPPLIES (Explain Unusual Circumstances)		E. DIAGNOSIS POINTER	F. $ CHARGES	G. DAYS OR UNITS	H. EPSDT Family Plan	I. ID. QUAL.	J. RENDERING PROVIDER ID. #
From MM	DD	YY	To MM	DD	YY			CPT/HCPCS	MODIFIER						
1														NPI	
2														NPI	
3														NPI	
4														NPI	
5														NPI	
6														NPI	

25. FEDERAL TAX I.D. NUMBER   SSN   EIN

26. PATIENT'S ACCOUNT NO.

27. ACCEPT ASSIGNMENT? (For govt. claims, see back)   YES   NO

28. TOTAL CHARGE $

29. AMOUNT PAID $

30. BALANCE DUE $

31. SIGNATURE OF PHYSICIAN OR SUPPLIER INCLUDING DEGREES OR CREDENTIALS (I certify that the statements on the reverse apply to this bill and are made a part thereof.)

SIGNED_____   DATE_____

32. SERVICE FACILITY LOCATION INFORMATION

a.   b.

33. BILLING PROVIDER INFO & PH #   (   )

a.   b.

NUCC Instruction Manual available at: www.nucc.org

OMB APPROVAL PENDING

PATIENT AND INSURED INFORMATION

PHYSICIAN OR SUPPLIER INFORMATION

Name:_____

Class/Section:_____

Date:_____

WORKBOOK cpTeach 2012

EXERCISE 6.15

Sid Moid, a patient returning from vacation after visiting relatives in Virginia, slipped on the wet cement after leaving a restaurant in your town. Mr. Moid had fallen flat on his back and is currently complaining of a very sore bottom and bleeding elbows. The patient is having difficulty walking. You examine the patient, paying special attention to the lower back and tailbone area. Additionally, you examine both elbows. You order some x-rays and get the patient's history finding nothing of any medical significance in the medical history. The patient's past history shows that the patient had received an ileostomy 5 years earlier but seems to have adapted well to that condition. The x-rays reveal that there are no broken bones, although there is some severe bruising of the lower back and left buttock.

Notes: _____

_____

_____

_____

_____

_____

_____

_____

_____

_____

_____

_____

_____

_____

_____

_____

DOC Form®
(Doctor's Office Checklist)

	OFFICE/OUTPATIENT		CONSULTATION	
	New (3)	Established (2)	Office/O.P. (3)	Inpatient (3)
Minimal Service		99211		

HISTORY

Problem Focused	99201	99212	99241	99251
Exp/Prob Focused	99202	99213	99242	99252
Detail	99203	99214	99243	99253
Comprehensive	99204/05	99215	99244/45	99254/55

EXAMINATION

Problem Focused	99201	99212	99241	99251
Exp/Prob Focused	99202	99213	99242	99252
Detail	99203	99214	99243	99253
Comprehensive	99204/05	99215	99244/45	99254/55

MEDICAL DECISION MAKING

Straight Forward	99201/2	99212	99241/42	99251/52
Low Complexity	99203	99213	99243	99253
Mod Complexity	99204	99214	99244	99254
High Complexity	99205	99215	99245	99255

TIME:_____　　Counsel/Coordination of Care:_____

10 Minutes	99201	99212		
15 Minutes		99213	99241	
20 Minutes	99202			99251
25 Minutes		99214		
30 Minutes	99203		99242	
40 Minutes		99215	99243	99252
45 Minutes	99204			
55 Minutes				99253
60 Minutes	99205		99244	
80 Minutes			99245	99254
110 Minutes				99255

EXERCISE 6.15

1500

HEALTH INSURANCE CLAIM FORM

APPROVED BY NATIONAL UNIFORM CLAIM COMMITTEE 08/05

| | PICA | | | | | | | | | | | | PICA | |

1. MEDICARE	MEDICAID	TRICARE CHAMPUS	CHAMPVA	GROUP HEALTH PLAN	FECA BLK LUNG	OTHER	1a. INSURED'S I.D. NUMBER	(For Program in Item 1)
(Medicare #)	(Medicaid #)	(Sponsor's SSN)	(Member ID#)	(SSN or ID)	(SSN)	(ID)		

2. PATIENT'S NAME (Last Name, First Name, Middle Initial)

9. PATIENT'S BIRTH DATE MM DD YY   SEX M [ ] F [ ]

4. INSURED'S NAME (Last Name, First Name, Middle Initial)

5. PATIENT'S ADDRESS (No., Street)

6. PATIENT RELATIONSHIP TO INSURED
Self [ ] Spouse [ ] Child [ ] Other [ ]

7. INSURED'S ADDRESS (No., Street)

CITY   STATE

8. PATIENT STATUS
Single [ ]   Married [ ]   Other [ ]

CITY   STATE

ZIP CODE   TELEPHONE (Include Area Code) (   )

Employed [ ]   Full-Time Student [ ]   Part-Time Student [ ]

ZIP CODE   TELEPHONE (Include Area Code) (   )

9. OTHER INSURED'S NAME (Last Name, First Name, Middle Initial)

10. IS PATIENT'S CONDITION RELATED TO:

11. INSURED'S POLICY GROUP OR FECA NUMBER

a. OTHER INSURED'S POLICY OR GROUP NUMBER

a. EMPLOYMENT? (Current or Previous)
YES [ ]   NO [ ]

a. INSURED'S DATE OF BIRTH MM DD YY   SEX M [ ] F [ ]

b. OTHER INSURED'S DATE OF BIRTH MM DD YY   SEX M [ ] F [ ]

b. AUTO ACCIDENT?   PLACE (State)
YES [ ]   NO [ ]

b. EMPLOYER'S NAME OR SCHOOL NAME

c. EMPLOYER'S NAME OR SCHOOL NAME

c. OTHER ACCIDENT?
YES [ ]   NO [ ]

c. INSURANCE PLAN NAME OR PROGRAM NAME

d. INSURANCE PLAN NAME OR PROGRAM NAME

10d. RESERVED FOR LOCAL USE

d. IS THERE ANOTHER HEALTH BENEFIT PLAN?
YES [ ]   NO [ ]   If yes, return to and complete item 9 a-d.

READ BACK OF FORM BEFORE COMPLETING & SIGNING THIS FORM.
12. PATIENT'S OR AUTHORIZED PERSON'S SIGNATURE I authorize the release of any medical or other information necessary to process this claim. I also request payment of government benefits either to myself or to the party who accepts assignment below.

SIGNED_____   DATE_____

13. INSURED'S OR AUTHORIZED PERSON'S SIGNATURE I authorize payment of medical benefits to the undersigned physician or supplier for services described below.

SIGNED_____

| 14. DATE OF CURRENT: MM DD YY ◄ ILLNESS (First symptom) OR INJURY (Accident) OR PREGNANCY(LMP) | 15. IF PATIENT HAS HAD SAME OR SIMILAR ILLNESS. GIVE FIRST DATE MM DD YY | 16. DATES PATIENT UNABLE TO WORK IN CURRENT OCCUPATION MM DD YY   MM DD YY FROM   TO |

17. NAME OF REFERRING PROVIDER OR OTHER SOURCE   17a.   17b. NPI

18. HOSPITALIZATION DATES RELATED TO CURRENT SERVICES MM DD YY   MM DD YY FROM   TO

19. RESERVED FOR LOCAL USE

20. OUTSIDE LAB? $ CHARGES
YES [ ]   NO [ ]

21. DIAGNOSIS OR NATURE OF ILLNESS OR INJURY (Relate items 1, 2, 3 or 4 to item 24E by Line)
1. |___.___   3. |___.___
2. |___.___   4. |___.___

22. MEDICAID RESUBMISSION CODE   ORIGINAL REF. NO.

23. PRIOR AUTHORIZATION NUMBER

24. A. DATE(S) OF SERVICE From MM DD YY To MM DD YY	B. PLACE OF SERVICE	C. EMG	D. PROCEDURES, SERVICES, OR SUPPLIES (Explain Unusual Circumstances) CPT/HCPCS MODIFIER	E. DIAGNOSIS POINTER	F. $ CHARGES	G. DAYS OR UNITS	H. EPSDT Family Plan	I. ID. QUAL.	J. RENDERING PROVIDER ID. #
1									NPI
2									NPI
3									NPI
4									NPI
5									NPI
6									NPI

25. FEDERAL TAX I.D. NUMBER   SSN EIN [ ]

26. PATIENT'S ACCOUNT NO.

27. ACCEPT ASSIGNMENT? (For govt. claims, see back) YES [ ]   NO [ ]

28. TOTAL CHARGE $

29. AMOUNT PAID $

30. BALANCE DUE $

31. SIGNATURE OF PHYSICIAN OR SUPPLIER INCLUDING DEGREES OR CREDENTIALS (I certify that the statements on the reverse apply to this bill and are made a part thereof.)

SIGNED_____   DATE_____

32. SERVICE FACILITY LOCATION INFORMATION

a.   b.

33. BILLING PROVIDER INFO & PH # (   )

a.   b.

NUCC Instruction Manual available at: www.nucc.org

OMB APPROVAL PENDING

PATIENT AND INSURED INFORMATION

PHYSICIAN OR SUPPLIER INFORMATION

	Name:_____
WORKBOOK cpTeach 2012	Class/Section:_____
	Date:_____

EXERCISE 6.16

Lea Shun has been a patient of yours for the past 5 years. Today, she presents herself in the office with an unscheduled appointment because she "can't breathe." You bring her in to your doctor who examines her and notices that her breathing is very labored and that due to her lifelong history of asthma, some treatment should begin and she should definitely be monitored. Your physician listens to the patient's lungs, discovers that the respiratory rate is 35 and that the bronchi seem to be constricted. He begins treating the patient with bronchodilators and subcutaneous epinephrine and monitors her progress for 2 ½ hours.

Notes: _____

_____

_____

_____

_____

_____

_____

_____

_____

_____

_____

_____

_____

_____

_____

_____

_____

_____

_____

_____

_____

DOC Form®
(Doctor's Office Checklist)

	OFFICE/OUTPATIENT		CONSULTATION	
	New (3)	Established (2)	Office/O.P. (3)	Inpatient (3)
Minimal Service		99211		
HISTORY				
Problem Focused	99201	99212	99241	99251
Exp/Prob Focused	99202	99213	99242	99252
Detail	99203	99214	99243	99253
Comprehensive	99204/05	99215	99244/45	99254/55
EXAMINATION				
Problem Focused	99201	99212	99241	99251
Exp/Prob Focused	99202	99213	99242	99252
Detail	99203	99214	99243	99253
Comprehensive	99204/05	99215	99244/45	99254/55
MEDICAL DECISION MAKING				
Straight Forward	99201/2	99212	99241/42	99251/52
Low Complexity	99203	99213	99243	99253
Mod Complexity	99204	99214	99244	99254
High Complexity	99205	99215	99245	99255

TIME:_____		Counsel/Coordination of Care:_____		
10 Minutes	99201	99212		
15 Minutes		99213	99241	
20 Minutes	99202			99251
25 Minutes		99214		
30 Minutes	99203		99242	
40 Minutes		99215	99243	99252
45 Minutes	99204			
55 Minutes				99253
60 Minutes	99205		99244	
80 Minutes			99245	99254
110 Minutes				99255

MedBooks, Inc.
101 W. Buckingham Road, Richardson, Tx. 75081 (800) 443-7397
Warning: This product is copyrighted and is not to be duplicated in any manner without the express written permission of MedBooks.

EXERCISE 6.16

WORKBOOK

cpTeach

2012

Name:_____

Class/Section:_____

Date:_____

1500

HEALTH INSURANCE CLAIM FORM

APPROVED BY NATIONAL UNIFORM CLAIM COMMITTEE 08/05

| | PICA | | | | | | | | PICA | |

| 1. MEDICARE   MEDICAID   TRICARE CHAMPUS   CHAMPVA   GROUP HEALTH PLAN   FECA BLK LUNG   OTHER | 1a. INSURED'S I.D. NUMBER   (For Program in Item 1) |
| (Medicare #)   (Medicaid #)   (Sponsor's SSN)   (Member ID#)   (SSN or ID)   (SSN)   (ID) | |

| 2. PATIENT'S NAME (Last Name, First Name, Middle Initial) | 3. PATIENT'S BIRTH DATE   MM   DD   YY   SEX   M □   F □ | 4. INSURED'S NAME (Last Name, First Name, Middle Initial) |

| 5. PATIENT'S ADDRESS (No., Street) | 6. PATIENT RELATIONSHIP TO INSURED   Self □   Spouse □   Child □   Other □ | 7. INSURED'S ADDRESS (No., Street) |

| CITY   STATE | 8. PATIENT STATUS   Single □   Married □   Other □ | CITY   STATE |

| ZIP CODE   TELEPHONE (Include Area Code) (   ) | Employed □   Full-Time Student □   Part-Time Student □ | ZIP CODE   TELEPHONE (Include Area Code) (   ) |

| 9. OTHER INSURED'S NAME (Last Name, First Name, Middle Initial) | 10. IS PATIENT'S CONDITION RELATED TO: | 11. INSURED'S POLICY GROUP OR FECA NUMBER |

| a. OTHER INSURED'S POLICY OR GROUP NUMBER | a. EMPLOYMENT? (Current or Previous)   YES □   NO □ | a. INSURED'S DATE OF BIRTH   MM   DD   YY   SEX   M □   F □ |

| b. OTHER INSURED'S DATE OF BIRTH   MM   DD   YY   SEX   M □   F □ | b. AUTO ACCIDENT?   PLACE (State)   YES □   NO □ | b. EMPLOYER'S NAME OR SCHOOL NAME |

| c. EMPLOYER'S NAME OR SCHOOL NAME | c. OTHER ACCIDENT?   YES □   NO □ | c. INSURANCE PLAN NAME OR PROGRAM NAME |

| d. INSURANCE PLAN NAME OR PROGRAM NAME | 10d. RESERVED FOR LOCAL USE | d. IS THERE ANOTHER HEALTH BENEFIT PLAN?   YES □   NO □   If yes, return to and complete item 9 a-d. |

READ BACK OF FORM BEFORE COMPLETING & SIGNING THIS FORM.

12. PATIENT'S OR AUTHORIZED PERSON'S SIGNATURE I authorize the release of any medical or other information necessary to process this claim. I also request payment of government benefits either to myself or to the party who accepts assignment below.

SIGNED_____   DATE_____

13. INSURED'S OR AUTHORIZED PERSON'S SIGNATURE I authorize payment of medical benefits to the undersigned physician or supplier for services described below.

SIGNED _____

| 14. DATE OF CURRENT: MM   DD   YY   ILLNESS (First symptom) OR INJURY (Accident) OR PREGNANCY(LMP) | 15. IF PATIENT HAS HAD SAME OR SIMILAR ILLNESS. GIVE FIRST DATE   MM   DD   YY | 16. DATES PATIENT UNABLE TO WORK IN CURRENT OCCUPATION   MM   DD   YY   MM   DD   YY   FROM   TO |

| 17. NAME OF REFERRING PROVIDER OR OTHER SOURCE | 17a. | 17b. NPI | 18. HOSPITALIZATION DATES RELATED TO CURRENT SERVICES   MM   DD   YY   MM   DD   YY   FROM   TO |

| 19. RESERVED FOR LOCAL USE | 20. OUTSIDE LAB? $ CHARGES   YES □   NO □ |

21. DIAGNOSIS OR NATURE OF ILLNESS OR INJURY (Relate Items 1, 2, 9 or 4 to Item 24E by Line)

1. |___.___| 3. |___.___|

2. |___.___| 4. |___.___|

| 22. MEDICAID RESUBMISSION CODE   ORIGINAL REF. NO. |
| 23. PRIOR AUTHORIZATION NUMBER |

24. A. DATE(S) OF SERVICE From To MM DD YY MM DD YY	B. PLACE OF SERVICE	C. EMG	D. PROCEDURES, SERVICES, OR SUPPLIES (Explain Unusual Circumstances) CPT/HCPCS MODIFIER	E. DIAGNOSIS POINTER	F. $ CHARGES	G. DAYS OR UNITS	H. EPSDT Family Plan	I. ID. QUAL.	J. RENDERING PROVIDER ID. #
1									NPI
2									NPI
3									NPI
4									NPI
5									NPI
6									NPI

| 25. FEDERAL TAX I.D. NUMBER   SSN □ EIN □ | 26. PATIENT'S ACCOUNT NO. | 27. ACCEPT ASSIGNMENT? (For govt. claims, see back)   YES □   NO □ | 28. TOTAL CHARGE $ | 29. AMOUNT PAID $ | 30. BALANCE DUE $ |

| 31. SIGNATURE OF PHYSICIAN OR SUPPLIER INCLUDING DEGREES OR CREDENTIALS (I certify that the statements on the reverse apply to this bill and are made a part thereof.)   SIGNED   DATE | 32. SERVICE FACILITY LOCATION INFORMATION   a. NPI   b. | 33. BILLING PROVIDER INFO & PH # (   )   a. NPI   b. |

NUCC Instruction Manual available at: www.nucc.org   OMB APPROVAL PENDING

PATIENT AND INSURED INFORMATION

PHYSICIAN OR SUPPLIER INFORMATION

Name:_____

Class/Section:_____

Date:_____

EXERCISE 6.17

Dakota Jones, a six-year-old boy, has been riding his bike without a helmet. On this particular day, Dakota, being the daredevil that he is, has decided to ride down the large hill at the end of his street which butts into a large dumpster. The brakes on Dakota's bike do not work properly and Dakota slammed into the dumpster going at top speed. When his mother found him, Dakota was unconscious and his right arm was bleeding. She carried him to her car and took him to the nearest emergency room. While there, Dakota received at CAT scan of his head, and his arm was x-rayed. The physician checked for any concussions, checked the patient's pupils and breathing, examined other bones for possible fractures, and reviewed the radiologist's reports. Dakota "came to" in the emergency room after having been unconscious for about 10 minutes. He seemed happy and relieved that both of his parents were there, and he was fairly active and responsive to questions. Since no fractures were found, and since Dakota's parents have no insurance or Medicaid and cannot afford hospital bills, Dakota was released with orders to wear his helmet, and for his parents to watch him for the evening to make sure that he did not experience any vomiting or further unconsciousness. Code for the emergency room physician.

Notes: _____

_____

_____

DOC Form®
(Doctor's Office Checklist)

	HOSPITAL		OBSERVATION		ER
	Initial (3)	Sub (2)	Discharge Date		New/Estab (3)
			Different (3)	Same (3)	

HISTORY

Problem Focused		99231			99281
Exp/Prob Focused		99232			99282/83
Detail	99221	99233	99218	99234	99284
Comprehensive	99221/2/3		99218/19/20	99234/35/36	99285

EXAMINATION

Problem Focused		99231			99281
Exp/Prob Focused		99232			99282/83
Detail	99221	99233	99218	99234	99284
Comprehensive	99221/2/3		99218/19/20	99234/35/36	99285

MEDICAL DECISION MAKING

Straight Forward	99221	99231	99218	99234	99281
Low Complexity	99221	99231	99218	99234	99282
Mod Complexity	99222	99232	99219	99235	99283/84
High Complexity	99223	99233	99220	99236	99285

DISCHARGE   99217

≤ 30 Minutes		99238			
> 30 Minutes		99239			

TIME

15 Minutes		99231			
20 Minutes					
25 Minutes		99232			
30 Minutes	99221				
35 Minutes		99233			
45 Minutes					
50 Minutes	99222				
60 Minutes					
70 Minutes	99223				

Patient Name:_____

Date:_____Physician Signature:_____

EXERCISE 6.17

<table>
<tr><td>WORKBOOK</td><td>Name:_____

Class/Section:_____

cpTeach Date:_____
2012</td></tr>
</table>

1500

HEALTH INSURANCE CLAIM FORM

APPROVED BY NATIONAL UNIFORM CLAIM COMMITTEE 08/05

[ ][ ] PICA   PICA [ ][ ]

1. MEDICARE MEDICAID TRICARE CHAMPUS CHAMPVA GROUP HEALTH PLAN FECA BLK LUNG OTHER	1a. INSURED'S I.D. NUMBER (For Program in Item 1)
[ ] (Medicare #) [ ] (Medicaid #) [ ] (Sponsor's SSN) [ ] (Member ID#) [ ] (SSN or ID) [ ] (SSN) [ ] (ID)	

2. PATIENT'S NAME (Last Name, First Name, Middle Initial)	3. PATIENT'S BIRTH DATE MM DD YY SEX M [ ] F [ ]	4. INSURED'S NAME (Last Name, First Name, Middle Initial)

5. PATIENT'S ADDRESS (No., Street)	6. PATIENT RELATIONSHIP TO INSURED Self [ ] Spouse [ ] Child [ ] Other [ ]	7. INSURED'S ADDRESS (No., Street)

CITY STATE	8. PATIENT STATUS Single [ ] Married [ ] Other [ ]	CITY STATE

ZIP CODE TELEPHONE (Include Area Code) ( )	Employed [ ] Full-Time Student [ ] Part-Time Student [ ]	ZIP CODE TELEPHONE (Include Area Code) ( )

9. OTHER INSURED'S NAME (Last Name, First Name, Middle Initial)	10. IS PATIENT'S CONDITION RELATED TO:	11. INSURED'S POLICY GROUP OR FECA NUMBER
a. OTHER INSURED'S POLICY OR GROUP NUMBER	a. EMPLOYMENT? (Current or Previous) [ ] YES [ ] NO	a. INSURED'S DATE OF BIRTH MM DD YY SEX M [ ] F [ ]
b. OTHER INSURED'S DATE OF BIRTH MM DD YY SEX M [ ] F [ ]	b. AUTO ACCIDENT? PLACE (State) [ ] YES [ ] NO	b. EMPLOYER'S NAME OR SCHOOL NAME
c. EMPLOYER'S NAME OR SCHOOL NAME	c. OTHER ACCIDENT? [ ] YES [ ] NO	c. INSURANCE PLAN NAME OR PROGRAM NAME
d. INSURANCE PLAN NAME OR PROGRAM NAME	10d. RESERVED FOR LOCAL USE	d. IS THERE ANOTHER HEALTH BENEFIT PLAN? [ ] YES [ ] NO If yes, return to and complete item 9 a-d.

READ BACK OF FORM BEFORE COMPLETING & SIGNING THIS FORM.

12. PATIENT'S OR AUTHORIZED PERSON'S SIGNATURE I authorize the release of any medical or other information necessary to process this claim. I also request payment of government benefits either to myself or to the party who accepts assignment below.

SIGNED_____   DATE_____

13. INSURED'S OR AUTHORIZED PERSON'S SIGNATURE I authorize payment of medical benefits to the undersigned physician or supplier for services described below.

SIGNED_____

14. DATE OF CURRENT: MM DD YY ◄ ILLNESS (First symptom) OR INJURY (Accident) OR PREGNANCY(LMP)	15. IF PATIENT HAS HAD SAME OR SIMILAR ILLNESS. GIVE FIRST DATE MM DD YY	16. DATES PATIENT UNABLE TO WORK IN CURRENT OCCUPATION MM DD YY MM DD YY FROM TO
17. NAME OF REFERRING PROVIDER OR OTHER SOURCE	17a. 17b. NPI	18. HOSPITALIZATION DATES RELATED TO CURRENT SERVICES MM DD YY MM DD YY FROM TO
19. RESERVED FOR LOCAL USE		20. OUTSIDE LAB? [ ] YES [ ] NO $ CHARGES

21. DIAGNOSIS OR NATURE OF ILLNESS OR INJURY (Relate Items 1, 2, 3 or 4 to Item 24E by Line)	22. MEDICAID RESUBMISSION CODE ORIGINAL REF. NO.
1. |____.____ 3. |____.____	
2. |____.____ 4. |____.____	23. PRIOR AUTHORIZATION NUMBER

24. A. DATE(S) OF SERVICE From To MM DD YY MM DD YY	B. PLACE OF SERVICE	C. EMG	D. PROCEDURES, SERVICES, OR SUPPLIES (Explain Unusual Circumstances) CPT/HCPCS	MODIFIER	E. DIAGNOSIS POINTER	F. $ CHARGES	G. DAYS OR UNITS	H. EPSDT Family Plan	I. ID. QUAL.	J. RENDERING PROVIDER ID. #
1										NPI
2										NPI
3										NPI
4										NPI
5										NPI
6										NPI

25. FEDERAL TAX I.D. NUMBER [ ] SSN [ ] EIN	26. PATIENT'S ACCOUNT NO.	27. ACCEPT ASSIGNMENT? (For govt. claims, see back) [ ] YES [ ] NO	28. TOTAL CHARGE $	29. AMOUNT PAID $	30. BALANCE DUE $
31. SIGNATURE OF PHYSICIAN OR SUPPLIER INCLUDING DEGREES OR CREDENTIALS (I certify that the statements on the reverse apply to this bill and are made a part thereof.) SIGNED_____ DATE_____	32. SERVICE FACILITY LOCATION INFORMATION a. b.	33. BILLING PROVIDER INFO & PH # ( ) a. b.			

NUCC Instruction Manual available at: www.nucc.org   OMB APPROVAL PENDING

PATIENT AND INSURED INFORMATION

PHYSICIAN OR SUPPLIER INFORMATION

EXERCISE 6.18

Greg Princeton, a 42-year-old alcoholic, is admitted to your hospital through the emergency room after being in a car accident. Mr. Princeton was in the car with his girlfriend who explained that he is severely depressed and has come to your town to get away from it all and to find some psychiatric help. Although no one was hurt, Mr. Princeton is incoherent and unconscious. The emergency room staff has checked Mr. Princeton's wallet and they discover that he is from out of town. Your physician, a psychiatrist, is called to render an opinion as to how/what treatment Mr. Princeton should receive while he is in the hospital. After a few hours, Mr. Princeton "comes to" and your physician is able to talk with him for about 45 minutes. He finds out that Mr. Princeton had been sober for the past five years, but that he just lost his son and wife in another car accident. Mr. Princeton has been active in AA, has come to your town to look for work, and will be staying with relatives who know about and are supportive of his continued therapy. He is cognizant of the fact that he needs further help at AA and is more than willing to submit to treatment. Code for this inpatient visit for the psychiatrist.

Notes: _____

_____

_____

_____

_____

_____

_____

_____

DOC Form®
(Doctor's Office Checklist)

	OFFICE/OUTPATIENT		CONSULTATION	
	New (3)	Established (2)	Office/O.P. (3)	Inpatient (3)
Minimal Service		99211		

HISTORY				
Problem Focused	99201	99212	99241	99251
Exp/Prob Focused	99202	99213	99242	99252
Detail	99203	99214	99243	99253
Comprehensive	99204/05	99215	99244/45	99254/55

EXAMINATION				
Problem Focused	99201	99212	99241	99251
Exp/Prob Focused	99202	99213	99242	99252
Detail	99203	99214	99243	99253
Comprehensive	99204/05	99215	99244/45	99254/55

MEDICAL DECISION MAKING				
Straight Forward	99201/2	99212	99241/42	99251/52
Low Complexity	99203	99213	99243	99253
Mod Complexity	99204	99214	99244	99254
High Complexity	99205	99215	99245	99255

TIME:_____		Counsel/Coordination of Care:_____		
10 Minutes	99201	99212		
15 Minutes		99213	99241	
20 Minutes	99202			99251
25 Minutes		99214		
30 Minutes	99203		99242	
40 Minutes		99215	99243	99252
45 Minutes	99204			
55 Minutes				99253
60 Minutes	99205		99244	
80 Minutes			99245	99254
110 Minutes				99255

MedBooks, Inc.
101 W. Buckingham Road, Richardson, Tx. 75081 (800) 443-7397
Warning: This product is copyrighted and is not to be duplicated in any manner without the express written permission of MedBooks.

EXERCISE 6.18

Name:_____

Class/Section:_____

Date:_____

1500

HEALTH INSURANCE CLAIM FORM

APPROVED BY NATIONAL UNIFORM CLAIM COMMITTEE 08/05

| | PICA | | | | | | | PICA | |

1. MEDICARE   MEDICAID   TRICARE CHAMPUS   CHAMPVA   GROUP HEALTH PLAN   FECA BLK LUNG   OTHER   1a. INSURED'S I.D. NUMBER   (For Program in Item 1)
  (Medicare #) (Medicaid #) (Sponsor's SSN) (Member ID#) (SSN or ID) (SSN) (ID)

2. PATIENT'S NAME (Last Name, First Name, Middle Initial)   3. PATIENT'S BIRTH DATE MM DD YY   SEX M   F   4. INSURED'S NAME (Last Name, First Name, Middle Initial)

5. PATIENT'S ADDRESS (No., Street)   6. PATIENT RELATIONSHIP TO INSURED   Self   Spouse   Child   Other   7. INSURED'S ADDRESS (No., Street)

CITY   STATE   8. PATIENT STATUS   Single   Married   Other   CITY   STATE

ZIP CODE   TELEPHONE (Include Area Code) (   )   Employed   Full-Time Student   Part-Time Student   ZIP CODE   TELEPHONE (Include Area Code) (   )

9. OTHER INSURED'S NAME (Last Name, First Name, Middle Initial)   10. IS PATIENT'S CONDITION RELATED TO: 11. INSURED'S POLICY GROUP OR FECA NUMBER

a. OTHER INSURED'S POLICY OR GROUP NUMBER   a. EMPLOYMENT? (Current or Previous)   YES   NO   a. INSURED'S DATE OF BIRTH MM DD YY   SEX M   F

b. OTHER INSURED'S DATE OF BIRTH MM DD YY   SEX M   F   b. AUTO ACCIDENT?   PLACE (State)   YES   NO   b. EMPLOYER'S NAME OR SCHOOL NAME

c. EMPLOYER'S NAME OR SCHOOL NAME   c. OTHER ACCIDENT?   YES   NO   c. INSURANCE PLAN NAME OR PROGRAM NAME

d. INSURANCE PLAN NAME OR PROGRAM NAME   10d. RESERVED FOR LOCAL USE   d. IS THERE ANOTHER HEALTH BENEFIT PLAN?   YES   NO   If yes, return to and complete item 9 a-d.

READ BACK OF FORM BEFORE COMPLETING & SIGNING THIS FORM.
12. PATIENT'S OR AUTHORIZED PERSON'S SIGNATURE I authorize the release of any medical or other information necessary to process this claim. I also request payment of government benefits either to myself or to the party who accepts assignment below.

SIGNED_____   DATE_____

13. INSURED'S OR AUTHORIZED PERSON'S SIGNATURE I authorize payment of medical benefits to the undersigned physician or supplier for services described below.

SIGNED_____

14. DATE OF CURRENT: MM DD YY   ILLNESS (First symptom) OR INJURY (Accident) OR PREGNANCY(LMP)   15. IF PATIENT HAS HAD SAME OR SIMILAR ILLNESS. GIVE FIRST DATE MM DD YY   16. DATES PATIENT UNABLE TO WORK IN CURRENT OCCUPATION MM DD YY FROM   TO MM DD YY

17. NAME OF REFERRING PROVIDER OR OTHER SOURCE   17a.   17b. NPI   18. HOSPITALIZATION DATES RELATED TO CURRENT SERVICES MM DD YY FROM   TO MM DD YY

19. RESERVED FOR LOCAL USE   20. OUTSIDE LAB?   YES   NO $ CHARGES

21. DIAGNOSIS OR NATURE OF ILLNESS OR INJURY (Relate Items 1, 2, 3 or 4 to Item 24E by Line)
1. |___.___   3. |___.___
2. |___.___   4. |___.___

22. MEDICAID RESUBMISSION CODE   ORIGINAL REF. NO.

23. PRIOR AUTHORIZATION NUMBER

24. A. DATE(S) OF SERVICE						B. PLACE OF SERVICE	C. EMG	D. PROCEDURES, SERVICES, OR SUPPLIES (Explain Unusual Circumstances)		E. DIAGNOSIS POINTER	F. $ CHARGES	G. DAYS OR UNITS	H. EPSDT Family Plan	I. ID. QUAL.	J. RENDERING PROVIDER ID. #
From			To					CPT/HCPCS	MODIFIER						
MM	DD	YY	MM	DD	YY										
1														NPI	
2														NPI	
3														NPI	
4														NPI	
5														NPI	
6														NPI	

25. FEDERAL TAX I.D. NUMBER   SSN EIN   26. PATIENT'S ACCOUNT NO.   27. ACCEPT ASSIGNMENT? (For govt. claims, see back)   YES   NO   28. TOTAL CHARGE $ 29. AMOUNT PAID $ 30. BALANCE DUE $

31. SIGNATURE OF PHYSICIAN OR SUPPLIER INCLUDING DEGREES OR CREDENTIALS (I certify that the statements on the reverse apply to this bill and are made a part thereof.)

SIGNED_____   DATE_____

32. SERVICE FACILITY LOCATION INFORMATION

a. NPI   b.

33. BILLING PROVIDER INFO & PH # (   )

a. NPI   b.

NUCC Instruction Manual available at: www.nucc.org   OMB APPROVAL PENDING

PATIENT AND INSURED INFORMATION

PHYSICIAN OR SUPPLIER INFORMATION

Name:_____

Class/Section:_____

Date:_____

cpTeach
2012

EXERCISE 6.19

Dr. Norman visits Janes Pulmones in the hospital a second time to reevaluate her lung condition. He performs an extensive review of her past medical management including an extended system review and an extended history of the present illness. He considers at least four possible diagnoses and checks on her progress with an examination of her lungs. During the exam, Dr. Norman looks at the affected body area as well as other symptomatic or related systems and recommends modifications to the attending physician on Ms. Pulmones' treatment.

Notes: _____

_____

_____

_____

_____

_____

_____

_____

_____

_____

_____

_____

_____

_____

_____

_____

DOC Form®
(Doctor's Office Checklist)

	HOSPITAL		OBSERVATION		ER
	Initial (3)	Sub (2)	Discharge Date Different (3) Same (3)		New/Estab (3)

HISTORY

Problem Focused		99231			99281
Exp/Prob Focused		99232			99282/83
Detail	99221	99233	99218	99234	99284
Comprehensive	99221/2/3		99218/19/20	99234/35/36	99285

EXAMINATION

Problem Focused		99231			99281
Exp/Prob Focused		99232			99282/83
Detail	99221	99233	99218	99234	99284
Comprehensive	99221/2/3		99218/19/20	99234/35/36	99285

MEDICAL DECISION MAKING

Straight Forward	99221	99231	99218	99234	99281
Low Complexity	99221	99231	99218	99234	99282
Mod Complexity	99222	99232	99219	99235	99283/84
High Complexity	99223	99233	99220	99236	99285

DISCHARGE   99217

≤ 30 Minutes		99238			
> 30 Minutes		99239			

TIME

15 Minutes		99231			
20 Minutes					
25 Minutes		99232			
30 Minutes	99221				
35 Minutes		99233			
45 Minutes					
50 Minutes	99222				
60 Minutes					
70 Minutes	99223				

Patient Name:_____

Date:_____Physician Signature:_____

MedBooks, Inc.
101 W. Buckingham Road, Richardson, Tx. 75081 (800) 443-7397
Warning: This product is copyrighted and is not to be duplicated in any manner without the express written permission of MedBooks.

EXERCISE 6.19

Name: _____

Class/Section: _____

cpTeach

Date: _____

2012

1500

HEALTH INSURANCE CLAIM FORM

APPROVED BY NATIONAL UNIFORM CLAIM COMMITTEE 08/05

☐☐ PICA   PICA ☐☐

1. MEDICARE MEDICAID TRICARE CHAMPUS CHAMPVA GROUP HEALTH PLAN FECA BLK LUNG OTHER	1a. INSURED'S I.D. NUMBER (For Program in Item 1)
☐ (Medicare #) ☐ (Medicaid #) ☐ (Sponsor's SSN) ☐ (Member ID#) ☐ (SSN or ID) ☐ (SSN) ☐ (ID)	

2. PATIENT'S NAME (Last Name, First Name, Middle Initial)	3. PATIENT'S BIRTH DATE SEX	4. INSURED'S NAME (Last Name, First Name, Middle Initial)
	MM DD YY M ☐ F ☐	

5. PATIENT'S ADDRESS (No., Street)	6. PATIENT RELATIONSHIP TO INSURED	7. INSURED'S ADDRESS (No., Street)
	Self ☐ Spouse ☐ Child ☐ Other ☐	

CITY STATE	8. PATIENT STATUS	CITY STATE
	Single ☐ Married ☐ Other ☐	
ZIP CODE TELEPHONE (Include Area Code) ( )	Employed ☐ Full-Time Student ☐ Part-Time Student ☐	ZIP CODE TELEPHONE (Include Area Code) ( )

9. OTHER INSURED'S NAME (Last Name, First Name, Middle Initial)	10. IS PATIENT'S CONDITION RELATED TO:	11. INSURED'S POLICY GROUP OR FECA NUMBER
a. OTHER INSURED'S POLICY OR GROUP NUMBER	a. EMPLOYMENT? (Current or Previous) ☐ YES ☐ NO	a. INSURED'S DATE OF BIRTH SEX MM DD YY M ☐ F ☐
b. OTHER INSURED'S DATE OF BIRTH SEX MM DD YY M ☐ F ☐	b. AUTO ACCIDENT? PLACE (State) ☐ YES ☐ NO	b. EMPLOYER'S NAME OR SCHOOL NAME
c. EMPLOYER'S NAME OR SCHOOL NAME	c. OTHER ACCIDENT? ☐ YES ☐ NO	c. INSURANCE PLAN NAME OR PROGRAM NAME
d. INSURANCE PLAN NAME OR PROGRAM NAME	10d. RESERVED FOR LOCAL USE	d. IS THERE ANOTHER HEALTH BENEFIT PLAN? ☐ YES ☐ NO If yes, return to and complete item 9 a-d.

READ BACK OF FORM BEFORE COMPLETING & SIGNING THIS FORM.

12. PATIENT'S OR AUTHORIZED PERSON'S SIGNATURE I authorize the release of any medical or other information necessary to process this claim. I also request payment of government benefits either to myself or to the party who accepts assignment below.

SIGNED_____ DATE_____

13. INSURED'S OR AUTHORIZED PERSON'S SIGNATURE I authorize payment of medical benefits to the undersigned physician or supplier for services described below.

SIGNED_____

14. DATE OF CURRENT: ILLNESS (First symptom) OR INJURY (Accident) OR PREGNANCY(LMP) MM DD YY	15. IF PATIENT HAS HAD SAME OR SIMILAR ILLNESS. GIVE FIRST DATE MM DD YY	16. DATES PATIENT UNABLE TO WORK IN CURRENT OCCUPATION MM DD YY FROM TO MM DD YY
17. NAME OF REFERRING PROVIDER OR OTHER SOURCE	17a. 17b. NPI	18. HOSPITALIZATION DATES RELATED TO CURRENT SERVICES MM DD YY FROM TO MM DD YY
19. RESERVED FOR LOCAL USE		20. OUTSIDE LAB? ☐ YES ☐ NO $ CHARGES

21. DIAGNOSIS OR NATURE OF ILLNESS OR INJURY (Relate Items 1, 2, 3 or 4 to Item 24E by Line)	22. MEDICAID RESUBMISSION CODE ORIGINAL REF. NO.
1. |_____ . _____ 3. |_____ . _____	
2. |_____ . _____ 4. |_____ . _____	23. PRIOR AUTHORIZATION NUMBER

24. A. DATE(S) OF SERVICE From To MM DD YY MM DD YY	B. PLACE OF SERVICE	C. EMG	D. PROCEDURES, SERVICES, OR SUPPLIES (Explain Unusual Circumstances) CPT/HCPCS MODIFIER	E. DIAGNOSIS POINTER	F. $ CHARGES	G. DAYS OR UNITS	H. EPSDT Family Plan	I. ID. QUAL.	J. RENDERING PROVIDER ID. #
1									NPI
2									NPI
3									NPI
4									NPI
5									NPI
6									NPI

25. FEDERAL TAX I.D. NUMBER SSN EIN	26. PATIENT'S ACCOUNT NO.	27. ACCEPT ASSIGNMENT? (For govt. claims, see back) ☐ YES ☐ NO	28. TOTAL CHARGE $	29. AMOUNT PAID $	30. BALANCE DUE $

31. SIGNATURE OF PHYSICIAN OR SUPPLIER INCLUDING DEGREES OR CREDENTIALS (I certify that the statements on the reverse apply to this bill and are made a part thereof.) SIGNED_____ DATE_____	32. SERVICE FACILITY LOCATION INFORMATION a. b.	33. BILLING PROVIDER INFO & PH # ( ) a. b.

NUCC Instruction Manual available at: www.nucc.org   OMB APPROVAL PENDING

PATIENT AND INSURED INFORMATION

PHYSICIAN OR SUPPLIER INFORMATION

Name:_____

Class/Section:_____

Date:_____

2012

EXERCISE 6.20

Ms. Barb Wire, a new patient of yours, falls off her exercise bike while working her way down to 450 lbs., and injures her wrist. Upon presentation in your office, your doctor completes a brief history of the incident with a problem pertinent system review and examines the wrist in an expanded problem focused exam. He orders some x-rays and makes a straightforward decision. He prescribes some Motrin and explains his findings to Ms. Wire.

Notes: _____

_____

_____

_____

_____

_____

_____

_____

_____

_____

_____

_____

_____

_____

_____

_____

_____

_____

_____

_____

_____

_____

_____

DOC Form®
(Doctor's Office Checklist)

	OFFICE/OUTPATIENT		CONSULTATION	
	New (3)	Established (2)	Office/O.P. (3)	Inpatient (3)
Minimal Service		99211		

HISTORY
	New (3)	Established (2)	Office/O.P. (3)	Inpatient (3)
Problem Focused	99201	99212	99241	99251
Exp/Prob Focused	99202	99213	99242	99252
Detail	99203	99214	99243	99253
Comprehensive	99204/05	99215	99244/45	99254/55

EXAMINATION
	New (3)	Established (2)	Office/O.P. (3)	Inpatient (3)
Problem Focused	99201	99212	99241	99251
Exp/Prob Focused	99202	99213	99242	99252
Detail	99203	99214	99243	99253
Comprehensive	99204/05	99215	99244/45	99254/55

MEDICAL DECISION MAKING
	New (3)	Established (2)	Office/O.P. (3)	Inpatient (3)
Straight Forward	99201/2	99212	99241/42	99251/52
Low Complexity	99203	99213	99243	99253
Mod Complexity	99204	99214	99244	99254
High Complexity	99205	99215	99245	99255

TIME:_____　　Counsel/Coordination of Care:_____
	New	Established	Office/O.P.	Inpatient
10 Minutes	99201	99212		
15 Minutes		99213	99241	
20 Minutes	99202			99251
25 Minutes		99214		
30 Minutes	99203		99242	
40 Minutes		99215	99243	99252
45 Minutes	99204			
55 Minutes				99253
60 Minutes	99205		99244	
80 Minutes			99245	99254
110 Minutes				99255

MedBooks, Inc.
101 W. Buckingham Road, Richardson, Tx. 75081 (800) 443-7397
Warning: This product is copyrighted and is not to be duplicated in any manner without the express written permission of MedBooks.

EXERCISE 6.20

WORKBOOK 24th Edition

McGUFFEY

cpTeach

2012

Name:_____

Class/Section:_____

Date:_____

```
1500
```

HEALTH INSURANCE CLAIM FORM
APPROVED BY NATIONAL UNIFORM CLAIM COMMITTEE 08/05

	PICA							PICA	

1. MEDICARE ☐ (Medicare #) MEDICAID ☐ (Medicaid #) TRICARE CHAMPUS ☐ (Sponsor's SSN) CHAMPVA ☐ (Member ID#) GROUP HEALTH PLAN ☐ (SSN or ID) FECA BLK LUNG ☐ (SSN) OTHER ☐ (ID)　　**1a. INSURED'S I.D. NUMBER**　　(For Program in Item 1)

2. PATIENT'S NAME (Last Name, First Name, Middle Initial)

3. PATIENT'S BIRTH DATE MM | DD | YY　　SEX M ☐ F ☐

4. INSURED'S NAME (Last Name, First Name, Middle Initial)

5. PATIENT'S ADDRESS (No., Street)

6. PATIENT RELATIONSHIP TO INSURED Self ☐ Spouse ☐ Child ☐ Other ☐

7. INSURED'S ADDRESS (No., Street)

CITY　　　　STATE

8. PATIENT STATUS Single ☐ Married ☐ Other ☐

CITY　　　　STATE

ZIP CODE　　TELEPHONE (Include Area Code) (　　)

Employed ☐ Full-Time Student ☐ Part-Time Student ☐

ZIP CODE　　TELEPHONE (Include Area Code) (　　)

9. OTHER INSURED'S NAME (Last Name, First Name, Middle Initial)

10. IS PATIENT'S CONDITION RELATED TO:

11. INSURED'S POLICY GROUP OR FECA NUMBER

a. OTHER INSURED'S POLICY OR GROUP NUMBER

a. EMPLOYMENT? (Current or Previous) YES ☐ NO ☐

a. INSURED'S DATE OF BIRTH MM | DD | YY　　SEX M ☐ F ☐

b. OTHER INSURED'S DATE OF BIRTH MM | DD | YY　SEX M ☐ F ☐

b. AUTO ACCIDENT? PLACE (State) YES ☐ NO ☐

b. EMPLOYER'S NAME OR SCHOOL NAME

c. EMPLOYER'S NAME OR SCHOOL NAME

c. OTHER ACCIDENT? YES ☐ NO ☐

c. INSURANCE PLAN NAME OR PROGRAM NAME

d. INSURANCE PLAN NAME OR PROGRAM NAME

10d. RESERVED FOR LOCAL USE

d. IS THERE ANOTHER HEALTH BENEFIT PLAN? YES ☐ NO ☐ If yes, return to and complete item 9 a-d.

READ BACK OF FORM BEFORE COMPLETING & SIGNING THIS FORM.
12. PATIENT'S OR AUTHORIZED PERSON'S SIGNATURE I authorize the release of any medical or other information necessary to process this claim. I also request payment of government benefits either to myself or to the party who accepts assignment below.

SIGNED_____ DATE_____

13. INSURED'S OR AUTHORIZED PERSON'S SIGNATURE I authorize payment of medical benefits to the undersigned physician or supplier for services described below.

SIGNED_____

14. DATE OF CURRENT: MM | DD | YY ◄ ILLNESS (First symptom) OR INJURY (Accident) OR PREGNANCY(LMP)

15. IF PATIENT HAS HAD SAME OR SIMILAR ILLNESS. GIVE FIRST DATE MM | DD | YY

16. DATES PATIENT UNABLE TO WORK IN CURRENT OCCUPATION MM | DD | YY FROM　TO MM | DD | YY

17. NAME OF REFERRING PROVIDER OR OTHER SOURCE

17a. | 17b. NPI

18. HOSPITALIZATION DATES RELATED TO CURRENT SERVICES MM | DD | YY FROM　TO MM | DD | YY

19. RESERVED FOR LOCAL USE

20. OUTSIDE LAB? YES ☐ NO ☐　$ CHARGES

21. DIAGNOSIS OR NATURE OF ILLNESS OR INJURY (Relate items 1, 2, 3 or 4 to Item 24E by Line)

1. |___.___ 　　3. |___.___

2. |___.___ 　　4. |___.___

22. MEDICAID RESUBMISSION CODE　ORIGINAL REF. NO.

23. PRIOR AUTHORIZATION NUMBER

24. A. DATE(S) OF SERVICE		B. PLACE OF SERVICE	C. EMG	D. PROCEDURES, SERVICES, OR SUPPLIES (Explain Unusual Circumstances)		E. DIAGNOSIS POINTER	F. $ CHARGES	G. DAYS OR UNITS	H. EPSDT Family Plan	I. ID. QUAL.	J. RENDERING PROVIDER ID. #
From MM DD YY	To MM DD YY			CPT/HCPCS	MODIFIER						
1										NPI	
2										NPI	
3										NPI	
4										NPI	
5										NPI	
6										NPI	

25. FEDERAL TAX I.D. NUMBER SSN ☐ EIN ☐

26. PATIENT'S ACCOUNT NO.

27. ACCEPT ASSIGNMENT? (For govt. claims, see back) YES ☐ NO ☐

28. TOTAL CHARGE $

29. AMOUNT PAID $

30. BALANCE DUE $

31. SIGNATURE OF PHYSICIAN OR SUPPLIER INCLUDING DEGREES OR CREDENTIALS (I certify that the statements on the reverse apply to this bill and are made a part thereof.)

SIGNED_____ DATE_____

32. SERVICE FACILITY LOCATION INFORMATION

a. NPI | b.

33. BILLING PROVIDER INFO & PH # (　　)

a. NPI | b.

NUCC Instruction Manual available at: www.nucc.org　　　　　　OMB APPROVAL PENDING

WORKBOOK	Name:_____
cpTeach 2012	Class/Section:_____
	Date:_____

EXERCISE 6.21

Ms. Sandy Beach has been a patient of yours for the past two weeks. She has been complaining of headaches that have persisted for 6 months. During this particular visit to your office, your doctor, Dr. U. Ken Too, questions Ms. Beach extensively about the history of the headaches, completes an extensive reexamination of her neurologically and obtains all pertinent past, current and family information concerning headaches, as well as completes a detailed examination of her medical records and tests performed during the visit. After considering all the information he has obtained from the tests and records for Ms. Beach, Dr. Too determines that the diagnoses options are limited, the amount of data reviewed is moderate, and the risk of mortality is low.

Notes: _____

_____

_____

_____

_____

_____

_____

_____

_____

_____

_____

_____

_____

_____

_____

_____

_____

_____

_____

DOC Form®
(Doctor's Office Checklist)

	OFFICE/OUTPATIENT		CONSULTATION	
	New (3)	Established (2)	Office/O.P. (3)	Inpatient (3)
Minimal Service		99211		

HISTORY

Problem Focused	99201	99212	99241	99251
Exp/Prob Focused	99202	99213	99242	99252
Detail	99203	99214	99243	99253
Comprehensive	99204/05	99215	99244/45	99254/55

EXAMINATION

Problem Focused	99201	99212	99241	99251
Exp/Prob Focused	99202	99213	99242	99252
Detail	99203	99214	99243	99253
Comprehensive	99204/05	99215	99244/45	99254/55

MEDICAL DECISION MAKING

Straight Forward	99201/2	99212	99241/42	99251/52
Low Complexity	99203	99213	99243	99253
Mod Complexity	99204	99214	99244	99254
High Complexity	99205	99215	99245	99255

TIME: _____　　**Counsel/Coordination of Care:** _____

10 Minutes	99201	99212		
15 Minutes		99213	99241	
20 Minutes	99202			99251
25 Minutes		99214		
30 Minutes	99203		99242	
40 Minutes		99215	99243	99252
45 Minutes	99204			
55 Minutes				99253
60 Minutes	99205		99244	
80 Minutes			99245	99254
110 Minutes				99255

MedBooks, Inc.
101 W. Buckingham Road, Richardson, Tx. 75081 (800) 443-7397
Warning: This product is copyrighted and is not to be duplicated in any manner without the express written permission of MedBooks.

EXERCISE 6.21

[1500]

HEALTH INSURANCE CLAIM FORM
APPROVED BY NATIONAL UNIFORM CLAIM COMMITTEE 08/05

WORKBOOK

Name:_____

Class/Section:_____

cpTeach
2012

Date:_____

| | PICA | | | | | | | | PICA | | |

1. MEDICARE MEDICAID TRICARE CHAMPUS CHAMPVA GROUP HEALTH PLAN FECA BLK LUNG OTHER
  (Medicare #) (Medicaid #) (Sponsor's SSN) (Member ID#) (SSN or ID) (SSN) (ID)

1a. INSURED'S I.D. NUMBER   (For Program in Item 1)

2. PATIENT'S NAME (Last Name, First Name, Middle Initial)

3. PATIENT'S BIRTH DATE SEX
  MM   DD   YY   M   F

4. INSURED'S NAME (Last Name, First Name, Middle Initial)

5. PATIENT'S ADDRESS (No., Street)

6. PATIENT RELATIONSHIP TO INSURED
  Self   Spouse   Child   Other

7. INSURED'S ADDRESS (No., Street)

CITY   STATE

8. PATIENT STATUS
  Single   Married   Other
  Employed   Full-Time Student   Part-Time Student

CITY   STATE

ZIP CODE   TELEPHONE (Include Area Code)
                    (   )

ZIP CODE   TELEPHONE (Include Area Code)
                    (   )

9. OTHER INSURED'S NAME (Last Name, First Name, Middle Initial)

10. IS PATIENT'S CONDITION RELATED TO:

11. INSURED'S POLICY GROUP OR FECA NUMBER

a. OTHER INSURED'S POLICY OR GROUP NUMBER

a. EMPLOYMENT? (Current or Previous)
  YES   NO

a. INSURED'S DATE OF BIRTH SEX
  MM   DD   YY   M   F

b. OTHER INSURED'S DATE OF BIRTH SEX
  MM   DD   YY   M   F

b. AUTO ACCIDENT? PLACE (State)
  YES   NO

b. EMPLOYER'S NAME OR SCHOOL NAME

c. EMPLOYER'S NAME OR SCHOOL NAME

c. OTHER ACCIDENT?
  YES   NO

c. INSURANCE PLAN NAME OR PROGRAM NAME

d. INSURANCE PLAN NAME OR PROGRAM NAME

10d. RESERVED FOR LOCAL USE

d. IS THERE ANOTHER HEALTH BENEFIT PLAN?
  YES   NO   If yes, return to and complete item 9 a-d.

READ BACK OF FORM BEFORE COMPLETING & SIGNING THIS FORM.
12. PATIENT'S OR AUTHORIZED PERSON'S SIGNATURE I authorize the release of any medical or other information necessary to process this claim. I also request payment of government benefits either to myself or to the party who accepts assignment below.

SIGNED_____   DATE_____

13. INSURED'S OR AUTHORIZED PERSON'S SIGNATURE I authorize payment of medical benefits to the undersigned physician or supplier for services described below.

SIGNED_____

14. DATE OF CURRENT: ILLNESS (First symptom) OR INJURY (Accident) OR PREGNANCY(LMP)
  MM   DD   YY

15. IF PATIENT HAS HAD SAME OR SIMILAR ILLNESS. GIVE FIRST DATE MM   DD   YY

16. DATES PATIENT UNABLE TO WORK IN CURRENT OCCUPATION
  MM   DD   YY   MM   DD   YY
  FROM   TO

17. NAME OF REFERRING PROVIDER OR OTHER SOURCE

17a.
17b. NPI

18. HOSPITALIZATION DATES RELATED TO CURRENT SERVICES
  MM   DD   YY   MM   DD   YY
  FROM   TO

19. RESERVED FOR LOCAL USE

20. OUTSIDE LAB? $ CHARGES
  YES   NO

21. DIAGNOSIS OR NATURE OF ILLNESS OR INJURY (Relate Items 1, 2, 3 or 4 to Item 24E by Line)

1. |____.____| 3. |____.____|

2. |____.____| 4. |____.____|

22. MEDICAID RESUBMISSION CODE   ORIGINAL REF. NO.

23. PRIOR AUTHORIZATION NUMBER

24. A. DATE(S) OF SERVICE						B. PLACE OF SERVICE	C. EMG	D. PROCEDURES, SERVICES, OR SUPPLIES (Explain Unusual Circumstances)		E. DIAGNOSIS POINTER	F. $ CHARGES	G. DAYS OR UNITS	H. EPSDT Family Plan	I. ID. QUAL.	J. RENDERING PROVIDER ID. #
From			To					CPT/HCPCS	MODIFIER						
MM	DD	YY	MM	DD	YY										
1														NPI	
2														NPI	
3														NPI	
4														NPI	
5														NPI	
6														NPI	

25. FEDERAL TAX I.D. NUMBER   SSN EIN

26. PATIENT'S ACCOUNT NO.

27. ACCEPT ASSIGNMENT? (For govt. claims, see back)
  YES   NO

28. TOTAL CHARGE $

29. AMOUNT PAID $

30. BALANCE DUE $

31. SIGNATURE OF PHYSICIAN OR SUPPLIER INCLUDING DEGREES OR CREDENTIALS (I certify that the statements on the reverse apply to this bill and are made a part thereof.)

SIGNED_____ DATE_____

32. SERVICE FACILITY LOCATION INFORMATION

a.   b.

33. BILLING PROVIDER INFO & PH # (   )

a.   b.

NUCC Instruction Manual available at: www.nucc.org   OMB APPROVAL PENDING

EXERCISE 6.22

Mr. T. Bone comes to your office to get his sutures removed. He is a regular patient of yours. The sutures were placed by another doctor when Mr. Bone was on vacation. Because the sutures are superficially located on the skin of Mr. Bone's arm and the healing looks good, the nurse removes the stitches and sends Mr. Bone home.

Notes: _____

_____

_____

_____

_____

_____

_____

_____

_____

_____

_____

_____

_____

_____

_____

_____

_____

_____

_____

_____

_____

_____

_____

DOC Form®
(Doctor's Office Checklist)

	OFFICE/OUTPATIENT		CONSULTATION	
	New (3)	Established (2)	Office/O.P. (3)	Inpatient (3)
Minimal Service		99211		
HISTORY				
Problem Focused	99201	99212	99241	99251
Exp/Prob Focused	99202	99213	99242	99252
Detail	99203	99214	99243	99253
Comprehensive	99204/05	99215	99244/45	99254/55
EXAMINATION				
Problem Focused	99201	99212	99241	99251
Exp/Prob Focused	99202	99213	99242	99252
Detail	99203	99214	99243	99253
Comprehensive	99204/05	99215	99244/45	99254/55
MEDICAL DECISION MAKING				
Straight Forward	99201/2	99212	99241/42	99251/52
Low Complexity	99203	99213	99243	99253
Mod Complexity	99204	99214	99244	99254
High Complexity	99205	99215	99245	99255

TIME:_____		**Counsel/Coordination of Care:**_____		
10 Minutes	99201	99212		
15 Minutes		99213	99241	
20 Minutes	99202			99251
25 Minutes		99214		
30 Minutes	99203		99242	
40 Minutes		99215	99243	99252
45 Minutes	99204			
55 Minutes				99253
60 Minutes	99205		99244	
80 Minutes			99245	99254
110 Minutes				99255

EXERCISE 6.22

Name:________________________

Class/Section:________________________

Date:________________________

1500

HEALTH INSURANCE CLAIM FORM

APPROVED BY NATIONAL UNIFORM CLAIM COMMITTEE 08/05

PICA PICA

1. MEDICARE (Medicare #) MEDICAID (Medicaid #) TRICARE CHAMPUS (Sponsor's SSN) CHAMPVA (Member ID#) GROUP HEALTH PLAN (SSN or ID) FECA BLK LUNG (SSN) OTHER (ID)

1a. INSURED'S I.D. NUMBER (For Program in Item 1)

2. PATIENT'S NAME (Last Name, First Name, Middle Initial)

3. PATIENT'S BIRTH DATE MM DD YY SEX M F

4. INSURED'S NAME (Last Name, First Name, Middle Initial)

5. PATIENT'S ADDRESS (No., Street)

6. PATIENT RELATIONSHIP TO INSURED Self Spouse Child Other

7. INSURED'S ADDRESS (No., Street)

CITY STATE

8. PATIENT STATUS Single Married Other

CITY STATE

ZIP CODE TELEPHONE (Include Area Code) ( )

Employed Full-Time Student Part-Time Student

ZIP CODE TELEPHONE (Include Area Code) ( )

9. OTHER INSURED'S NAME (Last Name, First Name, Middle Initial)

10. IS PATIENT'S CONDITION RELATED TO:

11. INSURED'S POLICY GROUP OR FECA NUMBER

a. OTHER INSURED'S POLICY OR GROUP NUMBER

a. EMPLOYMENT? (Current or Previous) YES NO

a. INSURED'S DATE OF BIRTH MM DD YY SEX M F

b. OTHER INSURED'S DATE OF BIRTH MM DD YY SEX M F

b. AUTO ACCIDENT? YES NO PLACE (State)

b. EMPLOYER'S NAME OR SCHOOL NAME

c. EMPLOYER'S NAME OR SCHOOL NAME

c. OTHER ACCIDENT? YES NO

c. INSURANCE PLAN NAME OR PROGRAM NAME

d. INSURANCE PLAN NAME OR PROGRAM NAME

10d. RESERVED FOR LOCAL USE

d. IS THERE ANOTHER HEALTH BENEFIT PLAN? YES NO *If yes*, return to and complete item 9 a-d.

READ BACK OF FORM BEFORE COMPLETING & SIGNING THIS FORM.

12. PATIENT'S OR AUTHORIZED PERSON'S SIGNATURE I authorize the release of any medical or other information necessary to process this claim. I also request payment of government benefits either to myself or to the party who accepts assignment below.

SIGNED________________ DATE________

13. INSURED'S OR AUTHORIZED PERSON'S SIGNATURE I authorize payment of medical benefits to the undersigned physician or supplier for services described below.

SIGNED________

PATIENT AND INSURED INFORMATION

14. DATE OF CURRENT: MM DD YY ILLNESS (First symptom) OR INJURY (Accident) OR PREGNANCY(LMP)

15. IF PATIENT HAS HAD SAME OR SIMILAR ILLNESS. GIVE FIRST DATE MM DD YY

16. DATES PATIENT UNABLE TO WORK IN CURRENT OCCUPATION MM DD YY FROM TO MM DD YY

17. NAME OF REFERRING PROVIDER OR OTHER SOURCE

17a. 17b. NPI

18. HOSPITALIZATION DATES RELATED TO CURRENT SERVICES MM DD YY FROM TO MM DD YY

19. RESERVED FOR LOCAL USE

20. OUTSIDE LAB? YES NO $ CHARGES

21. DIAGNOSIS OR NATURE OF ILLNESS OR INJURY (Relate Items 1, 2, 3 or 4 to Item 24E by Line)

1. ___ . ___ 3. ___ . ___

2. ___ . ___ 4. ___ . ___

22. MEDICAID RESUBMISSION CODE ORIGINAL REF. NO.

23. PRIOR AUTHORIZATION NUMBER

24. A. DATE(S) OF SERVICE From MM DD YY To MM DD YY	B. PLACE OF SERVICE	C. EMG	D. PROCEDURES, SERVICES, OR SUPPLIES (Explain Unusual Circumstances) CPT/HCPCS MODIFIER	E. DIAGNOSIS POINTER	F. $ CHARGES	G. DAYS OR UNITS	H. EPSDT Family Plan	I. ID. QUAL.	J. RENDERING PROVIDER ID. #
1								NPI	
2								NPI	
3								NPI	
4								NPI	
5								NPI	
6								NPI	

PHYSICIAN OR SUPPLIER INFORMATION

25. FEDERAL TAX I.D. NUMBER SSN EIN

26. PATIENT'S ACCOUNT NO.

27. ACCEPT ASSIGNMENT? (For govt. claims, see back) YES NO

28. TOTAL CHARGE $

29. AMOUNT PAID $

30. BALANCE DUE $

31. SIGNATURE OF PHYSICIAN OR SUPPLIER INCLUDING DEGREES OR CREDENTIALS (I certify that the statements on the reverse apply to this bill and are made a part thereof.)

SIGNED DATE

32. SERVICE FACILITY LOCATION INFORMATION

a. NPI b.

33. BILLING PROVIDER INFO & PH # ( )

a. NPI b.

NUCC Instruction Manual available at: www.nucc.org

OMB APPROVAL PENDING

EXERCISE 6.23

Mr. K. Pickett, a fence builder, is on vacation in your town and was involved in a serious automobile accident. Unconscious, he is rushed by ambulance to the nearest hospital where the emergency department is open. Dr. Quick, noticing the extensive bleeding of the head, asks that Dr. Crane, a neurologist, be summoned and begins the examination. Chest x-rays and tests (ECG's etc.) are ordered. By this time Mr. Pickett's friend has arrived and is thoroughly questioned concerning the patient's medical history. A phone call is placed to his family physician for more detailed medical information. Drs. Quick and Crane review all the medical information, x-rays and test data. Mr. Pickett is still unconscious and in critical condition; tests show probable brain damage, a skull fracture and internal bleeding. One and one-half hours later Mr. Pickett is moved to the intensive care unit for continued observation. Code for Dr. Quick.

Notes: _____

_____

_____

_____

_____

_____

_____

_____

_____

_____

_____

_____

DOC Form®
(Doctor's Office Checklist)

	HOSPITAL		OBSERVATION		ER
	Initial (3)	Sub (2)	Discharge Date Different (3) Same (3)		New/Estab (3)
HISTORY					
Problem Focused		99231			99281
Exp/Prob Focused		99232			99282/83
Detail	99221	99233	99218	99234	99284
Comprehensive	99221/2/3		99218/19/20	99234/35/36	99285
EXAMINATION					
Problem Focused		99231			99281
Exp/Prob Focused		99232			99282/83
Detail	99221	99233	99218	99234	99284
Comprehensive	99221/2/3		99218/19/20	99234/35/36	99285
MEDICAL DECISION MAKING					
Straight Forward	99221	99231	99218	99234	99281
Low Complexity	99221	99231	99218	99234	99282
Mod Complexity	99222	99232	99219	99235	99283/84
High Complexity	99223	99233	99220	99236	99285
DISCHARGE			99217		
≤ 30 Minutes		99238			
> 30 Minutes		99239			
TIME					
15 Minutes		99231			
20 Minutes					
25 Minutes		99232			
30 Minutes	99221				
35 Minutes		99233			
45 Minutes					
50 Minutes	99222				
60 Minutes					
70 Minutes	99223				

Patient Name:_____

Date:_____Physician Signature:_____

EXERCISE 6.23

1500
HEALTH INSURANCE CLAIM FORM
APPROVED BY NATIONAL UNIFORM CLAIM COMMITTEE 08/05

PICA ▭▭   PICA ▭▭

1. MEDICARE	MEDICAID	TRICARE CHAMPUS	CHAMPVA	GROUP HEALTH PLAN	FECA BLK LUNG	OTHER	1a. INSURED'S I.D. NUMBER	(For Program in Item 1)
▭ (Medicare #)	▭ (Medicaid #)	▭ (Sponsor's SSN)	▭ (Member ID#)	▭ (SSN or ID)	▭ (SSN)	▭ (ID)		

2. PATIENT'S NAME (Last Name, First Name, Middle Initial) | 3. PATIENT'S BIRTH DATE MM | DD | YY   SEX   M ▭ F ▭ | 4. INSURED'S NAME (Last Name, First Name, Middle Initial)

5. PATIENT'S ADDRESS (No., Street) | 6. PATIENT RELATIONSHIP TO INSURED   Self ▭ Spouse ▭ Child ▭ Other ▭ | 7. INSURED'S ADDRESS (No., Street)

CITY | STATE | 9. PATIENT STATUS   Single ▭ Married ▭ Other ▭ | CITY | STATE

ZIP CODE | TELEPHONE (Include Area Code) ( ) | Employed ▭ Full-Time Student ▭ Part-Time Student ▭ | ZIP CODE | TELEPHONE (Include Area Code) ( )

9. OTHER INSURED'S NAME (Last Name, First Name, Middle Initial) | 10. IS PATIENT'S CONDITION RELATED TO: | 11. INSURED'S POLICY GROUP OR FECA NUMBER

a. OTHER INSURED'S POLICY OR GROUP NUMBER | a. EMPLOYMENT? (Current or Previous) YES ▭ NO ▭ | a. INSURED'S DATE OF BIRTH MM | DD | YY   SEX   M ▭ F ▭

b. OTHER INSURED'S DATE OF BIRTH MM | DD | YY   SEX   M ▭ F ▭ | b. AUTO ACCIDENT?   PLACE (State)   YES ▭ NO ▭ | b. EMPLOYER'S NAME OR SCHOOL NAME

c. EMPLOYER'S NAME OR SCHOOL NAME | c. OTHER ACCIDENT?   YES ▭ NO ▭ | c. INSURANCE PLAN NAME OR PROGRAM NAME

d. INSURANCE PLAN NAME OR PROGRAM NAME | 10d. RESERVED FOR LOCAL USE | d. IS THERE ANOTHER HEALTH BENEFIT PLAN?   YES ▭ NO ▭   If yes, return to and complete item 9 a-d.

READ BACK OF FORM BEFORE COMPLETING & SIGNING THIS FORM.
12. PATIENT'S OR AUTHORIZED PERSON'S SIGNATURE I authorize the release of any medical or other information necessary to process this claim. I also request payment of government benefits either to myself or to the party who accepts assignment below.

SIGNED_____   DATE_____

13. INSURED'S OR AUTHORIZED PERSON'S SIGNATURE I authorize payment of medical benefits to the undersigned physician or supplier for services described below.

SIGNED_____

14. DATE OF CURRENT: MM | DD | YY   ILLNESS (First symptom) OR INJURY (Accident) OR PREGNANCY(LMP) | 15. IF PATIENT HAS HAD SAME OR SIMILAR ILLNESS. GIVE FIRST DATE MM | DD | YY | 16. DATES PATIENT UNABLE TO WORK IN CURRENT OCCUPATION FROM MM | DD | YY TO MM | DD | YY

17. NAME OF REFERRING PROVIDER OR OTHER SOURCE | 17a. | 17b. NPI | 18. HOSPITALIZATION DATES RELATED TO CURRENT SERVICES FROM MM | DD | YY TO MM | DD | YY

19. RESERVED FOR LOCAL USE | 20. OUTSIDE LAB?   YES ▭ NO ▭ $ CHARGES

21. DIAGNOSIS OR NATURE OF ILLNESS OR INJURY (Relate Items 1, 2, 3 or 4 to Item 24E by Line)
1. |___.___   3. |___.___
2. |___.___   4. |___.___

22. MEDICAID RESUBMISSION CODE | ORIGINAL REF. NO.

23. PRIOR AUTHORIZATION NUMBER

24. A. DATE(S) OF SERVICE						B. PLACE OF SERVICE	C. EMG	D. PROCEDURES, SERVICES, OR SUPPLIES (Explain Unusual Circumstances)		E. DIAGNOSIS POINTER	F. $ CHARGES	G. DAYS OR UNITS	H. EPSDT Family Plan	I. ID. QUAL.	J. RENDERING PROVIDER ID. #
From MM	DD	YY	To MM	DD	YY			CPT/HCPCS	MODIFIER						
1														NPI	
2														NPI	
3														NPI	
4														NPI	
5														NPI	
6														NPI	

25. FEDERAL TAX I.D. NUMBER   SSN ▭ EIN ▭ | 26. PATIENT'S ACCOUNT NO. | 27. ACCEPT ASSIGNMENT? (For govt. claims, see back) YES ▭ NO ▭ | 28. TOTAL CHARGE $ | 29. AMOUNT PAID $ | 30. BALANCE DUE $

31. SIGNATURE OF PHYSICIAN OR SUPPLIER INCLUDING DEGREES OR CREDENTIALS (I certify that the statements on the reverse apply to this bill and are made a part thereof.)

SIGNED_____   DATE_____ | 32. SERVICE FACILITY LOCATION INFORMATION   a.   b. | 33. BILLING PROVIDER INFO & PH # ( )   a.   b.

NUCC Instruction Manual available at: www.nucc.org   OMB APPROVAL PENDING

EXERCISE 6.24

Ms. Chip A. Dee presents her son (a new patient) to your office one afternoon after school. The 12-year-old boy is complaining of feeling dizzy and having a sore throat. As your doctor begins her exam, she notices some severe bruising on young Chip's body. Your physician does an extended history on Chip's illness, with a complete system review, and asks some serious questions of Chip's mom. Upon completing this comprehensive history, your physician performs a complete multisystem examination, checking for any broken bones as well as a thorough exam of Chip's throat. Your physician reviews a multiple number of diagnoses, and decides that the risk of complications or even death to young Chip is high. She leaves the room and reports Mr. & Mrs. Dee to the Children's Protective Services.

Notes: _____

_____

_____

_____

_____

_____

_____

_____

_____

_____

_____

_____

_____

_____

_____

_____

_____

DOC Form®
(Doctor's Office Checklist)

	OFFICE/OUTPATIENT		CONSULTATION	
	New (3)	Established (2)	Office/O.P. (3)	Inpatient (3)
Minimal Service		99211		

HISTORY

	New (3)	Established (2)	Office/O.P. (3)	Inpatient (3)
Problem Focused	99201	99212	99241	99251
Exp/Prob Focused	99202	99213	99242	99252
Detail	99203	99214	99243	99253
Comprehensive	99204/05	99215	99244/45	99254/55

EXAMINATION

	New (3)	Established (2)	Office/O.P. (3)	Inpatient (3)
Problem Focused	99201	99212	99241	99251
Exp/Prob Focused	99202	99213	99242	99252
Detail	99203	99214	99243	99253
Comprehensive	99204/05	99215	99244/45	99254/55

MEDICAL DECISION MAKING

	New (3)	Established (2)	Office/O.P. (3)	Inpatient (3)
Straight Forward	99201/2	99212	99241/42	99251/52
Low Complexity	99203	99213	99243	99253
Mod Complexity	99204	99214	99244	99254
High Complexity	99205	99215	99245	99255

TIME:_____   Counsel/Coordination of Care:_____

	New	Established	Office/O.P.	Inpatient
10 Minutes	99201	99212		
15 Minutes		99213	99241	
20 Minutes	99202			99251
25 Minutes		99214		
30 Minutes	99203		99242	
40 Minutes		99215	99243	99252
45 Minutes	99204			
55 Minutes				99253
60 Minutes	99205		99244	
80 Minutes			99245	99254
110 Minutes				99255

EXERCISE 6.24

1500
HEALTH INSURANCE CLAIM FORM
APPROVED BY NATIONAL UNIFORM CLAIM COMMITTEE 08/05

| | | PICA | | | | | | | | | PICA | |

1. MEDICARE ☐ (Medicare #) MEDICAID ☐ (Medicaid #) TRICARE CHAMPUS ☐ (Sponsor's SSN) CHAMPVA ☐ (Member ID#) GROUP HEALTH PLAN ☐ (SSN or ID) FECA BLK LUNG ☐ (SSN) OTHER ☐ (ID)   1a. INSURED'S I.D. NUMBER   (For Program in Item 1)

2. PATIENT'S NAME (Last Name, First Name, Middle Initial)

3. PATIENT'S BIRTH DATE   MM | DD | YY   SEX   M ☐   F ☐

4. INSURED'S NAME (Last Name, First Name, Middle Initial)

5. PATIENT'S ADDRESS (No., Street)

6. PATIENT RELATIONSHIP TO INSURED   Self ☐   Spouse ☐   Child ☐   Other ☐

7. INSURED'S ADDRESS (No., Street)

CITY   STATE

8. PATIENT STATUS   Single ☐   Married ☐   Other ☐

CITY   STATE

ZIP CODE   TELEPHONE (Include Area Code) (   )

Employed ☐   Full-Time Student ☐   Part-Time Student ☐

ZIP CODE   TELEPHONE (Include Area Code) (   )

9. OTHER INSURED'S NAME (Last Name, First Name, Middle Initial)

10. IS PATIENT'S CONDITION RELATED TO:

11. INSURED'S POLICY GROUP OR FECA NUMBER

a. OTHER INSURED'S POLICY OR GROUP NUMBER

a. EMPLOYMENT? (Current or Previous)   YES ☐   NO ☐

a. INSURED'S DATE OF BIRTH   MM | DD | YY   SEX   M ☐   F ☐

b. OTHER INSURED'S DATE OF BIRTH   MM | DD | YY   SEX   M ☐   F ☐

b. AUTO ACCIDENT?   PLACE (State)   YES ☐   NO ☐

b. EMPLOYER'S NAME OR SCHOOL NAME

c. EMPLOYER'S NAME OR SCHOOL NAME

c. OTHER ACCIDENT?   YES ☐   NO ☐

c. INSURANCE PLAN NAME OR PROGRAM NAME

d. INSURANCE PLAN NAME OR PROGRAM NAME

10d. RESERVED FOR LOCAL USE

d. IS THERE ANOTHER HEALTH BENEFIT PLAN?   YES ☐   NO ☐   If yes, return to and complete item 9 a-d.

READ BACK OF FORM BEFORE COMPLETING & SIGNING THIS FORM.
12. PATIENT'S OR AUTHORIZED PERSON'S SIGNATURE   I authorize the release of any medical or other information necessary to process this claim. I also request payment of government benefits either to myself or to the party who accepts assignment below.

SIGNED_____   DATE_____

13. INSURED'S OR AUTHORIZED PERSON'S SIGNATURE   I authorize payment of medical benefits to the undersigned physician or supplier for services described below.

SIGNED_____

14. DATE OF CURRENT: MM | DD | YY   ILLNESS (First symptom) OR INJURY (Accident) OR PREGNANCY(LMP)

15. IF PATIENT HAS HAD SAME OR SIMILAR ILLNESS. GIVE FIRST DATE   MM | DD | YY

16. DATES PATIENT UNABLE TO WORK IN CURRENT OCCUPATION   FROM MM | DD | YY   TO MM | DD | YY

17. NAME OF REFERRING PROVIDER OR OTHER SOURCE

17a.

17b. NPI

18. HOSPITALIZATION DATES RELATED TO CURRENT SERVICES   FROM MM | DD | YY   TO MM | DD | YY

19. RESERVED FOR LOCAL USE

20. OUTSIDE LAB?   YES ☐   NO ☐ $ CHARGES

21. DIAGNOSIS OR NATURE OF ILLNESS OR INJURY (Relate Items 1, 2, 3 or 4 to Item 24E by Line)
1. |____.____   3. |____.____
2. |____.____   4. |____.____

22. MEDICAID RESUBMISSION CODE   ORIGINAL REF. NO.

23. PRIOR AUTHORIZATION NUMBER

24. A. DATE(S) OF SERVICE						B. PLACE OF SERVICE	C. EMG	D. PROCEDURES, SERVICES, OR SUPPLIES (Explain Unusual Circumstances)		E. DIAGNOSIS POINTER	F. $ CHARGES	G. DAYS OR UNITS	H. EPSDT Family Plan	I. ID. QUAL.	J. RENDERING PROVIDER ID. #
From MM	DD	YY	To MM	DD	YY			CPT/HCPCS	MODIFIER						
1														NPI	
2														NPI	
3														NPI	
4														NPI	
5														NPI	
6														NPI	

25. FEDERAL TAX I.D. NUMBER   SSN ☐ EIN ☐

26. PATIENT'S ACCOUNT NO.

27. ACCEPT ASSIGNMENT? (For govt. claims, see back)   YES ☐   NO ☐

28. TOTAL CHARGE $

29. AMOUNT PAID $

30. BALANCE DUE $

31. SIGNATURE OF PHYSICIAN OR SUPPLIER INCLUDING DEGREES OR CREDENTIALS (I certify that the statements on the reverse apply to this bill and are made a part thereof.)

SIGNED_____   DATE_____

32. SERVICE FACILITY LOCATION INFORMATION

a.   b.

33. BILLING PROVIDER INFO & PH # (   )

a.   b.

NUCC Instruction Manual available at: www.nucc.org   OMB APPROVAL PENDING

EXERCISE 6.25

Ms. I Keri Nuff, a 95-year-old patient, presents herself in your office for the first time complaining of general malaise. Upon completion of a comprehensive history and a comprehensive exam, you decide that there are several diagnoses that may apply to Ms. Nuff's case and, because of her age, her risk of complications is moderate. You decide that Ms. Nuff should be admitted to the hospital for further tests. You admit Ms. Nuff on that same day.

Notes: _____

_____

_____

_____

_____

_____

_____

_____

_____

_____

_____

_____

_____

_____

_____

_____

_____

_____

DOC Form®
(Doctor's Office Checklist)

	HOSPITAL		OBSERVATION		ER
	Initial (3)	Sub (2)	Discharge Date Different (3)	Same (3)	New/Estab (3)
HISTORY					
Problem Focused		99231			99281
Exp/Prob Focused		99232			99282/83
Detail	99221	99233	99218	99234	99284
Comprehensive	99221/2/3		99218/19/20	99234/35/36	99285
EXAMINATION					
Problem Focused		99231			99281
Exp/Prob Focused		99232			99282/83
Detail	99221	99233	99218	99234	99284
Comprehensive	99221/2/3		99218/19/20	99234/35/36	99285
MEDICAL DECISION MAKING					
Straight Forward	99221	99231	99218	99234	99281
Low Complexity	99221	99231	99218	99234	99282
Mod Complexity	99222	99232	99219	99235	99283/84
High Complexity	99223	99233	99220	99236	99285
DISCHARGE			99217		
≤ 30 Minutes		99238			
> 30 Minutes		99239			
TIME					
15 Minutes		99231			
20 Minutes					
25 Minutes		99232			
30 Minutes	99221				
35 Minutes		99233			
45 Minutes					
50 Minutes	99222				
60 Minutes					
70 Minutes	99223				

Patient Name:_____

Date:_____ Physician Signature:_____

MedBooks, Inc.
101 W. Buckingham Road, Richardson, Tx. 75081 (800) 443-7397
Warning: This product is copyrighted and is not to be duplicated in any manner without the express written permission of MedBooks.

EXERCISE 6.25

1500

HEALTH INSURANCE CLAIM FORM

APPROVED BY NATIONAL UNIFORM CLAIM COMMITTEE 08/05

| | PICA | | | | | | | | | PICA | |

1. MEDICARE	MEDICAID	TRICARE CHAMPUS	CHAMPVA	GROUP HEALTH PLAN	FECA BLK LUNG	OTHER	1a. INSURED'S I.D. NUMBER	(For Program in Item 1)
(Medicare #)	(Medicaid #)	(Sponsor's SSN)	(Member ID#)	(SSN or ID)	(SSN)	(ID)		

2. PATIENT'S NAME (Last Name, First Name, Middle Initial)

9. PATIENT'S BIRTH DATE MM DD YY SEX M☐ F☐

4. INSURED'S NAME (Last Name, First Name, Middle Initial)

5. PATIENT'S ADDRESS (No., Street)

6. PATIENT RELATIONSHIP TO INSURED
Self☐ Spouse☐ Child☐ Other☐

7. INSURED'S ADDRESS (No., Street)

CITY   STATE

8. PATIENT STATUS
Single☐ Married☐ Other☐

CITY   STATE

ZIP CODE   TELEPHONE (Include Area Code)
(   )

Employed☐ Full-Time Student☐ Part-Time Student☐

ZIP CODE   TELEPHONE (Include Area Code)
(   )

9. OTHER INSURED'S NAME (Last Name, First Name, Middle Initial)

10. IS PATIENT'S CONDITION RELATED TO:

11. INSURED'S POLICY GROUP OR FECA NUMBER

a. OTHER INSURED'S POLICY OR GROUP NUMBER

a. EMPLOYMENT? (Current or Previous)
☐YES ☐NO

a. INSURED'S DATE OF BIRTH MM DD YY SEX M☐ F☐

b. OTHER INSURED'S DATE OF BIRTH MM DD YY SEX M☐ F☐

b. AUTO ACCIDENT? PLACE (State)
☐YES ☐NO

b. EMPLOYER'S NAME OR SCHOOL NAME

c. EMPLOYER'S NAME OR SCHOOL NAME

c. OTHER ACCIDENT?
☐YES ☐NO

c. INSURANCE PLAN NAME OR PROGRAM NAME

d. INSURANCE PLAN NAME OR PROGRAM NAME

10d. RESERVED FOR LOCAL USE

d. IS THERE ANOTHER HEALTH BENEFIT PLAN?
☐YES ☐NO If yes, return to and complete item 9 a-d.

READ BACK OF FORM BEFORE COMPLETING & SIGNING THIS FORM.
12. PATIENT'S OR AUTHORIZED PERSON'S SIGNATURE I authorize the release of any medical or other information necessary to process this claim. I also request payment of government benefits either to myself or to the party who accepts assignment below.

SIGNED_____ DATE_____

13. INSURED'S OR AUTHORIZED PERSON'S SIGNATURE I authorize payment of medical benefits to the undersigned physician or supplier for services described below.

SIGNED_____

14. DATE OF CURRENT: MM DD YY ◄ ILLNESS (First symptom) OR INJURY (Accident) OR PREGNANCY(LMP)	15. IF PATIENT HAS HAD SAME OR SIMILAR ILLNESS. GIVE FIRST DATE MM DD YY	16. DATES PATIENT UNABLE TO WORK IN CURRENT OCCUPATION MM DD YY MM DD YY FROM TO

17. NAME OF REFERRING PROVIDER OR OTHER SOURCE

17a.
17b. NPI

18. HOSPITALIZATION DATES RELATED TO CURRENT SERVICES MM DD YY MM DD YY
FROM   TO

19. RESERVED FOR LOCAL USE

20. OUTSIDE LAB? $ CHARGES
☐YES ☐NO

21. DIAGNOSIS OR NATURE OF ILLNESS OR INJURY (Relate Items 1, 2, 3 or 4 to Item 24E by Line)

1. |___.___   3. |___.___
2. |___.___   4. |___.___

22. MEDICAID RESUBMISSION CODE ORIGINAL REF. NO.

23. PRIOR AUTHORIZATION NUMBER

24. A. DATE(S) OF SERVICE From MM DD YY To MM DD YY	B. PLACE OF SERVICE	C. EMG	D. PROCEDURES, SERVICES, OR SUPPLIES (Explain Unusual Circumstances) CPT/HCPCS MODIFIER	E. DIAGNOSIS POINTER	F. $ CHARGES	G. DAYS OR UNITS	H. EPSDT Family Plan	I. ID. QUAL.	J. RENDERING PROVIDER ID. #
1									NPI
2									NPI
3									NPI
4									NPI
5									NPI
6									NPI

25. FEDERAL TAX I.D. NUMBER SSN EIN	26. PATIENT'S ACCOUNT NO.	27. ACCEPT ASSIGNMENT? (For govt. claims, see back) ☐YES ☐NO	28. TOTAL CHARGE $	29. AMOUNT PAID $	30. BALANCE DUE $

31. SIGNATURE OF PHYSICIAN OR SUPPLIER INCLUDING DEGREES OR CREDENTIALS (I certify that the statements on the reverse apply to this bill and are made a part thereof.)

SIGNED_____ DATE_____

32. SERVICE FACILITY LOCATION INFORMATION

a.   b.

33. BILLING PROVIDER INFO & PH # (   )

a.   b.

NUCC Instruction Manual available at: www.nucc.org

OMB APPROVAL PENDING

PATIENT AND INSURED INFORMATION

PHYSICIAN OR SUPPLIER INFORMATION

	Name:_____
	Class/Section:_____
cpTeach 2012	Date:_____

EXERCISE 6.26

Mr. U. Neever Doalot, an established patient of yours for years, comes into your office complaining of back pain. Mr. Doalot is a 32-year-old unemployed patient. You examine Mr. Doalot's back briefly to find out how long he has had this pain. Mr. Doalot says that he helped his brother-in-law move yesterday and it was last night that his pain began. You explain to Mr. Doalot that he should take some aspirin, and you begin to show him some exercises that should help alleviate his pain. Mr. Doalot has difficulty understanding your diagnosis and treatment plan and you spend the balance of your session explaining his therapy. The counseling/coordinator of care portion takes 30 minutes. The entire visit was 40 minutes.

Notes: _____

_____

_____

_____

_____

_____

_____

_____

_____

_____

_____

_____

_____

_____

_____

_____

_____

_____

_____

DOC Form®
(Doctor's Office Checklist)

OFFICE/OUTPATIENT   **CONSULTATION**

	New (3)	Established (2)	Office/O.P. (3)	Inpatient (3)
Minimal Service		99211		

HISTORY

	New (3)	Established (2)	Office/O.P. (3)	Inpatient (3)
Problem Focused	99201	99212	99241	99251
Exp/Prob Focused	99202	99213	99242	99252
Detail	99203	99214	99243	99253
Comprehensive	99204/05	99215	99244/45	99254/55

EXAMINATION

	New (3)	Established (2)	Office/O.P. (3)	Inpatient (3)
Problem Focused	99201	99212	99241	99251
Exp/Prob Focused	99202	99213	99242	99252
Detail	99203	99214	99243	99253
Comprehensive	99204/05	99215	99244/45	99254/55

MEDICAL DECISION MAKING

	New (3)	Established (2)	Office/O.P. (3)	Inpatient (3)
Straight Forward	99201/2	99212	99241/42	99251/52
Low Complexity	99203	99213	99243	99253
Mod Complexity	99204	99214	99244	99254
High Complexity	99205	99215	99245	99255

TIME:_____   Counsel/Coordination of Care:_____

	New (3)	Established (2)	Office/O.P. (3)	Inpatient (3)
10 Minutes	99201	99212		
15 Minutes		99213	99241	
20 Minutes	99202			99251
25 Minutes		99214		
30 Minutes	99203		99242	
40 Minutes		99215	99243	99252
45 Minutes	99204			
55 Minutes				99253
60 Minutes	99205		99244	
80 Minutes			99245	99254
110 Minutes				99255

MedBooks, Inc.
101 W. Buckingham Road, Richardson, Tx. 75081 (800) 443-7397
Warning: This product is copyrighted and is not to be duplicated in any manner without the express written permission of MedBooks.

EXERCISE 6.26

WORKBOOK

Name:_____

Class/Section:_____

cpTeach
2012

Date:_____

1500

HEALTH INSURANCE CLAIM FORM

APPROVED BY NATIONAL UNIFORM CLAIM COMMITTEE 08/05

PICA

PICA

1. MEDICARE MEDICAID TRICARE CHAMPUS CHAMPVA GROUP HEALTH PLAN FECA BLK LUNG OTHER	1a. INSURED'S I.D. NUMBER (For Program in Item 1)

(Medicare #)   (Medicaid #)   (Sponsor's SSN)   (Member ID#)   (SSN or ID)   (SSN)   (ID)

2. PATIENT'S NAME (Last Name, First Name, Middle Initial)

3. PATIENT'S BIRTH DATE MM DD YY   SEX   M   F

4. INSURED'S NAME (Last Name, First Name, Middle Initial)

5. PATIENT'S ADDRESS (No., Street)

6. PATIENT RELATIONSHIP TO INSURED   Self   Spouse   Child   Other

7. INSURED'S ADDRESS (No., Street)

CITY   STATE

8. PATIENT STATUS   Single   Married   Other

CITY   STATE

ZIP CODE   TELEPHONE (Include Area Code)   (   )

Employed   Full-Time Student   Part-Time Student

ZIP CODE   TELEPHONE (Include Area Code)   (   )

9. OTHER INSURED'S NAME (Last Name, First Name, Middle Initial)

10. IS PATIENT'S CONDITION RELATED TO:

11. INSURED'S POLICY GROUP OR FECA NUMBER

a. OTHER INSURED'S POLICY OR GROUP NUMBER

a. EMPLOYMENT? (Current or Previous)   YES   NO

a. INSURED'S DATE OF BIRTH MM DD YY   SEX   M   F

b. OTHER INSURED'S DATE OF BIRTH MM DD YY   SEX   M   F

b. AUTO ACCIDENT?   PLACE (State)   YES   NO

b. EMPLOYER'S NAME OR SCHOOL NAME

c. EMPLOYER'S NAME OR SCHOOL NAME

c. OTHER ACCIDENT?   YES   NO

c. INSURANCE PLAN NAME OR PROGRAM NAME

d. INSURANCE PLAN NAME OR PROGRAM NAME

10d. RESERVED FOR LOCAL USE

d. IS THERE ANOTHER HEALTH BENEFIT PLAN?   YES   NO   If yes, return to and complete item 9 a-d.

READ BACK OF FORM BEFORE COMPLETING & SIGNING THIS FORM.

12. PATIENT'S OR AUTHORIZED PERSON'S SIGNATURE I authorize the release of any medical or other information necessary to process this claim. I also request payment of government benefits either to myself or to the party who accepts assignment below.

SIGNED_____   DATE_____

13. INSURED'S OR AUTHORIZED PERSON'S SIGNATURE I authorize payment of medical benefits to the undersigned physician or supplier for services described below.

SIGNED_____

14. DATE OF CURRENT: MM DD YY   ILLNESS (First symptom) OR INJURY (Accident) OR PREGNANCY(LMP)

15. IF PATIENT HAS HAD SAME OR SIMILAR ILLNESS. GIVE FIRST DATE MM DD YY

16. DATES PATIENT UNABLE TO WORK IN CURRENT OCCUPATION MM DD YY FROM   TO   MM DD YY

17. NAME OF REFERRING PROVIDER OR OTHER SOURCE

17a.
17b. NPI

18. HOSPITALIZATION DATES RELATED TO CURRENT SERVICES MM DD YY FROM   TO   MM DD YY

19. RESERVED FOR LOCAL USE

20. OUTSIDE LAB?   YES   NO $ CHARGES

21. DIAGNOSIS OR NATURE OF ILLNESS OR INJURY (Relate Items 1, 2, 3 or 4 to Item 24E by Line)

1. |____.____
2. |____.____
3. |____.____
4. |____.____

22. MEDICAID RESUBMISSION CODE   ORIGINAL REF. NO.

23. PRIOR AUTHORIZATION NUMBER

24. A. DATE(S) OF SERVICE						B. PLACE OF SERVICE	C. EMG	D. PROCEDURES, SERVICES, OR SUPPLIES (Explain Unusual Circumstances)		E. DIAGNOSIS POINTER	F. $ CHARGES	G. DAYS OR UNITS	H. EPSDT Family Plan	I. ID. QUAL.	J. RENDERING PROVIDER ID. #
From			To					CPT/HCPCS	MODIFIER						
MM	DD	YY	MM	DD	YY										
1														NPI	
2														NPI	
3														NPI	
4														NPI	
5														NPI	
6														NPI	

25. FEDERAL TAX I.D. NUMBER   SSN   EIN

26. PATIENT'S ACCOUNT NO.

27. ACCEPT ASSIGNMENT? (For govt. claims, see back)   YES   NO

28. TOTAL CHARGE $

29. AMOUNT PAID $

30. BALANCE DUE $

31. SIGNATURE OF PHYSICIAN OR SUPPLIER INCLUDING DEGREES OR CREDENTIALS (I certify that the statements on the reverse apply to this bill and are made a part thereof.)

SIGNED_____   DATE_____

32. SERVICE FACILITY LOCATION INFORMATION

a. NPI   b.

33. BILLING PROVIDER INFO & PH #   (   )

a. NPI   b.

NUCC Instruction Manual available at: www.nucc.org

OMB APPROVAL PENDING

WORKBOOK	Name:_____
cpTeach 2012	Class/Section:_____
	Date:_____

EXERCISE 6.27

An 85-year-old patient of yours is admitted to the hospital by an orthopaedist to test for possible bone cancer. As the internist for the patient, you are asked to treat her for diabetes. During your initial visit to see the patient you complete a problem focused history and exam, making a straightforward decision to continue the patient's treatment as is.

Notes: _____

_____

_____

_____

_____

_____

_____

_____

_____

_____

_____

_____

_____

_____

_____

_____

_____

_____

_____

_____

_____

_____

_____

_____

_____

DOC Form®
(Doctor's Office Checklist)

	HOSPITAL		OBSERVATION		ER
	Initial (3)	Sub (2)	Discharge Date Different (3)	Same (3)	New/Estab (3)

HISTORY

Problem Focused		99231			99281
Exp/Prob Focused		99232			99282/83
Detail	99221	99233	99218	99234	99284
Comprehensive	99221/2/3		99218/19/20	99234/35/36	99285

EXAMINATION

Problem Focused		99231			99281
Exp/Prob Focused		99232			99282/83
Detail	99221	99233	99218	99234	99284
Comprehensive	99221/2/3		99218/19/20	99234/35/36	99285

MEDICAL DECISION MAKING

Straight Forward	99221	99231	99218	99234	99281
Low Complexity	99221	99231	99218	99234	99282
Mod Complexity	99222	99232	99219	99235	99283/84
High Complexity	99223	99233	99220	99236	99285

DISCHARGE   99217

≤ 30 Minutes		99238			
> 30 Minutes		99239			

TIME

15 Minutes		99231			
20 Minutes					
25 Minutes		99232			
30 Minutes	99221				
35 Minutes		99233			
45 Minutes					
50 Minutes	99222				
60 Minutes					
70 Minutes	99223				

Patient Name:_____

Date:_____Physician Signature:_____

MedBooks, Inc.
101 W. Buckingham Road, Richardson, Tx. 75081 (800) 443-7397
Warning: This product is copyrighted and is not to be duplicated in any manner without the express
written permission of MedBooks.

EXERCISE 6.27

Name: _____

Class/Section: _____

Date: _____

cpTeach 2012

(1500)

HEALTH INSURANCE CLAIM FORM

APPROVED BY NATIONAL UNIFORM CLAIM COMMITTEE 08/05

| | PICA | | | | | | | | PICA | |

1. MEDICARE (Medicare #)   **MEDICAID** (Medicaid #)   **TRICARE CHAMPUS** (Sponsor's SSN)   **CHAMPVA** (Member ID#)   **GROUP HEALTH PLAN** (SSN or ID)   **FECA BLK LUNG** (SSN)   **OTHER** (ID)   **1a. INSURED'S I.D. NUMBER** (For Program in Item 1)

2. PATIENT'S NAME (Last Name, First Name, Middle Initial)

3. PATIENT'S BIRTH DATE MM DD YY   **SEX** M   F

4. INSURED'S NAME (Last Name, First Name, Middle Initial)

5. PATIENT'S ADDRESS (No., Street)

6. PATIENT RELATIONSHIP TO INSURED   Self   Spouse   Child   Other

7. INSURED'S ADDRESS (No., Street)

CITY   **STATE**

8. PATIENT STATUS   Single   Married   Other

CITY   **STATE**

ZIP CODE   **TELEPHONE** (Include Area Code) ( )

Employed   Full-Time Student   Part-Time Student

ZIP CODE   **TELEPHONE** (Include Area Code) ( )

9. OTHER INSURED'S NAME (Last Name, First Name, Middle Initial)

10. IS PATIENT'S CONDITION RELATED TO:

11. INSURED'S POLICY GROUP OR FECA NUMBER

a. OTHER INSURED'S POLICY OR GROUP NUMBER

a. EMPLOYMENT? (Current or Previous)   YES   NO

a. INSURED'S DATE OF BIRTH MM DD YY   **SEX** M   F

b. OTHER INSURED'S DATE OF BIRTH MM DD YY   **SEX** M   F

b. AUTO ACCIDENT?   YES   NO   **PLACE** (State)

b. EMPLOYER'S NAME OR SCHOOL NAME

c. EMPLOYER'S NAME OR SCHOOL NAME

c. OTHER ACCIDENT?   YES   NO

c. INSURANCE PLAN NAME OR PROGRAM NAME

d. INSURANCE PLAN NAME OR PROGRAM NAME

10d. RESERVED FOR LOCAL USE

d. IS THERE ANOTHER HEALTH BENEFIT PLAN?   YES   NO   If yes, return to and complete item 9 a-d.

READ BACK OF FORM BEFORE COMPLETING & SIGNING THIS FORM.
12. PATIENT'S OR AUTHORIZED PERSON'S SIGNATURE I authorize the release of any medical or other information necessary to process this claim. I also request payment of government benefits either to myself or to the party who accepts assignment below.

SIGNED_____ DATE_____

13. INSURED'S OR AUTHORIZED PERSON'S SIGNATURE I authorize payment of medical benefits to the undersigned physician or supplier for services described below.

SIGNED_____

14. DATE OF CURRENT: MM DD YY   ILLNESS (First symptom) OR INJURY (Accident) OR PREGNANCY(LMP)

15. IF PATIENT HAS HAD SAME OR SIMILAR ILLNESS. GIVE FIRST DATE MM DD YY

16. DATES PATIENT UNABLE TO WORK IN CURRENT OCCUPATION MM DD YY FROM TO MM DD YY

17. NAME OF REFERRING PROVIDER OR OTHER SOURCE

17a.

17b. NPI

18. HOSPITALIZATION DATES RELATED TO CURRENT SERVICES MM DD YY FROM TO MM DD YY

19. RESERVED FOR LOCAL USE

20. OUTSIDE LAB?   YES   NO $ CHARGES

21. DIAGNOSIS OR NATURE OF ILLNESS OR INJURY (Relate Items 1, 2, 3 or 4 to Item 24E by Line)

1. |___.___   3. |___.___

2. |___.___   4. |___.___

22. MEDICAID RESUBMISSION CODE   ORIGINAL REF. NO.

23. PRIOR AUTHORIZATION NUMBER

24. A. DATE(S) OF SERVICE						B. PLACE OF SERVICE	C. EMG	D. PROCEDURES, SERVICES, OR SUPPLIES (Explain Unusual Circumstances) CPT/HCPCS	MODIFIER	E. DIAGNOSIS POINTER	F. $ CHARGES	G. DAYS OR UNITS	H. EPSDT Family Plan	I. ID. QUAL.	J. RENDERING PROVIDER ID. #
From MM	DD	YY	To MM	DD	YY										
1															NPI
2															NPI
3															NPI
4															NPI
5															NPI
6															NPI

25. FEDERAL TAX I.D. NUMBER   SSN EIN

26. PATIENT'S ACCOUNT NO.

27. ACCEPT ASSIGNMENT? (For govt. claims, see back)   YES   NO

28. TOTAL CHARGE $

29. AMOUNT PAID $

30. BALANCE DUE $

31. SIGNATURE OF PHYSICIAN OR SUPPLIER INCLUDING DEGREES OR CREDENTIALS (I certify that the statements on the reverse apply to this bill and are made a part thereof.)

SIGNED_____ DATE_____

32. SERVICE FACILITY LOCATION INFORMATION

a.   b.

33. BILLING PROVIDER INFO & PH # ( )

a.   b.

NUCC Instruction Manual available at: www.nucc.org   OMB APPROVAL PENDING

PATIENT AND INSURED INFORMATION

PHYSICIAN OR SUPPLIER INFORMATION

Name:_____

Class/Section:_____

Date:_____

2012

EXERCISE 6.28

Anne S. Thesia comes into your office complaining of the fact that she continues to get acne even at age 37. Your doctor has been seeing Anne for 2 years off and on. During the visit, your physician asks Anne about her diet and learns that Anne has gained a considerable amount of weight over the past 6 months (25 lbs.). Your physician asks Anne about her social life finding out that Anne has recently broken up with her boyfriend of 3 years, that her mother has been very, very sick and that she has recently lost her job as an accountant at the local hospital. Anne has begun smoking and realizes that she needs to quit. Your doctor, an OB/GYN, completes a review of Anne's history and then checks out Anne's face and back where she complains about the acne. No other part of her body is examined. Towards the end of the visit, Anne talks about not having a reason to live anymore. Your physician stays with Anne for an additional hour discussing this topic and then finally admits Anne to the hospital. (Hint: see also Inpatient/ Hospital DOC Form.)

Notes: _____

_____

_____

_____

_____

_____

_____

_____

_____

_____

_____

_____

_____

DOC Form®
(Doctor's Office Checklist)

OFFICE/OUTPATIENT   **CONSULTATION**

	New (3)	Established (2)	Office/O.P. (3)	Inpatient (3)
Minimal Service		99211		

HISTORY

	New (3)	Established (2)	Office/O.P. (3)	Inpatient (3)
Problem Focused	99201	99212	99241	99251
Exp/Prob Focused	99202	99213	99242	99252
Detail	99203	99214	99243	99253
Comprehensive	99204/05	99215	99244/45	99254/55

EXAMINATION

	New (3)	Established (2)	Office/O.P. (3)	Inpatient (3)
Problem Focused	99201	99212	99241	99251
Exp/Prob Focused	99202	99213	99242	99252
Detail	99203	99214	99243	99253
Comprehensive	99204/05	99215	99244/45	99254/55

MEDICAL DECISION MAKING

	New (3)	Established (2)	Office/O.P. (3)	Inpatient (3)
Straight Forward	99201/2	99212	99241/42	99251/52
Low Complexity	99203	99213	99243	99253
Mod Complexity	99204	99214	99244	99254
High Complexity	99205	99215	99245	99255

TIME:_____   Counsel/Coordination of Care:_____

	New (3)	Established (2)	Office/O.P. (3)	Inpatient (3)
10 Minutes	99201	99212		
15 Minutes		99213	99241	
20 Minutes	99202			99251
25 Minutes		99214		
30 Minutes	99203		99242	
40 Minutes		99215	99243	99252
45 Minutes	99204			
55 Minutes				99253
60 Minutes	99205		99244	
80 Minutes			99245	99254
110 Minutes				99255

EXERCISE 6.28

1500

HEALTH INSURANCE CLAIM FORM

APPROVED BY NATIONAL UNIFORM CLAIM COMMITTEE 08/05

☐☐☐ PICA

PICA ☐☐☐

| 1. MEDICARE ☐ (Medicare #) | MEDICAID ☐ (Medicaid #) | TRICARE CHAMPUS ☐ (Sponsor's SSN) | CHAMPVA ☐ (Member ID#) | GROUP HEALTH PLAN ☐ (SSN or ID) | FECA BLK LUNG ☐ (SSN) | OTHER ☐ (ID) | 1a. INSURED'S I.D. NUMBER (For Program in Item 1) |

2. PATIENT'S NAME (Last Name, First Name, Middle Initial)

3. PATIENT'S BIRTH DATE MM DD YY   SEX M ☐ F ☐

4. INSURED'S NAME (Last Name, First Name, Middle Initial)

5. PATIENT'S ADDRESS (No., Street)

6. PATIENT RELATIONSHIP TO INSURED
Self ☐ Spouse ☐ Child ☐ Other ☐

7. INSURED'S ADDRESS (No., Street)

CITY   STATE

8. PATIENT STATUS
Single ☐ Married ☐ Other ☐

CITY   STATE

ZIP CODE   TELEPHONE (Include Area Code) (   )

Employed ☐ Full-Time Student ☐ Part-Time Student ☐

ZIP CODE   TELEPHONE (Include Area Code) (   )

9. OTHER INSURED'S NAME (Last Name, First Name, Middle Initial)

10. IS PATIENT'S CONDITION RELATED TO:

11. INSURED'S POLICY GROUP OR FECA NUMBER

a. OTHER INSURED'S POLICY OR GROUP NUMBER

a. EMPLOYMENT? (Current or Previous)
YES ☐ NO ☐

a. INSURED'S DATE OF BIRTH MM DD YY   SEX M ☐ F ☐

b. OTHER INSURED'S DATE OF BIRTH MM DD YY   SEX M ☐ F ☐

b. AUTO ACCIDENT?   PLACE (State)
YES ☐ NO ☐

b. EMPLOYER'S NAME OR SCHOOL NAME

c. EMPLOYER'S NAME OR SCHOOL NAME

c. OTHER ACCIDENT?
YES ☐ NO ☐

c. INSURANCE PLAN NAME OR PROGRAM NAME

d. INSURANCE PLAN NAME OR PROGRAM NAME

10d. RESERVED FOR LOCAL USE

d. IS THERE ANOTHER HEALTH BENEFIT PLAN?
YES ☐ NO ☐ If yes, return to and complete item 9 a-d.

READ BACK OF FORM BEFORE COMPLETING & SIGNING THIS FORM.
12. PATIENT'S OR AUTHORIZED PERSON'S SIGNATURE I authorize the release of any medical or other information necessary to process this claim. I also request payment of government benefits either to myself or to the party who accepts assignment below.

SIGNED_____ DATE_____

13. INSURED'S OR AUTHORIZED PERSON'S SIGNATURE I authorize payment of medical benefits to the undersigned physician or supplier for services described below.

SIGNED_____

14. DATE OF CURRENT: MM DD YY ◄ ILLNESS (First symptom) OR INJURY (Accident) OR PREGNANCY(LMP)

15. IF PATIENT HAS HAD SAME OR SIMILAR ILLNESS. GIVE FIRST DATE MM DD YY

16. DATES PATIENT UNABLE TO WORK IN CURRENT OCCUPATION MM DD YY FROM   TO MM DD YY

17. NAME OF REFERRING PROVIDER OR OTHER SOURCE

17a.
17b. NPI

18. HOSPITALIZATION DATES RELATED TO CURRENT SERVICES MM DD YY FROM   TO MM DD YY

19. RESERVED FOR LOCAL USE

20. OUTSIDE LAB? $ CHARGES
YES ☐ NO ☐

21. DIAGNOSIS OR NATURE OF ILLNESS OR INJURY (Relate Items 1, 2, 3 or 4 to Item 24E by Line)

1. |____.____   3. |____.____

2. |____.____   4. |____.____

22. MEDICAID RESUBMISSION CODE   ORIGINAL REF. NO.

23. PRIOR AUTHORIZATION NUMBER

24. A. DATE(S) OF SERVICE From MM DD YY	To MM DD YY	B. PLACE OF SERVICE	C. EMG	D. PROCEDURES, SERVICES, OR SUPPLIES (Explain Unusual Circumstances) CPT/HCPCS	MODIFIER	E. DIAGNOSIS POINTER	F. $ CHARGES	G. DAYS OR UNITS	H. EPSDT Family Plan	I. ID. QUAL.	J. RENDERING PROVIDER ID. #
1											NPI
2											NPI
3											NPI
4											NPI
5											NPI
6											NPI

25. FEDERAL TAX I.D. NUMBER   SSN ☐ EIN ☐

26. PATIENT'S ACCOUNT NO.

27. ACCEPT ASSIGNMENT? (For govt. claims, see back)
YES ☐ NO ☐

28. TOTAL CHARGE $

29. AMOUNT PAID $

30. BALANCE DUE $

31. SIGNATURE OF PHYSICIAN OR SUPPLIER INCLUDING DEGREES OR CREDENTIALS (I certify that the statements on the reverse apply to this bill and are made a part thereof.)

SIGNED_____ DATE_____

32. SERVICE FACILITY LOCATION INFORMATION

a.   NPI   b.

33. BILLING PROVIDER INFO & PH # (   )

a.   NPI   b.

NUCC Instruction Manual available at: www.nucc.org

OMB APPROVAL PENDING

PATIENT AND INSURED INFORMATION

PHYSICIAN OR SUPPLIER INFORMATION

	Name:_____
WORKBOOK cpTeach 2012	Class/Section:_____
	Date:_____

EXERCISE 6.29

Your patient, Mr. Rusty Penny, a 42-year-old former football player, comes into your office because he is having pain in his foot. You examine the foot and find out that the pain is really localized in the toes including the big (great toe) and the second and third digits. You question Mr. Penny about whether or not there is any pain in his leg or if there is any pain in his other foot, and he denies any pain in those areas. You complete an exam which includes flexion and extension of the toes, an exam of the exterior of the feet both top and bottom, and a test of Mr. Penny's reflexes on his foot. You order some x-rays of the foot as well. You conclude at the end of the exam that Mr. Penny could be suffering from the onset of arthritis or some calcifications of the joint areas and that it would probably be best to prescribe some anti-inflammatories and have Mr. Penny revisit you in a month or so to see if his condition is improving.

Notes: _____

_____

_____

_____

_____

_____

_____

_____

_____

_____

_____

_____

_____

_____

_____

DOC Form®
(Doctor's Office Checklist)

OFFICE/OUTPATIENT CONSULTATION

	New (3)	Established (2)	Office/O.P. (3)	Inpatient (3)
Minimal Service		99211		

HISTORY

Problem Focused	99201	99212	99241	99251
Exp/Prob Focused	99202	99213	99242	99252
Detail	99203	99214	99243	99253
Comprehensive	99204/05	99215	99244/45	99254/55

EXAMINATION

Problem Focused	99201	99212	99241	99251
Exp/Prob Focused	99202	99213	99242	99252
Detail	99203	99214	99243	99253
Comprehensive	99204/05	99215	99244/45	99254/55

MEDICAL DECISION MAKING

Straight Forward	99201/2	99212	99241/42	99251/52
Low Complexity	99203	99213	99243	99253
Mod Complexity	99204	99214	99244	99254
High Complexity	99205	99215	99245	99255

TIME:_____ Counsel/Coordination of Care:_____

10 Minutes	99201	99212		
15 Minutes		99213	99241	
20 Minutes	99202			99251
25 Minutes		99214		
30 Minutes	99203		99242	
40 Minutes		99215	99243	99252
45 Minutes	99204			
55 Minutes				99253
60 Minutes	99205		99244	
80 Minutes			99245	99254
110 Minutes				99255

MedBooks, Inc.
101 W. Buckingham Road, Richardson, Tx. 75081 (800) 443-7397
Warning: This product is copyrighted and is not to be duplicated in any manner without the express written permission of MedBooks.

EXERCISE 6.29

Name:_____

Class/Section:_____

cpTeach

Date:_____

2012

1500

HEALTH INSURANCE CLAIM FORM

APPROVED BY NATIONAL UNIFORM CLAIM COMMITTEE 08/05

☐☐ PICA · · · · · PICA ☐☐

1. MEDICARE MEDICAID TRICARE CHAMPVA GROUP FECA OTHER	1a. INSURED'S I.D. NUMBER (For Program in Item 1)
☐ (Medicare #) ☐ (Medicaid #) ☐ CHAMPUS (Sponsor's SSN) ☐ (Member ID#) ☐ HEALTH PLAN (SSN or ID) ☐ BLK LUNG (SSN) ☐ (ID)	

2. PATIENT'S NAME (Last Name, First Name, Middle Initial)	3. PATIENT'S BIRTH DATE SEX	4. INSURED'S NAME (Last Name, First Name, Middle Initial)
	MM DD YY M ☐ F ☐	

5. PATIENT'S ADDRESS (No., Street)	6. PATIENT RELATIONSHIP TO INSURED	7. INSURED'S ADDRESS (No., Street)
	Self ☐ Spouse ☐ Child ☐ Other ☐	
CITY STATE	8. PATIENT STATUS Single ☐ Married ☐ Other ☐	CITY STATE
ZIP CODE TELEPHONE (Include Area Code) ( )	Employed ☐ Full-Time Student ☐ Part-Time Student ☐	ZIP CODE TELEPHONE (Include Area Code) ( )

9. OTHER INSURED'S NAME (Last Name, First Name, Middle Initial)	10. IS PATIENT'S CONDITION RELATED TO:	11. INSURED'S POLICY GROUP OR FECA NUMBER
a. OTHER INSURED'S POLICY OR GROUP NUMBER	a. EMPLOYMENT? (Current or Previous) ☐ YES ☐ NO	a. INSURED'S DATE OF BIRTH MM DD YY SEX M ☐ F ☐
b. OTHER INSURED'S DATE OF BIRTH MM DD YY SEX M ☐ F ☐	b. AUTO ACCIDENT? PLACE (State) ☐ YES ☐ NO	b. EMPLOYER'S NAME OR SCHOOL NAME
c. EMPLOYER'S NAME OR SCHOOL NAME	c. OTHER ACCIDENT? ☐ YES ☐ NO	c. INSURANCE PLAN NAME OR PROGRAM NAME
d. INSURANCE PLAN NAME OR PROGRAM NAME	10d. RESERVED FOR LOCAL USE	d. IS THERE ANOTHER HEALTH BENEFIT PLAN? ☐ YES ☐ NO If yes, return to and complete item 9 a-d.

READ BACK OF FORM BEFORE COMPLETING & SIGNING THIS FORM.

12. PATIENT'S OR AUTHORIZED PERSON'S SIGNATURE I authorize the release of any medical or other information necessary to process this claim. I also request payment of government benefits either to myself or to the party who accepts assignment below.	13. INSURED'S OR AUTHORIZED PERSON'S SIGNATURE I authorize payment of medical benefits to the undersigned physician or supplier for services described below.
SIGNED_____ DATE_____	SIGNED_____

14. DATE OF CURRENT: MM DD YY ◀ ILLNESS (First symptom) OR INJURY (Accident) OR PREGNANCY(LMP)	15. IF PATIENT HAS HAD SAME OR SIMILAR ILLNESS. GIVE FIRST DATE MM DD YY	16. DATES PATIENT UNABLE TO WORK IN CURRENT OCCUPATION MM DD YY MM DD YY FROM TO
17. NAME OF REFERRING PROVIDER OR OTHER SOURCE	17a. 17b. NPI	18. HOSPITALIZATION DATES RELATED TO CURRENT SERVICES MM DD YY MM DD YY FROM TO
19. RESERVED FOR LOCAL USE		20. OUTSIDE LAB? $ CHARGES ☐ YES ☐ NO

21. DIAGNOSIS OR NATURE OF ILLNESS OR INJURY (Relate Items 1, 2, 3 or 4 to Item 24E by Line)	22. MEDICAID RESUBMISSION CODE ORIGINAL REF. NO.
1. |___.___| 3. |___.___|	
2. |___.___| 4. |___.___|	23. PRIOR AUTHORIZATION NUMBER

24. A. DATE(S) OF SERVICE From To MM DD YY MM DD YY	B. PLACE OF SERVICE	C. EMG	D. PROCEDURES, SERVICES, OR SUPPLIES (Explain Unusual Circumstances) CPT/HCPCS MODIFIER	E. DIAGNOSIS POINTER	F. $ CHARGES	G. DAYS OR UNITS	H. EPSDT Family Plan	I. ID. QUAL.	J. RENDERING PROVIDER ID. #
1									NPI
2									NPI
3									NPI
4									NPI
5									NPI
6									NPI

25. FEDERAL TAX I.D. NUMBER SSN EIN	26. PATIENT'S ACCOUNT NO.	27. ACCEPT ASSIGNMENT? (For govt. claims, see back) ☐ YES ☐ NO	28. TOTAL CHARGE $	29. AMOUNT PAID $	30. BALANCE DUE $
31. SIGNATURE OF PHYSICIAN OR SUPPLIER INCLUDING DEGREES OR CREDENTIALS (I certify that the statements on the reverse apply to this bill and are made a part thereof.) SIGNED_____ DATE_____	32. SERVICE FACILITY LOCATION INFORMATION a. b.	33. BILLING PROVIDER INFO & PH # ( ) a. b.			

NUCC Instruction Manual available at: www.nucc.org · · · · · OMB APPROVAL PENDING

EXERCISE 6.30

Recode the previous example doing the opposite kind of visit than what you chose. For example, if you chose new, code established this time. Does coding for the other kind of service change the level of code that you are able to pick? Why or why not?

Notes: _____

_____
_____
_____
_____
_____
_____
_____
_____
_____
_____
_____
_____
_____
_____
_____
_____
_____
_____
_____
_____
_____
_____

DOC Form®
(Doctor's Office Checklist)

	OFFICE/OUTPATIENT		CONSULTATION	
	New (3)	Established (2)	Office/O.P. (3)	Inpatient (3)
Minimal Service		99211		

HISTORY

	New (3)	Established (2)	Office/O.P. (3)	Inpatient (3)
Problem Focused	99201	99212	99241	99251
Exp/Prob Focused	99202	99213	99242	99252
Detail	99203	99214	99243	99253
Comprehensive	99204/05	99215	99244/45	99254/55

EXAMINATION

	New (3)	Established (2)	Office/O.P. (3)	Inpatient (3)
Problem Focused	99201	99212	99241	99251
Exp/Prob Focused	99202	99213	99242	99252
Detail	99203	99214	99243	99253
Comprehensive	99204/05	99215	99244/45	99254/55

MEDICAL DECISION MAKING

	New (3)	Established (2)	Office/O.P. (3)	Inpatient (3)
Straight Forward	99201/2	99212	99241/42	99251/52
Low Complexity	99203	99213	99243	99253
Mod Complexity	99204	99214	99244	99254
High Complexity	99205	99215	99245	99255

TIME:_____   Counsel/Coordination of Care:_____

	New (3)	Established (2)	Office/O.P. (3)	Inpatient (3)
10 Minutes	99201	99212		
15 Minutes		99213	99241	
20 Minutes	99202			99251
25 Minutes		99214		
30 Minutes	99203		99242	
40 Minutes		99215	99243	99252
45 Minutes	99204			
55 Minutes				99253
60 Minutes	99205		99244	
80 Minutes			99245	99254
110 Minutes				99255

EXERCISE 6.30

1500

HEALTH INSURANCE CLAIM FORM

APPROVED BY NATIONAL UNIFORM CLAIM COMMITTEE 08/05

| | PICA | | | | | | | | PICA | |

| 1. MEDICARE | MEDICAID | TRICARE CHAMPUS | CHAMPVA | GROUP HEALTH PLAN | FECA BLK LUNG | OTHER | 1a. INSURED'S I.D. NUMBER | (For Program in Item 1) |

(Medicare #) (Medicaid #) (Sponsor's SSN) (Member ID#) (SSN or ID) (SSN) (ID)

2. PATIENT'S NAME (Last Name, First Name, Middle Initial)

3. PATIENT'S BIRTH DATE MM DD YY SEX M F

4. INSURED'S NAME (Last Name, First Name, Middle Initial)

5. PATIENT'S ADDRESS (No., Street)

6. PATIENT RELATIONSHIP TO INSURED Self Spouse Child Other

7. INSURED'S ADDRESS (No., Street)

CITY STATE

8. PATIENT STATUS Single Married Other

CITY STATE

ZIP CODE TELEPHONE (Include Area Code) ( )

Employed Full-Time Student Part-Time Student

ZIP CODE TELEPHONE (Include Area Code) ( )

9. OTHER INSURED'S NAME (Last Name, First Name, Middle Initial)

10. IS PATIENT'S CONDITION RELATED TO:

11. INSURED'S POLICY GROUP OR FECA NUMBER

a. OTHER INSURED'S POLICY OR GROUP NUMBER

a. EMPLOYMENT? (Current or Previous) YES NO

a. INSURED'S DATE OF BIRTH MM DD YY SEX M F

b. OTHER INSURED'S DATE OF BIRTH MM DD YY SEX M F

b. AUTO ACCIDENT? PLACE (State) YES NO

b. EMPLOYER'S NAME OR SCHOOL NAME

c. EMPLOYER'S NAME OR SCHOOL NAME

c. OTHER ACCIDENT? YES NO

c. INSURANCE PLAN NAME OR PROGRAM NAME

d. INSURANCE PLAN NAME OR PROGRAM NAME

10d. RESERVED FOR LOCAL USE

d. IS THERE ANOTHER HEALTH BENEFIT PLAN? YES NO If yes, return to and complete item 9 a-d.

READ BACK OF FORM BEFORE COMPLETING & SIGNING THIS FORM.

12. PATIENT'S OR AUTHORIZED PERSON'S SIGNATURE I authorize the release of any medical or other information necessary to process this claim. I also request payment of government benefits either to myself or to the party who accepts assignment below.

SIGNED_____ DATE_____

13. INSURED'S OR AUTHORIZED PERSON'S SIGNATURE I authorize payment of medical benefits to the undersigned physician or supplier for services described below.

SIGNED _____

14. DATE OF CURRENT: MM DD YY ILLNESS (First symptom) OR INJURY (Accident) OR PREGNANCY(LMP)

15. IF PATIENT HAS HAD SAME OR SIMILAR ILLNESS. GIVE FIRST DATE MM DD YY

16. DATES PATIENT UNABLE TO WORK IN CURRENT OCCUPATION MM DD YY MM DD YY FROM TO

17. NAME OF REFERRING PROVIDER OR OTHER SOURCE

17a. 17b. NPI

18. HOSPITALIZATION DATES RELATED TO CURRENT SERVICES MM DD YY MM DD YY FROM TO

19. RESERVED FOR LOCAL USE

20. OUTSIDE LAB? YES NO $ CHARGES

21. DIAGNOSIS OR NATURE OF ILLNESS OR INJURY (Relate items 1, 2, 9 or 4 to Item 24E by Line)

1. _____ 3. _____

2. _____ 4. _____

22. MEDICAID RESUBMISSION CODE ORIGINAL REF. NO.

23. PRIOR AUTHORIZATION NUMBER

24. A. DATE(S) OF SERVICE From MM DD YY To MM DD YY	B. PLACE OF SERVICE	C. EMG	D. PROCEDURES, SERVICES, OR SUPPLIES (Explain Unusual Circumstances) CPT/HCPCS MODIFIER	E. DIAGNOSIS POINTER	F. $ CHARGES	G. DAYS OR UNITS	H. EPSDT Family Plan	I. ID. QUAL.	J. RENDERING PROVIDER ID. #
1								NPI	
2								NPI	
3								NPI	
4								NPI	
5								NPI	
6								NPI	

25. FEDERAL TAX I.D. NUMBER SSN EIN

26. PATIENT'S ACCOUNT NO.

27. ACCEPT ASSIGNMENT? (For govt. claims, see back) YES NO

28. TOTAL CHARGE $

29. AMOUNT PAID $

30. BALANCE DUE $

31. SIGNATURE OF PHYSICIAN OR SUPPLIER INCLUDING DEGREES OR CREDENTIALS (I certify that the statements on the reverse apply to this bill and are made a part thereof.)

SIGNED DATE

32. SERVICE FACILITY LOCATION INFORMATION

a. NPI b.

33. BILLING PROVIDER INFO & PH # ( )

a. NPI b.

NUCC Instruction Manual available at: www.nucc.org

OMB APPROVAL PENDING

EXERCISE 6.31

Ms. I. M. Sneezy, a 24-year-old established patient, comes into your office following a visit that she made last week. She is complaining of severe itching and a lot of sneezing since she received an allergy injection last week. You examine her skin and the itchy parts (located on her back and chest) and determine that since nothing else in her life has changed since last week (no new detergents or food) that she is probably having a hypersensitive reaction to the immunotherapy. You readjust her dose, decreasing it a bit, and explain that she should call you if the itching and sneezing persist.

Notes: _____

_____
_____
_____
_____
_____
_____
_____
_____
_____
_____
_____
_____
_____
_____
_____
_____
_____
_____
_____
_____
_____
_____

DOC Form®
(Doctor's Office Checklist)

	OFFICE/OUTPATIENT		CONSULTATION	
	New (3)	Established (2)	Office/O.P. (3)	Inpatient (3)
Minimal Service		99211		

HISTORY

	New (3)	Established (2)	Office/O.P. (3)	Inpatient (3)
Problem Focused	99201	99212	99241	99251
Exp/Prob Focused	99202	99213	99242	99252
Detail	99203	99214	99243	99253
Comprehensive	99204/05	99215	99244/45	99254/55

EXAMINATION

	New (3)	Established (2)	Office/O.P. (3)	Inpatient (3)
Problem Focused	99201	99212	99241	99251
Exp/Prob Focused	99202	99213	99242	99252
Detail	99203	99214	99243	99253
Comprehensive	99204/05	99215	99244/45	99254/55

MEDICAL DECISION MAKING

	New (3)	Established (2)	Office/O.P. (3)	Inpatient (3)
Straight Forward	99201/2	99212	99241/42	99251/52
Low Complexity	99203	99213	99243	99253
Mod Complexity	99204	99214	99244	99254
High Complexity	99205	99215	99245	99255

TIME:_____　　Counsel/Coordination of Care:_____

	New (3)	Established (2)	Office/O.P. (3)	Inpatient (3)
10 Minutes	99201	99212		
15 Minutes		99213	99241	
20 Minutes	99202			99251
25 Minutes		99214		
30 Minutes	99203		99242	
40 Minutes		99215	99243	99252
45 Minutes	99204			
55 Minutes				99253
60 Minutes	99205		99244	
80 Minutes			99245	99254
110 Minutes				99255

MedBooks, Inc.
101 W. Buckingham Road, Richardson, Tx. 75081 (800) 443-7397

EXERCISE 6.31

Name: ____________________
Class/Section: ____________________
Date: ____________________

cpTeach 2012 Workbook

1500

HEALTH INSURANCE CLAIM FORM

APPROVED BY NATIONAL UNIFORM CLAIM COMMITTEE 08/05

PICA PICA

1. MEDICARE (Medicare #) MEDICAID (Medicaid #) TRICARE CHAMPUS (Sponsor's SSN) CHAMPVA (Member ID#) GROUP HEALTH PLAN (SSN or ID) FECA BLK LUNG (SSN) OTHER (ID)

1a. INSURED'S I.D. NUMBER (For Program in Item 1)

2. PATIENT'S NAME (Last Name, First Name, Middle Initial)

3. PATIENT'S BIRTH DATE MM DD YY SEX M F

4. INSURED'S NAME (Last Name, First Name, Middle Initial)

5. PATIENT'S ADDRESS (No., Street) CITY STATE ZIP CODE TELEPHONE (Include Area Code) ( )

6. PATIENT RELATIONSHIP TO INSURED Self Spouse Child Other

7. INSURED'S ADDRESS (No., Street) CITY STATE ZIP CODE TELEPHONE (Include Area Code) ( )

8. PATIENT STATUS Single Married Other Employed Full-Time Student Part-Time Student

9. OTHER INSURED'S NAME (Last Name, First Name, Middle Initial)

a. OTHER INSURED'S POLICY OR GROUP NUMBER

b. OTHER INSURED'S DATE OF BIRTH MM DD YY SEX M F

c. EMPLOYER'S NAME OR SCHOOL NAME

d. INSURANCE PLAN NAME OR PROGRAM NAME

10. IS PATIENT'S CONDITION RELATED TO:

a. EMPLOYMENT? (Current or Previous) YES NO

b. AUTO ACCIDENT? YES NO PLACE (State)

c. OTHER ACCIDENT? YES NO

10d. RESERVED FOR LOCAL USE

11. INSURED'S POLICY GROUP OR FECA NUMBER

a. INSURED'S DATE OF BIRTH MM DD YY SEX M F

b. EMPLOYER'S NAME OR SCHOOL NAME

c. INSURANCE PLAN NAME OR PROGRAM NAME

d. IS THERE ANOTHER HEALTH BENEFIT PLAN? YES NO *If yes*, return to and complete item 9 a-d.

READ BACK OF FORM BEFORE COMPLETING & SIGNING THIS FORM.

12. PATIENT'S OR AUTHORIZED PERSON'S SIGNATURE I authorize the release of any medical or other information necessary to process this claim. I also request payment of government benefits either to myself or to the party who accepts assignment below.

SIGNED ____________ DATE ____________

13. INSURED'S OR AUTHORIZED PERSON'S SIGNATURE I authorize payment of medical benefits to the undersigned physician or supplier for services described below.

SIGNED ____________

PATIENT AND INSURED INFORMATION

14. DATE OF CURRENT: MM DD YY ILLNESS (First symptom) OR INJURY (Accident) OR PREGNANCY(LMP)

15. IF PATIENT HAS HAD SAME OR SIMILAR ILLNESS. GIVE FIRST DATE MM DD YY

16. DATES PATIENT UNABLE TO WORK IN CURRENT OCCUPATION FROM MM DD YY TO MM DD YY

17. NAME OF REFERRING PROVIDER OR OTHER SOURCE 17a. 17b. NPI

18. HOSPITALIZATION DATES RELATED TO CURRENT SERVICES FROM MM DD YY TO MM DD YY

19. RESERVED FOR LOCAL USE

20. OUTSIDE LAB? YES NO $ CHARGES

21. DIAGNOSIS OR NATURE OF ILLNESS OR INJURY (Relate Items 1, 2, 3 or 4 to Item 24E by Line)

1. ____ . ____ 3. ____ . ____
2. ____ . ____ 4. ____ . ____

22. MEDICAID RESUBMISSION CODE ORIGINAL REF. NO.

23. PRIOR AUTHORIZATION NUMBER

	24. A. DATE(S) OF SERVICE From MM DD YY To MM DD YY	B. PLACE OF SERVICE	C. EMG	D. PROCEDURES, SERVICES, OR SUPPLIES (Explain Unusual Circumstances) CPT/HCPCS MODIFIER	E. DIAGNOSIS POINTER	F. $ CHARGES	G. DAYS OR UNITS	H. EPSDT Family Plan	I. ID. QUAL.	J. RENDERING PROVIDER ID. #
1									NPI	
2									NPI	
3									NPI	
4									NPI	
5									NPI	
6									NPI	

25. FEDERAL TAX I.D. NUMBER SSN EIN

26. PATIENT'S ACCOUNT NO.

27. ACCEPT ASSIGNMENT? (For govt. claims, see back) YES NO

28. TOTAL CHARGE $

29. AMOUNT PAID $

30. BALANCE DUE $

31. SIGNATURE OF PHYSICIAN OR SUPPLIER INCLUDING DEGREES OR CREDENTIALS (I certify that the statements on the reverse apply to this bill and are made a part thereof.)

SIGNED DATE

32. SERVICE FACILITY LOCATION INFORMATION a. b.

33. BILLING PROVIDER INFO & PH # ( ) a. b.

PHYSICIAN OR SUPPLIER INFORMATION

NUCC Instruction Manual available at: www.nucc.org OMB APPROVAL PENDING

Name:_____

Class/Section:_____

Date:_____

2012

EXERCISE 6.32

Re-code the previous example pretending that Ms. Sneezy is a new patient to your office. How does this change your coding? Are you able to get as high a level of service as you did in the example above? Why or why not?

Notes: _____

_____

DOC Form®
(Doctor's Office Checklist)

	OFFICE/OUTPATIENT		CONSULTATION	
	New (3)	Established (2)	Office/O.P. (3)	Inpatient (3)
Minimal Service		99211		

HISTORY
Problem Focused	99201	99212	99241	99251
Exp/Prob Focused	99202	99213	99242	99252
Detail	99203	99214	99243	99253
Comprehensive	99204/05	99215	99244/45	99254/55

EXAMINATION
Problem Focused	99201	99212	99241	99251
Exp/Prob Focused	99202	99213	99242	99252
Detail	99203	99214	99243	99253
Comprehensive	99204/05	99215	99244/45	99254/55

MEDICAL DECISION MAKING
Straight Forward	99201/2	99212	99241/42	99251/52
Low Complexity	99203	99213	99243	99253
Mod Complexity	99204	99214	99244	99254
High Complexity	99205	99215	99245	99255

TIME:_____ Counsel/Coordination of Care:_____
10 Minutes	99201	99212		
15 Minutes		99213	99241	
20 Minutes	99202			99251
25 Minutes		99214		
30 Minutes	99203		99242	
40 Minutes		99215	99243	99252
45 Minutes	99204			
55 Minutes				99253
60 Minutes	99205		99244	
80 Minutes			99245	99254
110 Minutes				99255

MedBooks, Inc.
101 W. Buckingham Road, Richardson, Tx. 75081 (800) 443-7397
Warning: This product is copyrighted and is not to be duplicated in any manner without the express written permission of MedBooks.

EXERCISE 6.32

WORKBOOK

cpTeach

2012

Name:_____

Class/Section:_____

Date:_____

1500
HEALTH INSURANCE CLAIM FORM
APPROVED BY NATIONAL UNIFORM CLAIM COMMITTEE 08/05

	PICA						PICA	

1. MEDICARE (Medicare #)   **MEDICAID** (Medicaid #)   **TRICARE CHAMPUS** (Sponsor's SSN)   **CHAMPVA** (Member ID#)   **GROUP HEALTH PLAN** (SSN or ID)   **FECA BLK LUNG** (SSN)   **OTHER** (ID)   **1a. INSURED'S I.D. NUMBER**   (For Program in Item 1)

2. PATIENT'S NAME (Last Name, First Name, Middle Initial)

3. PATIENT'S BIRTH DATE MM DD YY   **SEX** M ☐ F ☐

4. INSURED'S NAME (Last Name, First Name, Middle Initial)

5. PATIENT'S ADDRESS (No., Street)

6. PATIENT RELATIONSHIP TO INSURED Self ☐ Spouse ☐ Child ☐ Other ☐

7. INSURED'S ADDRESS (No., Street)

CITY   STATE

8. PATIENT STATUS Single ☐ Married ☐ Other ☐

CITY   STATE

ZIP CODE   TELEPHONE (Include Area Code) ( )

Employed ☐ Full-Time Student ☐ Part-Time Student ☐

ZIP CODE   TELEPHONE (Include Area Code) ( )

9. OTHER INSURED'S NAME (Last Name, First Name, Middle Initial)

10. IS PATIENT'S CONDITION RELATED TO:

11. INSURED'S POLICY GROUP OR FECA NUMBER

a. OTHER INSURED'S POLICY OR GROUP NUMBER

a. EMPLOYMENT? (Current or Previous) YES ☐ NO ☐

a. INSURED'S DATE OF BIRTH MM DD YY   **SEX** M ☐ F ☐

b. OTHER INSURED'S DATE OF BIRTH MM DD YY   **SEX** M ☐ F ☐

b. AUTO ACCIDENT? PLACE (State) YES ☐ NO ☐

b. EMPLOYER'S NAME OR SCHOOL NAME

c. EMPLOYER'S NAME OR SCHOOL NAME

c. OTHER ACCIDENT? YES ☐ NO ☐

c. INSURANCE PLAN NAME OR PROGRAM NAME

d. INSURANCE PLAN NAME OR PROGRAM NAME

10d. RESERVED FOR LOCAL USE

d. IS THERE ANOTHER HEALTH BENEFIT PLAN? YES ☐ NO ☐ If yes, return to and complete item 9 a-d.

READ BACK OF FORM BEFORE COMPLETING & SIGNING THIS FORM.
12. PATIENT'S OR AUTHORIZED PERSON'S SIGNATURE I authorize the release of any medical or other information necessary to process this claim. I also request payment of government benefits either to myself or to the party who accepts assignment below.

SIGNED_____ DATE_____

13. INSURED'S OR AUTHORIZED PERSON'S SIGNATURE I authorize payment of medical benefits to the undersigned physician or supplier for services described below.

SIGNED_____

14. DATE OF CURRENT: MM DD YY   ILLNESS (First symptom) OR INJURY (Accident) OR PREGNANCY(LMP)

15. IF PATIENT HAS HAD SAME OR SIMILAR ILLNESS. GIVE FIRST DATE MM DD YY

16. DATES PATIENT UNABLE TO WORK IN CURRENT OCCUPATION FROM MM DD YY TO MM DD YY

17. NAME OF REFERRING PROVIDER OR OTHER SOURCE   17a.   17b. NPI

18. HOSPITALIZATION DATES RELATED TO CURRENT SERVICES FROM MM DD YY TO MM DD YY

19. RESERVED FOR LOCAL USE

20. OUTSIDE LAB? YES ☐ NO ☐ $ CHARGES

21. DIAGNOSIS OR NATURE OF ILLNESS OR INJURY (Relate Items 1, 2, 3 or 4 to Item 24E by Line)
1. |___.___   3. |___.___
2. |___.___   4. |___.___

22. MEDICAID RESUBMISSION CODE   ORIGINAL REF. NO.

23. PRIOR AUTHORIZATION NUMBER

24. A. DATE(S) OF SERVICE From MM DD YY To MM DD YY	**B. PLACE OF SERVICE**	**C. EMG**	**D. PROCEDURES, SERVICES, OR SUPPLIES** (Explain Unusual Circumstances) CPT/HCPCS MODIFIER	**E. DIAGNOSIS POINTER**	**F. $ CHARGES**	**G. DAYS OR UNITS**	**H. EPSDT Family Plan**	**I. ID. QUAL.**	**J. RENDERING PROVIDER ID. #**
1								NPI
2								NPI
3								NPI
4								NPI
5								NPI
6								NPI

25. FEDERAL TAX I.D. NUMBER SSN ☐ EIN ☐

26. PATIENT'S ACCOUNT NO.

27. ACCEPT ASSIGNMENT? (For govt. claims, see back) YES ☐ NO ☐

28. TOTAL CHARGE $

29. AMOUNT PAID $

30. BALANCE DUE $

31. SIGNATURE OF PHYSICIAN OR SUPPLIER INCLUDING DEGREES OR CREDENTIALS (I certify that the statements on the reverse apply to this bill and are made a part thereof.)

SIGNED_____ DATE_____

32. SERVICE FACILITY LOCATION INFORMATION

a. NPI   b.

33. BILLING PROVIDER INFO & PH # ( )

a. NPI   b.

NUCC Instruction Manual available at: www.nucc.org

OMB APPROVAL PENDING

PATIENT AND INSURED INFORMATION   *PHYSICIAN OR SUPPLIER INFORMATION*

Name:_____

Class/Section:_____

Date:_____

EXERCISE 6.33

Angela Angelique, a new patient, presents in your office with her mother. Angela is 5 years old. Upon seeing the patient, you notice that the she is severely retarded and question her mother about the pregnancy and discover, according to the mother, she was in labor for 9 days. The mother proceeds to tell you that Angela is deaf, blind, and spastic, and has no control over her bowels and is still in diapers. She has no ability to feed herself and is afraid of most touches from people. Mrs. Angelique explains that other physicians have said that poor Angela will probably not live very long. You also find out that Angela's father had a retarded brother and that he is no longer with the family. Mrs. Angelique has a history of cardiac problems and asthma. There are no smokers in the family and no one is alcoholic, although Mr. Angelique has had a history of drug abuse. Today's visit concerns the difficulty that Angela has had in breathing lately. Mrs. Angelique describes this as being heavy and wheezing. Sometimes the baby will wake up in the middle of the night crying. She will be red and look as if she cannot breathe. In fact, this happened last night. Upon examination of Angela you notice her lungs sound terrible and may have pneumonia. You also notice her ears are infected and red. Abdominal exam indicates a mass of unknown orgin. Mrs. Angelique is very poor, has no health insurance and is not quite sure that she knows how to handle all of the stresses that come along with raising her child. You talk to her about some agencies that can help, make some phone calls to set up meetings while she is present, and tell her you would like to admit Angela to the hospital for some further testing. You do the admission that day.

DOC Form®
(Doctor's Office Checklist)

HOSPITAL		OBSERVATION		ER
Initial (3) Sub (2)		Discharge Date		New/Estab (3)
		Different (3) Same (3)		

HISTORY

Problem Focused		99231			99281
Exp/Prob Focused		99232			99282/83
Detail	99221	99233	99218	99234	99284
Comprehensive	99221/2/3		99218/19/20	99234/35/36	99285

EXAMINATION

Problem Focused		99231			99281
Exp/Prob Focused		99232			99282/83
Detail	99221	99233	99218	99234	99284
Comprehensive	99221/2/3		99218/19/20	99234/35/36	99285

MEDICAL DECISION MAKING

Straight Forward	99221	99231	99218	99234	99281
Low Complexity	99221	99231	99218	99234	99282
Mod Complexity	99222	99232	99219	99235	99283/84
High Complexity	99223	99233	99220	99236	99285

DISCHARGE 99217

≤ 30 Minutes	99238
> 30 Minutes	99239

TIME

15 Minutes	99231
20 Minutes	
25 Minutes	99232
30 Minutes	99221
35 Minutes	99233
45 Minutes	
50 Minutes	99222
60 Minutes	
70 Minutes	99223

Patient Name:_____

Date:_____Physician Signature:_____

EXERCISE 6.33

[1500]

HEALTH INSURANCE CLAIM FORM

APPROVED BY NATIONAL UNIFORM CLAIM COMMITTEE 08/05

☐☐ PICA   PICA ☐☐

1. MEDICARE MEDICAID TRICARE CHAMPUS CHAMPVA GROUP HEALTH PLAN FECA BLK LUNG OTHER	1a. INSURED'S I.D. NUMBER (For Program in Item 1)
☐ (Medicare #) ☐ (Medicaid #) ☐ (Sponsor's SSN) ☐ (Member ID#) ☐ (SSN or ID) ☐ (SSN) ☐ (ID)	

2. PATIENT'S NAME (Last Name, First Name, Middle Initial)	3. PATIENT'S BIRTH DATE MM DD YY SEX M ☐ F ☐	4. INSURED'S NAME (Last Name, First Name, Middle Initial)

5. PATIENT'S ADDRESS (No., Street)	6. PATIENT RELATIONSHIP TO INSURED Self ☐ Spouse ☐ Child ☐ Other ☐	7. INSURED'S ADDRESS (No., Street)

CITY STATE	8. PATIENT STATUS Single ☐ Married ☐ Other ☐	CITY STATE

ZIP CODE TELEPHONE (Include Area Code) ( )	Employed ☐ Full-Time Student ☐ Part-Time Student ☐	ZIP CODE TELEPHONE (Include Area Code) ( )

9. OTHER INSURED'S NAME (Last Name, First Name, Middle Initial)	10. IS PATIENT'S CONDITION RELATED TO:	11. INSURED'S POLICY GROUP OR FECA NUMBER
a. OTHER INSURED'S POLICY OR GROUP NUMBER	a. EMPLOYMENT? (Current or Previous) ☐ YES ☐ NO	a. INSURED'S DATE OF BIRTH MM DD YY SEX M ☐ F ☐
b. OTHER INSURED'S DATE OF BIRTH MM DD YY SEX M ☐ F ☐	b. AUTO ACCIDENT? PLACE (State) ☐ YES ☐ NO	b. EMPLOYER'S NAME OR SCHOOL NAME
c. EMPLOYER'S NAME OR SCHOOL NAME	c. OTHER ACCIDENT? ☐ YES ☐ NO	c. INSURANCE PLAN NAME OR PROGRAM NAME
d. INSURANCE PLAN NAME OR PROGRAM NAME	10d. RESERVED FOR LOCAL USE	d. IS THERE ANOTHER HEALTH BENEFIT PLAN? ☐ YES ☐ NO If yes, return to and complete item 9 a-d.

READ BACK OF FORM BEFORE COMPLETING & SIGNING THIS FORM.

12. PATIENT'S OR AUTHORIZED PERSON'S SIGNATURE I authorize the release of any medical or other information necessary to process this claim. I also request payment of government benefits either to myself or to the party who accepts assignment below. SIGNED_____ DATE_____	13. INSURED'S OR AUTHORIZED PERSON'S SIGNATURE I authorize payment of medical benefits to the undersigned physician or supplier for services described below. SIGNED_____

14. DATE OF CURRENT: MM DD YY ◄ ILLNESS (First symptom) OR INJURY (Accident) OR PREGNANCY(LMP)	15. IF PATIENT HAS HAD SAME OR SIMILAR ILLNESS. GIVE FIRST DATE MM DD YY	16. DATES PATIENT UNABLE TO WORK IN CURRENT OCCUPATION MM DD YY MM DD YY FROM TO
17. NAME OF REFERRING PROVIDER OR OTHER SOURCE	17a. 17b. NPI	18. HOSPITALIZATION DATES RELATED TO CURRENT SERVICES MM DD YY MM DD YY FROM TO
19. RESERVED FOR LOCAL USE		20. OUTSIDE LAB? ☐ YES ☐ NO $ CHARGES

21. DIAGNOSIS OR NATURE OF ILLNESS OR INJURY (Relate Items 1, 2, 3 or 4 to Item 24E by Line)	22. MEDICAID RESUBMISSION CODE ORIGINAL REF. NO.
1. |____.____| 3. |____.____|	
2. |____.____| 4. |____.____|	23. PRIOR AUTHORIZATION NUMBER

24. A. DATE(S) OF SERVICE From To MM DD YY MM DD YY	B. PLACE OF SERVICE	C. EMG	D. PROCEDURES, SERVICES, OR SUPPLIES (Explain Unusual Circumstances) CPT/HCPCS MODIFIER	E. DIAGNOSIS POINTER	F. $ CHARGES	G. DAYS OR UNITS	H. EPSDT Family Plan	I. ID. QUAL.	J. RENDERING PROVIDER ID. #
1									NPI
2									NPI
3									NPI
4									NPI
5									NPI
6									NPI

25. FEDERAL TAX I.D. NUMBER ☐ SSN ☐ EIN	26. PATIENT'S ACCOUNT NO.	27. ACCEPT ASSIGNMENT? (For govt. claims, see back) ☐ YES ☐ NO	28. TOTAL CHARGE $	29. AMOUNT PAID $	30. BALANCE DUE $
31. SIGNATURE OF PHYSICIAN OR SUPPLIER INCLUDING DEGREES OR CREDENTIALS (I certify that the statements on the reverse apply to this bill and are made a part thereof.) SIGNED_____ DATE_____	32. SERVICE FACILITY LOCATION INFORMATION a. b.	33. BILLING PROVIDER INFO & PH # ( ) a. b.

NUCC Instruction Manual available at: www.nucc.org   OMB APPROVAL PENDING

(text running vertically on right side: PATIENT AND INSURED INFORMATION ... PHYSICIAN OR SUPPLIER INFORMATION)

EXERCISE 6.34

Audry Lill, comes into your office complaining of severe weight gain in the past few years (over 100 pounds), a significant amount of hair loss, and of persistent lower right abdominal pain. She has come to you because her last doctor told her that she was losing a lot of hair due to the fact that she wore pony tails as a child. She heard from her friend that you were an OB/GYN who also had your Ph.D. in endocrinology and would like your opinion on her condition. During her history, you learn that one of her cousins has thyroid problems, and that she had been in a severe car accident back in 1983. You also learn that one of her doctors suggested that she have a hysterectomy a few years ago due to the fact that she was having irregular bleeding. At her last visit with her regular doctor which was about one month ago, she was told that she had a 4 cm cyst on her ovaries. Knowing that she had received a complete hysterectomy, she explained to the doctor that this could not be true. He requested that she come back in a week for another test and told her that the cyst was gone. Ms. Lill stills feels the pain, and is worried about her condition. She eats oatmeal in the morning, has a salad for lunch and often does not eat dinner. She is an active person, 40 years of age, and is single with no children. She is gainfully employed and travels a bit. She drinks a mild amount of alcohol, but only socially, and never gets drunk. Her grandmother lived to age 94, both parents are still living, there is no history of cancer or other diseases in her family that she is aware of. You decide to order some extensive blood work, as well as a level three ultrasound. You also complete a general multi-system exam and explain to Ms. Lill that she should come back in a week to discuss the results of her tests and to make a plan of action going forward.

DOC Form®
(Doctor's Office Checklist)

OFFICE/OUTPATIENT   **CONSULTATION**

	New (3)	Established (2)	Office/O.P. (3)	Inpatient (3)
Minimal Service		99211		

HISTORY

Problem Focused	99201	99212	99241	99251
Exp/Prob Focused	99202	99213	99242	99252
Detail	99203	99214	99243	99253
Comprehensive	99204/05	99215	99244/45	99254/55

EXAMINATION

Problem Focused	99201	99212	99241	99251
Exp/Prob Focused	99202	99213	99242	99252
Detail	99203	99214	99243	99253
Comprehensive	99204/05	99215	99244/45	99254/55

MEDICAL DECISION MAKING

Straight Forward	99201/2	99212	99241/42	99251/52
Low Complexity	99203	99213	99243	99253
Mod Complexity	99204	99214	99244	99254
High Complexity	99205	99215	99245	99255

TIME:_____   **Counsel/Coordination of Care:_____**

10 Minutes	99201	99212		
15 Minutes		99213	99241	
20 Minutes	99202			99251
25 Minutes		99214		
30 Minutes	99203		99242	
40 Minutes		99215	99243	99252
45 Minutes	99204			
55 Minutes				99253
60 Minutes	99205		99244	
80 Minutes			99245	99254
110 Minutes				99255

MedBooks, Inc.
101 W. Buckingham Road, Richardson, Tx. 75081 (800) 443-7397
Warning: This product is copyrighted and is not to be duplicated in any manner without the express written permission of MedBooks.

EXERCISE 6.34

Name:_____

Class/Section:_____

Date:_____

cpTeach 2012

1500

HEALTH INSURANCE CLAIM FORM

APPROVED BY NATIONAL UNIFORM CLAIM COMMITTEE 08/05

[ ][ ] PICA · PICA [ ][ ]

| 1. MEDICARE [ ] (Medicare #) · MEDICAID [ ] (Medicaid #) · TRICARE CHAMPUS [ ] (Sponsor's SSN) · CHAMPVA [ ] (Member ID#) · GROUP HEALTH PLAN [ ] (SSN or ID) · FECA BLK LUNG [ ] (SSN) · OTHER [ ] (ID) | 1a. INSURED'S I.D. NUMBER (For Program in Item 1) |

2. PATIENT'S NAME (Last Name, First Name, Middle Initial)

3. PATIENT'S BIRTH DATE MM | DD | YY   SEX M [ ]   F [ ]

4. INSURED'S NAME (Last Name, First Name, Middle Initial)

5. PATIENT'S ADDRESS (No., Street)

6. PATIENT RELATIONSHIP TO INSURED
Self [ ]   Spouse [ ]   Child [ ]   Other [ ]

7. INSURED'S ADDRESS (No., Street)

CITY | STATE

8. PATIENT STATUS
Single [ ]   Married [ ]   Other [ ]
Employed [ ]   Full-Time Student [ ]   Part-Time Student [ ]

CITY | STATE

ZIP CODE | TELEPHONE (Include Area Code) ( )

ZIP CODE | TELEPHONE (Include Area Code) ( )

9. OTHER INSURED'S NAME (Last Name, First Name, Middle Initial)

10. IS PATIENT'S CONDITION RELATED TO:

11. INSURED'S POLICY GROUP OR FECA NUMBER

a. OTHER INSURED'S POLICY OR GROUP NUMBER

a. EMPLOYMENT? (Current or Previous)
YES [ ]   NO [ ]

a. INSURED'S DATE OF BIRTH MM | DD | YY   SEX M [ ]   F [ ]

b. OTHER INSURED'S DATE OF BIRTH MM | DD | YY   SEX M [ ]   F [ ]

b. AUTO ACCIDENT?   PLACE (State)
YES [ ]   NO [ ]

b. EMPLOYER'S NAME OR SCHOOL NAME

c. EMPLOYER'S NAME OR SCHOOL NAME

c. OTHER ACCIDENT?
YES [ ]   NO [ ]

c. INSURANCE PLAN NAME OR PROGRAM NAME

d. INSURANCE PLAN NAME OR PROGRAM NAME

10d. RESERVED FOR LOCAL USE

d. IS THERE ANOTHER HEALTH BENEFIT PLAN?
YES [ ]   NO [ ]   If yes, return to and complete item 9 a-d.

READ BACK OF FORM BEFORE COMPLETING & SIGNING THIS FORM.
12. PATIENT'S OR AUTHORIZED PERSON'S SIGNATURE   I authorize the release of any medical or other information necessary to process this claim. I also request payment of government benefits either to myself or to the party who accepts assignment below.
SIGNED_____   DATE_____

13. INSURED'S OR AUTHORIZED PERSON'S SIGNATURE   I authorize payment of medical benefits to the undersigned physician or supplier for services described below.
SIGNED_____

14. DATE OF CURRENT: MM | DD | YY   ILLNESS (First symptom) OR INJURY (Accident) OR PREGNANCY(LMP)

15. IF PATIENT HAS HAD SAME OR SIMILAR ILLNESS. GIVE FIRST DATE MM | DD | YY

16. DATES PATIENT UNABLE TO WORK IN CURRENT OCCUPATION
FROM MM | DD | YY   TO MM | DD | YY

17. NAME OF REFERRING PROVIDER OR OTHER SOURCE

17a.
17b. NPI

18. HOSPITALIZATION DATES RELATED TO CURRENT SERVICES
FROM MM | DD | YY   TO MM | DD | YY

19. RESERVED FOR LOCAL USE

20. OUTSIDE LAB? $ CHARGES
YES [ ]   NO [ ]

21. DIAGNOSIS OR NATURE OF ILLNESS OR INJURY (Relate Items 1, 2, 3 or 4 to Item 24E by Line)
1. |___.___   3. |___.___
2. |___.___   4. |___.___

22. MEDICAID RESUBMISSION CODE   ORIGINAL REF. NO.

23. PRIOR AUTHORIZATION NUMBER

24. A. DATE(S) OF SERVICE From MM DD YY To MM DD YY	B. PLACE OF SERVICE	C. EMG	D. PROCEDURES, SERVICES, OR SUPPLIES (Explain Unusual Circumstances) CPT/HCPCS	MODIFIER	E. DIAGNOSIS POINTER	F. $ CHARGES	G. DAYS OR UNITS	H. EPSDT Family Plan	I. ID. QUAL.	J. RENDERING PROVIDER ID. #
1									NPI	
2									NPI	
3									NPI	
4									NPI	
5									NPI	
6									NPI	

25. FEDERAL TAX I.D. NUMBER   SSN [ ] EIN [ ]

26. PATIENT'S ACCOUNT NO.

27. ACCEPT ASSIGNMENT? (For govt. claims, see back)
YES [ ]   NO [ ]

28. TOTAL CHARGE $

29. AMOUNT PAID $

30. BALANCE DUE $

31. SIGNATURE OF PHYSICIAN OR SUPPLIER INCLUDING DEGREES OR CREDENTIALS (I certify that the statements on the reverse apply to this bill and are made a part thereof.)
SIGNED_____   DATE_____

32. SERVICE FACILITY LOCATION INFORMATION
a. NPI   b.

33. BILLING PROVIDER INFO & PH # ( )
a. NPI   b.

NUCC Instruction Manual available at: www.nucc.org

OMB APPROVAL PENDING

X

Name:	
Class/Section:	
cpTeach 2012	Date:

EXERCISE 6.35

Pretend that in the case above, the patient came to you as an established patient. Would this change your coding? Would you pick a higher level of service than you had in the example above? Why or why not?

Notes: _____

_____

_____

DOC Form®
(Doctor's Office Checklist)

OFFICE/OUTPATIENT   CONSULTATION

	New (3)	Established (2)	Office/O.P. (3)	Inpatient (3)
Minimal Service		99211		

HISTORY

	New (3)	Established (2)	Office/O.P. (3)	Inpatient (3)
Problem Focused	99201	99212	99241	99251
Exp/Prob Focused	99202	99213	99242	99252
Detail	99203	99214	99243	99253
Comprehensive	99204/05	99215	99244/45	99254/55

EXAMINATION

	New (3)	Established (2)	Office/O.P. (3)	Inpatient (3)
Problem Focused	99201	99212	99241	99251
Exp/Prob Focused	99202	99213	99242	99252
Detail	99203	99214	99243	99253
Comprehensive	99204/05	99215	99244/45	99254/55

MEDICAL DECISION MAKING

	New (3)	Established (2)	Office/O.P. (3)	Inpatient (3)
Straight Forward	99201/2	99212	99241/42	99251/52
Low Complexity	99203	99213	99243	99253
Mod Complexity	99204	99214	99244	99254
High Complexity	99205	99215	99245	99255

TIME:_____   Counsel/Coordination of Care:_____

	New (3)	Established (2)	Office/O.P. (3)	Inpatient (3)
10 Minutes	99201	99212		
15 Minutes		99213	99241	
20 Minutes	99202			99251
25 Minutes		99214		
30 Minutes	99203		99242	
40 Minutes		99215	99243	99252
45 Minutes	99204			
55 Minutes				99253
60 Minutes	99205		99244	
80 Minutes			99245	99254
110 Minutes				99255

MedBooks, Inc.
101 W. Buckingham Road, Richardson, Tx. 75081 (800) 443-7397
Warning: This product is copyrighted and is not to be duplicated in any manner without the express written permission of MedBooks.

Exercise 6.35

1500

HEALTH INSURANCE CLAIM FORM

APPROVED BY NATIONAL UNIFORM CLAIM COMMITTEE 08/05

☐☐ PICA | PICA ☐☐

| 1. MEDICARE MEDICAID TRICARE CHAMPUS CHAMPVA GROUP HEALTH PLAN FECA BLK LUNG OTHER | 1a. INSURED'S I.D. NUMBER (For Program in Item 1) |
| (Medicare #) (Medicaid #) (Sponsor's SSN) (Member ID#) (SSN or ID) (SSN) (ID) | |

2. PATIENT'S NAME (Last Name, First Name, Middle Initial)

3. PATIENT'S BIRTH DATE MM DD YY SEX M ☐ F ☐

4. INSURED'S NAME (Last Name, First Name, Middle Initial)

5. PATIENT'S ADDRESS (No., Street)

6. PATIENT RELATIONSHIP TO INSURED
Self ☐ Spouse ☐ Child ☐ Other ☐

7. INSURED'S ADDRESS (No., Street)

CITY | STATE

8. PATIENT STATUS
Single ☐ Married ☐ Other ☐
Employed ☐ Full-Time Student ☐ Part-Time Student ☐

CITY | STATE

ZIP CODE | TELEPHONE (Include Area Code) ( )

ZIP CODE | TELEPHONE (Include Area Code) ( )

9. OTHER INSURED'S NAME (Last Name, First Name, Middle Initial)

10. IS PATIENT'S CONDITION RELATED TO:

11. INSURED'S POLICY GROUP OR FECA NUMBER

a. OTHER INSURED'S POLICY OR GROUP NUMBER

a. EMPLOYMENT? (Current or Previous) ☐ YES ☐ NO

a. INSURED'S DATE OF BIRTH MM DD YY SEX M ☐ F ☐

b. OTHER INSURED'S DATE OF BIRTH MM DD YY SEX M ☐ F ☐

b. AUTO ACCIDENT? PLACE (State) ☐ YES ☐ NO

b. EMPLOYER'S NAME OR SCHOOL NAME

c. EMPLOYER'S NAME OR SCHOOL NAME

c. OTHER ACCIDENT? ☐ YES ☐ NO

c. INSURANCE PLAN NAME OR PROGRAM NAME

d. INSURANCE PLAN NAME OR PROGRAM NAME

10d. RESERVED FOR LOCAL USE

d. IS THERE ANOTHER HEALTH BENEFIT PLAN? ☐ YES ☐ NO If yes, return to and complete item 9 a-d.

READ BACK OF FORM BEFORE COMPLETING & SIGNING THIS FORM.
12. PATIENT'S OR AUTHORIZED PERSON'S SIGNATURE I authorize the release of any medical or other information necessary to process this claim. I also request payment of government benefits either to myself or to the party who accepts assignment below.

SIGNED_____ DATE_____

13. INSURED'S OR AUTHORIZED PERSON'S SIGNATURE I authorize payment of medical benefits to the undersigned physician or supplier for services described below.

SIGNED_____

14. DATE OF CURRENT: MM DD YY ◄ ILLNESS (First symptom) OR INJURY (Accident) OR PREGNANCY(LMP)

15. IF PATIENT HAS HAD SAME OR SIMILAR ILLNESS. GIVE FIRST DATE MM DD YY

16. DATES PATIENT UNABLE TO WORK IN CURRENT OCCUPATION MM DD YY FROM TO MM DD YY

17. NAME OF REFERRING PROVIDER OR OTHER SOURCE

17a.
17b. NPI

18. HOSPITALIZATION DATES RELATED TO CURRENT SERVICES MM DD YY FROM TO MM DD YY

19. RESERVED FOR LOCAL USE

20. OUTSIDE LAB? ☐ YES ☐ NO $ CHARGES

21. DIAGNOSIS OR NATURE OF ILLNESS OR INJURY (Relate items 1, 2, 3 or 4 to Item 24E by Line)
1. |____.____
2. |____.____
3. |____.____
4. |____.____

22. MEDICAID RESUBMISSION CODE ORIGINAL REF. NO.

23. PRIOR AUTHORIZATION NUMBER

24. A. DATE(S) OF SERVICE						B. PLACE OF SERVICE	C. EMG	D. PROCEDURES, SERVICES, OR SUPPLIES (Explain Unusual Circumstances) CPT/HCPCS MODIFIER	E. DIAGNOSIS POINTER	F. $ CHARGES	G. DAYS OR UNITS	H. EPSDT Family Plan	I. ID. QUAL.	J. RENDERING PROVIDER ID. #
From			To											
MM	DD	YY	MM	DD	YY									
1														NPI
2														NPI
3														NPI
4														NPI
5														NPI
6														NPI

25. FEDERAL TAX I.D. NUMBER SSN EIN ☐ ☐

26. PATIENT'S ACCOUNT NO.

27. ACCEPT ASSIGNMENT? (For govt. claims, see back) ☐ YES ☐ NO

28. TOTAL CHARGE $

29. AMOUNT PAID $

30. BALANCE DUE $

31. SIGNATURE OF PHYSICIAN OR SUPPLIER INCLUDING DEGREES OR CREDENTIALS (I certify that the statements on the reverse apply to this bill and are made a part thereof.)

SIGNED_____ DATE_____

32. SERVICE FACILITY LOCATION INFORMATION

a. | b.

33. BILLING PROVIDER INFO & PH # ( )

a. | b.

NUCC Instruction Manual available at: www.nucc.org

OMB APPROVAL PENDING

EXERCISE 6.36

Red LeBleu comes to your office with his 14-month-old daughter who has persistent diarrhea. Red is fed up with his current pediatrician and explains to you that his daughter has had a lot of ear infections and that she always seems to be sick. He wants a second opinion on the current treatment plan for his daughter which is basically to let her grow out of any of the ailments that she has. You talk to Mr. LeBleu about the baby and find out that she has been teething for a number of months. You also learn that there is a cat at home and that the baby seems to sneeze a lot when they are there. Further, you learn that the baby drinks quite a bit of whole milk and constantly seems congested. You perform a head to toe exam, get information on her past shots and immunization records, check out the baby's ears and see that another infection is starting. You place the baby on another antibiotic and explain to Mr. LeBleu that he should get some acidophilus (a natural bacteria present in the digestive tract) at the health food store and that this be placed in the baby's drink. You further explain that this will help replace the flora in her intestine which have been killed as a result of the antibiotic therapy and that this should cut her diarrhea. Finally, you remind Mr. LeBleu to keep the baby away from the cat, off of milk, and for him to cease giving her any apple juice until the diarrhea is cleared, as apple juice will exacerbate the bowel movements.

Notes: _____

_____

_____

_____

_____

DOC Form®
(Doctor's Office Checklist)

	OFFICE/OUTPATIENT		CONSULTATION	
	New (3)	Established (2)	Office/O.P. (3)	Inpatient (3)
Minimal Service		99211		

HISTORY

Problem Focused	99201	99212	99241	99251
Exp/Prob Focused	99202	99213	99242	99252
Detail	99203	99214	99243	99253
Comprehensive	99204/05	99215	99244/45	99254/55

EXAMINATION

Problem Focused	99201	99212	99241	99251
Exp/Prob Focused	99202	99213	99242	99252
Detail	99203	99214	99243	99253
Comprehensive	99204/05	99215	99244/45	99254/55

MEDICAL DECISION MAKING

Straight Forward	99201/2	99212	99241/42	99251/52
Low Complexity	99203	99213	99243	99253
Mod Complexity	99204	99214	99244	99254
High Complexity	99205	99215	99245	99255

TIME:_____　　Counsel/Coordination of Care:_____

10 Minutes	99201	99212		
15 Minutes		99213	99241	
20 Minutes	99202			99251
25 Minutes		99214		
30 Minutes	99203		99242	
40 Minutes		99215	99243	99252
45 Minutes	99204			
55 Minutes				99253
60 Minutes	99205		99244	
80 Minutes			99245	99254
110 Minutes				99255

EXERCISE 6.36

1500
HEALTH INSURANCE CLAIM FORM
APPROVED BY NATIONAL UNIFORM CLAIM COMMITTEE 08/05

		PICA							PICA		

1. MEDICARE (Medicare #) **MEDICAID** (Medicaid #) **TRICARE CHAMPUS** (Sponsor's SSN) **CHAMPVA** (Member ID#) **GROUP HEALTH PLAN** (SSN or ID) **FECA BLK LUNG** (SSN) **OTHER** (ID)

1a. INSURED'S I.D. NUMBER (For Program in Item 1)

2. PATIENT'S NAME (Last Name, First Name, Middle Initial)

3. PATIENT'S BIRTH DATE MM DD YY **SEX** M F

4. INSURED'S NAME (Last Name, First Name, Middle Initial)

5. PATIENT'S ADDRESS (No., Street)

6. PATIENT RELATIONSHIP TO INSURED Self Spouse Child Other

7. INSURED'S ADDRESS (No., Street)

CITY **STATE**

8. PATIENT STATUS Single Married Other

CITY **STATE**

ZIP CODE **TELEPHONE** (Include Area Code) ( )

Employed Full-Time Student Part-Time Student

ZIP CODE **TELEPHONE** (Include Area Code) ( )

9. OTHER INSURED'S NAME (Last Name, First Name, Middle Initial)

10. IS PATIENT'S CONDITION RELATED TO:

11. INSURED'S POLICY GROUP OR FECA NUMBER

a. OTHER INSURED'S POLICY OR GROUP NUMBER

a. EMPLOYMENT? (Current or Previous) YES NO

a. INSURED'S DATE OF BIRTH MM DD YY **SEX** M F

b. OTHER INSURED'S DATE OF BIRTH MM DD YY **SEX** M F

b. AUTO ACCIDENT? YES NO **PLACE** (State)

b. EMPLOYER'S NAME OR SCHOOL NAME

c. EMPLOYER'S NAME OR SCHOOL NAME

c. OTHER ACCIDENT? YES NO

c. INSURANCE PLAN NAME OR PROGRAM NAME

d. INSURANCE PLAN NAME OR PROGRAM NAME

10d. RESERVED FOR LOCAL USE

d. IS THERE ANOTHER HEALTH BENEFIT PLAN? YES NO If yes, return to and complete item 9 a-d.

READ BACK OF FORM BEFORE COMPLETING & SIGNING THIS FORM.
12. PATIENT'S OR AUTHORIZED PERSON'S SIGNATURE I authorize the release of any medical or other information necessary to process this claim. I also request payment of government benefits either to myself or to the party who accepts assignment below.

SIGNED_____ DATE_____

13. INSURED'S OR AUTHORIZED PERSON'S SIGNATURE I authorize payment of medical benefits to the undersigned physician or supplier for services described below.

SIGNED_____

14. DATE OF CURRENT: MM DD YY ILLNESS (First symptom) OR INJURY (Accident) OR PREGNANCY(LMP)

15. IF PATIENT HAS HAD SAME OR SIMILAR ILLNESS. GIVE FIRST DATE MM DD YY

16. DATES PATIENT UNABLE TO WORK IN CURRENT OCCUPATION MM DD YY FROM TO MM DD YY

17. NAME OF REFERRING PROVIDER OR OTHER SOURCE

17a.
17b. NPI

18. HOSPITALIZATION DATES RELATED TO CURRENT SERVICES MM DD YY FROM TO MM DD YY

19. RESERVED FOR LOCAL USE

20. OUTSIDE LAB? YES NO **$ CHARGES**

21. DIAGNOSIS OR NATURE OF ILLNESS OR INJURY (Relate Items 1, 2, 3 or 4 to Item 24E by Line)

1. _____ . _____
2. _____ . _____
3. _____ . _____
4. _____ . _____

22. MEDICAID RESUBMISSION CODE ORIGINAL REF. NO.

23. PRIOR AUTHORIZATION NUMBER

24. A. DATE(S) OF SERVICE						B. PLACE OF SERVICE	C. EMG	D. PROCEDURES, SERVICES, OR SUPPLIES (Explain Unusual Circumstances)		E. DIAGNOSIS POINTER	F. $ CHARGES	G. DAYS OR UNITS	H. EPSDT Family Plan	I. ID. QUAL.	J. RENDERING PROVIDER ID. #
From			To					CPT/HCPCS	MODIFIER						
MM	DD	YY	MM	DD	YY										
1															NPI
2															NPI
3															NPI
4															NPI
5															NPI
6															NPI

25. FEDERAL TAX I.D. NUMBER SSN EIN

26. PATIENT'S ACCOUNT NO.

27. ACCEPT ASSIGNMENT? (For govt. claims, see back) YES NO

28. TOTAL CHARGE $

29. AMOUNT PAID $

30. BALANCE DUE $

31. SIGNATURE OF PHYSICIAN OR SUPPLIER INCLUDING DEGREES OR CREDENTIALS (I certify that the statements on the reverse apply to this bill and are made a part thereof.)

SIGNED_____ DATE_____

32. SERVICE FACILITY LOCATION INFORMATION

a. NPI b.

33. BILLING PROVIDER INFO & PH # ( )

a. NPI b.

NUCC Instruction Manual available at: www.nucc.org

OMB APPROVAL PENDING

PATIENT AND INSURED INFORMATION

PHYSICIAN OR SUPPLIER INFORMATION

Name:_____

Class/Section:_____

cpTeach

Date:_____

2012

EXERCISE 6.37

Re-code the example above pretending that this patient is an established patient of yours. How does this change your coding? Is the level of service you chose for the established patient higher or lower than the one you chose for the answer above? Why?

Notes: _____

_____

_____

_____

_____

_____

_____

_____

_____

_____

_____

_____

_____

_____

_____

_____

_____

_____

_____

_____

_____

_____

_____

DOC Form®
(Doctor's Office Checklist)

	OFFICE/OUTPATIENT		CONSULTATION	
	New (3)	Established (2)	Office/O.P. (3)	Inpatient (3)
Minimal Service		99211		

HISTORY

Problem Focused	99201	99212	99241	99251
Exp/Prob Focused	99202	99213	99242	99252
Detail	99203	99214	99243	99253
Comprehensive	99204/05	99215	99244/45	99254/55

EXAMINATION

Problem Focused	99201	99212	99241	99251
Exp/Prob Focused	99202	99213	99242	99252
Detail	99203	99214	99243	99253
Comprehensive	99204/05	99215	99244/45	99254/55

MEDICAL DECISION MAKING

Straight Forward	99201/2	99212	99241/42	99251/52
Low Complexity	99203	99213	99243	99253
Mod Complexity	99204	99214	99244	99254
High Complexity	99205	99215	99245	99255

TIME:_____   Counsel/Coordination of Care:_____

10 Minutes	99201	99212		
15 Minutes		99213	99241	
20 Minutes	99202			99251
25 Minutes		99214		
30 Minutes	99203		99242	
40 Minutes		99215	99243	99252
45 Minutes	99204			
55 Minutes				99253
60 Minutes	99205		99244	
80 Minutes			99245	99254
110 Minutes				99255

EXERCISE 6.37

Name: _____

Class/Section: _____

Date: _____

1500

HEALTH INSURANCE CLAIM FORM

APPROVED BY NATIONAL UNIFORM CLAIM COMMITTEE 08/05

| | PICA | | | | | | | PICA | |

1. MEDICARE ☐ (Medicare #) MEDICAID ☐ (Medicaid #) TRICARE CHAMPUS ☐ (Sponsor's SSN) CHAMPVA ☐ (Member ID#) GROUP HEALTH PLAN ☐ (SSN or ID) FECA BLK LUNG ☐ (SSN) OTHER ☐ (ID)   **1a.** INSURED'S I.D. NUMBER   (For Program in Item 1)

2. PATIENT'S NAME (Last Name, First Name, Middle Initial)   **3.** PATIENT'S BIRTH DATE MM DD YY   SEX M ☐ F ☐   **4.** INSURED'S NAME (Last Name, First Name, Middle Initial)

5. PATIENT'S ADDRESS (No., Street)   **6.** PATIENT RELATIONSHIP TO INSURED   Self ☐ Spouse ☐ Child ☐ Other ☐   **7.** INSURED'S ADDRESS (No., Street)

CITY   STATE   **9.** PATIENT STATUS   Single ☐ Married ☐ Other ☐   CITY   STATE

ZIP CODE   TELEPHONE (Include Area Code) ( )   Employed ☐ Full-Time Student ☐ Part-Time Student ☐   ZIP CODE   TELEPHONE (Include Area Code) ( )

9. OTHER INSURED'S NAME (Last Name, First Name, Middle Initial)   **10.** IS PATIENT'S CONDITION RELATED TO: **11.** INSURED'S POLICY GROUP OR FECA NUMBER

a. OTHER INSURED'S POLICY OR GROUP NUMBER   **a.** EMPLOYMENT? (Current or Previous) YES ☐ NO ☐   **a.** INSURED'S DATE OF BIRTH MM DD YY   SEX M ☐ F ☐

b. OTHER INSURED'S DATE OF BIRTH MM DD YY   SEX M ☐ F ☐   **b.** AUTO ACCIDENT? YES ☐ NO ☐ PLACE (State)   **b.** EMPLOYER'S NAME OR SCHOOL NAME

c. EMPLOYER'S NAME OR SCHOOL NAME   **c.** OTHER ACCIDENT? YES ☐ NO ☐   **c.** INSURANCE PLAN NAME OR PROGRAM NAME

d. INSURANCE PLAN NAME OR PROGRAM NAME   **10d.** RESERVED FOR LOCAL USE   **d.** IS THERE ANOTHER HEALTH BENEFIT PLAN? YES ☐ NO ☐ If yes, return to and complete item 9 a-d.

READ BACK OF FORM BEFORE COMPLETING & SIGNING THIS FORM.
12. PATIENT'S OR AUTHORIZED PERSON'S SIGNATURE I authorize the release of any medical or other information necessary to process this claim. I also request payment of government benefits either to myself or to the party who accepts assignment below.

SIGNED_____ DATE_____

13. INSURED'S OR AUTHORIZED PERSON'S SIGNATURE I authorize payment of medical benefits to the undersigned physician or supplier for services described below.

SIGNED_____

14. DATE OF CURRENT: ILLNESS (First symptom) OR INJURY (Accident) OR PREGNANCY(LMP) MM DD YY   **15.** IF PATIENT HAS HAD SAME OR SIMILAR ILLNESS. GIVE FIRST DATE MM DD YY   **16.** DATES PATIENT UNABLE TO WORK IN CURRENT OCCUPATION FROM MM DD YY TO MM DD YY

17. NAME OF REFERRING PROVIDER OR OTHER SOURCE   **17a.** **17b.** NPI   **18.** HOSPITALIZATION DATES RELATED TO CURRENT SERVICES FROM MM DD YY TO MM DD YY

19. RESERVED FOR LOCAL USE   **20.** OUTSIDE LAB? YES ☐ NO ☐ $ CHARGES

21. DIAGNOSIS OR NATURE OF ILLNESS OR INJURY (Relate Items 1, 2, 3 or 4 to Item 24E by Line)
1. |___.___ 3. |___.___
2. |___.___ 4. |___.___

22. MEDICAID RESUBMISSION CODE   ORIGINAL REF. NO.

23. PRIOR AUTHORIZATION NUMBER

24. A. DATE(S) OF SERVICE From To MM DD YY MM DD YY	B. PLACE OF SERVICE	C. EMG	D. PROCEDURES, SERVICES, OR SUPPLIES (Explain Unusual Circumstances) CPT/HCPCS MODIFIER	E. DIAGNOSIS POINTER	F. $ CHARGES	G. DAYS OR UNITS	H. EPSDT Family Plan	I. ID. QUAL.	J. RENDERING PROVIDER ID. #
1									NPI
2									NPI
3									NPI
4									NPI
5									NPI
6									NPI

25. FEDERAL TAX I.D. NUMBER   SSN ☐ EIN ☐   **26.** PATIENT'S ACCOUNT NO.   **27.** ACCEPT ASSIGNMENT? (For govt. claims, see back) YES ☐ NO ☐   **28.** TOTAL CHARGE $ **29.** AMOUNT PAID $ **30.** BALANCE DUE $

31. SIGNATURE OF PHYSICIAN OR SUPPLIER INCLUDING DEGREES OR CREDENTIALS (I certify that the statements on the reverse apply to this bill and are made a part thereof.)

SIGNED_____ DATE_____

32. SERVICE FACILITY LOCATION INFORMATION

a.   b.

33. BILLING PROVIDER INFO & PH # ( )

a.   b.

NUCC Instruction Manual available at: www.nucc.org   OMB APPROVAL PENDING

PATIENT AND INSURED INFORMATION

PHYSICIAN OR SUPPLIER INFORMATION

EXERCISE 6.38

Ms. Rosie Rosita, a new patient to your neurosurgery practice, comes into your office complaining of paralysis to the right side of her face. She has been sent to you by a friend of yours who is also a friend of her family's, an internal medicine doctor. When she arrives, she is handed a questionnaire which asks her questions about her current condition, her past medical history including any prior surgeries she may have had, her family history including who has suffered from what ailments/diseases and a social history. Following the completion of this questionnaire, she is brought into the examining room where you review her history, ask a few more questions and then perform an exam of her face using special techniques to test reflexes and such. Due to the fact that she is unable to whistle, make the movement for the letter "O" (at least on one side) and other such things, you suspect that she probably has suffered a case of Bell's Palsy. However, also due to the fact that she has been complaining of bad headaches in the front and side of her head, you think it best to schedule a CAT Scan and go from there. You record your findings, and reschedule a visit for one week. You report all information to your friend, the internal medicine doctor, and move on to the next patient.

Notes: _____

_____

_____

_____

_____

_____

DOC Form®
(Doctor's Office Checklist)

	OFFICE/OUTPATIENT		CONSULTATION	
	New (3)	Established (2)	Office/O.P. (3)	Inpatient (3)
Minimal Service		99211		

HISTORY

Problem Focused	99201	99212	99241	99251
Exp/Prob Focused	99202	99213	99242	99252
Detail	99203	99214	99243	99253
Comprehensive	99204/05	99215	99244/45	99254/55

EXAMINATION

Problem Focused	99201	99212	99241	99251
Exp/Prob Focused	99202	99213	99242	99252
Detail	99203	99214	99243	99253
Comprehensive	99204/05	99215	99244/45	99254/55

MEDICAL DECISION MAKING

Straight Forward	99201/2	99212	99241/42	99251/52
Low Complexity	99203	99213	99243	99253
Mod Complexity	99204	99214	99244	99254
High Complexity	99205	99215	99245	99255

TIME:_____   Counsel/Coordination of Care:_____

10 Minutes	99201	99212		
15 Minutes		99213	99241	
20 Minutes	99202			99251
25 Minutes		99214		
30 Minutes	99203		99242	
40 Minutes		99215	99243	99252
45 Minutes	99204			
55 Minutes				99253
60 Minutes	99205		99244	
80 Minutes			99245	99254
110 Minutes				99255

MedBooks, Inc.
101 W. Buckingham Road, Richardson, Tx. 75081 (800) 443-7397
Warning: This product is copyrighted and is not to be duplicated in any manner without the express written permission of MedBooks.

EXERCISE 6.38

1500

HEALTH INSURANCE CLAIM FORM

APPROVED BY NATIONAL UNIFORM CLAIM COMMITTEE 08/05

| | | PICA | | | | | | | | PICA | | |

1. MEDICARE   MEDICAID   TRICARE CHAMPUS   CHAMPVA   GROUP HEALTH PLAN   FECA BLK LUNG   OTHER
(Medicare #) (Medicaid #) (Sponsor's SSN) (Member ID#) (SSN or ID) (SSN) (ID)

1a. INSURED'S I.D. NUMBER   (For Program in Item 1)

2. PATIENT'S NAME (Last Name, First Name, Middle Initial)

3. PATIENT'S BIRTH DATE   MM DD YY   **SEX**   M   F

4. INSURED'S NAME (Last Name, First Name, Middle Initial)

5. PATIENT'S ADDRESS (No., Street)

6. PATIENT RELATIONSHIP TO INSURED
Self   Spouse   Child   Other

7. INSURED'S ADDRESS (No., Street)

CITY   STATE

8. PATIENT STATUS
Single   Married   Other
Employed   Full-Time Student   Part-Time Student

CITY   STATE

ZIP CODE   TELEPHONE (Include Area Code)
(   )

ZIP CODE   TELEPHONE (Include Area Code)
(   )

9. OTHER INSURED'S NAME (Last Name, First Name, Middle Initial)

10. IS PATIENT'S CONDITION RELATED TO:

11. INSURED'S POLICY GROUP OR FECA NUMBER

a. OTHER INSURED'S POLICY OR GROUP NUMBER

a. EMPLOYMENT? (Current or Previous)
YES   NO

a. INSURED'S DATE OF BIRTH   MM DD YY   **SEX**   M   F

b. OTHER INSURED'S DATE OF BIRTH   MM DD YY   **SEX**   M   F

b. AUTO ACCIDENT?   PLACE (State)
YES   NO

b. EMPLOYER'S NAME OR SCHOOL NAME

c. EMPLOYER'S NAME OR SCHOOL NAME

c. OTHER ACCIDENT?
YES   NO

c. INSURANCE PLAN NAME OR PROGRAM NAME

d. INSURANCE PLAN NAME OR PROGRAM NAME

10d. RESERVED FOR LOCAL USE

d. IS THERE ANOTHER HEALTH BENEFIT PLAN?
YES   NO   If yes, return to and complete item 9 a-d.

READ BACK OF FORM BEFORE COMPLETING & SIGNING THIS FORM.
12. PATIENT'S OR AUTHORIZED PERSON'S SIGNATURE I authorize the release of any medical or other information necessary to process this claim. I also request payment of government benefits either to myself or to the party who accepts assignment below.

SIGNED_____   DATE_____

13. INSURED'S OR AUTHORIZED PERSON'S SIGNATURE I authorize payment of medical benefits to the undersigned physician or supplier for services described below.

SIGNED_____

14. DATE OF CURRENT: MM DD YY   ILLNESS (First symptom) OR INJURY (Accident) OR PREGNANCY(LMP)

15. IF PATIENT HAS HAD SAME OR SIMILAR ILLNESS. GIVE FIRST DATE MM DD YY

16. DATES PATIENT UNABLE TO WORK IN CURRENT OCCUPATION MM DD YY   FROM   TO   MM DD YY

17. NAME OF REFERRING PROVIDER OR OTHER SOURCE

17a.
17b. NPI

18. HOSPITALIZATION DATES RELATED TO CURRENT SERVICES MM DD YY   FROM   TO   MM DD YY

19. RESERVED FOR LOCAL USE

20. OUTSIDE LAB? $ CHARGES
YES   NO

21. DIAGNOSIS OR NATURE OF ILLNESS OR INJURY (Relate Items 1, 2, 3 or 4 to Item 24E by Line)
1. |___.___   3. |___.___
2. |___.___   4. |___.___

22. MEDICAID RESUBMISSION CODE   ORIGINAL REF. NO.

23. PRIOR AUTHORIZATION NUMBER

24. A. DATE(S) OF SERVICE						B. PLACE OF SERVICE	C. EMG	D. PROCEDURES, SERVICES, OR SUPPLIES (Explain Unusual Circumstances)		E. DIAGNOSIS POINTER	F. $ CHARGES	G. DAYS OR UNITS	H. EPSDT Family Plan	I. ID. QUAL.	J. RENDERING PROVIDER ID. #
From			To					CPT/HCPCS	MODIFIER						
MM	DD	YY	MM	DD	YY										
1														NPI	
2														NPI	
3														NPI	
4														NPI	
5														NPI	
6														NPI	

25. FEDERAL TAX I.D. NUMBER   SSN EIN

26. PATIENT'S ACCOUNT NO.

27. ACCEPT ASSIGNMENT? (For govt. claims, see back)
YES   NO

28. TOTAL CHARGE $

29. AMOUNT PAID $

30. BALANCE DUE $

31. SIGNATURE OF PHYSICIAN OR SUPPLIER INCLUDING DEGREES OR CREDENTIALS (I certify that the statements on the reverse apply to this bill and are made a part thereof.)

SIGNED_____   DATE_____

32. SERVICE FACILITY LOCATION INFORMATION

a. NPI   b.

33. BILLING PROVIDER INFO & PH # (   )

a. NPI   b.

NUCC Instruction Manual available at: www.nucc.org

OMB APPROVAL PENDING

WORKBOOK		Name:_____
cpTeach 2012		Class/Section:_____
		Date:_____

EXERCISE 6.39

Alice Veolar, an established patient of yours for years, comes to your office for her regular annual exam. She is 42 years old and a single mother of one. Her pelvic region, head, ears, eyes, nose, throat, reflexes, cervix --everything-- seemed normal except her breast. Upon examination, you notice that she has an unusual lump in her right breast. You ask her about it, noting how long she has had it, and whether or not it has grown. You also review her family history to see if anyone in her family has had any history of breast cancer. There is no history of breast cancer, but since she is "at that age" you insist that she have a mammogram and that it be performed right away. Your nurse schedules the mammogram for the next day. Ms. Veolar is scared and you explain to her that mammograms are routine now and even if she hadn't had the lump, you still would've requested this test. Your total visit takes 15 minutes.

Notes: _____

_____

_____

_____

_____

_____

_____

_____

_____

_____

_____

_____

_____

_____

DOC Form®
(Doctor's Office Checklist)

OFFICE/OUTPATIENT   CONSULTATION

	New (3)	Established (2)	Office/O.P. (3)	Inpatient (3)
Minimal Service		99211		

HISTORY

	New (3)	Established (2)	Office/O.P. (3)	Inpatient (3)
Problem Focused	99201	99212	99241	99251
Exp/Prob Focused	99202	99213	99242	99252
Detail	99203	99214	99243	99253
Comprehensive	99204/05	99215	99244/45	99254/55

EXAMINATION

	New (3)	Established (2)	Office/O.P. (3)	Inpatient (3)
Problem Focused	99201	99212	99241	99251
Exp/Prob Focused	99202	99213	99242	99252
Detail	99203	99214	99243	99253
Comprehensive	99204/05	99215	99244/45	99254/55

MEDICAL DECISION MAKING

	New (3)	Established (2)	Office/O.P. (3)	Inpatient (3)
Straight Forward	99201/2	99212	99241/42	99251/52
Low Complexity	99203	99213	99243	99253
Mod Complexity	99204	99214	99244	99254
High Complexity	99205	99215	99245	99255

TIME:_____   Counsel/Coordination of Care:_____

	New (3)	Established (2)	Office/O.P. (3)	Inpatient (3)
10 Minutes	99201	99212		
15 Minutes		99213	99241	
20 Minutes	99202			99251
25 Minutes		99214		
30 Minutes	99203		99242	
40 Minutes		99215	99243	99252
45 Minutes	99204			
55 Minutes				99253
60 Minutes	99205		99244	
80 Minutes			99245	99254
110 Minutes				99255

MedBooks, Inc.
101 W. Buckingham Road, Richardson, Tx. 75081 (800) 443-7397
Warning: This product is copyrighted and is not to be duplicated in any manner without the express written permission of MedBooks.

EXERCISE 6.39

Name: _____

Class/Section: _____

Date: _____

cpTeach 2012

1500
HEALTH INSURANCE CLAIM FORM
APPROVED BY NATIONAL UNIFORM CLAIM COMMITTEE 08/05

| | PICA | | | | | | | PICA | |

1. MEDICARE	MEDICAID	TRICARE CHAMPUS	CHAMPVA	GROUP HEALTH PLAN	FECA BLK LUNG	OTHER	1a. INSURED'S I.D. NUMBER	(For Program in Item 1)
(Medicare #)	(Medicaid #)	(Sponsor's SSN)	(Member ID#)	(SSN or ID)	(SSN)	(ID)		

2. PATIENT'S NAME (Last Name, First Name, Middle Initial)	3. PATIENT'S BIRTH DATE MM DD YY SEX M F	4. INSURED'S NAME (Last Name, First Name, Middle Initial)

5. PATIENT'S ADDRESS (No., Street)	6. PATIENT RELATIONSHIP TO INSURED Self Spouse Child Other	7. INSURED'S ADDRESS (No., Street)

CITY	STATE	8. PATIENT STATUS Single Married Other	CITY	STATE

ZIP CODE	TELEPHONE (Include Area Code) ( )	Employed Full-Time Student Part-Time Student	ZIP CODE	TELEPHONE (Include Area Code) ( )

9. OTHER INSURED'S NAME (Last Name, First Name, Middle Initial)	10. IS PATIENT'S CONDITION RELATED TO:	11. INSURED'S POLICY GROUP OR FECA NUMBER

a. OTHER INSURED'S POLICY OR GROUP NUMBER	a. EMPLOYMENT? (Current or Previous) YES NO	a. INSURED'S DATE OF BIRTH MM DD YY SEX M F

b. OTHER INSURED'S DATE OF BIRTH MM DD YY SEX M F	b. AUTO ACCIDENT? PLACE (State) YES NO	b. EMPLOYER'S NAME OR SCHOOL NAME

c. EMPLOYER'S NAME OR SCHOOL NAME	c. OTHER ACCIDENT? YES NO	c. INSURANCE PLAN NAME OR PROGRAM NAME

d. INSURANCE PLAN NAME OR PROGRAM NAME	10d. RESERVED FOR LOCAL USE	d. IS THERE ANOTHER HEALTH BENEFIT PLAN? YES NO If yes, return to and complete item 9 a-d.

READ BACK OF FORM BEFORE COMPLETING & SIGNING THIS FORM.

12. PATIENT'S OR AUTHORIZED PERSON'S SIGNATURE I authorize the release of any medical or other information necessary to process this claim. I also request payment of government benefits either to myself or to the party who accepts assignment below. SIGNED_____ DATE_____	13. INSURED'S OR AUTHORIZED PERSON'S SIGNATURE I authorize payment of medical benefits to the undersigned physician or supplier for services described below. SIGNED_____

14. DATE OF CURRENT: ILLNESS (First symptom) OR INJURY (Accident) OR PREGNANCY(LMP) MM DD YY	15. IF PATIENT HAS HAD SAME OR SIMILAR ILLNESS. GIVE FIRST DATE MM DD YY	16. DATES PATIENT UNABLE TO WORK IN CURRENT OCCUPATION MM DD YY MM DD YY FROM TO

17. NAME OF REFERRING PROVIDER OR OTHER SOURCE	17a. 17b. NPI	18. HOSPITALIZATION DATES RELATED TO CURRENT SERVICES MM DD YY MM DD YY FROM TO

19. RESERVED FOR LOCAL USE		20. OUTSIDE LAB? $ CHARGES YES NO

21. DIAGNOSIS OR NATURE OF ILLNESS OR INJURY (Relate Items 1, 2, 3 or 4 to Item 24E by Line) 1. ___.___ 3. ___.___ 2. ___.___ 4. ___.___	22. MEDICAID RESUBMISSION CODE ORIGINAL REF. NO. 23. PRIOR AUTHORIZATION NUMBER

24. A. DATE(S) OF SERVICE From MM DD YY To MM DD YY	B. PLACE OF SERVICE	C. EMG	D. PROCEDURES, SERVICES, OR SUPPLIES (Explain Unusual Circumstances) CPT/HCPCS MODIFIER	E. DIAGNOSIS POINTER	F. $ CHARGES	G. DAYS OR UNITS	H. EPSDT Family Plan	I. ID. QUAL.	J. RENDERING PROVIDER ID. #
1									NPI
2									NPI
3									NPI
4									NPI
5									NPI
6									NPI

25. FEDERAL TAX I.D. NUMBER SSN EIN	26. PATIENT'S ACCOUNT NO.	27. ACCEPT ASSIGNMENT? (For govt. claims, see back) YES NO	28. TOTAL CHARGE $	29. AMOUNT PAID $	30. BALANCE DUE $

31. SIGNATURE OF PHYSICIAN OR SUPPLIER INCLUDING DEGREES OR CREDENTIALS (I certify that the statements on the reverse apply to this bill and are made a part thereof.) SIGNED_____ DATE_____	32. SERVICE FACILITY LOCATION INFORMATION a. b.	33. BILLING PROVIDER INFO & PH # ( ) a. b.

NUCC Instruction Manual available at: www.nucc.org

OMB APPROVAL PENDING

PATIENT AND INSURED INFORMATION — *PHYSICIAN OR SUPPLIER INFORMATION*

Name:_____

Class/Section:_____

Date:_____

cpTeach
2012

EXERCISE 6.40

Warren Peace has just received treatment for his total hip replacement and is in the hospital recovering from the surgery done by a local orthopedists. He is now complaining of itching of his genitals. Your doctor, an internal medicine physician, comes to see him in the hospital and decides that the itching is no big deal, prescribing some anti-itch cream to be administered to Mr. Peace.

Notes: _____

_____

_____

_____

_____

_____

_____

_____

_____

_____

_____

_____

_____

_____

_____

_____

_____

_____

_____

_____

_____

_____

_____

DOC Form®
(Doctor's Office Checklist)

	HOSPITAL		OBSERVATION		ER
	Initial (3) Sub (2)		Discharge Date Different (3) Same (3)		New/Estab (3)
HISTORY					
Problem Focused		99231			99281
Exp/Prob Focused		99232			99282/83
Detail	99221	99233	99218	99234	99284
Comprehensive	99221/2/3		99218/19/20	99234/35/36	99285
EXAMINATION					
Problem Focused		99231			99281
Exp/Prob Focused		99232			99282/83
Detail	99221	99233	99218	99234	99284
Comprehensive	99221/2/3		99218/19/20	99234/35/36	99285
MEDICAL DECISION MAKING					
Straight Forward	99221	99231	99218	99234	99281
Low Complexity	99221	99231	99218	99234	99282
Mod Complexity	99222	99232	99219	99235	99283/84
High Complexity	99223	99233	99220	99236	99285
DISCHARGE			99217		
≤ 30 Minutes		99238			
> 30 Minutes		99239			
TIME					
15 Minutes		99231			
20 Minutes					
25 Minutes		99232			
30 Minutes	99221				
35 Minutes		99233			
45 Minutes					
50 Minutes	99222				
60 Minutes					
70 Minutes	99223				

Patient Name:_____

Date:_____Physician Signature:_____

MedBooks, Inc.
101 W. Buckingham Road, Richardson, Tx. 75081 (800) 443-7397
Warning: This product is copyrighted and is not to be duplicated in any manner without the express written permission of MedBooks.

EXERCISE 6.40

1500

HEALTH INSURANCE CLAIM FORM

APPROVED BY NATIONAL UNIFORM CLAIM COMMITTEE 08/05

Name:_____

Class/Section:_____

Date:_____

2012

| | PICA | | | | | | PICA | |

1. MEDICARE MEDICAID TRICARE CHAMPUS CHAMPVA GROUP HEALTH PLAN FECA BLK LUNG OTHER	1a. INSURED'S I.D. NUMBER (For Program in Item 1)
(Medicare #) (Medicaid #) (Sponsor's SSN) (Member ID#) (SSN or ID) (SSN) (ID)	

2. PATIENT'S NAME (Last Name, First Name, Middle Initial)	3. PATIENT'S BIRTH DATE MM DD YY SEX M □ F □	4. INSURED'S NAME (Last Name, First Name, Middle Initial)
5. PATIENT'S ADDRESS (No., Street)	6. PATIENT RELATIONSHIP TO INSURED Self □ Spouse □ Child □ Other □	7. INSURED'S ADDRESS (No., Street)
CITY STATE	8. PATIENT STATUS Single □ Married □ Other □	CITY STATE
ZIP CODE TELEPHONE (Include Area Code) ( )	Employed □ Full-Time Student □ Part-Time Student □	ZIP CODE TELEPHONE (Include Area Code) ( )

9. OTHER INSURED'S NAME (Last Name, First Name, Middle Initial)	10. IS PATIENT'S CONDITION RELATED TO:	11. INSURED'S POLICY GROUP OR FECA NUMBER
a. OTHER INSURED'S POLICY OR GROUP NUMBER	a. EMPLOYMENT? (Current or Previous) YES □ NO □	a. INSURED'S DATE OF BIRTH MM DD YY SEX M □ F □
b. OTHER INSURED'S DATE OF BIRTH MM DD YY SEX M □ F □	b. AUTO ACCIDENT? PLACE (State) YES □ NO □	b. EMPLOYER'S NAME OR SCHOOL NAME
c. EMPLOYER'S NAME OR SCHOOL NAME	c. OTHER ACCIDENT? YES □ NO □	c. INSURANCE PLAN NAME OR PROGRAM NAME
d. INSURANCE PLAN NAME OR PROGRAM NAME	10d. RESERVED FOR LOCAL USE	d. IS THERE ANOTHER HEALTH BENEFIT PLAN? YES □ NO □ If yes, return to and complete item 9 a-d.

READ BACK OF FORM BEFORE COMPLETING & SIGNING THIS FORM.

12. PATIENT'S OR AUTHORIZED PERSON'S SIGNATURE I authorize the release of any medical or other information necessary to process this claim. I also request payment of government benefits either to myself or to the party who accepts assignment below.

SIGNED_____   DATE_____

13. INSURED'S OR AUTHORIZED PERSON'S SIGNATURE I authorize payment of medical benefits to the undersigned physician or supplier for services described below.

SIGNED_____

14. DATE OF CURRENT: MM DD YY ◄ ILLNESS (First symptom) OR INJURY (Accident) OR PREGNANCY(LMP)	15. IF PATIENT HAS HAD SAME OR SIMILAR ILLNESS. GIVE FIRST DATE MM DD YY	16. DATES PATIENT UNABLE TO WORK IN CURRENT OCCUPATION MM DD YY FROM TO MM DD YY
17. NAME OF REFERRING PROVIDER OR OTHER SOURCE	17a. 17b. NPI	18. HOSPITALIZATION DATES RELATED TO CURRENT SERVICES MM DD YY FROM TO MM DD YY
19. RESERVED FOR LOCAL USE		20. OUTSIDE LAB? YES □ NO □ $ CHARGES
21. DIAGNOSIS OR NATURE OF ILLNESS OR INJURY (Relate Items 1, 2, 9 or 4 to Item 24E by Line) 1. ___.___ 2. ___.___ 3. ___.___ 4. ___.___		22. MEDICAID RESUBMISSION CODE ___ ORIGINAL REF. NO. ___ 23. PRIOR AUTHORIZATION NUMBER

24. A. DATE(S) OF SERVICE From To MM DD YY MM DD YY	B. PLACE OF SERVICE	C. EMG	D. PROCEDURES, SERVICES, OR SUPPLIES (Explain Unusual Circumstances) CPT/HCPCS MODIFIER	E. DIAGNOSIS POINTER	F. $ CHARGES	G. DAYS OR UNITS	H. EPSDT Family Plan	I. ID. QUAL.	J. RENDERING PROVIDER ID. #
1								NPI	
2								NPI	
3								NPI	
4								NPI	
5								NPI	
6								NPI	

25. FEDERAL TAX I.D. NUMBER SSN □ EIN □	26. PATIENT'S ACCOUNT NO.	27. ACCEPT ASSIGNMENT? (For govt. claims, see back) YES □ NO □	28. TOTAL CHARGE $	29. AMOUNT PAID $	30. BALANCE DUE $
31. SIGNATURE OF PHYSICIAN OR SUPPLIER INCLUDING DEGREES OR CREDENTIALS (I certify that the statements on the reverse apply to this bill and are made a part thereof.) SIGNED_____ DATE_____	32. SERVICE FACILITY LOCATION INFORMATION a. NPI b.	33. BILLING PROVIDER INFO & PH # ( ) a. NPI b.

PATIENT AND INSURED INFORMATION

PHYSICIAN OR SUPPLIER INFORMATION

NUCC Instruction Manual available at: www.nucc.org   OMB APPROVAL PENDING

Name:_____

Class/Section:_____

Date:_____

2012

EXERCISE 6.41

Lutrell Togurt is your interior designer and a personal acquaintance. Unfortunately, he has AIDS and is doing everything he can to stay in good health. He presents to your ophthalmology practice at the request of his internal medicine doctor, because he has had recent visual acuity changes which could be indicative of just about anything. You perform a complete single system exam, take a complete history, finding out about his family's history, past history and his social history (even though he is your friend, you have never seen him as a patient before), and come up with five or six possible diagnoses. You send him in for some lab work, perform some specialized tests in your office, and still have not arrived at a single definitive diagnosis. You will wait to see how the lab results come back.

Notes: _____

_____

_____

_____

_____

_____

_____

_____

_____

_____

_____

_____

_____

_____

_____

_____

_____

_____

_____

DOC Form®
(Doctor's Office Checklist)

	OFFICE/OUTPATIENT		CONSULTATION	
	New (3)	Established (2)	Office/O.P. (3)	Inpatient (3)
Minimal Service		99211		

HISTORY

Problem Focused	99201	99212	99241	99251
Exp/Prob Focused	99202	99213	99242	99252
Detail	99203	99214	99243	99253
Comprehensive	99204/05	99215	99244/45	99254/55

EXAMINATION

Problem Focused	99201	99212	99241	99251
Exp/Prob Focused	99202	99213	99242	99252
Detail	99203	99214	99243	99253
Comprehensive	99204/05	99215	99244/45	99254/55

MEDICAL DECISION MAKING

Straight Forward	99201/2	99212	99241/42	99251/52
Low Complexity	99203	99213	99243	99253
Mod Complexity	99204	99214	99244	99254
High Complexity	99205	99215	99245	99255

TIME: _____ Counsel/Coordination of Care: _____

10 Minutes	99201	99212		
15 Minutes		99213	99241	
20 Minutes	99202			99251
25 Minutes		99214		
30 Minutes	99203		99242	
40 Minutes		99215	99243	99252
45 Minutes	99204			
55 Minutes				99253
60 Minutes	99205		99244	
80 Minutes			99245	99254
110 Minutes				99255

MedBooks, Inc.
101 W. Buckingham Road, Richardson, Tx. 75081 (800) 443-7397
Warning: This product is copyrighted and is not to be duplicated in any manner without the express written permission of MedBooks.

EXERCISE 6.41

1500

HEALTH INSURANCE CLAIM FORM

APPROVED BY NATIONAL UNIFORM CLAIM COMMITTEE 08/05

| | PICA | | | | | | | | PICA | |

| 1. MEDICARE | MEDICAID | TRICARE CHAMPUS | CHAMPVA | GROUP HEALTH PLAN | FECA BLK LUNG | OTHER | 1a. INSURED'S I.D. NUMBER | (For Program in Item 1) |

(Medicare #)   (Medicaid #)   (Sponsor's SSN)   (Member ID#)   (SSN or ID)   (SSN)   (ID)

2. PATIENT'S NAME (Last Name, First Name, Middle Initial)

3. PATIENT'S BIRTH DATE MM DD YY   SEX   M   F

4. INSURED'S NAME (Last Name, First Name, Middle Initial)

5. PATIENT'S ADDRESS (No., Street)

6. PATIENT RELATIONSHIP TO INSURED   Self   Spouse   Child   Other

7. INSURED'S ADDRESS (No., Street)

CITY   STATE

8. PATIENT STATUS   Single   Married   Other

CITY   STATE

ZIP CODE   TELEPHONE (Include Area Code) ( )

Employed   Full-Time Student   Part-Time Student

ZIP CODE   TELEPHONE (Include Area Code) ( )

9. OTHER INSURED'S NAME (Last Name, First Name, Middle Initial)

10. IS PATIENT'S CONDITION RELATED TO:

11. INSURED'S POLICY GROUP OR FECA NUMBER

a. OTHER INSURED'S POLICY OR GROUP NUMBER

a. EMPLOYMENT? (Current or Previous)   YES   NO

a. INSURED'S DATE OF BIRTH MM DD YY   SEX   M   F

b. OTHER INSURED'S DATE OF BIRTH MM DD YY   SEX   M   F

b. AUTO ACCIDENT?   PLACE (State)   YES   NO

b. EMPLOYER'S NAME OR SCHOOL NAME

c. EMPLOYER'S NAME OR SCHOOL NAME

c. OTHER ACCIDENT?   YES   NO

c. INSURANCE PLAN NAME OR PROGRAM NAME

d. INSURANCE PLAN NAME OR PROGRAM NAME

10d. RESERVED FOR LOCAL USE

d. IS THERE ANOTHER HEALTH BENEFIT PLAN?   YES   NO   If yes, return to and complete item 9 a-d.

READ BACK OF FORM BEFORE COMPLETING & SIGNING THIS FORM.
12. PATIENT'S OR AUTHORIZED PERSON'S SIGNATURE I authorize the release of any medical or other information necessary to process this claim. I also request payment of government benefits either to myself or to the party who accepts assignment below.

SIGNED_____   DATE_____

13. INSURED'S OR AUTHORIZED PERSON'S SIGNATURE I authorize payment of medical benefits to the undersigned physician or supplier for services described below.

SIGNED_____

14. DATE OF CURRENT: MM DD YY   ILLNESS (First symptom) OR INJURY (Accident) OR PREGNANCY(LMP)

15. IF PATIENT HAS HAD SAME OR SIMILAR ILLNESS. GIVE FIRST DATE MM DD YY

16. DATES PATIENT UNABLE TO WORK IN CURRENT OCCUPATION MM DD YY   FROM   TO MM DD YY

17. NAME OF REFERRING PROVIDER OR OTHER SOURCE

17a.
17b. NPI

18. HOSPITALIZATION DATES RELATED TO CURRENT SERVICES MM DD YY   FROM   TO MM DD YY

19. RESERVED FOR LOCAL USE

20. OUTSIDE LAB?   YES   NO $ CHARGES

21. DIAGNOSIS OR NATURE OF ILLNESS OR INJURY (Relate Items 1, 2, 3 or 4 to Item 24E by Line)

1. _____ . _____   3. _____ . _____

2. _____ . _____   4. _____ . _____

22. MEDICAID RESUBMISSION CODE   ORIGINAL REF. NO.

23. PRIOR AUTHORIZATION NUMBER

24. A. DATE(S) OF SERVICE		B. PLACE OF SERVICE	C. EMG	D. PROCEDURES, SERVICES, OR SUPPLIES (Explain Unusual Circumstances)		E. DIAGNOSIS POINTER	F. $ CHARGES	G. DAYS OR UNITS	H. EPSDT Family Plan	I. ID. QUAL.	J. RENDERING PROVIDER ID. #
From MM DD YY	To MM DD YY			CPT/HCPCS	MODIFIER						
1										NPI	
2										NPI	
3										NPI	
4										NPI	
5										NPI	
6										NPI	

25. FEDERAL TAX I.D. NUMBER   SSN EIN

26. PATIENT'S ACCOUNT NO.

27. ACCEPT ASSIGNMENT? (For govt. claims, see back)   YES   NO

28. TOTAL CHARGE $

29. AMOUNT PAID $

30. BALANCE DUE $

31. SIGNATURE OF PHYSICIAN OR SUPPLIER INCLUDING DEGREES OR CREDENTIALS (I certify that the statements on the reverse apply to this bill and are made a part thereof.)

SIGNED_____   DATE_____

32. SERVICE FACILITY LOCATION INFORMATION

a.   b.

33. BILLING PROVIDER INFO & PH # ( )

a.   b.

NUCC Instruction Manual available at: www.nucc.org

OMB APPROVAL PENDING

EXERCISE 6.42

Ben Dover, a 21-year-old male, presents to the emergency room complaining of fever, diarrhea and abdominal cramps. He appears well hydrated, is not vomiting and is tolerating oral fluids well. You take his temperature (it measures 100.2 degrees) and perform some lab tests on his blood to get a CBC. You complete the patient's history as it pertains to his condition, and do a general multi-system examination. You are unable to find anything "wrong" with Ben and decide that he has a mild case of the flu and send him home.

Notes: _____

_____

_____

_____

_____

_____

_____

_____

_____

_____

_____

_____

_____

_____

_____

_____

_____

_____

_____

_____

DOC Form®
(Doctor's Office Checklist)

	HOSPITAL		**OBSERVATION**		**ER**
	Initial (3)　Sub (2)		Discharge Date		New/Estab (3)
			Different (3)　Same (3)		

HISTORY

	HOSPITAL Initial	HOSPITAL Sub	OBS Different	OBS Same	ER
Problem Focused		99231			99281
Exp/Prob Focused		99232			99282/83
Detail	99221	99233	99218	99234	99284
Comprehensive	99221/2/3		99218/19/20	99234/35/36	99285

EXAMINATION

	HOSPITAL Initial	HOSPITAL Sub	OBS Different	OBS Same	ER
Problem Focused		99231			99281
Exp/Prob Focused		99232			99282/83
Detail	99221	99233	99218	99234	99284
Comprehensive	99221/2/3		99218/19/20	99234/35/36	99285

MEDICAL DECISION MAKING

	HOSPITAL Initial	HOSPITAL Sub	OBS Different	OBS Same	ER
Straight Forward	99221	99231	99218	99234	99281
Low Complexity	99221	99231	99218	99234	99282
Mod Complexity	99222	99232	99219	99235	99283/84
High Complexity	99223	99233	99220	99236	99285

DISCHARGE　　　　　　　99217

	HOSPITAL Initial	HOSPITAL Sub	OBS Different	OBS Same	ER
≤ 30 Minutes		99238			
> 30 Minutes		99239			

TIME

	HOSPITAL Initial	HOSPITAL Sub	OBS Different	OBS Same	ER
15　Minutes		99231			
20　Minutes					
25　Minutes		99232			
30　Minutes	99221				
35　Minutes		99233			
45　Minutes					
50　Minutes	99222				
60　Minutes					
70　Minutes	99223				

Patient Name:_____

Date:_____Physician Signature:_____

MedBooks, Inc.
101 W. Buckingham Road, Richardson, Tx. 75081 (800) 443-7397
Warning: This product is copyrighted and is not to be duplicated in any manner without the express written permission of MedBooks.

EXERCISE 6.42

1500
HEALTH INSURANCE CLAIM FORM
APPROVED BY NATIONAL UNIFORM CLAIM COMMITTEE 08/05

| | | PICA | | | | | | | | | | PICA | |

1. MEDICARE	MEDICAID	TRICARE CHAMPUS	CHAMPVA	GROUP HEALTH PLAN	FECA BLK LUNG	OTHER	1a. INSURED'S I.D. NUMBER	(For Program in Item 1)
(Medicare #)	(Medicaid #)	(Sponsor's SSN)	(Member ID#)	(SSN or ID)	(SSN)	(ID)		

2. PATIENT'S NAME (Last Name, First Name, Middle Initial)

3. PATIENT'S BIRTH DATE MM DD YY   SEX M F

4. INSURED'S NAME (Last Name, First Name, Middle Initial)

5. PATIENT'S ADDRESS (No., Street)

6. PATIENT RELATIONSHIP TO INSURED   Self Spouse Child Other

7. INSURED'S ADDRESS (No., Street)

CITY   STATE

8. PATIENT STATUS   Single Married Other

CITY   STATE

ZIP CODE   TELEPHONE (Include Area Code) ( )

Employed Full-Time Student Part-Time Student

ZIP CODE   TELEPHONE (Include Area Code) ( )

9. OTHER INSURED'S NAME (Last Name, First Name, Middle Initial)

10. IS PATIENT'S CONDITION RELATED TO:

11. INSURED'S POLICY GROUP OR FECA NUMBER

a. OTHER INSURED'S POLICY OR GROUP NUMBER

a. EMPLOYMENT? (Current or Previous) YES NO

a. INSURED'S DATE OF BIRTH MM DD YY   SEX M F

b. OTHER INSURED'S DATE OF BIRTH MM DD YY   SEX M F

b. AUTO ACCIDENT?   PLACE (State) YES NO

b. EMPLOYER'S NAME OR SCHOOL NAME

c. EMPLOYER'S NAME OR SCHOOL NAME

c. OTHER ACCIDENT? YES NO

c. INSURANCE PLAN NAME OR PROGRAM NAME

d. INSURANCE PLAN NAME OR PROGRAM NAME

10d. RESERVED FOR LOCAL USE

d. IS THERE ANOTHER HEALTH BENEFIT PLAN? YES NO If yes, return to and complete item 9 a-d.

READ BACK OF FORM BEFORE COMPLETING & SIGNING THIS FORM.
12. PATIENT'S OR AUTHORIZED PERSON'S SIGNATURE I authorize the release of any medical or other information necessary to process this claim. I also request payment of government benefits either to myself or to the party who accepts assignment below.

SIGNED_____ DATE_____

13. INSURED'S OR AUTHORIZED PERSON'S SIGNATURE I authorize payment of medical benefits to the undersigned physician or supplier for services described below.

SIGNED_____

14. DATE OF CURRENT: MM DD YY ILLNESS (First symptom) OR INJURY (Accident) OR PREGNANCY(LMP)

15. IF PATIENT HAS HAD SAME OR SIMILAR ILLNESS. GIVE FIRST DATE MM DD YY

16. DATES PATIENT UNABLE TO WORK IN CURRENT OCCUPATION MM DD YY FROM   TO MM DD YY

17. NAME OF REFERRING PROVIDER OR OTHER SOURCE

17a.
17b. NPI

18. HOSPITALIZATION DATES RELATED TO CURRENT SERVICES MM DD YY FROM   TO MM DD YY

19. RESERVED FOR LOCAL USE

20. OUTSIDE LAB? YES NO $ CHARGES

21. DIAGNOSIS OR NATURE OF ILLNESS OR INJURY (Relate Items 1, 2, 3 or 4 to Item 24E by Line)

1. |___.___
2. |___.___
3. |___.___
4. |___.___

22. MEDICAID RESUBMISSION CODE   ORIGINAL REF. NO.

23. PRIOR AUTHORIZATION NUMBER

24. A. DATE(S) OF SERVICE From MM DD YY To MM DD YY	B. PLACE OF SERVICE	C. EMG	D. PROCEDURES, SERVICES, OR SUPPLIES (Explain Unusual Circumstances) CPT/HCPCS MODIFIER	E. DIAGNOSIS POINTER	F. $ CHARGES	G. DAYS OR UNITS	H. EPSDT Family Plan	I. ID. QUAL.	J. RENDERING PROVIDER ID. #
1									NPI
2									NPI
3									NPI
4									NPI
5									NPI
6									NPI

25. FEDERAL TAX I.D. NUMBER SSN EIN

26. PATIENT'S ACCOUNT NO.

27. ACCEPT ASSIGNMENT? (For govt. claims, see back) YES NO

28. TOTAL CHARGE $

29. AMOUNT PAID $

30. BALANCE DUE $

31. SIGNATURE OF PHYSICIAN OR SUPPLIER INCLUDING DEGREES OR CREDENTIALS (I certify that the statements on the reverse apply to this bill and are made a part thereof.)

SIGNED_____ DATE_____

32. SERVICE FACILITY LOCATION INFORMATION

a. NPI   b.

33. BILLING PROVIDER INFO & PH # ( )

a. NPI   b.

Name:_____

Class/Section:_____

Date:_____

EXERCISE 6.43

Diane Taceeya presents to the emergency room for removal of sutures that were placed 12 days ago. You are on-call and as such, review the lesion, decide that it has healed properly and remove the stitches.

Notes:_____

_____

_____

_____

_____

_____

_____

_____

_____

_____

_____

_____

_____

_____

_____

_____

_____

_____

_____

_____

_____

_____

_____

_____

_____

_____

_____

_____

_____

DOC Form®
(Doctor's Office Checklist)

	HOSPITAL		OBSERVATION		ER
	Initial (3)	Sub (2)	Discharge Date		New/Estab (3)
			Different (3)	Same (3)	

HISTORY

	HOSPITAL Initial	HOSPITAL Sub	OBSERVATION Different	OBSERVATION Same	ER
Problem Focused		99231			99281
Exp/Prob Focused		99232			99282/83
Detail	99221	99233	99218	99234	99284
Comprehensive	99221/2/3		99218/19/20	99234/35/36	99285

EXAMINATION

	HOSPITAL Initial	HOSPITAL Sub	OBSERVATION Different	OBSERVATION Same	ER
Problem Focused		99231			99281
Exp/Prob Focused		99232			99282/83
Detail	99221	99233	99218	99234	99284
Comprehensive	99221/2/3		99218/19/20	99234/35/36	99285

MEDICAL DECISION MAKING

	HOSPITAL Initial	HOSPITAL Sub	OBSERVATION Different	OBSERVATION Same	ER
Straight Forward	99221	99231	99218	99234	99281
Low Complexity	99221	99231	99218	99234	99282
Mod Complexity	99222	99232	99219	99235	99283/84
High Complexity	99223	99233	99220	99236	99285

DISCHARGE 99217

	HOSPITAL Sub	
≤ 30 Minutes	99238	
> 30 Minutes	99239	

TIME

	HOSPITAL Initial	HOSPITAL Sub	
15 Minutes		99231	
20 Minutes			
25 Minutes		99232	
30 Minutes	99221		
35 Minutes		99233	
45 Minutes			
50 Minutes	99222		
60 Minutes			
70 Minutes	99223		

Patient Name:_____

Date:_____Physician Signature:_____

MedBooks, Inc.
101 W. Buckingham Road, Richardson, Tx. 75081 (800) 443-7397
Warning: This product is copyrighted and is not to be duplicated in any manner without the express written permission of MedBooks.

EXERCISE 6.43

Name:_____

Class/Section:_____

Date:_____

cpTeach
2012

```
1500
```

HEALTH INSURANCE CLAIM FORM

APPROVED BY NATIONAL UNIFORM CLAIM COMMITTEE 08/05

| | PICA | | | | | | | | PICA | |

1. MEDICARE	MEDICAID	TRICARE CHAMPUS	CHAMPVA	GROUP HEALTH PLAN	FECA BLK LUNG	OTHER	1a. INSURED'S I.D. NUMBER	(For Program in Item 1)
(Medicare #)	(Medicaid #)	(Sponsor's SSN)	(Member ID#)	(SSN or ID)	(SSN)	(ID)		

2. PATIENT'S NAME (Last Name, First Name, Middle Initial)

3. PATIENT'S BIRTH DATE MM DD YY   SEX M F

4. INSURED'S NAME (Last Name, First Name, Middle Initial)

5. PATIENT'S ADDRESS (No., Street)

6. PATIENT RELATIONSHIP TO INSURED   Self Spouse Child Other

7. INSURED'S ADDRESS (No., Street)

CITY   STATE

8. PATIENT STATUS   Single Married Other

CITY   STATE

ZIP CODE   TELEPHONE (Include Area Code) ( )

Employed Full-Time Student Part-Time Student

ZIP CODE   TELEPHONE (Include Area Code) ( )

9. OTHER INSURED'S NAME (Last Name, First Name, Middle Initial)

10. IS PATIENT'S CONDITION RELATED TO:

11. INSURED'S POLICY GROUP OR FECA NUMBER

a. OTHER INSURED'S POLICY OR GROUP NUMBER

a. EMPLOYMENT? (Current or Previous) YES NO

a. INSURED'S DATE OF BIRTH MM DD YY   SEX M F

b. OTHER INSURED'S DATE OF BIRTH MM DD YY   SEX M F

b. AUTO ACCIDENT? YES NO PLACE (State)

b. EMPLOYER'S NAME OR SCHOOL NAME

c. EMPLOYER'S NAME OR SCHOOL NAME

c. OTHER ACCIDENT? YES NO

c. INSURANCE PLAN NAME OR PROGRAM NAME

d. INSURANCE PLAN NAME OR PROGRAM NAME

10d. RESERVED FOR LOCAL USE

d. IS THERE ANOTHER HEALTH BENEFIT PLAN? YES NO If yes, return to and complete item 9 a-d.

READ BACK OF FORM BEFORE COMPLETING & SIGNING THIS FORM.

12. PATIENT'S OR AUTHORIZED PERSON'S SIGNATURE I authorize the release of any medical or other information necessary to process this claim. I also request payment of government benefits either to myself or to the party who accepts assignment below.

SIGNED_____   DATE_____

13. INSURED'S OR AUTHORIZED PERSON'S SIGNATURE I authorize payment of medical benefits to the undersigned physician or supplier for services described below.

SIGNED_____

14. DATE OF CURRENT: MM DD YY   ILLNESS (First symptom) OR INJURY (Accident) OR PREGNANCY(LMP)

15. IF PATIENT HAS HAD SAME OR SIMILAR ILLNESS. GIVE FIRST DATE MM DD YY

16. DATES PATIENT UNABLE TO WORK IN CURRENT OCCUPATION MM DD YY   FROM   TO

17. NAME OF REFERRING PROVIDER OR OTHER SOURCE

17a.

17b. NPI

18. HOSPITALIZATION DATES RELATED TO CURRENT SERVICES MM DD YY   FROM   TO

19. RESERVED FOR LOCAL USE

20. OUTSIDE LAB? YES NO $ CHARGES

21. DIAGNOSIS OR NATURE OF ILLNESS OR INJURY (Relate Items 1, 2, 3 or 4 to Item 24E by Line)

1. |___.___   3. |___.___

2. |___.___   4. |___.___

22. MEDICAID RESUBMISSION CODE   ORIGINAL REF. NO.

23. PRIOR AUTHORIZATION NUMBER

24. A. DATE(S) OF SERVICE						B. PLACE OF SERVICE	C. EMG	D. PROCEDURES, SERVICES, OR SUPPLIES (Explain Unusual Circumstances)		E. DIAGNOSIS POINTER	F. $ CHARGES	G. DAYS OR UNITS	H. EPSDT Family Plan	I. ID. QUAL.	J. RENDERING PROVIDER ID. #
From			To					CPT/HCPCS	MODIFIER						
MM	DD	YY	MM	DD	YY										
1														NPI	
2														NPI	
3														NPI	
4														NPI	
5														NPI	
6														NPI	

25. FEDERAL TAX I.D. NUMBER   SSN EIN

26. PATIENT'S ACCOUNT NO.

27. ACCEPT ASSIGNMENT? (For govt. claims, see back) YES NO

28. TOTAL CHARGE $

29. AMOUNT PAID $

30. BALANCE DUE $

31. SIGNATURE OF PHYSICIAN OR SUPPLIER INCLUDING DEGREES OR CREDENTIALS (I certify that the statements on the reverse apply to this bill and are made a part thereof.)

SIGNED_____   DATE_____

32. SERVICE FACILITY LOCATION INFORMATION

a.   b.

33. BILLING PROVIDER INFO & PH # ( )

a.   b.

NUCC Instruction Manual available at: www.nucc.org

OMB APPROVAL PENDING

EXERCISE 6.44

Stan Byerman is a 72-year-old male who has multiple medical problems including, but not limited to, hypertension, diabetes, heart condition with a history of a triple bypass a few years ago, and arthritis. At this visit, you listen to his heart and lungs and order an EKG. You discover that the results of his EKG do not look good. Since he has come to your office with his daughter, you request that you get an opportunity to speak with her about your patient's condition. The patient waits in the waiting room and you talk to the daughter reviewing the patient's complex, detailed medical records that have been transferred from previous physicians. You then complete a comprehensive treatment plan which requires that you to personally initiate and coordinate the care with a local home health agency and dietician. The entire service takes about 60 minutes.

Notes: _____

_____

_____

_____

_____

_____

_____

_____

_____

_____

_____

_____

_____

_____

_____

_____

DOC Form®
(Doctor's Office Checklist)

	OFFICE/OUTPATIENT		CONSULTATION	
	New (3)	Established (2)	Office/O.P. (3)	Inpatient (3)
Minimal Service		99211		

HISTORY

Problem Focused	99201	99212	99241	99251
Exp/Prob Focused	99202	99213	99242	99252
Detail	99203	99214	99243	99253
Comprehensive	99204/05	99215	99244/45	99254/55

EXAMINATION

Problem Focused	99201	99212	99241	99251
Exp/Prob Focused	99202	99213	99242	99252
Detail	99203	99214	99243	99253
Comprehensive	99204/05	99215	99244/45	99254/55

MEDICAL DECISION MAKING

Straight Forward	99201/2	99212	99241/42	99251/52
Low Complexity	99203	99213	99243	99253
Mod Complexity	99204	99214	99244	99254
High Complexity	99205	99215	99245	99255

TIME:_____   Counsel/Coordination of Care:_____

10 Minutes	99201	99212		
15 Minutes		99213	99241	
20 Minutes	99202			99251
25 Minutes		99214		
30 Minutes	99203		99242	
40 Minutes		99215	99243	99252
45 Minutes	99204			
55 Minutes				99253
60 Minutes	99205		99244	
80 Minutes			99245	99254
110 Minutes				99255

MedBooks, Inc.
101 W. Buckingham Road, Richardson, Tx. 75081 (800) 443-7397
Warning: This product is copyrighted and is not to be duplicated in any manner without the express written permission of MedBooks.

EXERCISE 6.44

1500
HEALTH INSURANCE CLAIM FORM
APPROVED BY NATIONAL UNIFORM CLAIM COMMITTEE 08/05

[ ] [ ] PICA   PICA [ ] [ ]

1. MEDICARE	MEDICAID	TRICARE CHAMPUS	CHAMPVA	GROUP HEALTH PLAN	FECA BLK LUNG	OTHER	1a. INSURED'S I.D. NUMBER	(For Program in Item 1)
(Medicare #)	(Medicaid #)	(Sponsor's SSN)	(Member ID#)	(SSN or ID)	(SSN)	(ID)		

2. PATIENT'S NAME (Last Name, First Name, Middle Initial)

3. PATIENT'S BIRTH DATE MM | DD | YY   SEX M [ ] F [ ]

4. INSURED'S NAME (Last Name, First Name, Middle Initial)

5. PATIENT'S ADDRESS (No., Street)

6. PATIENT RELATIONSHIP TO INSURED   Self [ ] Spouse [ ] Child [ ] Other [ ]

7. INSURED'S ADDRESS (No., Street)

CITY   STATE

8. PATIENT STATUS   Single [ ]   Married [ ]   Other [ ]

CITY   STATE

ZIP CODE   TELEPHONE (Include Area Code) (   )

Employed [ ]   Full-Time Student [ ]   Part-Time Student [ ]

ZIP CODE   TELEPHONE (Include Area Code) (   )

9. OTHER INSURED'S NAME (Last Name, First Name, Middle Initial)

10. IS PATIENT'S CONDITION RELATED TO:

11. INSURED'S POLICY GROUP OR FECA NUMBER

a. OTHER INSURED'S POLICY OR GROUP NUMBER

a. EMPLOYMENT? (Current or Previous)   YES [ ]   NO [ ]

a. INSURED'S DATE OF BIRTH MM | DD | YY   SEX M [ ] F [ ]

b. OTHER INSURED'S DATE OF BIRTH MM | DD | YY   SEX M [ ] F [ ]

b. AUTO ACCIDENT?   YES [ ]   NO [ ]   PLACE (State)

b. EMPLOYER'S NAME OR SCHOOL NAME

c. EMPLOYER'S NAME OR SCHOOL NAME

c. OTHER ACCIDENT?   YES [ ]   NO [ ]

c. INSURANCE PLAN NAME OR PROGRAM NAME

d. INSURANCE PLAN NAME OR PROGRAM NAME

10d. RESERVED FOR LOCAL USE

d. IS THERE ANOTHER HEALTH BENEFIT PLAN?   YES [ ]   NO [ ]   If yes, return to and complete item 9 a-d.

READ BACK OF FORM BEFORE COMPLETING & SIGNING THIS FORM.
12. PATIENT'S OR AUTHORIZED PERSON'S SIGNATURE I authorize the release of any medical or other information necessary to process this claim. I also request payment of government benefits either to myself or to the party who accepts assignment below.

SIGNED_____ DATE_____

13. INSURED'S OR AUTHORIZED PERSON'S SIGNATURE I authorize payment of medical benefits to the undersigned physician or supplier for services described below.

SIGNED_____

14. DATE OF CURRENT: MM | DD | YY   ILLNESS (First symptom) OR INJURY (Accident) OR PREGNANCY(LMP)

15. IF PATIENT HAS HAD SAME OR SIMILAR ILLNESS. GIVE FIRST DATE MM | DD | YY

16. DATES PATIENT UNABLE TO WORK IN CURRENT OCCUPATION MM | DD | YY FROM   TO MM | DD | YY

17. NAME OF REFERRING PROVIDER OR OTHER SOURCE

17a.
17b. NPI

18. HOSPITALIZATION DATES RELATED TO CURRENT SERVICES MM | DD | YY FROM   TO MM | DD | YY

19. RESERVED FOR LOCAL USE

20. OUTSIDE LAB?   YES [ ]   NO [ ] $ CHARGES

21. DIAGNOSIS OR NATURE OF ILLNESS OR INJURY (Relate Items 1, 2, 3 or 4 to Item 24E by Line)

1. |___.___| 3. |___.___|
2. |___.___| 4. |___.___|

22. MEDICAID RESUBMISSION CODE   ORIGINAL REF. NO.

23. PRIOR AUTHORIZATION NUMBER

24. A. DATE(S) OF SERVICE		B. PLACE OF SERVICE	C. EMG	D. PROCEDURES, SERVICES, OR SUPPLIES (Explain Unusual Circumstances) CPT/HCPCS	MODIFIER	E. DIAGNOSIS POINTER	F. $ CHARGES	G. DAYS OR UNITS	H. EPSDT Family Plan	I. ID. QUAL.	J. RENDERING PROVIDER ID. #
From MM DD YY	To MM DD YY										
1											NPI
2											NPI
3											NPI
4											NPI
5											NPI
6											NPI

25. FEDERAL TAX I.D. NUMBER   SSN [ ] EIN [ ]

26. PATIENT'S ACCOUNT NO.

27. ACCEPT ASSIGNMENT? (For govt. claims, see back)   YES [ ]   NO [ ]

28. TOTAL CHARGE $

29. AMOUNT PAID $

30. BALANCE DUE $

31. SIGNATURE OF PHYSICIAN OR SUPPLIER INCLUDING DEGREES OR CREDENTIALS (I certify that the statements on the reverse apply to this bill and are made a part thereof.)

SIGNED_____ DATE_____

32. SERVICE FACILITY LOCATION INFORMATION

a. NPI   b.

33. BILLING PROVIDER INFO & PH # (   )

a. NPI   b.

NUCC Instruction Manual available at: www.nucc.org

OMB APPROVAL PENDING

EXERCISE 6.45

Irene Negotiate is 14 years old. She is a new patient to your office who presents with persistent back pain, and her mother explains that her shoulders don't seem to be straight. During the history, you find out that there is a history of scoliosis on her father's side and that this patient is one of the school's athletes. She has not had any prior surgeries or other medical conditions and has led a fairly normal life. Upon examination, you perform a complete head-to-toe exam, checking her gait, her reflexes, her back, neck, shoulders, arms and legs. You order an x-ray. It confirms your suspicions that she does have scoliosis, albeit mild. You explain to the mother that Ms. Negotiate should be monitored and what the potential treatments are.

Notes: _____

_____

_____

_____

_____

_____

_____

_____

_____

_____

_____

_____

_____

_____

_____

_____

_____

_____

_____

DOC Form®
(Doctor's Office Checklist)

OFFICE/OUTPATIENT   **CONSULTATION**

	New (3)	Established (2)	Office/O.P. (3)	Inpatient (3)
Minimal Service		99211		

HISTORY

Problem Focused	99201	99212	99241	99251
Exp/Prob Focused	99202	99213	99242	99252
Detail	99203	99214	99243	99253
Comprehensive	99204/05	99215	99244/45	99254/55

EXAMINATION

Problem Focused	99201	99212	99241	99251
Exp/Prob Focused	99202	99213	99242	99252
Detail	99203	99214	99243	99253
Comprehensive	99204/05	99215	99244/45	99254/55

MEDICAL DECISION MAKING

Straight Forward	99201/2	99212	99241/42	99251/52
Low Complexity	99203	99213	99243	99253
Mod Complexity	99204	99214	99244	99254
High Complexity	99205	99215	99245	99255

TIME:_____ **Counsel/Coordination of Care:**_____

10 Minutes	99201	99212		
15 Minutes		99213	99241	
20 Minutes	99202			99251
25 Minutes		99214		
30 Minutes	99203		99242	
40 Minutes		99215	99243	99252
45 Minutes	99204			
55 Minutes				99253
60 Minutes	99205		99244	
80 Minutes			99245	99254
110 Minutes				99255

MedBooks, Inc.
101 W. Buckingham Road, Richardson, Tx. 75081 (800) 443-7397
Warning: This product is copyrighted and is not to be duplicated in any manner without the express written permission of MedBooks.

EXERCISE 6.45

1500

HEALTH INSURANCE CLAIM FORM

APPROVED BY NATIONAL UNIFORM CLAIM COMMITTEE 08/05

| | PICA | | | | | | | | PICA | |

| 1. MEDICARE | MEDICAID | TRICARE CHAMPUS | CHAMPVA | GROUP HEALTH PLAN | FECA BLK LUNG | OTHER | 1a. INSURED'S I.D. NUMBER | (For Program in Item 1) |
| (Medicare #) | (Medicaid #) | (Sponsor's SSN) | (Member ID#) | (SSN or ID) | (SSN) | (ID) | | |

2. PATIENT'S NAME (Last Name, First Name, Middle Initial)

3. PATIENT'S BIRTH DATE MM DD YY   SEX M □ F □

4. INSURED'S NAME (Last Name, First Name, Middle Initial)

5. PATIENT'S ADDRESS (No., Street)

6. PATIENT RELATIONSHIP TO INSURED   Self □ Spouse □ Child □ Other □

7. INSURED'S ADDRESS (No., Street)

CITY   STATE

8. PATIENT STATUS   Single □ Married □ Other □

CITY   STATE

ZIP CODE   TELEPHONE (Include Area Code) (   )

Employed □ Full-Time Student □ Part-Time Student □

ZIP CODE   TELEPHONE (Include Area Code) (   )

9. OTHER INSURED'S NAME (Last Name, First Name, Middle Initial)

10. IS PATIENT'S CONDITION RELATED TO:

11. INSURED'S POLICY GROUP OR FECA NUMBER

a. OTHER INSURED'S POLICY OR GROUP NUMBER

a. EMPLOYMENT? (Current or Previous)   YES □ NO □

a. INSURED'S DATE OF BIRTH MM DD YY   SEX M □ F □

b. OTHER INSURED'S DATE OF BIRTH MM DD YY   SEX M □ F □

b. AUTO ACCIDENT?   YES □ NO □   PLACE (State)

b. EMPLOYER'S NAME OR SCHOOL NAME

c. EMPLOYER'S NAME OR SCHOOL NAME

c. OTHER ACCIDENT?   YES □ NO □

c. INSURANCE PLAN NAME OR PROGRAM NAME

d. INSURANCE PLAN NAME OR PROGRAM NAME

10d. RESERVED FOR LOCAL USE

d. IS THERE ANOTHER HEALTH BENEFIT PLAN?   YES □ NO □   If yes, return to and complete item 9 a-d.

READ BACK OF FORM BEFORE COMPLETING & SIGNING THIS FORM.

12. PATIENT'S OR AUTHORIZED PERSON'S SIGNATURE I authorize the release of any medical or other information necessary to process this claim. I also request payment of government benefits either to myself or to the party who accepts assignment below.

SIGNED _____ DATE _____

13. INSURED'S OR AUTHORIZED PERSON'S SIGNATURE I authorize payment of medical benefits to the undersigned physician or supplier for services described below.

SIGNED _____

14. DATE OF CURRENT: MM DD YY   ILLNESS (First symptom) OR INJURY (Accident) OR PREGNANCY(LMP)

15. IF PATIENT HAS HAD SAME OR SIMILAR ILLNESS. GIVE FIRST DATE MM DD YY

16. DATES PATIENT UNABLE TO WORK IN CURRENT OCCUPATION FROM MM DD YY TO MM DD YY

17. NAME OF REFERRING PROVIDER OR OTHER SOURCE

17a.

17b. NPI

18. HOSPITALIZATION DATES RELATED TO CURRENT SERVICES FROM MM DD YY TO MM DD YY

19. RESERVED FOR LOCAL USE

20. OUTSIDE LAB?   YES □ NO □ $ CHARGES

21. DIAGNOSIS OR NATURE OF ILLNESS OR INJURY (Relate Items 1, 2, 3 or 4 to Item 24E by Line)

1. |___.___| 3. |___.___|

2. |___.___| 4. |___.___|

22. MEDICAID RESUBMISSION CODE   ORIGINAL REF. NO.

23. PRIOR AUTHORIZATION NUMBER

24. A. DATE(S) OF SERVICE From MM DD YY To MM DD YY	B. PLACE OF SERVICE	C. EMG	D. PROCEDURES, SERVICES, OR SUPPLIES (Explain Unusual Circumstances) CPT/HCPCS	MODIFIER	E. DIAGNOSIS POINTER	F. $ CHARGES	G. DAYS OR UNITS	H. EPSDT Family Plan	I. ID. QUAL.	J. RENDERING PROVIDER ID. #
1										NPI
2										NPI
3										NPI
4										NPI
5										NPI
6										NPI

25. FEDERAL TAX I.D. NUMBER   SSN □ EIN □

26. PATIENT'S ACCOUNT NO.

27. ACCEPT ASSIGNMENT? (For govt. claims, see back)   YES □ NO □

28. TOTAL CHARGE $

29. AMOUNT PAID $

30. BALANCE DUE $

31. SIGNATURE OF PHYSICIAN OR SUPPLIER INCLUDING DEGREES OR CREDENTIALS (I certify that the statements on the reverse apply to this bill and are made a part thereof.)

SIGNED _____ DATE _____

32. SERVICE FACILITY LOCATION INFORMATION

a.   b.

33. BILLING PROVIDER INFO & PH # (   )

a.   b.

NUCC Instruction Manual available at: www.nucc.org

OMB APPROVAL PENDING

PATIENT AND INSURED INFORMATION

PHYSICIAN OR SUPPLIER INFORMATION

EXERCISE 6.46

Re-code this example pretending that the patient is established. Is the level of service you chose for the established patient visit higher or lower than the one you chose when the patient was a new patient? Why?

Notes: _____

_____

_____				

DOC Form®
(Doctor's Office Checklist)

OFFICE/OUTPATIENT   CONSULTATION

	New (3)	Established (2)	Office/O.P. (3)	Inpatient (3)
Minimal Service		99211		

HISTORY

	New (3)	Established (2)	Office/O.P. (3)	Inpatient (3)
Problem Focused	99201	99212	99241	99251
Exp/Prob Focused	99202	99213	99242	99252
Detail	99203	99214	99243	99253
Comprehensive	99204/05	99215	99244/45	99254/55

EXAMINATION

	New (3)	Established (2)	Office/O.P. (3)	Inpatient (3)
Problem Focused	99201	99212	99241	99251
Exp/Prob Focused	99202	99213	99242	99252
Detail	99203	99214	99243	99253
Comprehensive	99204/05	99215	99244/45	99254/55

MEDICAL DECISION MAKING

	New (3)	Established (2)	Office/O.P. (3)	Inpatient (3)
Straight Forward	99201/2	99212	99241/42	99251/52
Low Complexity	99203	99213	99243	99253
Mod Complexity	99204	99214	99244	99254
High Complexity	99205	99215	99245	99255

TIME:_____   Counsel/Coordination of Care:_____

	New (3)	Established (2)	Office/O.P. (3)	Inpatient (3)
10 Minutes	99201	99212		
15 Minutes		99213	99241	
20 Minutes	99202			99251
25 Minutes		99214		
30 Minutes	99203		99242	
40 Minutes		99215	99243	99252
45 Minutes	99204			
55 Minutes				99253
60 Minutes	99205		99244	
80 Minutes			99245	99254
110 Minutes				99255

MedBooks, Inc.
101 W. Buckingham Road, Richardson, Tx. 75081 (800) 443-7397
Warning: This product is copyrighted and is not to be duplicated in any manner without the express written permission of MedBooks.

EXERCISE 6.46

1500
HEALTH INSURANCE CLAIM FORM

APPROVED BY NATIONAL UNIFORM CLAIM COMMITTEE 08/05

| | | PICA | | | | | | | PICA | | |

1. MEDICARE MEDICAID TRICARE CHAMPVA GROUP FECA OTHER	1a. INSURED'S I.D. NUMBER (For Program in Item 1)
(Medicare #) (Medicaid #) CHAMPUS (Sponsor's SSN) (Member ID#) HEALTH PLAN (SSN or ID) BLK LUNG (SSN) (ID)	

2. PATIENT'S NAME (Last Name, First Name, Middle Initial)

3. PATIENT'S BIRTH DATE MM DD YY   SEX M F

4. INSURED'S NAME (Last Name, First Name, Middle Initial)

5. PATIENT'S ADDRESS (No., Street)

6. PATIENT RELATIONSHIP TO INSURED   Self Spouse Child Other

7. INSURED'S ADDRESS (No., Street)

CITY   STATE

8. PATIENT STATUS   Single Married Other

CITY   STATE

ZIP CODE   TELEPHONE (Include Area Code) (   )

Employed Full-Time Student Part-Time Student

ZIP CODE   TELEPHONE (Include Area Code) (   )

9. OTHER INSURED'S NAME (Last Name, First Name, Middle Initial)

10. IS PATIENT'S CONDITION RELATED TO:

11. INSURED'S POLICY GROUP OR FECA NUMBER

a. OTHER INSURED'S POLICY OR GROUP NUMBER

a. EMPLOYMENT? (Current or Previous) YES NO

a. INSURED'S DATE OF BIRTH MM DD YY   SEX M F

b. OTHER INSURED'S DATE OF BIRTH MM DD YY   SEX M F

b. AUTO ACCIDENT? YES NO   PLACE (State)

b. EMPLOYER'S NAME OR SCHOOL NAME

c. EMPLOYER'S NAME OR SCHOOL NAME

c. OTHER ACCIDENT? YES NO

c. INSURANCE PLAN NAME OR PROGRAM NAME

d. INSURANCE PLAN NAME OR PROGRAM NAME

10d. RESERVED FOR LOCAL USE

d. IS THERE ANOTHER HEALTH BENEFIT PLAN? YES NO If yes, return to and complete item 9 a-d.

READ BACK OF FORM BEFORE COMPLETING & SIGNING THIS FORM.
12. PATIENT'S OR AUTHORIZED PERSON'S SIGNATURE I authorize the release of any medical or other information necessary to process this claim. I also request payment of government benefits either to myself or to the party who accepts assignment below.

SIGNED_____ DATE_____

13. INSURED'S OR AUTHORIZED PERSON'S SIGNATURE I authorize payment of medical benefits to the undersigned physician or supplier for services described below.

SIGNED_____

14. DATE OF CURRENT: MM DD YY ILLNESS (First symptom) OR INJURY (Accident) OR PREGNANCY(LMP)

15. IF PATIENT HAS HAD SAME OR SIMILAR ILLNESS. GIVE FIRST DATE MM DD YY

16. DATES PATIENT UNABLE TO WORK IN CURRENT OCCUPATION MM DD YY FROM   TO MM DD YY

17. NAME OF REFERRING PROVIDER OR OTHER SOURCE

17a.
17b. NPI

18. HOSPITALIZATION DATES RELATED TO CURRENT SERVICES MM DD YY FROM   TO MM DD YY

19. RESERVED FOR LOCAL USE

20. OUTSIDE LAB? YES NO $ CHARGES

21. DIAGNOSIS OR NATURE OF ILLNESS OR INJURY (Relate Items 1, 2, 3 or 4 to Item 24E by Line)
1. |___.___   3. |___.___
2. |___.___   4. |___.___

22. MEDICAID RESUBMISSION CODE   ORIGINAL REF. NO.

23. PRIOR AUTHORIZATION NUMBER

24. A. DATE(S) OF SERVICE		B. PLACE OF SERVICE	C. EMG	D. PROCEDURES, SERVICES, OR SUPPLIES (Explain Unusual Circumstances)		E. DIAGNOSIS POINTER	F. $ CHARGES	G. DAYS OR UNITS	H. EPSDT Family Plan	I. ID. QUAL.	J. RENDERING PROVIDER ID. #
From MM DD YY	To MM DD YY			CPT/HCPCS	MODIFIER						
1											NPI
2											NPI
3											NPI
4											NPI
5											NPI
6											NPI

25. FEDERAL TAX I.D. NUMBER   SSN EIN

26. PATIENT'S ACCOUNT NO.

27. ACCEPT ASSIGNMENT? (For govt. claims, see back) YES NO

28. TOTAL CHARGE $

29. AMOUNT PAID $

30. BALANCE DUE $

31. SIGNATURE OF PHYSICIAN OR SUPPLIER INCLUDING DEGREES OR CREDENTIALS (I certify that the statements on the reverse apply to this bill and are made a part thereof.)

SIGNED_____ DATE_____

32. SERVICE FACILITY LOCATION INFORMATION

33. BILLING PROVIDER INFO & PH # (   )

a.   b.

a. NPI   b.

EXERCISE 6.47

El Johnway, a 19-year-old football player, presents to your office complaining of pain in his knee. He is a new patient. You ask him the usual questions about when the pain started, how it might have been precipitated and exactly where it hurts. He explains to you that during the game on Friday night, he was injured but really didn't think too much about it until today (Monday). When he woke up, the pain was still there and the swelling had increased. Since the injury was 3 days ago, and since it appears to be getting worse instead of better, you order some x-rays of both knees, both AP and lateral views, to check for any fractures. You examine both knees (comparing one to the other) and test rotation, flexion and extension. Since the knee is so swollen, you don't test the reflexes. Once you receive the films, you decide that there is no fracture but that there could be some torn ligaments. You explain this to your patient and give him the information about surgical treatments.

Notes: _____

_____

_____

_____

_____

_____

_____

_____

_____

_____

_____

_____

_____

DOC Form®
(Doctor's Office Checklist)

OFFICE/OUTPATIENT   **CONSULTATION**

	New (3)	Established (2)	Office/O.P. (3)	Inpatient (3)
Minimal Service		99211		

HISTORY

Problem Focused	99201	99212	99241	99251
Exp/Prob Focused	99202	99213	99242	99252
Detail	99203	99214	99243	99253
Comprehensive	99204/05	99215	99244/45	99254/55

EXAMINATION

Problem Focused	99201	99212	99241	99251
Exp/Prob Focused	99202	99213	99242	99252
Detail	99203	99214	99243	99253
Comprehensive	99204/05	99215	99244/45	99254/55

MEDICAL DECISION MAKING

Straight Forward	99201/2	99212	99241/42	99251/52
Low Complexity	99203	99213	99243	99253
Mod Complexity	99204	99214	99244	99254
High Complexity	99205	99215	99245	99255

TIME:_____   **Counsel/Coordination of Care:_____**

10 Minutes	99201	99212		
15 Minutes		99213	99241	
20 Minutes	99202			99251
25 Minutes		99214		
30 Minutes	99203		99242	
40 Minutes		99215	99243	99252
45 Minutes	99204			
55 Minutes				99253
60 Minutes	99205		99244	
80 Minutes			99245	99254
110 Minutes				99255

EXERCISE 6.47

Name:_____

Class/Section:_____

cpTeach 2012   Date:_____

1500

HEALTH INSURANCE CLAIM FORM

APPROVED BY NATIONAL UNIFORM CLAIM COMMITTEE 08/05

☐☐ PICA   PICA ☐☐

1. MEDICARE ☐ (Medicare #)   MEDICAID ☐ (Medicaid #)   TRICARE CHAMPUS ☐ (Sponsor's SSN)   CHAMPVA ☐ (Member ID#)   GROUP HEALTH PLAN ☐ (SSN or ID)   FECA BLK LUNG ☐ (SSN)   OTHER ☐ (ID)   **1a.** INSURED'S I.D. NUMBER   (For Program in Item 1)

2. PATIENT'S NAME (Last Name, First Name, Middle Initial)   **3.** PATIENT'S BIRTH DATE MM DD YY   SEX M☐ F☐   **4.** INSURED'S NAME (Last Name, First Name, Middle Initial)

5. PATIENT'S ADDRESS (No., Street)   **6.** PATIENT RELATIONSHIP TO INSURED   Self ☐ Spouse ☐ Child ☐ Other ☐   **7.** INSURED'S ADDRESS (No., Street)

CITY   STATE   **8.** PATIENT STATUS   Single ☐ Married ☐ Other ☐   CITY   STATE

ZIP CODE   TELEPHONE (Include Area Code) ( )   Employed ☐ Full-Time Student ☐ Part-Time Student ☐   ZIP CODE   TELEPHONE (Include Area Code) ( )

9. OTHER INSURED'S NAME (Last Name, First Name, Middle Initial)   **10.** IS PATIENT'S CONDITION RELATED TO: **11.** INSURED'S POLICY GROUP OR FECA NUMBER

a. OTHER INSURED'S POLICY OR GROUP NUMBER   **a.** EMPLOYMENT? (Current or Previous) YES ☐ NO ☐   **a.** INSURED'S DATE OF BIRTH MM DD YY   SEX M☐ F☐

b. OTHER INSURED'S DATE OF BIRTH MM DD YY   SEX M☐ F☐   **b.** AUTO ACCIDENT?   PLACE (State) YES ☐ NO ☐   **b.** EMPLOYER'S NAME OR SCHOOL NAME

c. EMPLOYER'S NAME OR SCHOOL NAME   **c.** OTHER ACCIDENT? YES ☐ NO ☐   **c.** INSURANCE PLAN NAME OR PROGRAM NAME

d. INSURANCE PLAN NAME OR PROGRAM NAME   **10d.** RESERVED FOR LOCAL USE   **d.** IS THERE ANOTHER HEALTH BENEFIT PLAN? YES ☐ NO ☐ If yes, return to and complete item 9 a-d.

READ BACK OF FORM BEFORE COMPLETING & SIGNING THIS FORM.

12. PATIENT'S OR AUTHORIZED PERSON'S SIGNATURE I authorize the release of any medical or other information necessary to process this claim. I also request payment of government benefits either to myself or to the party who accepts assignment below.

SIGNED_____ DATE_____

13. INSURED'S OR AUTHORIZED PERSON'S SIGNATURE I authorize payment of medical benefits to the undersigned physician or supplier for services described below.

SIGNED_____

14. DATE OF CURRENT: MM DD YY ◄ ILLNESS (First symptom) OR INJURY (Accident) OR PREGNANCY(LMP)   **15.** IF PATIENT HAS HAD SAME OR SIMILAR ILLNESS. GIVE FIRST DATE MM DD YY   **16.** DATES PATIENT UNABLE TO WORK IN CURRENT OCCUPATION MM DD YY FROM TO MM DD YY

17. NAME OF REFERRING PROVIDER OR OTHER SOURCE   17a.   17b. NPI   **18.** HOSPITALIZATION DATES RELATED TO CURRENT SERVICES MM DD YY FROM TO MM DD YY

19. RESERVED FOR LOCAL USE   **20.** OUTSIDE LAB? YES ☐ NO ☐ $ CHARGES

21. DIAGNOSIS OR NATURE OF ILLNESS OR INJURY (Relate Items 1, 2, 3 or 4 to Item 24E by Line)

1. |___.___   3. |___.___

2. |___.___   4. |___.___

22. MEDICAID RESUBMISSION CODE   ORIGINAL REF. NO.

23. PRIOR AUTHORIZATION NUMBER

24. A. DATE(S) OF SERVICE From MM DD YY To MM DD YY | **B.** PLACE OF SERVICE | **C.** EMG | **D.** PROCEDURES, SERVICES, OR SUPPLIES (Explain Unusual Circumstances) CPT/HCPCS MODIFIER | **E.** DIAGNOSIS POINTER | **F.** $ CHARGES | **G.** DAYS OR UNITS | **H.** EPSDT Family Plan | **I.** ID. QUAL. | **J.** RENDERING PROVIDER ID. #

1   NPI

2   NPI

3   NPI

4   NPI

5   NPI

6   NPI

25. FEDERAL TAX I.D. NUMBER   SSN ☐ EIN ☐   **26.** PATIENT'S ACCOUNT NO.   **27.** ACCEPT ASSIGNMENT? (For govt. claims, see back) YES ☐ NO ☐   **28.** TOTAL CHARGE $ **29.** AMOUNT PAID $ **30.** BALANCE DUE $

31. SIGNATURE OF PHYSICIAN OR SUPPLIER INCLUDING DEGREES OR CREDENTIALS (I certify that the statements on the reverse apply to this bill and are made a part thereof.)

SIGNED_____ DATE_____

32. SERVICE FACILITY LOCATION INFORMATION

a.   b.

33. BILLING PROVIDER INFO & PH # ( )

a.   b.

NUCC Instruction Manual available at: www.nucc.org   OMB APPROVAL PENDING

PATIENT AND INSURED INFORMATION

PHYSICIAN OR SUPPLIER INFORMATION

	Name:_____
	Class/Section:_____
	Date:_____
2012	

EXERCISE 6.48

Re-code this same example above, but this time pretend that this patient has been an established patient of yours. Is the level of service you pick for this patient as an established patient higher or lower than the one you picked for him as a new patient? Why?

Notes: _____

_____

_____

_____

_____

_____

_____

_____

_____

_____

_____

_____

_____

_____

_____

_____

_____

_____

_____

_____

_____

_____

_____

_____

_____

_____

_____

DOC Form®
(Doctor's Office Checklist)

	OFFICE/OUTPATIENT		CONSULTATION	
	New (3)	Established (2)	Office/O.P. (3)	Inpatient (3)
Minimal Service		99211		

HISTORY
Problem Focused	99201	99212	99241	99251
Exp/Prob Focused	99202	99213	99242	99252
Detail	99203	99214	99243	99253
Comprehensive	99204/05	99215	99244/45	99254/55

EXAMINATION
Problem Focused	99201	99212	99241	99251
Exp/Prob Focused	99202	99213	99242	99252
Detail	99203	99214	99243	99253
Comprehensive	99204/05	99215	99244/45	99254/55

MEDICAL DECISION MAKING
Straight Forward	99201/2	99212	99241/42	99251/52
Low Complexity	99203	99213	99243	99253
Mod Complexity	99204	99214	99244	99254
High Complexity	99205	99215	99245	99255

TIME:　　　　Counsel/Coordination of Care:
10 Minutes	99201	99212		
15 Minutes		99213	99241	
20 Minutes	99202			99251
25 Minutes		99214		
30 Minutes	99203		99242	
40 Minutes		99215	99243	99252
45 Minutes	99204			
55 Minutes				99253
60 Minutes	99205		99244	
80 Minutes			99245	99254
110 Minutes				99255

MedBooks, Inc.
101 W. Buckingham Road, Richardson, Tx. 75081 (800) 443-7397
Warning: This product is copyrighted and is not to be duplicated in any manner without the express written permission of MedBooks.

EXERCISE 6.48

1500

HEALTH INSURANCE CLAIM FORM

APPROVED BY NATIONAL UNIFORM CLAIM COMMITTEE 08/05

| | PICA | | | | | | | | | PICA | |

| 1. MEDICARE MEDICAID TRICARE CHAMPUS CHAMPVA GROUP HEALTH PLAN FECA BLK LUNG OTHER | 1a. INSURED'S I.D. NUMBER   (For Program in Item 1) |
| (Medicare #) (Medicaid #) (Sponsor's SSN) (Member ID#) (SSN or ID) (SSN) (ID) | |

| 2. PATIENT'S NAME (Last Name, First Name, Middle Initial) | 3. PATIENT'S BIRTH DATE MM DD YY   SEX M   F | 4. INSURED'S NAME (Last Name, First Name, Middle Initial) |

| 5. PATIENT'S ADDRESS (No., Street) | 6. PATIENT RELATIONSHIP TO INSURED Self   Spouse   Child   Other | 7. INSURED'S ADDRESS (No., Street) |

| CITY   STATE | 8. PATIENT STATUS Single   Married   Other | CITY   STATE |

| ZIP CODE   TELEPHONE (Include Area Code) (   ) | Employed   Full-Time Student   Part-Time Student | ZIP CODE   TELEPHONE (Include Area Code) (   ) |

| 9. OTHER INSURED'S NAME (Last Name, First Name, Middle Initial) | 10. IS PATIENT'S CONDITION RELATED TO: | 11. INSURED'S POLICY GROUP OR FECA NUMBER |

| a. OTHER INSURED'S POLICY OR GROUP NUMBER | a. EMPLOYMENT? (Current or Previous) YES   NO | a. INSURED'S DATE OF BIRTH MM DD YY   SEX M   F |

| b. OTHER INSURED'S DATE OF BIRTH MM DD YY   SEX M   F | b. AUTO ACCIDENT?   PLACE (State) YES   NO | b. EMPLOYER'S NAME OR SCHOOL NAME |

| c. EMPLOYER'S NAME OR SCHOOL NAME | c. OTHER ACCIDENT? YES   NO | c. INSURANCE PLAN NAME OR PROGRAM NAME |

| d. INSURANCE PLAN NAME OR PROGRAM NAME | 10d. RESERVED FOR LOCAL USE | d. IS THERE ANOTHER HEALTH BENEFIT PLAN? YES   NO   If yes, return to and complete item 9 a-d. |

READ BACK OF FORM BEFORE COMPLETING & SIGNING THIS FORM.

12. PATIENT'S OR AUTHORIZED PERSON'S SIGNATURE I authorize the release of any medical or other information necessary to process this claim. I also request payment of government benefits either to myself or to the party who accepts assignment below.

SIGNED_____ DATE_____

13. INSURED'S OR AUTHORIZED PERSON'S SIGNATURE I authorize payment of medical benefits to the undersigned physician or supplier for services described below.

SIGNED_____

| 14. DATE OF CURRENT: ILLNESS (First symptom) OR MM DD YY   INJURY (Accident) OR PREGNANCY(LMP) | 15. IF PATIENT HAS HAD SAME OR SIMILAR ILLNESS. GIVE FIRST DATE MM DD YY | 16. DATES PATIENT UNABLE TO WORK IN CURRENT OCCUPATION MM DD YY   MM DD YY FROM   TO |

| 17. NAME OF REFERRING PROVIDER OR OTHER SOURCE | 17a. 17b. NPI | 18. HOSPITALIZATION DATES RELATED TO CURRENT SERVICES MM DD YY   MM DD YY FROM   TO |

| 19. RESERVED FOR LOCAL USE | 20. OUTSIDE LAB? $ CHARGES YES   NO |

| 21. DIAGNOSIS OR NATURE OF ILLNESS OR INJURY (Relate Items 1, 2, 3 or 4 to Item 24E by Line) 1. |____.____   3. |____.____ 2. |____.____   4. |____.____ | 22. MEDICAID RESUBMISSION CODE   ORIGINAL REF. NO. 23. PRIOR AUTHORIZATION NUMBER |

24. A. DATE(S) OF SERVICE From To MM DD YY MM DD YY	B. PLACE OF SERVICE	C. EMG	D. PROCEDURES, SERVICES, OR SUPPLIES (Explain Unusual Circumstances) CPT/HCPCS MODIFIER	E. DIAGNOSIS POINTER	F. $ CHARGES	G. DAYS OR UNITS	H. EPSDT Family Plan	I. ID. QUAL.	J. RENDERING PROVIDER ID. #
1									NPI
2									NPI
3									NPI
4									NPI
5									NPI
6									NPI

| 25. FEDERAL TAX I.D. NUMBER   SSN EIN | 26. PATIENT'S ACCOUNT NO. | 27. ACCEPT ASSIGNMENT? (For govt. claims, see back) YES   NO | 28. TOTAL CHARGE $ | 29. AMOUNT PAID $ | 30. BALANCE DUE $ |

| 31. SIGNATURE OF PHYSICIAN OR SUPPLIER INCLUDING DEGREES OR CREDENTIALS (I certify that the statements on the reverse apply to this bill and are made a part thereof.) SIGNED_____ DATE_____ | 32. SERVICE FACILITY LOCATION INFORMATION a. NPI   b. | 33. BILLING PROVIDER INFO & PH # (   ) a. NPI   b. |

NUCC Instruction Manual available at: www.nucc.org

OMB APPROVAL PENDING

WORKBOOK cpTeach 24th Edition 2012	Name:_____
	Class/Section:_____
	Date:_____

EXERCISE 6.49

Your doctor plans the care for a terminally ill patient named Marge N. Overa. She is 63 years old and has cancer that has advanced to her lungs and brain. Care includes oxygen in the home, diuretics, intravenous infusion of morphine, etc. The physician has phone contacts with the nurse, family and social-worker. There are discussions planned with the social-worker concerning advanced life support issues as per the patient's request. The documentation includes review and modification of care plan and certifications from nurses, pharmacy, social workers and DME personnel. The total length of the service is about 40 minutes. Code for your physician.

Notes: _____

_____

_____

_____

_____

_____

_____

_____

_____

_____

_____

_____

_____

_____

_____

_____

_____

_____

DOC Form®
(Doctor's Office Checklist)

	OFFICE/OUTPATIENT		CONSULTATION	
	New (3)	Established (2)	Office/O.P. (3)	Inpatient (3)
Minimal Service		99211		

HISTORY

Problem Focused	99201	99212	99241	99251
Exp/Prob Focused	99202	99213	99242	99252
Detail	99203	99214	99243	99253
Comprehensive	99204/05	99215	99244/45	99254/55

EXAMINATION

Problem Focused	99201	99212	99241	99251
Exp/Prob Focused	99202	99213	99242	99252
Detail	99203	99214	99243	99253
Comprehensive	99204/05	99215	99244/45	99254/55

MEDICAL DECISION MAKING

Straight Forward	99201/2	99212	99241/42	99251/52
Low Complexity	99203	99213	99243	99253
Mod Complexity	99204	99214	99244	99254
High Complexity	99205	99215	99245	99255

TIME:_____   Counsel/Coordination of Care:_____

10 Minutes	99201	99212		
15 Minutes		99213	99241	
20 Minutes	99202			99251
25 Minutes		99214		
30 Minutes	99203		99242	
40 Minutes		99215	99243	99252
45 Minutes	99204			
55 Minutes				99253
60 Minutes	99205		99244	
80 Minutes			99245	99254
110 Minutes				99255

MedBooks, Inc.
101 W. Buckingham Road, Richardson, Tx. 75081 (800) 443-7397
Warning: This product is copyrighted and is not to be duplicated in any manner without the express written permission of MedBooks.

EXERCISE 6.49

Name:_____

Class/Section:_____

Date:_____

2012

(1500)

HEALTH INSURANCE CLAIM FORM

APPROVED BY NATIONAL UNIFORM CLAIM COMMITTEE 08/05

| | PICA | | | | | | | | | PICA | | |

| 1. MEDICARE | MEDICAID | TRICARE CHAMPUS | CHAMPVA | GROUP HEALTH PLAN | FECA BLK LUNG | OTHER | 1a. INSURED'S I.D. NUMBER | (For Program in Item 1) |

(Medicare #)   (Medicaid #)   (Sponsor's SSN)   (Member ID#)   (SSN or ID)   (SSN)   (ID)

2. PATIENT'S NAME (Last Name, First Name, Middle Initial)

9. PATIENT'S BIRTH DATE MM DD YY   SEX   M   F

4. INSURED'S NAME (Last Name, First Name, Middle Initial)

5. PATIENT'S ADDRESS (No., Street)

6. PATIENT RELATIONSHIP TO INSURED   Self   Spouse   Child   Other

7. INSURED'S ADDRESS (No., Street)

CITY   STATE

8. PATIENT STATUS   Single   Married   Other

Employed   Full-Time Student   Part-Time Student

CITY   STATE

ZIP CODE   TELEPHONE (Include Area Code) (   )

ZIP CODE   TELEPHONE (Include Area Code) (   )

9. OTHER INSURED'S NAME (Last Name, First Name, Middle Initial)

10. IS PATIENT'S CONDITION RELATED TO:

11. INSURED'S POLICY GROUP OR FECA NUMBER

a. OTHER INSURED'S POLICY OR GROUP NUMBER

a. EMPLOYMENT? (Current or Previous)   YES   NO

a. INSURED'S DATE OF BIRTH MM DD YY   SEX   M   F

b. OTHER INSURED'S DATE OF BIRTH MM DD YY   SEX   M   F

b. AUTO ACCIDENT?   PLACE (State)   YES   NO

b. EMPLOYER'S NAME OR SCHOOL NAME

c. EMPLOYER'S NAME OR SCHOOL NAME

c. OTHER ACCIDENT?   YES   NO

c. INSURANCE PLAN NAME OR PROGRAM NAME

d. INSURANCE PLAN NAME OR PROGRAM NAME

10d. RESERVED FOR LOCAL USE

d. IS THERE ANOTHER HEALTH BENEFIT PLAN?   YES   NO   If yes, return to and complete item 9 a-d.

READ BACK OF FORM BEFORE COMPLETING & SIGNING THIS FORM.
12. PATIENT'S OR AUTHORIZED PERSON'S SIGNATURE I authorize the release of any medical or other information necessary to process this claim. I also request payment of government benefits either to myself or to the party who accepts assignment below.

SIGNED_____   DATE_____

13. INSURED'S OR AUTHORIZED PERSON'S SIGNATURE I authorize payment of medical benefits to the undersigned physician or supplier for services described below.

SIGNED_____

14. DATE OF CURRENT: MM DD YY   ILLNESS (First symptom) OR INJURY (Accident) OR PREGNANCY(LMP)

15. IF PATIENT HAS HAD SAME OR SIMILAR ILLNESS. GIVE FIRST DATE MM DD YY

16. DATES PATIENT UNABLE TO WORK IN CURRENT OCCUPATION MM DD YY   FROM   TO   MM DD YY

17. NAME OF REFERRING PROVIDER OR OTHER SOURCE

17a.
17b. NPI

18. HOSPITALIZATION DATES RELATED TO CURRENT SERVICES MM DD YY   FROM   TO   MM DD YY

19. RESERVED FOR LOCAL USE

20. OUTSIDE LAB?   YES   NO $ CHARGES

21. DIAGNOSIS OR NATURE OF ILLNESS OR INJURY (Relate Items 1, 2, 3 or 4 to Item 24E by Line)

1. _____ . _____   3. _____ . _____

2. _____ . _____   4. _____ . _____

22. MEDICAID RESUBMISSION CODE   ORIGINAL REF. NO.

23. PRIOR AUTHORIZATION NUMBER

24. A. DATE(S) OF SERVICE						B. PLACE OF SERVICE	C. EMG	D. PROCEDURES, SERVICES, OR SUPPLIES (Explain Unusual Circumstances) CPT/HCPCS	MODIFIER	E. DIAGNOSIS POINTER	F. $ CHARGES	G. DAYS OR UNITS	H. EPSDT Family Plan	I. ID. QUAL.	J. RENDERING PROVIDER ID. #
From MM	DD	YY	To MM	DD	YY										
1														NPI	
2														NPI	
3														NPI	
4														NPI	
5														NPI	
6														NPI	

25. FEDERAL TAX I.D. NUMBER   SSN   EIN

26. PATIENT'S ACCOUNT NO.

27. ACCEPT ASSIGNMENT? (For govt. claims, see back)   YES   NO

28. TOTAL CHARGE $

29. AMOUNT PAID $

30. BALANCE DUE $

31. SIGNATURE OF PHYSICIAN OR SUPPLIER INCLUDING DEGREES OR CREDENTIALS (I certify that the statements on the reverse apply to this bill and are made a part thereof.)

SIGNED_____   DATE_____

32. SERVICE FACILITY LOCATION INFORMATION

a.   b.

33. BILLING PROVIDER INFO & PH # (   )

a.   b.

NUCC Instruction Manual available at: www.nucc.org

OMB APPROVAL PENDING

PATIENT AND INSURED INFORMATION

PHYSICIAN OR SUPPLIER INFORMATION

Name:_____

Class/Section:_____

Date:_____

cpTeach
2012

EXERCISE 6.50

Lise T. Vall has been a patient of your for 5 years. She is on Accupril for her high blood pressure. She comes into your office this day for a blood pressure check which the nurse performs. No other services are provided.

Notes: _____

_____

DOC Form®
(Doctor's Office Checklist)

	OFFICE/OUTPATIENT		CONSULTATION	
	New (3)	Established (2)	Office/O.P. (3)	Inpatient (3)
Minimal Service		99211		

HISTORY

	New (3)	Established (2)	Office/O.P. (3)	Inpatient (3)
Problem Focused	99201	99212	99241	99251
Exp/Prob Focused	99202	99213	99242	99252
Detail	99203	99214	99243	99253
Comprehensive	99204/05	99215	99244/45	99254/55

EXAMINATION

	New (3)	Established (2)	Office/O.P. (3)	Inpatient (3)
Problem Focused	99201	99212	99241	99251
Exp/Prob Focused	99202	99213	99242	99252
Detail	99203	99214	99243	99253
Comprehensive	99204/05	99215	99244/45	99254/55

MEDICAL DECISION MAKING

	New (3)	Established (2)	Office/O.P. (3)	Inpatient (3)
Straight Forward	99201/2	99212	99241/42	99251/52
Low Complexity	99203	99213	99243	99253
Mod Complexity	99204	99214	99244	99254
High Complexity	99205	99215	99245	99255

TIME:_____   Counsel/Coordination of Care:_____

	New (3)	Established (2)	Office/O.P. (3)	Inpatient (3)
10 Minutes	99201	99212		
15 Minutes		99213	99241	
20 Minutes	99202			99251
25 Minutes		99214		
30 Minutes	99203		99242	
40 Minutes		99215	99243	99252
45 Minutes	99204			
55 Minutes				99253
60 Minutes	99205		99244	
80 Minutes			99245	99254
110 Minutes				99255

MedBooks, Inc.
101 W. Buckingham Road, Richardson, Tx. 75081 (800) 443-7397
Warning: This product is copyrighted and is not to be duplicated in any manner without the express written permission of MedBooks.

EXERCISE 6.50

1500

HEALTH INSURANCE CLAIM FORM
APPROVED BY NATIONAL UNIFORM CLAIM COMMITTEE 08/05

[ ][ ] PICA   PICA [ ][ ]

1. MEDICARE MEDICAID TRICARE CHAMPUS CHAMPVA GROUP HEALTH PLAN FECA BLK LUNG OTHER	1a. INSURED'S I.D. NUMBER (For Program in Item 1)
(Medicare #) (Medicaid #) (Sponsor's SSN) (Member ID#) (SSN or ID) (SSN) (ID)	

2. PATIENT'S NAME (Last Name, First Name, Middle Initial)	3. PATIENT'S BIRTH DATE MM DD YY SEX M F	4. INSURED'S NAME (Last Name, First Name, Middle Initial)
5. PATIENT'S ADDRESS (No., Street)	6. PATIENT RELATIONSHIP TO INSURED Self Spouse Child Other	7. INSURED'S ADDRESS (No., Street)
CITY STATE	8. PATIENT STATUS Single Married Other Employed Full-Time Student Part-Time Student	CITY STATE
ZIP CODE TELEPHONE (Include Area Code) ( )		ZIP CODE TELEPHONE (Include Area Code) ( )
9. OTHER INSURED'S NAME (Last Name, First Name, Middle Initial)	10. IS PATIENT'S CONDITION RELATED TO:	11. INSURED'S POLICY GROUP OR FECA NUMBER
a. OTHER INSURED'S POLICY OR GROUP NUMBER	a. EMPLOYMENT? (Current or Previous) YES NO	a. INSURED'S DATE OF BIRTH MM DD YY SEX M F
b. OTHER INSURED'S DATE OF BIRTH MM DD YY SEX M F	b. AUTO ACCIDENT? PLACE (State) YES NO	b. EMPLOYER'S NAME OR SCHOOL NAME
c. EMPLOYER'S NAME OR SCHOOL NAME	c. OTHER ACCIDENT? YES NO	c. INSURANCE PLAN NAME OR PROGRAM NAME
d. INSURANCE PLAN NAME OR PROGRAM NAME	10d. RESERVED FOR LOCAL USE	d. IS THERE ANOTHER HEALTH BENEFIT PLAN? YES NO If yes, return to and complete item 9 a-d.

READ BACK OF FORM BEFORE COMPLETING & SIGNING THIS FORM.

12. PATIENT'S OR AUTHORIZED PERSON'S SIGNATURE I authorize the release of any medical or other information necessary to process this claim. I also request payment of government benefits either to myself or to the party who accepts assignment below.

SIGNED_____ DATE_____

13. INSURED'S OR AUTHORIZED PERSON'S SIGNATURE I authorize payment of medical benefits to the undersigned physician or supplier for services described below.

SIGNED_____

14. DATE OF CURRENT: ILLNESS (First symptom) OR MM DD YY INJURY (Accident) OR PREGNANCY(LMP)	15. IF PATIENT HAS HAD SAME OR SIMILAR ILLNESS. GIVE FIRST DATE MM DD YY	16. DATES PATIENT UNABLE TO WORK IN CURRENT OCCUPATION MM DD YY MM DD YY FROM TO
17. NAME OF REFERRING PROVIDER OR OTHER SOURCE	17a. 17b. NPI	18. HOSPITALIZATION DATES RELATED TO CURRENT SERVICES MM DD YY MM DD YY FROM TO
19. RESERVED FOR LOCAL USE		20. OUTSIDE LAB? YES NO $ CHARGES

21. DIAGNOSIS OR NATURE OF ILLNESS OR INJURY (Relate Items 1, 2, 3 or 4 to Item 24E by Line)

1. |___.___   3. |___.___
2. |___.___   4. |___.___

22. MEDICAID RESUBMISSION CODE   ORIGINAL REF. NO.
23. PRIOR AUTHORIZATION NUMBER

24. A. DATE(S) OF SERVICE From To MM DD YY MM DD YY	B. PLACE OF SERVICE	C. EMG	D. PROCEDURES, SERVICES, OR SUPPLIES (Explain Unusual Circumstances) CPT/HCPCS	MODIFIER	E. DIAGNOSIS POINTER	F. $ CHARGES	G. DAYS OR UNITS	H. EPSDT Family Plan	I. ID. QUAL.	J. RENDERING PROVIDER ID. #
1										NPI
2										NPI
3										NPI
4										NPI
5										NPI
6										NPI

25. FEDERAL TAX I.D. NUMBER SSN EIN	26. PATIENT'S ACCOUNT NO.	27. ACCEPT ASSIGNMENT? (For govt. claims, see back) YES NO	28. TOTAL CHARGE $	29. AMOUNT PAID $	30. BALANCE DUE $
31. SIGNATURE OF PHYSICIAN OR SUPPLIER INCLUDING DEGREES OR CREDENTIALS (I certify that the statements on the reverse apply to this bill and are made a part thereof.) SIGNED DATE	32. SERVICE FACILITY LOCATION INFORMATION a. NPI b.	33. BILLING PROVIDER INFO & PH # ( ) a. NPI b.			

NUCC Instruction Manual available at: www.nucc.org   OMB APPROVAL PENDING

PATIENT AND INSURED INFORMATION

PHYSICIAN OR SUPPLIER INFORMATION

	Name:_____
WORKBOOK cpTeach 2012	Class/Section:_____
	Date:_____

EXERCISE 6.51

Lilly Pad returns to your office for a recheck following her antibiotic therapy for acute tonsillitis. Upon performing the exam, you notice that although mildly improved, her tonsils are still quite inflamed and you conclude that the antibiotics probably aren't the ones to rid her of this disease. You prescribe another one and ask her to return to your office in 10 days.

Notes: _____
_____
_____
_____
_____
_____
_____
_____
_____
_____
_____
_____
_____
_____
_____
_____
_____
_____
_____
_____
_____
_____
_____
_____
_____
_____
_____

DOC Form®
(Doctor's Office Checklist)

	OFFICE/OUTPATIENT		CONSULTATION	
	New (3)	Established (2)	Office/O.P. (3)	Inpatient (3)
Minimal Service		99211		

HISTORY

Problem Focused	99201	99212	99241	99251
Exp/Prob Focused	99202	99213	99242	99252
Detail	99203	99214	99243	99253
Comprehensive	99204/05	99215	99244/45	99254/55

EXAMINATION

Problem Focused	99201	99212	99241	99251
Exp/Prob Focused	99202	99213	99242	99252
Detail	99203	99214	99243	99253
Comprehensive	99204/05	99215	99244/45	99254/55

MEDICAL DECISION MAKING

Straight Forward	99201/2	99212	99241/42	99251/52
Low Complexity	99203	99213	99243	99253
Mod Complexity	99204	99214	99244	99254
High Complexity	99205	99215	99245	99255

TIME:_____ Counsel/Coordination of Care:_____

10 Minutes	99201	99212		
15 Minutes		99213	99241	
20 Minutes	99202			99251
25 Minutes		99214		
30 Minutes	99203		99242	
40 Minutes		99215	99243	99252
45 Minutes	99204			
55 Minutes				99253
60 Minutes	99205		99244	
80 Minutes			99245	99254
110 Minutes				99255

MedBooks, Inc.
101 W. Buckingham Road, Richardson, Tx. 75081 (800) 443-7397
Warning: This product is copyrighted and is not to be duplicated in any manner without the express written permission of MedBooks.

EXERCISE 6.51

Name:_____

Class/Section:_____

Date:_____

cpTeach
2012

1500

HEALTH INSURANCE CLAIM FORM

APPROVED BY NATIONAL UNIFORM CLAIM COMMITTEE 08/05

| | PICA | | | | | | | PICA | |

1. MEDICARE MEDICAID TRICARE CHAMPVA GROUP FECA OTHER	1a. INSURED'S I.D. NUMBER (For Program in Item 1)
(Medicare #) *(Medicaid #)* CHAMPUS *(Sponsor's SSN)* *(Member ID#)* HEALTH PLAN *(SSN or ID)* BLK LUNG *(SSN)* *(ID)*	

2. PATIENT'S NAME (Last Name, First Name, Middle Initial)	3. PATIENT'S BIRTH DATE MM DD YY SEX M F	4. INSURED'S NAME (Last Name, First Name, Middle Initial)
5. PATIENT'S ADDRESS (No., Street)	6. PATIENT RELATIONSHIP TO INSURED Self Spouse Child Other	7. INSURED'S ADDRESS (No., Street)
CITY STATE	8. PATIENT STATUS Single Married Other	CITY STATE
ZIP CODE TELEPHONE (Include Area Code) ( )	Employed Full-Time Student Part-Time Student	ZIP CODE TELEPHONE (Include Area Code) ( )

9. OTHER INSURED'S NAME (Last Name, First Name, Middle Initial)	10. IS PATIENT'S CONDITION RELATED TO:	11. INSURED'S POLICY GROUP OR FECA NUMBER
a. OTHER INSURED'S POLICY OR GROUP NUMBER	a. EMPLOYMENT? (Current or Previous) YES NO	a. INSURED'S DATE OF BIRTH MM DD YY SEX M F
b. OTHER INSURED'S DATE OF BIRTH MM DD YY SEX M F	b. AUTO ACCIDENT? PLACE (State) YES NO	b. EMPLOYER'S NAME OR SCHOOL NAME
c. EMPLOYER'S NAME OR SCHOOL NAME	c. OTHER ACCIDENT? YES NO	c. INSURANCE PLAN NAME OR PROGRAM NAME
d. INSURANCE PLAN NAME OR PROGRAM NAME	10d. RESERVED FOR LOCAL USE	d. IS THERE ANOTHER HEALTH BENEFIT PLAN? YES NO If yes, return to and complete item 9 a-d.

READ BACK OF FORM BEFORE COMPLETING & SIGNING THIS FORM.
12. PATIENT'S OR AUTHORIZED PERSON'S SIGNATURE I authorize the release of any medical or other information necessary to process this claim. I also request payment of government benefits either to myself or to the party who accepts assignment below.

SIGNED_____ DATE_____

13. INSURED'S OR AUTHORIZED PERSON'S SIGNATURE I authorize payment of medical benefits to the undersigned physician or supplier for services described below.

SIGNED_____

14. DATE OF CURRENT: ILLNESS (First symptom) OR MM DD YY INJURY (Accident) OR PREGNANCY(LMP)	15. IF PATIENT HAS HAD SAME OR SIMILAR ILLNESS. GIVE FIRST DATE MM DD YY	16. DATES PATIENT UNABLE TO WORK IN CURRENT OCCUPATION MM DD YY MM DD YY FROM TO
17. NAME OF REFERRING PROVIDER OR OTHER SOURCE	17a. 17b. NPI	18. HOSPITALIZATION DATES RELATED TO CURRENT SERVICES MM DD YY MM DD YY FROM TO
19. RESERVED FOR LOCAL USE		20. OUTSIDE LAB? YES NO $ CHARGES
21. DIAGNOSIS OR NATURE OF ILLNESS OR INJURY (Relate Items 1, 2, 3 or 4 to Item 24E by Line) 1. |_____._____ 3. |_____._____ 2. |_____._____ 4. |_____._____		22. MEDICAID RESUBMISSION CODE ORIGINAL REF. NO. 23. PRIOR AUTHORIZATION NUMBER

24. A. DATE(S) OF SERVICE From To MM DD YY MM DD YY	B. PLACE OF SERVICE	C. EMG	D. PROCEDURES, SERVICES, OR SUPPLIES (Explain Unusual Circumstances) CPT/HCPCS MODIFIER	E. DIAGNOSIS POINTER	F. $ CHARGES	G. DAYS OR UNITS	H. EPSDT Family Plan	I. ID. QUAL.	J. RENDERING PROVIDER ID. #
1								NPI	
2								NPI	
3								NPI	
4								NPI	
5								NPI	
6								NPI	

25. FEDERAL TAX I.D. NUMBER SSN EIN	26. PATIENT'S ACCOUNT NO.	27. ACCEPT ASSIGNMENT? (For govt. claims, see back) YES NO	28. TOTAL CHARGE $	29. AMOUNT PAID $	30. BALANCE DUE $
31. SIGNATURE OF PHYSICIAN OR SUPPLIER INCLUDING DEGREES OR CREDENTIALS (I certify that the statements on the reverse apply to this bill and are made a part thereof.) SIGNED DATE	32. SERVICE FACILITY LOCATION INFORMATION a. b.	33. BILLING PROVIDER INFO & PH # ( ) a. b.			

NUCC Instruction Manual available at: www.nucc.org

OMB APPROVAL PENDING

PATIENT AND INSURED INFORMATION

PHYSICIAN OR SUPPLIER INFORMATION

EXERCISE 6.52

This same patient comes back to you in ten days. Upon checking her tonsils this time, you notice that the condition has cleared, but Ms. Pad begins to tell you about her son who is performing poorly in school and who has recently been expelled. She also tells you that this boy has begun to associate with a gang and has come home drunk several nights in a row. She then proceeds to tell you that she found a white looking powder in his bedroom, and she is afraid that he is also on drugs. You give her some advice about different groups that can help and suggest that she too get some counseling and join a support group. The entire visit takes about 40 minutes.

Notes: _____

_____

_____

_____

_____

_____

_____

_____

_____

_____

_____

_____

_____

_____

_____

_____

_____

_____

_____

_____

DOC Form®
(Doctor's Office Checklist)

OFFICE/OUTPATIENT　　CONSULTATION

	New (3)	Established (2)	Office/O.P. (3)	Inpatient (3)
Minimal Service		99211		

HISTORY

	New (3)	Established (2)	Office/O.P. (3)	Inpatient (3)
Problem Focused	99201	99212	99241	99251
Exp/Prob Focused	99202	99213	99242	99252
Detail	99203	99214	99243	99253
Comprehensive	99204/05	99215	99244/45	99254/55

EXAMINATION

	New (3)	Established (2)	Office/O.P. (3)	Inpatient (3)
Problem Focused	99201	99212	99241	99251
Exp/Prob Focused	99202	99213	99242	99252
Detail	99203	99214	99243	99253
Comprehensive	99204/05	99215	99244/45	99254/55

MEDICAL DECISION MAKING

	New (3)	Established (2)	Office/O.P. (3)	Inpatient (3)
Straight Forward	99201/2	99212	99241/42	99251/52
Low Complexity	99203	99213	99243	99253
Mod Complexity	99204	99214	99244	99254
High Complexity	99205	99215	99245	99255

TIME:_____　　Counsel/Coordination of Care:_____

	New (3)	Established (2)	Office/O.P. (3)	Inpatient (3)
10 Minutes	99201	99212		
15 Minutes		99213	99241	
20 Minutes	99202			99251
25 Minutes		99214		
30 Minutes	99203		99242	
40 Minutes		99215	99243	99252
45 Minutes	99204			
55 Minutes				99253
60 Minutes	99205		99244	
80 Minutes			99245	99254
110 Minutes				99255

MedBooks, Inc.
101 W. Buckingham Road, Richardson, Tx. 75081 (800) 443-7397
Warning: This product is copyrighted and is not to be duplicated in any manner without the express written permission of MedBooks.

EXERCISE 6.52

WORKBOOK

Name:_____

Class/Section:_____

cpTeach

2012

Date:_____

1500

HEALTH INSURANCE CLAIM FORM

APPROVED BY NATIONAL UNIFORM CLAIM COMMITTEE 08/05

| | PICA | | | | | | | | PICA | |

| 1. MEDICARE | MEDICAID | TRICARE CHAMPUS | CHAMPVA | GROUP HEALTH PLAN | FECA BLK LUNG | OTHER | 1a. INSURED'S I.D. NUMBER | (For Program in Item 1) |

(Medicare #) (Medicaid #) (Sponsor's SSN) (Member ID#) (SSN or ID) (SSN) (ID)

| 2. PATIENT'S NAME (Last Name, First Name, Middle Initial) | 3. PATIENT'S BIRTH DATE MM DD YY SEX M F | 4. INSURED'S NAME (Last Name, First Name, Middle Initial) |

| 5. PATIENT'S ADDRESS (No., Street) | 6. PATIENT RELATIONSHIP TO INSURED Self Spouse Child Other | 7. INSURED'S ADDRESS (No., Street) |

| CITY | STATE | 8. PATIENT STATUS Single Married Other | CITY | STATE |

| ZIP CODE | TELEPHONE (Include Area Code) ( ) | Employed Full-Time Student Part-Time Student | ZIP CODE | TELEPHONE (Include Area Code) ( ) |

9. OTHER INSURED'S NAME (Last Name, First Name, Middle Initial)

10. IS PATIENT'S CONDITION RELATED TO:

11. INSURED'S POLICY GROUP OR FECA NUMBER

a. OTHER INSURED'S POLICY OR GROUP NUMBER

a. EMPLOYMENT? (Current or Previous) YES NO

a. INSURED'S DATE OF BIRTH MM DD YY SEX M F

b. OTHER INSURED'S DATE OF BIRTH MM DD YY SEX M F

b. AUTO ACCIDENT? PLACE (State) YES NO

b. EMPLOYER'S NAME OR SCHOOL NAME

c. EMPLOYER'S NAME OR SCHOOL NAME

c. OTHER ACCIDENT? YES NO

c. INSURANCE PLAN NAME OR PROGRAM NAME

d. INSURANCE PLAN NAME OR PROGRAM NAME

10d. RESERVED FOR LOCAL USE

d. IS THERE ANOTHER HEALTH BENEFIT PLAN? YES NO If yes, return to and complete item 9 a-d.

READ BACK OF FORM BEFORE COMPLETING & SIGNING THIS FORM.

12. PATIENT'S OR AUTHORIZED PERSON'S SIGNATURE I authorize the release of any medical or other information necessary to process this claim. I also request payment of government benefits either to myself or to the party who accepts assignment below.

SIGNED_____ DATE_____

13. INSURED'S OR AUTHORIZED PERSON'S SIGNATURE I authorize payment of medical benefits to the undersigned physician or supplier for services described below.

SIGNED_____

PATIENT AND INSURED INFORMATION

| 14. DATE OF CURRENT: MM DD YY ILLNESS (First symptom) OR INJURY (Accident) OR PREGNANCY(LMP) | 15. IF PATIENT HAS HAD SAME OR SIMILAR ILLNESS. GIVE FIRST DATE MM DD YY | 16. DATES PATIENT UNABLE TO WORK IN CURRENT OCCUPATION MM DD YY FROM TO MM DD YY |

| 17. NAME OF REFERRING PROVIDER OR OTHER SOURCE | 17a. 17b. NPI | 18. HOSPITALIZATION DATES RELATED TO CURRENT SERVICES MM DD YY FROM TO MM DD YY |

| 19. RESERVED FOR LOCAL USE | 20. OUTSIDE LAB? YES NO $ CHARGES |

21. DIAGNOSIS OR NATURE OF ILLNESS OR INJURY (Relate Items 1, 2, 9 or 4 to Item 24E by Line)

1. |___.___   3. |___.___

2. |___.___   4. |___.___

22. MEDICAID RESUBMISSION CODE ORIGINAL REF. NO.

23. PRIOR AUTHORIZATION NUMBER

24. A. DATE(S) OF SERVICE			B. PLACE OF SERVICE	C. EMG	D. PROCEDURES, SERVICES, OR SUPPLIES (Explain Unusual Circumstances) CPT/HCPCS MODIFIER	E. DIAGNOSIS POINTER	F. $ CHARGES	G. DAYS OR UNITS	H. EPSDT Family Plan	I. ID. QUAL.	J. RENDERING PROVIDER ID. #
From MM DD YY	To MM DD YY										
1										NPI	
2										NPI	
3										NPI	
4										NPI	
5										NPI	
6										NPI	

| 25. FEDERAL TAX I.D. NUMBER SSN EIN | 26. PATIENT'S ACCOUNT NO. | 27. ACCEPT ASSIGNMENT? (For govt. claims, see back) YES NO | 28. TOTAL CHARGE $ | 29. AMOUNT PAID $ | 30. BALANCE DUE $ |

| 31. SIGNATURE OF PHYSICIAN OR SUPPLIER INCLUDING DEGREES OR CREDENTIALS (I certify that the statements on the reverse apply to this bill and are made a part thereof.) SIGNED_____ DATE | 32. SERVICE FACILITY LOCATION INFORMATION a. NPI b. | 33. BILLING PROVIDER INFO & PH # ( ) a. NPI b. |

PHYSICIAN OR SUPPLIER INFORMATION

NUCC Instruction Manual available at: www.nucc.org

OMB APPROVAL PENDING

What is Anesthesia?

We have now arrived at the part of the CPT® book where you will find codes that address Anesthesia. The codes found in this section normally begin with the number "0" with a few exceptions noted in the Anesthesia Guidelines, where qualifying circumstances for anesthesia call for the initial digit of "9." There also some dental anesthesia codes in the HCPCS National Coding Manual, but we will not address them here.

An example of an anesthesia code is the following:

> *00100   Anesthesia for procedures on salivary glands, including biopsy*

Copyright AMA, 2011

As you can see, the first digit is a zero with four other digits that follow. Remember, as with the other sections in CPT® it is the first digit of the code that will clue you in on where (within the CPT®) you can find the codes.

In this chapter we will only discuss anesthesia administered by an anesthesia provider; that is, anesthesia provided by an anesthesiologist, a certified registered nurse anesthetist (CRNA) or an anesthesia assistant (AA). This is because if a surgeon provides his own anesthesia, you simply append the modifier -47 to the surgical procedure.

Like the other sections in CPT®, the Anesthesia section is divided into basic subsections. The first 15 of these subsections are anatomical categories from the top of the head to the toes. The last 4 categories end with several smaller subsections that are more general, based upon the types of services (i.e., radiological procedures, burn excisions or debridement, obstetric cases, and a category of "other" procedures that could not be properly placed in one of the others already listed). Knowing that the Anesthesia section is arranged this way makes

---

Tip

There are other CPT® codes that start with "0" in categories II and III. But these will begin with a "0" and end in either an "F" or a "T."

it easy to find a code, if you know the part of the body operated upon, or if the case fits into the last categories just mentioned.

Once you find the general subsection in CPT® that describes where the procedure took place (e.g., head, thorax), you can then read the descriptions of the codes to find the specific procedure. For the most part, the services found in Anesthesia are organized by the type of procedure (e.g., open, closed). Each code describes certain generalized services done to a particular body area. You will note, interestingly enough, that the Anesthesia codes are not specifically related to a certain surgical service. They are more general. Consider the following:

> *01650   Anesthesia for procedures on arteries of shoulder and axilla; not otherwise specified*
>
> Copyright AMA, 2011

As you can see, the anesthesia code listed above could cover a variety of surgical services, as the description of the code is very generalized. This is because anesthesia coding is based on the difficulty of the anesthesia, not the surgical procedure itself. Anesthesia care is complicated by conditions which impact oxygenation, such as procedures involving the lungs and trachea. So, anesthesia on the shoulder and axilla are all grouped together because there is not much in that location which would cause a problem with oxygenation of the patient. Anesthesia coding is also impacted by the level of consciousness, so if the patient needed to be conscious during parts of a diagnostic procedure, but would not be conscious during the same therapeutic procedure, there may be different anesthesia codes that you would use.

REIMBURSEMENT

Using Anesthesia codes to obtain reimbursement differs from that which applies to other codes in the CPT® book. Most codes have Relative Value Units (RVU's) assigned to them. These Relative Value Units compare the time and resources to provide one service to another, such as the comparison of a colonoscopy to an office visit. To better understand this concept, think of a Relative Value Unit almost like you would think of the number of pounds of meat. The more the meat weighs, the higher the number of pounds (or in this case, Relative Value Units). As you already know, once you have the weight of the beef or chicken you are buying, all you need is the price per pound to calculate how much the meat will cost you at check out.

Likewise, in assessing prices, different insurance companies (including Medicare) assign a conversion factor (price per pound) for each of the different sections in the CPT® book. Put in another way, the Surgery section has one price per pound assigned to it, the Evaluation and Management yet another, and Anesthesia yet another still. For Medicare, this conversion factor (price per pound) is multiplied by the RVU (number of pounds) to generate a price for the procedure.

Key

The bottom line: Think about the problems the physician or the CRNA might have in the administration of anesthesia, not the surgeon's problems in providing the surgery. Each person (i.e., the anesthesiologist and the surgeon) will code their own services that they provide to the patient.

Many physicians do not pay attention to the RVU's and simply assign a reasonable price directly to a procedure code. And while we do not recommend this methodology (of simply assigning a price without at least looking at the RVU's), many doctors will check with their colleagues at medical meetings and price their services accordingly. In using the Anesthesia codes, however, the simple math of applying the price per pound (Conversion Factor) to the number of pounds (RVU) does not exactly apply, and you will need to take several things in to account. You will need to use a formula to come up with a total fee. We will show you the formula below so that you will understand where we are leading you. Then, we will discuss the different components that are taken into account within the formula itself.

No two codes are alike...

The formulas for calculating anesthesia charges are:

Base Units + Time Units + Modifying Units = Total Units
Total Units x Conversion Factor = Total Fee

As with any mathematical equation, you will just need to take it one step at a time. Remember, anyone can eat an elephant one bite at a time. We will take it piece by piece, so that by the end of this chapter you will be an expert!

WHO CAME UP WITH THESE FORMULAS?

The responsibility for developing the Anesthesia section fell to two organizations. One of these was the American Medical Association (AMA) and the other was the American Society of Anesthesiologists (ASA).

While the AMA publishes the codes for anesthesia in the CPT® book, the ASA publishes a book that employs these codes and gives you the additional information you need to complete the formula. This additional information supplements the CPT® Anesthesia section codes by listing additional codes for services that anesthesiologists can also perform as well as the base units for each of these procedures. Relative Value Units are to procedures and Evaluation and Management services what Base Units are to anesthesia services. (See formula above.) For anesthesia services, base units are figures that permit calculation of the cost or value of each anesthesia service relative to other anesthesia services. As mentioned before, these formulas are similar to figuring out the price per pound of red meat (if you were working in the meat department at a local grocery store). That is, once you know the price per pound of the steak or hamburger, all you need is the weight of the meat (relative value) in order to figure out how much to charge the customer. Obviously, steak will cost more than hamburger. Likewise, services like surgeries will cost more than office visits.

You can learn more about relative values or base units by consulting the ASA's Relative Value Guide, or by contacting the ASA directly at 1-800-562-8666 or 847-825-5586. Their mailing address is ASA, 520 N. Northwest Highway, Park Ridge, Il 60068-2573, or you can email them at www.asahq.org. Just keep in mind that, in all likelihood, you will need several resources such as a "cross-walk" or "cross coder" in addition to the CPT® book in order to code Anesthesia services effectively. That being said, it will be the main purpose of this chapter to give you an overview of the general rules of coding for anesthesia using the CPT® book while providing you with hints and tips that you may need if you decide to actually work in an anesthesia office.

How is the Anesthesia Section Different from the Other Sections in CPT®?

As you have already learned, each section in CPT® has been fairly self-contained. That is, the Guidelines for each section supply the doctor and coder with the information they need to code the services within that section. It is in the Guidelines of each section that you learn about what modifiers apply and also about the rules for using the codes in that section. When you use most of the codes in the CPT® book, you know that each will describe a specific service and each should have its own unique price that you should use when you submit a charge to either a patient or a third party payer. Codes in the Anesthesia section are different in that the codes are more generalized. Just like prolonged E/M codes, the amount of time spent providing the anesthesia services is also a factor. That is, you could provide a service such as anesthesia for an arthroscopic procedure of the hip and, depending upon many variables (e.g., the number of loose bodies removed, the amount of shaving, the patient's age, condition, and length of time it took to provide the service), the end price of the service would vary.

Additionally, the Anesthesia section is a bit different from the other sections in CPT® in that some of the information you may need to completely code the claim correctly is not given to you within the Anesthesia section itself but will be something that you will have to obtain from your doctor, other parts of the CPT® book, the HCPCS National Coding Manual (discussed previously), and the ASA's Relative Value Book available at www.asahq.org. In contrast, when we studied E/M, you knew that in most cases, with the exception of the established patient minimal service, it was the doctor who provided the service for these visits. In the E/M section, the information you needed to get from the doctor was the kind of history, the kind of exam, and the kind of medical decision making that was used in order to completely determine the kind of visit that took place.

Remember, the ultimate goal for you is to be able to bill someone for the anesthesia services you rendered. Based upon that, let's recall the formula described above.

Base Value + Time Units + Modifying Units = Total Units
Total Units x Conversion Factor = Total Fee

> ### Tip
>
> Codes in the Anesthesia section are different in that the codes are more generalized. Just like prolonged E/M codes, the amount of time spent providing the anesthesia services is also a factor
>
>

In the Anesthesia section, in order to get the information you need to be able to effectively use the formula above you will need to find out the following:

a. ***Which code will you use?*** This involves determining the Anesthesia code. Ask yourself: What surgical services were provided? What type of anesthesia was provided? Was the anesthesia general, regional, monitored anesthesia care, or moderate sedation? What part of the body was the anesthesia provided to? If abdominal, was the surgery above or below the umbilicus (waistline)? To code effectively, you will need to identify the correct anesthesia code for every procedure. Then you need to identify which procedure links to the anesthesia service with the highest number of base units. This will tell you which CPT® code to use which will help you determine the base units.

b. ***How much time was spent providing the anesthesia to the patient?*** How long did the anesthesia provider furnish care? This is the amount of time spent in hours and minutes starting from when the provider began preparing the patient to receive anesthesia and ending when the patient was no longer under the care of the anesthesia provider. This will help you fill in the time units portion of the formula.

c. ***Which carrier are you going to be submitting your claim to and how many minutes are included in their time unit?*** Different carriers have different definitions of the number of minutes involved in a "time unit." In general, a time unit is 15 minutes. Sometimes anesthesia practices negotiate different "time unit" definitions. To get the total time (in units) that you provided anesthesia, you divide the total time, such as 180 minutes by the number of minutes in the time unit (such as 15 minutes) to obtain the number of time units (180/15 = 12). NOTE: There is a movement to change this to billing per minute (none of this 15 minutes per unit stuff), particularly as electronic billing progresses and they standardize anesthesia billing. It sure would make things a lot easier.

d. ***Who provided the service(s) (e.g., an anesthesiologist, a certified registered nurse anesthetist)?*** This will help you obtain information on modifiers that may be needed to explain who provided the service(s).

e. ***What condition was the patient in and were there any qualifying circumstances that need to be taken into account (e.g., the patient had an emergency condition, medical necessity or condition, extreme age)?*** This will help you fill in the portion under modifying units in the formula.

Some of this is the kind of information that you will be able to get from the patient's chart. You may also find that you are able to get some of the information from the office of the surgeon. Other information can be obtained by researching a variety of sources such as the carriers with whom you deal and the ASA.

Putting all of the data together on the claim form will help insure that you get paid properly.

Obviously the CPT® book will not tell you who provided the service. This information should be on the documentation of the service. Additionally, since multiple procedures are often done during one anesthesia episode and not all patients are the same, and since we have no way of predicting any complications or setbacks, the length of time that it may take to provide one patient with anesthesia may differ from the length of time that it takes for another. As a result, in coding for anesthesia, you will need to take the amount of time that was spent with the patient into account.

We will discuss these issues in detail as we go through this chapter.

WHAT IS ANESTHESIA?

For this chapter, we will define anesthesia as the administration of a gas or a drug resulting in partial or complete loss of feeling. Through the use of drugs administered by the provider (e.g., a surgeon, an anesthesiologist, a CRNA, or an anesthesia assistant), anesthesia allows for the loss of sensation or feeling so that the patient feels no pain during the medical procedure, or at least doesn't remember it.

BASIC TYPES OF ANESTHESIA

There are four basic or overall types of anesthesia that are administered so that a patient can endure a surgery (or other invasive or painful procedure). They are:

<u>Basic Types of Anesthesia</u>

1.   **general anesthesia**
2.   **monitored anesthesia care (MAC)**
3.   **regional anesthesia**
4.   **local anesthesia**

COMPARING GENERAL ANESTHESIA & MONITORED ANESTHESIA CARE (MAC)

In both general anesthesia and monitored anesthesia care (MAC), the anesthesia provider is at the patient's side and is completely devoted to monitoring and caring for the patient so that the surgeon can focus on the operation.

Usually when the patient is placed "under," the form of anesthesia would be a general type of anesthesia where the patient would not be cognizant of what was going on. According to the American Society of Anesthesiologists' definition of general anesthesia, the patient is considered to be under general anesthesia if he or she "loses consciousness and the ability to respond purposefully… irrespective of whether airway instrumentation is required."

It refers to a total body anesthesia where the body is brought to a level of sleep where there is no sensation, memory, or voluntary skeletal muscle movement. The medications given to support a general anesthesia are given either intravenously or they are inhaled. The level of anesthesia given is monitored constantly so that it can be fine-tuned to serve the individual needs of the patient. General anesthesia is discontinued and medications are given to reverse the effects of the anesthetic agent at the end of the surgery, and the patient is brought to the recovery room.

Like the general anesthesia patient, the MAC, (monitored anesthesia care) patient is also given the sedative and other agent but the dosage is low enough that the patient remains responsive and can breathe without assistance. MAC is often used to supplement local and regional anesthesia, particularly during simple procedures and minor surgery. It can also be used when the planned procedure is uncomfortable and on surgeries which do not require general anesthesia.

The purpose of MAC is to provide the patient with anxiety and pain relief, amnesia, comfort, and safety during the procedure. While the physician performing the service generally orders MAC, it can also be requested by the patient himself, or even the primary care physician.

During the monitored anesthesia care, the patient is sedated and cannot remember what is happening but is also responsive to touch and may even "wake" from time to time. As explained above, this is not the case with general anesthesia. The patient is usually awake at the end of the MAC service and can be readily discharged from the recovery room. Because MAC requires the same level of monitoring as a general anesthesia would, it is treated the same as a general anesthesia except that the appropriate modifiers must be used for payment purposes.

Although you have not yet studied modifiers, there are some modifiers that are unique to the coding of anesthesia claims. Modifiers are nothing more than adjectives, and they help further describe (or limit) the code that you are using. They are usually appended to the end of the code. While you will find many modifiers at the end of your CPT® book, you will also find modifiers in the HCPCS National Coding Manual. The following MAC modifiers are examples of those that you will find in the HCPCS National Coding Manual.

> ## Tip
>
> General anesthesia places the patient in a deep sleep; the patient loses consciousness and usually requires assisted ventilation.
>
>  ▶

QS –   Monitored anesthesia care (MAC) services

G8 –   Monitored Anesthesia care (MAC) for deep complex, complicated, or markedly invasive surgical procedures

G9 –   Monitored anesthesia care (MAC) for patient who has a history of severe cardiopulmonary condition

COMPARING REGIONAL AND LOCAL ANESTHESIA

Regional anesthesia refers to numbing only a region of the body. Medications called local anesthetics are injected to block nerves from transmitting the feeling of pain to the brain. Patients can either be awake or sleeping. If they are awake, the patient may feel movement or pressure, but no pain.

The three most common types of regional anesthesia are:

1.   **Spinals = injection of local anesthetics into the subarachnoid spaces at specific levels of the spine corresponding to the place of surgery to make it "sleep";**

2.   **Epidurals = same as a spinal only the anesthesia is placed between the vertebral spine and beneath the ligamentum flavum and into the extradural space;**

3.   **Peripheral Nerve Blocks = specific nerves coming from the surgery site are numbed to prevent the pain being transmitted to the brain.**

In local anesthesia, the injection is placed at the actual site of the surgery. Local anesthesia is usually only useful for operations on small areas. Local anesthetics are sometimes used with monitored anesthesia care or MAC.

PAIN MANAGEMENT

Pain management is an integral part of the array of services offered by the anesthesiologist. Various methods are used to control chronic, intractable pain resulting from an injury or illness. These same methods are used to control postoperative pain. It will not be the scope of this chapter to cover pain management specifics.

THE GLOBAL CONCEPT OR BLUE PLATE SPECIAL FOR ANESTHESIA

When anesthesia services are rendered, no matter which type, they are considered to be "global" in nature, meaning that you do not need to bill out separately for different components. You can think of the "global" concept as being similar to the blue plate special. That is, you get everything (including the baked potato, green beans, and meat loaf) for one price. Remember, the global period ends when the anesthesia provider releases the patient to the nurse or other provider in the post anesthesia area. If the patient is returned to the operating room that same day, it is a totally new global period. Unlike for surgeons, the anesthesia provider would not use modifier -78 (Return to the Operating Room for a Related Procedure During the Postoperative Period), because there is no postoperative period for anesthesia services.

For the Anesthesia section, this global concept (or blue plate special) includes the following:

1. **Work done in advance of the anesthesia administration (pre-op) (e.g., evaluating the pre-anesthesia questionnaire completed by the patient, seeing the patient in advance of the surgery, transporting, positioning, prepping, and draping of the patient for satisfactory anesthesia);**

2. **The anesthesia service itself, along with the administration of any other necessary fluids, or testing (e.g., ECG, monitoring temperature, blood pressure) that may be required to keep the patient as stable as possible (e.g., placement of external devices necessary for cardiac monitoring), oximetry (to determine how much oxygen is actually in the blood), capnography where the exhaled carbon dioxide is monitored to determine the adequacy of the patient's ventilation, temperature, EEG, central nervous system (CNS) evoked responses, and Doppler flow where the patient's cardiovascular blood flow is measured, placement of peripheral intravenous lines necessary for fluid and medication administration, placement of airway (e.g., endotracheal, orotracheal, nasogastric tubes), laryngoscopy for placement of airway tube, intraoperative interpretation of heart rate, respirations, temperature, laboratory determinations such as arterial blood gases (pH, pO2, pCO2, bicarbonate), hematology, blood chemistries, lactate, nerve stimulation for the determination of the level of paralysis or localization of nerves, insertion of urinary bladder catheter, and blood sample procurement through existing lines or requiring only venipuncture or arterial puncture;**

3. **Post-anesthesia follow-up/recovery (post-op).**

When you use the codes 00100 through 01999, remember that they all include the components listed above (the blue plate special) and it is not necessary to list them out separately. If, however, your anesthesia provider also provided a service that is not listed here (e.g., a surgical service, specialized echocardiogram, line insertion), you will need to make sure there is documentation by the surgeon requesting it (e.g., for postoperative pain management), then find the appropriate code in the CPT® book and bill it accordingly in addition to the code for the anesthesia.

Let's now discuss how anesthesia can be administered.

ANESTHESIA ADMINISTRATION
There are several ways anesthesia can be given to the patient. These are:

1. **Through the patient's breathing (via inhalation);**

2. **Through the patient's blood (intravenously);**

3. **Through the patient's rectum (rectally), meaning inserted into the rectum and then absorbed through the mucus membrane of the rectum;**

4. **Through a certain part of the patient's body to "anesthetize" that part of the body (know as "regional" anesthesia) such as a spinal, epidural, or nerve block (used often for pain alleviation);**

5. **Direct application such as cocaine for nasal surgeries.**

You will know which method your doctor used once you read the patient's chart. Once you become more familiar with the types of anesthesia that are available it will be easier. Do not despair…the code numbers and descriptions take all of this into account.

WHO PROVIDES THE ANESTHESIA?
There are several types of anesthesia providers. These are:

a. *An Anesthesiologist: an M.D. or D.O*. with additional training specializing in anesthesia and pain management;

b. *A Certified Registered Nurse Anesthetist (CRNA)*, who has had graduate-level education, training, and certification to administer anesthesia;

c. *An Anesthesia Assistant (AA)*, who has a pre-medical background, a baccalaureate degree, graduate-level studies, and training to monitor anesthesia administration.

Anesthesiologists may practice independently and bill independently. CRNA's may practice independently and bill independently.

A LITTLE MORE ABOUT CRNAS
As previously stated, a CRNA is an advanced practice nurse who specializes in providing/administering anesthesia either independently or under the "supervision" or "medical direction" of a physician. This nursing specialty has existed

since the Civil War. CRNAs were the first nurses to be awarded reimbursement rights under the Medicare program.

From a reimbursement standpoint, one of the most important aspects to consider is who employs the CRNA. A survey conducted in 2003 showed that, at that time, about 37% of the practicing CRNAs were employed with a physician group, 32% were employed by the hospital, 16% were independent contractors and 3% were employed by free standing surgical centers. Your insurance company will know who provided the services based upon several bits of information that you give them on the claim form, mainly because of the modifier you use to indicate who provided the service, but also by the HIPAA taxonomy used. While you have not yet studied modifiers, keep in mind that a modifier is simply an adjective. It tells the insurance company something extra about the service you provided. In this case it will identify "who" provided the service. While in other sections of this book we have chosen to withhold a thorough analysis on modifiers until a later chapter, we felt that since many people only need to study the chapter on Anesthesia and not any others (i.e., they do not code for anyone other than an anesthesiologist), it was appropriate to list some of the modifiers you would be seeing for the Anesthesia section here so that a discussion of how to report "who" actually provided the service would make sense to you. We will be discussing the "who" modifiers later in this chapter.

If the CRNA is self-employed and providing services to Medicare patients, he must "accept assignment." This means that he must agree to get the bulk of his payment, for the services he provides, directly from Medicare. The reimbursement will be at the rate that Medicare has predetermined will be the value of the services provided by the CRNA. This being said however, several states determine whether or not the CRNA must be "supervised" or "medically directed" by a physician. While not within the scope of this book to discuss all of the ins and outs of the requirements for CRNAs and anesthesiologist teams, please make sure that if you find yourself billing for any anesthesiologists, you check with the carriers in your state to determine who gets what payment (e.g., how much of the payment for services does the CRNA get while being supervised or medically directed by the physician and how much does the physician receive) and how both the billing is to be done and how the payment is split.

THE DIFFERENCE BETWEEN MEDICAL SUPERVISION & MEDICAL DIRECTION

Normally, it is the anesthesiologist who will provide the anesthesia for the patient and, in some cases he may employ a CRNA or an AA. If either the CRNA or the AA is working for the physician, the CRNA and AA may provide services under the medical direction of the anesthesiologist, or under supervision.

Some misguided individuals use the terms "medical direction" and "medical supervision" interchangeably; that is, people use them as if they mean the same thing. Be careful, as the terms have two entirely different meanings.

> ### Tip
> If you find yourself billing for any anesthesiologists, check with the carrier in your state to determine who gets what payment.
>
>

Medical direction means that the physician has met all of the requirements by a particular state for being able to direct the CRNA or AA and that this physician will receive 100% of the reimbursement for the claim.

To many carriers, medical supervision means that the physician anesthesiologist was either involved with more than four concurrent rooms/cases or that he failed to meet the medical direction steps required by some states. In these cases, you will either see (if you are reviewing claims) or use the modifier "AD." Some carriers will not reimburse a claim when they see the modifier "AD" as the carriers feel that more than four consecutive cases exceed standards or proper medical care.

MEDICAL DIRECTION (MODIFIER QK)

Anesthesiologists can only bill for services provided under "medical direction" if the following conditions are met:

1. **The physician (anesthesiologist) is present supervising* the CRNA or the AA, even though the anesthesiologist is not actually performing the anesthesia care;**

2. **There are not more than four simultaneous cases being done by CRNAs or AAs under the anesthesiologist's direction.**

The physician can bill for the anesthesia services provided by the CRNA and the AA if the physician:

1. **Also performs the pre-anesthesia evaluation of the patient;**

2. **Determines and prescribes the exact plan for the anesthesia;**

3. **Personally participates in the challenging portion of the service(s) such as induction and emergence;**

4. **Is present and available in the event of any emergencies;**

5. **Monitors the course of the anesthesia administration at intervals;**

6. **Also performs the post-anesthesia care to the patient.**

7. **Ensures that all procedures are performed by qualified CRNAs or AAs.**

Now, the anesthesiologist can't do just anything while providing medical direction (as if he would have time). In general, he must remain "behind the red line" in the operating suite so he can respond to emergencies. So, if the labor and delivery is a floor up, he probably should not be going there.

Key

Supervision can mean that the physician can also be providing other services at the same time (e.g., working on discharge notes, checking on patients periodically in post-anesthesia recovery) while still monitoring the work of the CRNA and the AA.

What he can do is:

1. **Address an emergency of short duration in the immediate area;**

2. **Administer an epidural or caudal anesthetic to ease labor pain;**

3. **Perform periodic, rather than continuous, monitoring of an obstetrical patient;**

4. **Receive patients entering the operating suite for the next surgery;**

5. **Check on or discharge patients from the recovery room;**

6. **Coordinate scheduling matters.**

MEDICAL SUPERVISION (MODIFIER AD)

In anesthesia, medical supervision differs from medical direction. Medical supervision can fall into one of two scenarios. The first is when the doctor supervises more than four cases that are going on concurrently. An example of this would be an outpatient surgical setting where a face-lift is performed in Room A, a tummy tuck in Room B, a blepharoplasty in Room C, a breast augmentation in Room D, and a liposuction in Room E. The anesthesiologist does not have to be physically present in each room, but rather he/she is supervising the work of the CRNAs or AAs who are actually providing the anesthesia.

The second is when there are only four concurrent cases (or less) going on (which would imply that the doctor is directing and not supervising) and then there is an emergency in one room upon which he must focus his attention. In situations like this, the medical direction of the other cases falls to "medical supervision" in that the doctor is only supervising the other cases while he attends to the emergency situation.

MODIFIERS THAT EXPLAIN WHO PROVIDED THE ANESTHESIA SERVICE: THE "WHO" MODIFIERS

If you are planning on studying all of cpTeach®, you will see that in our chapter on Modifiers we explain that modifiers are two digit codes that are used like adjectives. They simply describe something additional about the noun (code) to which they are appended.

For instance, if you wanted to say that we are experiencing blue skies today, you would know that the adjective (or modifier) was the word "blue" and that it referred to the "skies." Likewise, in CPT®, when you want to say that the CRNA provided the anesthesia service, you would use the modifier to express that it was a CRNA.

Unlike in English where adjectives tend to precede the noun, modifiers in coding come after the code. An example would look like the following:

00100-AA

There are several modifiers that let the carrier know who provided the anesthesia to the patient. Each of these is unique and has something different to say, so please read them individually. You will notice that there is a two-digit alpha code (two letters of the alphabet) and then a description that follows each code. None of these modifiers will be found in the CPT® book but can be located by looking in the HCPCS National Coding Manual and in the ASA's Relative Value Guide.

The modifiers that tell the carrier who provided the service are:

AA **(Physician Modifier) Anesthesia services are performed personally by the Anesthesiologist himself.**

AD **(Physician Modifier) Anesthesia services are medically supervised by the physician with more than four concurrent (simultaneous) cases. The physician will use this modifier while the CRNA will also submit a bill with the modifier -QX to indicate that the CRNA provided services under an anesthesiologist's medical direction.**

QK **(Physician Modifier) Anesthesia services are medically directed by the physician for two, three, or four concurrent cases done by qualified individuals.**

QY **(Physician Modifier) This will be the modifier that the anesthesiologist uses to report the medical direction of one CRNA.**

Q6 **(Physician Modifier) This shows that the services for the anesthesia were done by a locum tenens physician (i.e., a physician who is substituting for another physician for a certain period of time).**

The following modifiers can be billed by a CRNA:

QX **(Modifier used by the CRNA) CRNA provided the services under the direction of the anesthesiologist who has met all of the requirements to be able to direct the CRNA. Each provider (i.e., the CRNA and the anesthesiologist) will be paid a portion of the fees.**

QZ **(CRNA modifier) When you use this modifier, the CRNA will be paid 100% of the reimbursed fees. QZ indicates that the CRNA provided the services without the medical direction of the Anesthesiologist (physician).**

Tip

An anesthesiologist must remain in the operating room during the entire procedure for the case to be considered a personally performed service.

Key

When you are billing for both the CRNA and the anesthesiologist on the same claim form, you will need to make sure that both modifiers are used. That is, use the modifier -QX on the end of the CPT® code to show the CRNA's role and the modifier QY on the end of the CPT® code to indicate the physician's role.

WHAT ANESTHESIA SERVICE WAS PROVIDED?

Once you know who provided the service, you should ask yourself about what service they provided. For instance, did they provide anesthesia for an obstetric service, or one for a breast reduction? On which part of the body did the service occur? Knowing that the Anesthesia section is arranged mostly from the head to the feet, and recognizing (from the patient's medical chart) what the anesthesia was provided for will help you find the correct CPT® code.

Let's take an example. Assume a patient was being operated on for a breast reduction.

Option 1 Locate the CPT® code for the breast reduction. Use that code in a crosswalk (the ASA has a good one) that will lead you from the CPT® procedure code to the most frequently used anesthesia code. The crosswalk also has the narrative of the anesthesia code completely stated, as well as the base units. It also lists the other anesthesia codes that might be used.

Option 2 Look in the CPT® index under "Anesthesia." For the modifier you may use either the location or, frequently, the type of procedure. Find the modifier that most closely matches the location of the procedure. In this case, look under "Anesthesia, breast, breast reduction." It directs you to 00402.

Option 3 Look in the Anesthesia section of the CPT® book realizing that the section is mostly in order from head to toe. Since the procedure on the breast would be in the location of the thorax, you would find that particular subdivision and look for a description of the code that most closely resembles the kind of anesthesia you provided.

Consider the following:

00402 *Anesthesia for procedures on the integumentary system on the extremities, anterior trunk and perineum; reconstructive procedures on breast (e.g., reduction or augmentation mammoplasty, muscle flaps)*

                 Copyright AMA, 2011

After you have located the code that tells you what was done to the patient, you must also let the carrier know who provided the service. Using one of the modifiers we described above, you can let the carrier know that it was the CRNA who provided the anesthesia service under the direction of the physician.

00402-QX *Anesthesia for procedures on the integumentary system on the extremities, anterior trunk and perineum; reconstructive procedures on breast (e.g., reduction or augmentation mammoplasty, muscle flaps) - CRNA provided the services under the direction of the Anesthesiologist*

               Copyright AMA, 2011

Tip

Placing the modifier at the end of the CPT® code indicates to the carrier both what was done and who did it.

Key

Anesthesia codes do not use RT, LT, or 50 (See the chapter on Modifiers for more information on what the RT, LT and –50 are.).

ABOUT THE CONDITION OF THE PATIENT

It is also important for the carrier (and even more so for the physician) to know about the patient's condition. For instance, is the patient a normal healthy patient, does he have some sort of disease, or is he close to dying and at risk at the time the anesthesia is being administered? Each of these conditions will determine a lot about when, how, and if the anesthesia is even provided. The patient's condition also may have a fair impact on the length of time needed for the anesthesia provider and surgeon to provide the service.

In order to better convey the physical status of the patient, the CPT® book lists six separate modifiers that describe the different general statuses of the patient.

These are:

PATIENT STATUS MODIFIERS

Modifier	Description	Physical Status Modifying Units
P1	Normal healthy patient	0
P2	Patient with mild systemic disease	0
P3	Patient with severe systemic disease	1
P4	Patient with severe systemic disease that is a constant threat to life	2
P5	Moribund (dying) patient who is not expected to survive without the operation	3
P6	A declared brain-dead patient whose organs are being removed for donor purposes	0

You will note that these physical status modifiers all start with the letter P for "physical" and end with a number from 1 through 6. Do NOT mistake it for the 1P, 2P, 3P, and 8P which are modifiers for the category II codes. The way you would use the anesthesia physical status modifiers (P1,P2, P3, P4, P5, P6) is similar to how you would use any modifier; you would place it at the end of the CPT® code that you chose. You will also note the physical status modifying units at the end of the modifiers. These amounts (0 through a maximum of 3) will be used in the formula that you employ when you calculate your total fees (more on this a little later in this chapter).

Let's take an example.

Suppose the surgeon was going to operate on a patient who had a small 0.2 cm lesion in her nose. The doctor and the patient had decided that, at a minimum, the lesion was unsightly and that it needed to come off. The patient, a normal, healthy 10 year old, was brought to the operating room for her day surgery. The physician performed the surgery without any complications, and the anesthesiologist provided the anesthesia services. In coding for the anesthesiologist, you would notice several things. First is that the service occurred on the upper part of the body (toward the head). Because of this, and knowing how the Anesthesia section of CPT® is arranged, you would look under "Head" to see which code most closely resembled the service provided by your doctor.

In all likelihood, you would choose the following:

> *00160*   *Anesthesia for procedures on nose and accessory sinuses; not otherwise specified*
>
> Copyright AMA, 2011

As you look at the description of this code, however, you can see that nowhere in it are you given any information about the fact that the patient was a normal, healthy 10 year old. This is where the Physical Status Modifiers come in. By looking at the listing above, you would see that the physical status modifier P1 most closely describes the situation you have with this patient; that is, that your patient is normal and healthy. You would take this modifier and append it to the end of the CPT® code that you used to report the anesthesia for the nose.

> *00160-P1*   *Anesthesia for procedures on nose and accessory sinuses; not otherwise specified; normal healthy patient*
>
> Copyright AMA, 2011

When you look at the physical status modifying units associated with the P1 modifier you will note that it is "0." Basically, this means that the fact that the patient was normal and healthy will have no impact on the reimbursement either in a positive or negative way. If the physical status modifier has some value (e.g., a 1, 2, or 3) then the calculated fee would be affected.

There are also other codes that you will find in the CPT® book that address the condition of the patient. These codes can be found in the Medicine section (specifically located toward the end) under the Qualifying Circumstances for Anesthesia subsection. When you look at these codes, you will see the following codes and descriptions. We have taken the liberty of including the ASA modifying units so that you can see how the use of any of these extra codes will impact your overall fees.

CPT Code	Description	ASA Modifying Units
✚99100	*Anesthesia for patient of extreme age, younger than 1 year and older than 70 (List separately in addition to the code for primary anesthesia procedure)*	*1*
✚99116	*Anesthesia complicated by utilization of total body hypothermia (List separately in addition to the code for primary anesthesia procedure)*	*5*
✚99135	*Anesthesia complicated by utilization of controlled hypotension (List separately in addition to code for primary anesthesia procedure)*	*5*
✚99140	*Anesthesia complicated by emergency conditions (specify) (List separately in addition to code for primary anesthesia procedure)*	*2*

Copyright AMA, 2011

You will notice three main things about each of the codes listed above. The first is that they all ask for you to use them in addition to the code for the primary anesthesia procedure(s). The second is that they all describe something additional about the patient that you can't get by simply looking at the regular anesthesia code. The third is the number of Relative Value Units that are attributed to each code. These RVUs will be used in the "modifying units" portion of the formula for calculating your overall fee.

You may ask yourself how these differ from the physical status modifiers that also described something about the patient. The answer is simple. You will always use a physical status modifier on the end of every Anesthesia code that you employ as it describes the overall health of the patient with no specifics. You may or may not use the Qualifying Circumstances for Anesthesia subsection codes, as these describe more specific things about the patient (e.g., total body hypothermia, hypotension).

Let's take another example.

> *Suppose you had a patient who seemed to be a normal, otherwise healthy 9 month old with a cleft lip. In coding for the anesthesia portion of the services provided for this patient you would first look up the code at the beginning of the Anesthesia section to see which one closely resembles the description of what it was that you did. Secondly, you would add the Physical Status modifier to the end of that code to indicate that the patient was a healthy person. Thirdly, if applicable, attach a Qualifying Circumstance for Anesthesia code to show the carrier that the patient was considered to be of "extreme" age (under the age of 1).*

Your coding would look like the following:

> *00102-P1*   *Anesthesia for procedures involving plastic repair of cleft lip-normal healthy patient*
>
> *+99100*   *Anesthesia for patient of extreme age, younger than 1 year and older than 70 (List separately in addition to code for primary anesthesia procedure)*
>
> Copyright AMA, 2011

Key

Notice that each code says something a bit different to the insurance company and each will also have its own unique price.

MEDICAL NECESSITY

As with every service you code, there must be documentation that the service is medically necessary. You will document the medical necessity through the proper use of the diagnostic codes that explain why the patient was being seen (i.e., his disease or condition. ICD (diagnostic) codes are not discussed in this book). As we have already discussed, some services that require anesthesia will be major procedures, such as coronary artery bypass graft or the repair of a hip fracture. Anesthesia can also be deemed necessary in a minor procedure, such as in a patient with a history of cardiopulmonary disease who needs to have vital signs monitored and cannot do so without anesthesia. Anesthesia may also be necessary for a small child who must remain still for a minor procedure.

You will find that frequently you will need to use various components, whether they are multiple CPT® codes, modifiers, or whatever to completely describe everything you can about the patient and the conditions that you were working under. Do not be afraid to use as many of these components (e.g., physical status modifiers, qualifying circumstances for anesthesia) as you need.

To determine the sequence of modifiers, usually those that impact the price are listed first. But with anesthesia, the provider specialty modifiers (e.g., AA and QX pay 100% so they would not modify payment) and patient status modifiers (e.g., P1 do not modify payment) sometimes modify payment and sometimes don't. Check with the carrier and submit modifiers in the order they prescribe.

HOW LONG DID THE PROVIDER SPEND WITH THE PATIENT?

TIME

Once you have answered the questions above, it will be important to investigate the total time that the provider spent with the patient. We have explained that looking at the total amount of time is important to you, because time is one of the factors that you will look at in determining the overall reimbursement for each case. Don't worry. We will pull all of these details together for you toward the end of this chapter after we have explained what the variables are, and why you need them.

In Anesthesia, time is measured by looking at the total time from the moment the provider first began to prepare the patient for anesthesia until the time when, after post-anesthesia recovery, the patient was released from the care of the anesthesia provider to the qualified nursing staff. All of this time is considered to be part of the global fee period that we discussed earlier in this chapter, where the blue plate special applies and where everything will be included in that one price.

So to determine what you will do for coding for anesthesia services, find the anesthesia start and stop times. This is not just the time when the anesthetic agent was being administered, but the time before and after administration also. Determine the time in minutes. This is usually done by lining up the hours and minutes (in "military time") of the anesthesia stop time above the anesthesia start hours and minutes. Then subtract.

Stop	12 (hours)	47 (minutes)	
Start	09 (hours)	23 (minutes)	
Total	03 (hours)	24 (minutes)	= (3 hours x 60 minutes/hour + 24 minutes)
			= 204 minutes

When you have a smaller minutes number at the stop time than the start time (e.g., end 12:23, begin 09:47), subtract 1 from the stop hour (e.g., 12-1=11) and add 60 to the stop minutes (e.g., 23 + 60 = 83). Then your calculation will look like:

Stop	11 (hours)	83 (minutes)	
Start	09 (hours)	47 (minutes)	
Total	02 (hours)	36 (minutes)	= (120 minutes + 36 minutes)
			= 156 minutes

When you look at the total time (that should be listed in the patient's medical record), it will be important to check with your carrier to see if they divide the time in increments of 15 minutes or something else. This could make all of the difference in the world to you from a reimbursement standpoint. The most common time increment, however, is the 15-minute time increment.

Let's take an example.

Suppose the service that you provided to the patient started at 7:00 a.m. and ended at 9:35 a.m. If the custom in your region is to base the time increments on 15 minutes, you would look at the total time and then divide by 15. In this case, the total time would be 2 hours and 35 minutes (a total of 155 minutes). By dividing the 155 by the 15-minute increment value, you will see that the total time incre-

ments would be equal to 10.33 units. If, however, the accepted time increment were 30 minutes, the number of units for this same example would be 5.166.   You can see how important it is to know what the accepted time increments are before you start to do the math.

As you can see by looking at the examples listed above, the number of time units ended up being fractional. That is, when we calculated the total number of units by dividing the total time (in minutes) by the number of the time increment (e.g., 15, 30), the end result was not a whole number. In some states when this happens, you are asked to go ahead and round up or down to the nearest whole number. Some carriers want it submitted to the tenths, so you would have submitted 10.3. In other states, you will be allowed to use the entire number, fractional or not, as part of your overall calculation. Please check with your carriers to see what they want you to do and make sure that you do a broad range check. Some carriers in your same region may want it done one way and the one next door to them may want it done another. Also, make sure that you update your calls to these carriers annually to make sure that you have the latest requirement on how they want you to do the calculations. Time spent on the front end could save you literally thousands on the back.

Multiple Procedures

Sometimes patients have more than one procedure done during a surgical encounter. It would be labor intensive, add no benefit, as well as be risky to bring the patient out of an anesthetized state between each procedure. So how do you code if there were multiple procedures on different parts of the body? For instance, if a patient were shot by another hunter while out at his local ranch, there could be injuries requiring removal of buck shot from the superficial facial and scalp as well as removal of shrapnel from the lungs. For this, code out all of the surgical procedures done (and check with the surgeon's coder to make sure your codes match). Check each surgical code using a crosswalk to the applicable anesthesia code. The anesthesia code with the highest number of base units would be the code reported by the anesthesia provider. Sometimes the primary surgical procedure does not match the anesthesia service with the highest base units, so don't be concerned if this happens. How do you account for all the other services? They are accounted for with the time units.

Cancelled/Discontinued Services

Remember that anesthesia services are professional services, not institutional services. Therefore, when determining the correct modifier for anesthesia, do not be tempted to use the ambulatory surgery center codes. Those are for the institutional component.

When a surgery is cancelled or discontinued the day upon which it was scheduled, check with the carrier or the contract on how to submit. In general:

Key

If the anesthesia provider has NOT begun administering anesthesia when the surgery is cancelled, code the preoperative assessment and services up to the cancellation using an E/M code.

If the anesthesia provider has begun administering anesthesia, code the surgical procedure that was scheduled/started. The number of minutes will indicate that something happened. Be sure to use a diagnosis code to indicate why the surgery was cancelled.

BASE UNITS

Base Units are those values that are assigned to the great majority of the Anesthesia codes by the American Society of Anesthesiologists. These values are determined based upon two main factors. The first is the global package; that is, what is involved by the physician in order to provide the pre-op work, the intra-surgery anesthesia, and the post-anesthesia recovery work. The second factor is the cost of doing business for the anesthesiologist. This could be the cost of the rent, the billing service company, malpractice insurance, any employees, etc. All of these "costs" are evaluated and then broken down into a number that is assigned to each anesthesia code based upon what it would take for the physician to provide that service. For instance, if you were to look at the base units for the following codes, notice how they would be different based upon the amount of work and cost that is involved in providing those services to the patient.

CPT Code	Description	Base Units
00100	*Anesthesia for procedures on salivary glands, including biopsy*	*5*
00474	*Anesthesia for partial rib resection; radical procedures (e.g., pectus excavatum)*	*13*

Copyright AMA, 2011

CONVERSION FACTORS

Each physician will have what most of us would compare to an "hourly rate." In other words, some dollar amount that, depending upon how long we worked, our overall pay would be based upon. In the world of anesthesia coding and billing, this rate is called a conversion factor and it is unique both to the physician or provider and to the region of the country in which this provider practices. You will need to know what your provider's conversion factor is in order to be able to complete the formula for calculating the overall fee for the services you provide. Do not despair. The physician should be able to give this to you. If the provider does not have his or her conversion factor, you will need to get help from someone in the field (perhaps you could try calling the ASA) to learn how to calculate one.

PUTTING IT ALL TOGETHER

It is now time to look at everything that has been discussed and put it all together so that you can make sense out of not only the coding portion but the billing

Tip

Base units are important to the anesthesia coder because they are used in calculating the overall fee that is charged to the patient and third-party payer.

portion of the Anesthesia section. Let's consider the formula for calculating the fee once more before putting it all together.

> **Base Units + Time Units + Modifying Units = Total Units**
> **Total Units x Conversion Factor = Total Fee**

As we have already discussed, there are many things that you need to look at in calculating the fee charged. The first thing you will need to do is to find the anesthesia code that you feel most closely describes what kind of anesthesia you provided for your patient. This will give you the first piece of the required information by giving you the base units that are based upon the procedure you provided.

Let's take an example.

> *Suppose a patient with a breast mass is scheduled for a biopsy. The patient is a normal healthy patient who has no modifying circumstances that need to be reported. The code for excision of a breast mass is 00402. If you had access to the ASA's Relative Value book, you could look up this number, 00402, and see that this code has 5 base units.*

Tip

Remember: Base units are a measure of the degree of work required to provide the procedure to the patient or, put another way, the degree of difficulty.

> **Base units for code 00402 (see ASA Relative Value Guide) = 5 base units**

In continuing to examine the formula for calculating the fee for a certain service, you examine the patient's chart and see that the anesthesiologist has recorded the time of the initial contact with the patient as 10:00 a.m. and the finish time with the patient as 11:00 a.m., making the total time spent with the patient equal to 60 minutes.

Assuming, for the sake of this example, that the local carrier mandates that they will award one time unit for every 15 minutes spent with the patient, you will take the 60 minutes of total time and divide it by the 15 minute increment (mandated by the carrier) to get the total time units spent.

> **60 minutes spent with the patient divided by 15 minute base increment**
> **= 4 time units**

When we look at the formula again, we see the following:

> **Base Units (5) + Time Units (4) + Modifying Units (0)　= Total Units (9)**
> **Total Units x Conversion Factor = Total Fee**

Let's say for the sake of this example that the provider conversion factor is $100 per unit.

Base Units (5) + Time Units (4) + Modifying Units (0) = Total Units (9)
Total Units (9) x Conversion Factor ($100) = Total Fee ($900)

Let's take another example.

This time, you have the same case but the patient is 72 years old. You would use the following CPT® codes.

CPT Code	Description	Base/Modifying Units
00402	*Anesthesia for procedures on the integumentary system on the extremities, anterior trunk and perineum; reconstructive procedures on breast (e.g. reduction or augmentation mamoplasty, muscle flaps)*	5
+99100	*Anesthesia for patients of extreme age, younger than 1 year older than 70 (List separately in addition to code for primary anesthesia procedure).*	1

Copyright AMA, 2011

In putting this all together in order to calculate a fee, here is what you would see.

Base Unit (5) + Time Units (4) + Modifying Units (1) = Total Units (10)
Total Units (10) x Conversion Factor ($100) = Total Fee ($1000)

As you can see, the addition of the 99100 and its modifying unit of 1 added $100 extra to this provider's overall charge.

Here is another example.

Suppose that again, we had the same 72-year-old patient, only she was having a repair of an aortic aneurysm. This time, the anesthesiologist used controlled hypotension because an aneurysm was involved and you sure don't want any increased pressure during these procedures. Say the procedure was 33875, a graft of the descending thoracic aorta, without bypass.

Your CPT® coding would look like this:

CPT Code	Description	Base/Modifying Units
00560	*Anesthesia for procedures on heart, pericardial sac, and great vessels of chest; without pump oxygenator*	20
+99100	*Anesthesia for patients of extreme age, younger than 1 year older than 70 (List separately in addition to code for primary anesthesia procedure)*	1

+99135 *Anesthesia complicated by utilization of controlled* *5*
hypotension (List separately in addition to code for
primary anesthesia procedure)

Copyright AMA, 2011

Anesthesia time was four hours (240 minutes), which is 16 fifteen-minute time units.

Using the formula above, we would just plug in all of the values accordingly.

Base Units (20) + Time Units (16) + Modifying Units (1+5)
= Total Units (42)
Total Units (42) x Conversion Factor ($100) = Total Fee ($4200)

All of these examples, for simplicity sake, do not include any reductions for con-tractual obligations, patient deductible, or co-insurance.

The base units have a wide range of values, as can be seen above, with the low-est at 3 units (for something such as a knee scope), and up to 30 units (for the re-cipient of a liver transplant). Medicaid and Medicare reimbursements for a base unit start in the teens and range up, depending on the region of the country and the county, with the average around $17.00 per unit. Commercial carriers have higher values for the base units (which is why providers tend to have patients with insurance rather than patients whose care is paid by the Federal govern-ment), but these rates vary depending on contracts they have with the physician and/or other variables.

Like any other service that you try to bill for, it is important to check with your insurance carriers to see if they have provisions to pay for anesthesia services at a contracted rate, even if the provider is not contracted. If there are such provisions to pay non-contracted providers, these provisions for may be found under various acronyms such as RAP (radiologists, anesthesiolo-gists, pathologists) and PARE (pathologist, anesthesiologist, radiologists and emergency room physicians). Carriers will often have provisions for non-con-tracted provider payments to take into account services furnished to patients (who are subscribers to their plan) but for whom services were provided by a non-contracted physician.

Let's take an example.

Suppose an anesthesiologist for a patient who has BCBS insurance performs a service. If the anesthesiologist is not "contracted" as a provider of service under BCBS, the insurance company may have a provision that allows for the anesthesiologist to receive payment for the services he/she provided. The insurance companies realize that in cases such as this, the patient has no choice in choosing the anesthesiologist from the health plans they participate with, as the anesthesiologist has most likely been referred by the surgeon or hospital and is considered to be an "unseen" physician by the patient.

This concludes this portion on anesthesia. As with most topics on coding, there is always more to learn. Check on the Internet and with your carriers for more specifics on anesthesia topics.

Name:_____

Class/Section:_____

Date:_____

2012

EXERCISE 7.1

1. _____ Burn Excisions or Debridement

2. _____ Shoulder and Axilla

3. _____ Lower Leg (Below Knee, Includes Ankle and Foot)

4. _____ Knee and Popliteal Area

5. _____ Head

6. _____ Forearm, Wrist, and Hand

7. _____ Other Procedures

8. _____ Upper Leg (Except Knee)

9. _____ Radiological Procedures

10. _____ Pelvis (Except Hip)

11. _____ Neck

12. _____ Perineum

13. _____ Thorax (Chest Wall and Shoulder Girdle)

14. _____ Lower Abdomen

15. _____ Intrathoracic

16. _____ Upper Abdomen

17. _____ Upper Arm and Elbow

18. _____ Obstetric

19. _____ Spine and Spinal Cord

Before You Begin:
Read Chapter 7 in cpTeach® on "Anesthesia." Follow along in your CPT® with the points illustrated in cpTeach®.

Purpose of this Lesson:
To familiarize the student with the overall arrangement of the Anesthesia chapter.

Instructions:
1. Read the following subsections of the Anesthesia chapter listed below.

2. Place the subsections in the order in which they appear in your CPT® codebook by writing 1, 2, 3, etc. in the space to the left of each description.

WORKBOOK

cpTeach
2012

Name:_____

Class/Section:_____

Date:_____

Before You Begin:

Read Chapter 7 in cpTeach® on "Anesthesia." Follow along in your CPT® with the points illustrated in cpTeach®.

Purpose of this Lesson:

To familiarize the student with the overall arrangement of the Anesthesia chapter.

Instructions:

1. Look up the definition to the words listed below in cpTeach®.

2. Write the correct definition by each word below.

Exercise 7.2

1. RVU_____

2. Base Unit_____

3. Regional Anesthesia_____

4. Total Units_____

5. MAC_____

6. General Anesthesia_____

7. Time Units_____

8. CRNA_____

9. Medical Supervision_____

10. Medical Direction_____

11. Local Anesthesia_____

12. Modifying Units_____

Name:_____

Class/Section:_____

Date:_____

EXERCISE 7.3

a. _____

   _____

   _____

b. _____

   _____

   _____

c. _____

   _____

   _____

d. _____

   _____

   _____

e. _____

   _____

   _____

Before You Begin:
Read Chapter 7 in cpTeach® on "Anesthesia." Follow along in your CPT® with the points illustrated in cpTeach®.

Purpose of this Lesson:
To familiarize the student with the overall arrangement of the Anesthesia chapter.

Instructions:
1. Look up the various ways in cpTeach® to obtain information that will allow the coder to effectively use the formula for calculating anesthesia charges.

2. Write the 5 distinct ways below including a brief definition of each.

WORKBOOK

McGUFFEY

cpTeach

2012

Name:_____

Class/Section:_____

Date:_____

Before You Begin:

Read Chapter 7 in cpTeach® on "Anesthesia." Follow along in your CPT® with the points illustrated in cpTeach®.

Purpose of this Lesson:

To familiarize the student with the overall arrangement of the Anesthesia chapter.

Instructions:

1. Look up the various ways in cpTeach® that anesthesia can be administered to a patient.

2. Write the 5 individual ways below.

EXERCISE 7.4

a. _____

_____

_____

b. _____

_____

_____

c. _____

_____

_____

d. _____

_____

_____

e. _____

_____

_____

Name:_____

Class/Section:_____

cpTeach

Date:_____

2012

EXERCISE 7.5

	Physical Modifier	**CRNA Modifier**
Modifier QX:		
Modifier QY:		
Modifier AA:		
Modifier QK:		
Modifier AD:		
Modifier QZ:		
Modifier Q6:		

Before You Begin:
Read Chapter 7 in cpTeach® on "Anesthesia." Follow along in your CPT® with the points illustrated in cpTeach®.

Purpose of this Lesson:
To familiarize the student with the overall arrangement of the Anesthesia chapter.

Instructions:
1. Look up the following anesthesia modifiers listed below in cpTeach®.

2. Place the modifier under the appropriate usage category.

WORKBOOK

McGUFFEY

cpTeach

2012

*Name:*_____

*Class/Section:*_____

*Date:*_____

Before You Begin:
Read Chapter 7 in cpTeach®
on "Anesthesia." Follow
along in your CPT® with
the points illustrated in
cpTeach®.

Purpose of this Lesson:
To familiarize the student
with the overall arrangement
of the Anesthesia chapter.

Instructions:
1. Look up the following
   physical status anesthesia
   modifiers listed below in
   cpTeach®.

2. Write the definition of
   each physical status
   modifier below.

EXERCISE 7.6

1. P1 _____

_____

2. P2 _____

_____

3. P3 _____

_____

4. P4 _____

_____

5. P5 _____

_____

6. P6 _____

_____

WORKBOOK

cpTeach

2012

Name:_____

Class/Section:_____

Date:_____

EXERCISE 7.7

1. P1 _____

2. P2 _____

3. P3 _____

4. P4 _____

5. P5 _____

6. P6 _____

Before You Begin:
Read Chapter 7 in cpTeach® on "Anesthesia." Follow along in your CPT® with the points illustrated in cpTeach®.

Purpose of this Lesson:
To familiarize the student with the overall arrangement of the Anesthesia chapter.

Instructions:
1. Look up the following physical status anesthesia modifiers listed below in cpTeach®.

2. Place the correct amount of modifying units next to each.

Before You Begin:
Read Chapter 7 in cpTeach® on "Anesthesia." Follow along in your CPT® with the points illustrated in cpTeach®.

Purpose of this Lesson:
To familiarize the student with the overall arrangement of the Anesthesia chapter.

Instructions:
1. Read the examples listed below to determine which level of physical status modifier best describes each one.

2. Place the correct physical status modifier next to each one.

EXERCISE 7.8

_____ 1. The patient is brought to the ER and after a 3-hour surgery, is pronounced brain-dead. Upon notifying the next of kin, the patient's relative determines that the organs are to be donated.

_____ 2. A 21-year-old woman in active labor, showing signs of preeclampsia.

_____ 3. A healthy 32-year-old man presents himself for a routine tonsillectomy.

_____ 4. A 50-year-old woman, in her third trimester, presents herself with congestive heart failure for a cesarean section delivery in a breech position.

_____ 5. Two 13-year-old Siamese twin males, joined at the head and shoulder.

_____ 6. An 23-year-old woman with acute appendicitis, presents for an emergency appendectomy.

Name:_____

Class/Section:_____

cpTeach
2012

Date:_____

Example:

A patient is scheduled for surgery today. She is a healthy 38-year-old with no modifying circumstances. Today's procedure is a simple, uncomplicated vaginal delivery. The anesthesia code is 01960. Assume that you had access to the ASA's RVU book and the Base Units for 01960 is equal to "5." The initial contact with the patient was at 8:46 a.m., and the finish time was 11:13 a.m., making the time spent 2 hours and 27 minutes (147 minutes). Assume that 15 minutes = 1 Time Unit. Assume the Conversion Factor for this procedure is $100.00. What is the total fee?

Base Units 5 + Time Units 0 = Total Units 14.8
Total Units 14.8 x Conversion Factor $100.00 = Total Fee $1480.00

Before You Begin:
Read Chapter 7 in cpTeach® on "Anesthesia." Follow along in your CPT® with the points illustrated in cpTeach®.

Purpose of this Lesson:
To familiarize the student with the overall arrangement of the Anesthesia chapter.

Instructions:
1. Read the following examples below.

2. Fill in the blanks using the information provided, and determine the Total Fee.

Exercise 7.9

1. A patient in an accident presents to the ER with a broken nose. He is a 16-year-old male in relatively good health. There are no modifying circumstances. Today's procedure is a closed treatment of the nasal bone fracture, without stabilization. The anesthesia code is 00160. Assume that you had access to the ASA's RVU book and the Base Units for 00160 is equal to "5." The initial contact with the patient was at 6:02 a.m., and the finish time was 7:03 a.m., making the time spent 1 hours and 1 minute (61 minutes). Assume that 15 minutes = 1 Time Unit. Assume the Conversion Factor for this procedure is $35.00. What is the total fee?

Base Units _____ + Time Units _____ + Modifying Units _____ = Total Units _____

Total Units _____ x Conversion Factor $_____ = Total Fee $_____

2. A 92-year-old patient has fallen in the shower and fractured his left forearm. The patient has cataracts on both eyes and has cardiac issues. Today's procedure is to apply a cast to the forearm. The anesthesia code is 01860. Assume that you had access to the ASA's RVU book and the Base Units for 01860 is equal to "3." The initial contact with the patient was at 2:10 a.m., and the finish time was 2:33 a.m., making the time spent 0 hours and 23 minutes (23 minutes). Assume that 15 minutes = 1 Time Unit. Assume the Conversion Factor for this procedure is $35.00. What is the total fee?

Base Units_____ + Time Units_____ + Modifying Units_____ = Total Units_____

Total Units_____   x Conversion Factor $_____ = Total Fee $_____

3. A patient is presented with severe (total body) hypothermia (CPT® code 99116) and a ruptured achilles tendon. She is a 34-year-old female. Today's procedure is to repair the ruptured tendon. The anesthesia code is 01472. Assume that you had access to the ASA's RVU book and the Base Units for 01472 is equal to "5." The initial contact with the patient was at 3:59 p.m., and the finish time was 7:58 p.m., making the time spent 3 hours and 59 minutes (239 minutes). Assume that 15 minutes = 1 Time Unit. Assume the Conversion Factor for this procedure is $75.00. What is the total fee?

Base Units_____ + Time Units_____ + Modifying Units_____ = Total Units_____

Total Units_____   x Conversion Factor $_____ = Total Fee $_____

4. The patient is requiring anesthesia for an open or surgical arthroscopy procedure of the shoulder joint (CPT® code 29805). The patient is a 47-year-old man with no known problems, appearing to be in good health. There are no modifying circumstances. The anesthesia code is 01630. Assume that you had access to the ASA's RVU book and the Base Units for 01630 is equal to "5." The initial contact with the patient was at 11:22 a.m., and the finish time was 1:15 p.m., making the time spent 1 hours and 53 minutes (113 minutes). Assume that 15 minutes = 1 Time Unit. Assume the Conversion Factor for this procedure is $42.63. What is the total fee?

Base Units_____ + Time Units_____ + Modifying Units_____ = Total Units_____

Total Units_____   x Conversion Factor $_____ = Total Fee $_____

Name:_____

Class/Section:_____

Date:_____

5. A 51-year-old severe alcoholic male has become unconscious. Upon admitting to the ER, it is determined that the patient's liver has stopped working. The patient is non-responsive and a brain-dead donor has an organ available. Today's procedure is to transplant the donor liver (CPT® code 47135). The anesthesia code is 00796. Assume that you had access to the ASA's RVU book and the Base Units for 00796 is equal to "30." The initial contact with the patient was at 11:10 p.m., and the finish time was 5:18 a.m., making the time spent 6 hours and 8 minutes (368 minutes). Assume that 15 minutes = 1 Time Unit. Assume the Conversion Factor for this procedure is $92.17. What is the total fee?

Base Units_____ + **Time Units**_____ + **Modifying Units**_____ = **Total Units**_____

Total Units_____ x **Conversion Factor $**_____ = **Total Fee $**_____

Surgery

The codes in the Surgery section begin with the numbers 1 through 6. Keeping this in mind will help you in abiding by the guidelines found in the Surgery section.

According to the CPT® codebook, there are two kinds of surgeries. These are:

1. **Those that include the entire surgical package concept;**

2. **Those that do not include the surgical package concept.**

The AMA's surgical package concept includes (according to the CPT® codebook):

1. **Local infiltration, metacarpal, digital block or topical anesthesia when used, and one related E/M visit on the date immediately prior to or on the date of the procedure (including history and physical);**

2. **The operation per se;**

3. **Immediate post-op care, including dictation of the notes and talking with the family and other physicians, writing orders, evaluating the patient in the post-anesthesia recovery area and typical postoperative follow-up care.**

Many carriers employ a slightly different one than the AMA describes. The carrier surgical package includes:

1. **Pre-op;**

2. **Surgery;**

3. **Post-op.**

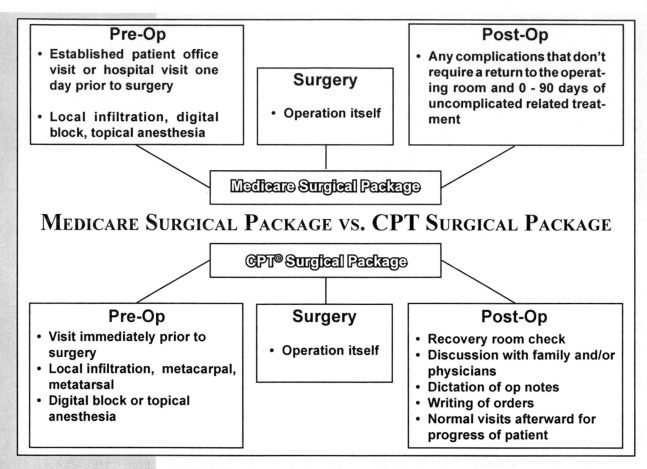

Pre-Op
- Established patient office visit or hospital visit one day prior to surgery
- Local infiltration, digital block, topical anesthesia

Surgery
- Operation itself

Post-Op
- Any complications that don't require a return to the operating room and 0 - 90 days of uncomplicated related treatment

Medicare Surgical Package

MEDICARE SURGICAL PACKAGE VS. CPT SURGICAL PACKAGE

CPT® Surgical Package

Pre-Op
- Visit immediately prior to surgery
- Local infiltration, metacarpal, metatarsal
- Digital block or topical anesthesia

Surgery
- Operation itself

Post-Op
- Recovery room check
- Discussion with family and/or physicians
- Dictation of op notes
- Writing of orders
- Normal visits afterward for progress of patient

Notice that, although not huge, the main difference between these two is found in the portion of the package that occurs after the surgery. For Medicare, the surgical package concept (known as the National Global Surgery Policy) includes the following:

1. **Visits one day prior to surgery;**

2. **Surgery;**

3. **Complications that do not require a trip back to the operating room and between zero and 90 days post-op care.**

Medicare and the AMA agree that the visit upon which the decision to operate on the patient was made is a billable service. Addition of the modifier -57 may be helpful in getting this service paid, or you may even use the modifier –25 for significant, separately identifiable E/M Service by the same physician on the same day of the procedure or other service. The total price for the surgery should include all of the components of the surgical package (i.e., the pre-op, surgery and post-op). According to CPT®, any complications or exacerbations of the surgery are not included in the surgical package, and procedures performed to correct or alleviate these problems should be coded separately. According to Medicare, complications that do not require a revisit to the operating room are included with the price of the surgery.

Uncomplicated follow-up care is included with the total surgical package. In CPT®, you should use the code 99024 with "no charge" to code for the patient's follow-up visits. The book, Medicare RBRVS: A Physician's Guide will give you valuable information on the number of follow-up days for each surgical procedure. You may also find some valuable information on coding for surgeries in the Correct Coding Initiative book produced by CMS. Using these books to code is extremely helpful when you find out the number of follow-up days and use that information to know when to begin to bill the patient. You can obtain a copy of these publications by calling 1-800-443-7397 or by logging onto **www. medbooks.com**.

According to CPT®, follow-up care for diagnostic services includes only that care that relates to the diagnostic procedure itself; it does not include care for the condition for which the diagnostic procedure was performed in the first place.

Also, according to CPT® rules, a physician may choose to bill for supplies and materials over and above those usually included with the office/outpatient visit or other services rendered.

It is important to list multiple procedures occurring on the same day with separate entries, as long as they are not part of the overall global service. Multiple procedures should be placed on the claim form in order from major to minor service, with a separate price listed for each service.

The words "separate procedure" mean that you can bill for the service only when that procedure is performed alone (not as part of a larger more global service) or for a specific purpose. More information on separate procedures can be found in the guidelines in the Surgery section. Some examples of separate procedures include arthroscopies that may start out being diagnostic in character and then turn into services that are therapeutic in nature. Make sure that you read all of the notes in and around any code that you use, as the notes will give you valuable information on how to use the code. If you see the inverted triangles that indicate that a change has taken place in the text in and around the codes, make sure that you read this portion in case the change impacts your coding.

In using an unlisted procedure code, always be sure to check the Category III codes to see if you can find a code for the service you performed. If there is no Category III code available, use the unlisted procedure code and make sure that you submit a special report explaining to the claims processor (in layman's terms) the unusual circumstances of the service and why you chose the unlisted procedure code.

In coding procedures that do not include the entire surgical package, remember that you are coding only for the surgical service itself and that you should strive to complete the surgical package by coding separately for any pre-op, regional or general anesthesia, and post-op components provided. (See Medicare RBRVS: A Physician's Guide to determine which services have no postoperative follow-up.) If you do code for a pre-op (such as an office visit), make sure to use the modifier -25 (for Separately Identifiable E/M Service on the Same Day as Another Procedure or Service) on the end of the E/M code.

The Surgery section is arranged (for the most part) from outside the body (Integumentary System) inward (Musculoskeletal, Respiratory, Cardiovascular System...).

Three different kinds of repairs are listed in the Integumentary System. These include:

A simple repair requires one layer closure.

1. **Simple repair**   **Superficial layer(s) only;**

2. **Intermediate repair**   **Layer closure of epidermal and dermal closure plus deeper layers of subcutaneous tissue and non-muscle fascia;**

3. **Complex repair**   **Plastic repair; more than layered closure.**

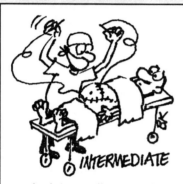

An intermediate repair includes a multiple layer closure.

In coding repairs, you should measure and record the size of the lesion in centimeters and code the repair according to its kind (simple, intermediate, or complex). Repairs of the same classification and location (as given in the description of the code) should be added together and reported as a single item.

In coding for the first fracture repair where "treatment" of the fracture is involved, make sure to use codes found between 20005 and 28899. Codes found between 29000 and 29750 are used for second- or third-time cast placement or for first-time cast placement done for the purposes of stabilizing or protecting the bone. Placing a modifier -76 following the procedure code number should indicate re-reduction of a fracture by the same physician. Placing a -77 following a procedure code number should indicate re-reduction by a different physician.

Codes for vascular injection procedures include necessary local anesthesia, introduction of the needle or intracatheter, injection of any contrast medium, and any associated pre- or post-op.

Complex repair is similar to a plastic repair.

Endoscopic descriptors include all related and secondary procedures that are performed at the same time. It is not necessary to list out these related procedures unless they are performed independently of the larger, more global service or unless they require additional time, effort or judgment.

Maternity care includes care associated with a normal vaginal delivery or Cesarean delivery. This means the nine or so months of prenatal care, the delivery itself, and the postnatal care in the hospital and office. Complications of the delivery are not included and should be coded separately.

Name:_____

Class/Section:_____

cpTeach Date:_____
2012

EXERCISE: 8.1

1. Respiratory System   _____

2. Musculoskeletal System   _____

3. Digestive System   _____

4. Cardiovascular System   _____

5. Integumentary System   _____

Before You Begin:
Read Chapter 8 in cpTeach® on "Surgery." Follow along in CPT® with the points illustrated in cpTeach®.

Purpose of this Lesson:
To familiarize you with the arrangement of the Surgery section.

Instructions:
1. Look at the following diagram.

2. Pretend that the woman is being cut and place the body systems in order as they would be cut through. This will be the same order as the Surgery section.

Name:_____

Class/Section:_____

Date:_____

Before You Begin:
Read Chapter 8 in cpTeach® on the Surgery section. Follow along in CPT® with the points illustrated in cpTeach®.

Purpose of this Lesson:
To familiarize the student with the different surgical packages (i.e., Medicare surgical package and AMA CPT® surgical package).

Instructions:
1. Refer to the Guidelines in the Surgery section of your CPT® codebook and read about the listed surgical procedures.

2. Read the Surgery section in your cpTeach® about the Medicare surgical package.

3. Complete the diagrams below.

EXERCISE: 8.2

AMA's SURGICAL PACKAGE

MEDICARE's SURGICAL PACKAGE

Name: _____

Class/Section: _____

Date: _____

WORKBOOK

cpTeach
Expert Medical Coding Made Easy!

2012

EXERCISE: 8.3

LABEL THE COMPONENTS OF THE
"BLUE PLATE SPECIAL" AS:
1. PRE-OP
2. SUGERY
3. POST-OP

Before You Begin:
Read Chapter 8 in cpTeach®
on "Surgery." Follow along
in CPT® with the points
illustrated in cpTeach®.
Notice how the surgical
package can be likened to
the blue plate special.

Purpose of this Lesson:
To familiarize the student
with the all inclusive (global)
concept of the AMA CPT®-4
surgical package.

Instructions:
1. Label each part of the
   meal below as if it
   were a component of
   the Medicare surgical
   package.

WORKBOOK

McGUFFEY

cpTeach

2012

Name:_____

Class/Section:_____

Date:_____

Before You Begin:

Read Chapter 8 in cpTeach® on "Surgery." Follow along in CPT® with the points illustrated in cpTeach®.

Purpose of this Lesson:

To familiarize you with add-on codes.

Instructions:

1. Look up each of the following codes in your CPT® codebook.

2. Place the correct notation in front of each code for "add-on" codes.

3. If the code is not an "add-on" code, indicate that by placing the initials NAC for "not add-on code" in the space to the left.

EXERCISE: 8.4

1. _____   11100   Biopsy of skin, subcutaneous tissue and/or mucous membrane (including simple closure), unless otherwise listed; single lesion

    _____   11101   each seperate/additional lesion

2. _____   11200   Removal of skin tags, multiple fibro-cutaneous tags, any area; up to and including 15 lesions

    _____   11201   each additional 10 lesions

3. _____   11055   Paring or cutting of benign hyperkera-totic lesion (eg, corn or callus); single lesion

    _____   11056   2 to 4 lesions

4. _____   11730   Avulsion of nail plate, partial or complete, simple; single

    _____   11732   each additional nail plate

Why or why not? Answer here._____

_____

_____

_____

_____

	Name: _____
WORKBOOK	Class/Section: _____
cpTeach 2012	Date: _____

Exercise: 8.5

YES OR NO   **WHY OR WHY NOT?**

1. _____   29805 and 29806 _____

2. _____   22100 and 22103 _____

3. _____   46600 and 46606 _____

4. _____   47140 and 47142 _____

5. _____   12006 and 12014 _____

Before You Begin:
Read Chapter 8 in cpTeach® on "Surgery." Follow along in CPT® with the points illustrated in cpTeach®.

Purpose of this Lesson:
To familiarize the student with separate procedures, add-on procedures and regular services.

Instructions:
1. Look up the codes below in your CPT® codebook.

2. Compare the codes to one another (e.g., 29805 and 29806). Indicate in the space provided a "yes" or "no" to tell which ones could be added to another service or placed on the same claim form and which ones could not. Why or why not? (Assume that all services are done on the same body part).

Name:_____

Class/Section:_____

cpTeach
2012 Date:_____

Before You Begin:
Read Chapter 8 in cpTeach®
on "Surgery." Follow along
in CPT® with the points
illustrated in cpTeach®.

Purpose of this Lesson:
To summarize some of the
concepts learned about in
the Surgery section and
continue to reinforce the
concepts learned throughout
the cpTeach® text.

Instructions:
1. Read each statement
below.

2. Fill in the answers to each
statement by completing
the crossword puzzle.

EXERCISE: 8.6

ACROSS:

6. Code numbers that can be used when you cannot find a description for either in the Category III codes or in the regular section of CPT and that a doctor has performed are called _____ procedures.

7. The part of the Surgical Package that includes local infiltration, topical anesthesia, metacarpal/digital block and the E/M immediately preceding the surgery.

8. The part of the Surgical Package which must be normal and uncomplicated in order to be included as part of the Surgical Package.

9. Some procedures can be done alone or as part of a larger more global service. When these procedures are done alone, they can be coded and are called _____ procedures.

10. The code number used to describe a postoperative follow-up service that is <u>included in the Surgical Package</u> is found in this section.

11. When the pre-op, surgery, and post-op are included in one price, it is called the _____ fee period.

DOWN:

1. The Surgical Package can be likened to this.

2. Codes found in the series 11100 - 11101 describe a _____ of skin, subcutaneous tissue and/or mucous membrane.

3. The first code numbers in the Surgery Section begin with this number.

4. A written document submitted to the carrier that explains unusual circumstances or procedures that vary from the norm is called a _____.

EXERCISE: 8.6

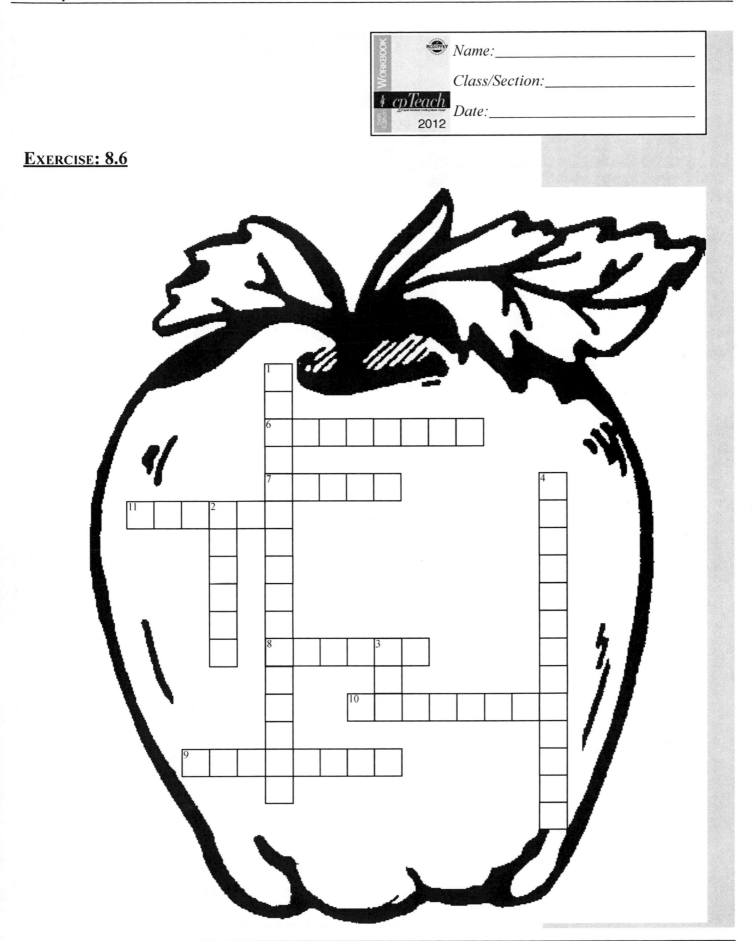

WORKBOOK

McGUFFEY

cpTeach

24th Edition

2012

*Name:*_____

*Class/Section:*_____

*Date:*_____

Before You Begin:
Read Chapter 8 in cpTeach® on "Surgery." Follow along in CPT® with the points illustrated in cpTeach®.

Purpose of this Lesson:
To exercise your knowledge of the more difficult concepts in the Surgery section and to assist the student in deeper understanding of surgery coding.

Instructions:
1. Read each statement below.

2. Check the statement that best completes each sentence.

EXERCISE: 8.7

1. **Follow-up care for diagnostic procedures includes:**

    _____   a.   All care for that patient for the next 100 years.

    _____   b.   Global care for the condition itself.

    _____   c.   Care for the diagnostic procedure itself.

    _____   d.   Care until the patient is cured.

2. **Follow up care for therapeutic procedures includes:**

    _____   a.   All care for that patient for the next 100 years.

    _____   b.   Care for the surgical procedure itself.

    _____   c.   Care for the surgical procedure plus any major complications that may occur due to the physician performing that procedure.

    _____   d.   Care until the patient is cured.

3. **In billing for multiple procedures for the physician you can:**

    _____   a.   Code only for the major service.

    _____   b.   Code for all services unless one is part of a larger, more global service.

    _____   c.   Code only for the most expensive service.

    _____   d.   Code for all procedures no matter what.

4. **When you code for removal of a lesion, you need to measure:**

    _____   a.   The size of the lesion after it is taken off.

    _____   b.   The size of the lesion before it is removed.

    _____   c.   The size of the lesion plus the size of the margins after removal.

    _____   d.   The size of the lesion plus the size of the margins before removal.

Name:_____

Class/Section:_____

Date:_____

2012

EXERCISE: 8.7

5. When you remove a lesion, the following is included:

_____ a. The only thing included is the removal and the follow-up care.

_____ b. The removal itself and the simple repair of the lesion is included, plus the normal other parts of the surgical package.

_____ c. The removal is included plus any kind of follow-up care.

_____ d. The removal is included plus any kind of closure of the wound.

6. When you code for repairs, it is important to:

_____ a. Add together the lengths of the repair in the same classification and report them as a single item.

_____ b. Add together all the repairs and report only as one code.

_____ c. Code each repair separately.

_____ d. You don't need to code repairs, because they are included with the excision of the lesion.

7. When you code for cast removals, it is important to:

_____ a. Code an office visit to get reimbursed for the time it took to remove the cast.

_____ b. Code the 99024 for post-operative follow-up visit.

_____ c. You don't need to code anything if you don't want to.

_____ d. a, b, and c are true.

_____ e. b and c are true.

Before You Begin:
Read Chapter 6 in cpTeach® on "Evaluation and Management" and follow along in CPT®.

Purpose of this Lesson:
To familiarize the student with the Evaluation and Management codes found in the first chapter of CPT®.

Instructions:
1. Complete the following definitions.

WORKBOOK

McGUFFEY
cpTeach

Name:_____

Class/Section:_____

Date:_____

2012

EXERCISE: 8.7

8. **When you code for a diagnostic service (e.g., arthroscopy of the knee) that turns into a larger more global service (e.g., it starts off as a diagnostic service and then becomes one in which you remove loose bodies), you should:**

_____   a. Code for all of the services that you did including both the diagnostic and therapeutic services.

_____   b. Code for just the diagnostic service.

_____   c. Code for the therapeutic service only.

_____   d. You don't need to code for either service, because the surgical package no longer exists.

9. **For procedures that are considered to be "add-on" codes you should:**

_____   a. Add all the procedures together and only consider the highest numeric CPT® code.

_____   b. Code all the services that apply.

_____   c. Add the modifier –51 for Multiple Services to each code, because the plus sign means "add-on".

_____   d. Do not do anything except code for the first service only.

10. **When you code for services in the ophthalmology subsection of the Surgery section you should:**

_____   a. Keep in mind that since you have two eyes, all surgeries in this subsection will be bilateral to account for both eyes.

_____   b. Keep in mind that the surgeries only cover one eye.

_____   c. Keep in mind that in order to code for both eyes, you must use a modifier.

_____   d. B and C are true.

_____   e. None of the above.

Name:_____

Class/Section:_____

Date:_____

2012

EXAMPLE:

Q. 29870

A. <u>When this code is looked up, it reads as follows:</u>

> **29870   *Arthroscopy, knee, diagnostic, with or without synovial
> biopsy (separate procedure).*
>
> Copyright AMA 2011

The words "separate procedure" follow the description and identify
this service as potentially being part of the service included in code #'s
29871 through 29887.

Purpose of this Lesson:
To exercise your knowledge
of separate procedures and
the nuances connected with
coding separate procedures.
Remember: coding out a
separate procedure in
conjunction with the larger,
more global service is
unbundling.

EXERCISE **8.8**

1. **Q. 29800**
    A. _____
    _____

2. **Q. 29819**
    A. _____
    _____

3. **Q. 46600**
    A. _____
    _____

4. **Q. 50605**
    A. _____
    _____

5. **Q. 49320**
    A. _____
    _____

6. **Q. 43235**
    A. _____
    _____

Instructions:
1. Read each statement
    below.

2. Identify which
    procedures are
    "separate" procedures.

3. If you find out that a
    procedure is a "separate"
    procedure, explain why
    and identify some of the
    code(s) which would
    constitute the larger,
    more global service.

WORKBOOK

McGUFFEY

cpTeach
Export Medical Coding Made Easy!
24th EDITION
2012

*Name:*_____

*Class/Section:*_____

*Date:*_____

EXERCISE 8.8

7. **Q. 43201**
    A. _____
    _____

8. **Q. 44360**
    A. _____
    _____

9. **Q. 44377**
    A. _____
    _____

10. **Q. 44390**
    A. _____
    _____

Name:_____

Class/Section:_____

Date:_____

2012

EXERCISE: 8.9

1. Endoscopy/Laryngoscopy with the removal of a lesion

   _____   a.   31526

   _____   b.   31528

   _____   c.   31512

   _____   d.   31530

2. Nasal endoscopy with control of nasal hemorrhage

   _____   a.   30901

   _____   b.   30903

   _____   c.   31238

   _____   d.   30905

3. Insertion of ventricular assist device; extracorporeal, biventricular

   _____   a.   33978

   _____   b.   33975

   _____   c.   33976

   _____   d.   33980

Before You Begin:
Read Chapter 8 in cpTeach® on "Surgery." Follow along in CPT® with the points illustrated in cpTeach®.

Purpose of this Lesson:
To exercise your knowledge of the Surgery section, the nuances connected with coding add-on codes, and in proper code selection.

Instructions:
1. Read each procedure below.

2. Find the procedure(s) in the CPT® codebook and select the correct answer from one of the choices given below.

WORKBOOK

cpTeach
2012

Name:_____

Class/Section:_____

Date:_____

EXERCISE: 8.9

4. Thoracotomy, with exploration

   _____   a.   32095

   _____   b.   32035

   _____   c.   32100

   _____   d.   32140

5. Orbitotomy with bone flap; with removal of foreign body

   _____   a.   67430

   _____   b.   67440

   _____   c.   67413

   _____   d.   67414

6. Strabismus surgery, recession or resection procedure; two horizontal muscles on patient with previous eye surgery or injury that did not involve the extraocular muscles

   _____   a.   67311

   _____   b.   67312

   _____   c.   67312, 67331

   _____   d.   67316

Name:_____

Class/Section:_____

cpTeach

Date:_____

2012

EXERCISE: 8.9

7. Vertebral corpectomy; partial or complete, transthoracic approach with decompression of spinal cord and/or nerve roots, thoracic, 3 segments

    _____   a.   63085 x 3

    _____   b.   63086 x 3

    _____   c.   63085, 63086 x2

    _____   d.   63085, 63088, 63086

8. Repair of strangulated ventral hernia using implantation of mesh

    _____   a.   49561, 49568

    _____   b.   49572, 49568

    _____   c.   49565, 49568

    _____   d.   49568, 49587

9. Partial colectomy and take down of splenic flexure

    _____   a.   44141, 44143

    _____   b.   44143

    _____   c.   44140, 44139

    _____   d.   44141, 44128

Name:_____

Class/Section:_____

Date:_____

2012

EXERCISE: 8.9

10. Excision of bone cyst or tumor of femur with internal fixation

    _____   a.   27356, 27358

    _____   b.   27357, 27358

    _____   c.   27355, 27358

    _____   d.   27355

11. Open reduction of cervical fracture, (three fractured vertebrae) posterior approach

    _____   a.   22325, 22328 x 2

    _____   b.   22325, 22328

    _____   c.   63087, 63088 x2

    _____   d.   22326, 22328 x2

12. Open treatment of two lumbar vertebral fractures, posterior approach and one cervical vertebral fracture

    _____   a.   22325 x 2, 22326

    _____   b.   22325, 22326

    _____   c.   22325, 22328, 22326

    _____   d.   22325, 22328 x 2

Instructions:

Think of your skin, subcutaneous tissue, muscle and bone as a four story building. The basement floor, usually the most structurally solid, is the bone. The ground floor is the muscle. The second floor is the subcutaneous/adipose tissue; the 3rd, the dermis; and the top floor, the epidermis. If a branch were to fall on the roof of this building, it may do some damage. If, however, a larger object such as a crane were to fall on the building, it may penetrate the roof and ruin the third floor. Obviously, the more stories (layers) affected by the falling object - the greater the damage to the building and the more extensive your repair (and bill) would be.

Assume that none of the wounds that will be described in the following exercises happened with a knife or gunshot, and assume that none of them require exploration. Consider the following diagram:

Before You Begin:

Read Chapter 8 in cpTeach® on "Surgery." Follow along in CPT® with the points illustrated in cpTeach®.

Purpose of this Lesson:

To assist you in understanding how repairs should be coded according to the number of layers closed and the kind of repair performed.

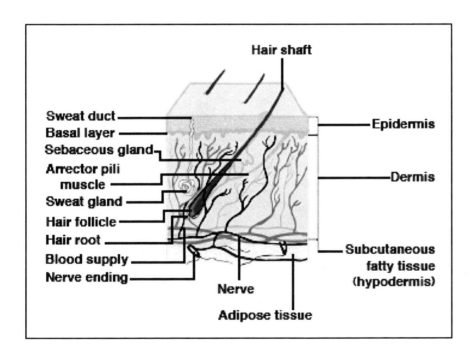

WORKBOOK

cpTeach
Expert Medical Coding Made Easy
2012

Name:_____

Class/Section:_____

Date:_____

EXERCISE: 8.10

Based on the diagram given under the instructions and the explanation cited there, identify the following lacerations for type of repairs required as well as the layers repaired:

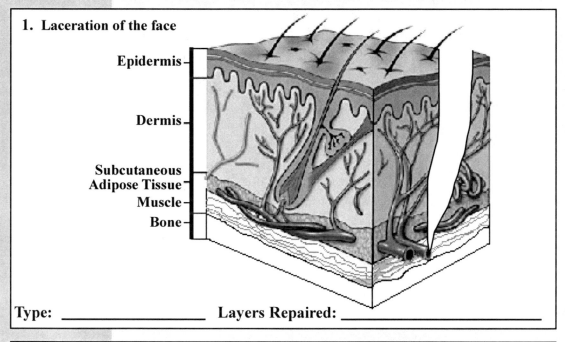

1. **Laceration of the face**

Epidermis–

Dermis–

Subcutaneous
Adipose Tissue–
Muscle–
Bone–

Type: _____   **Layers Repaired:** _____

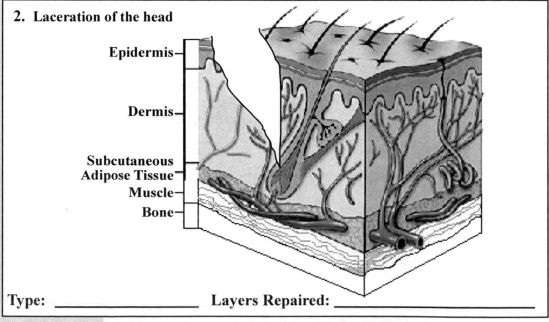

2. **Laceration of the head**

Epidermis–

Dermis–

Subcutaneous
Adipose Tissue–
Muscle–
Bone–

Type: _____   **Layers Repaired:** _____

EXERCISE: 8.10

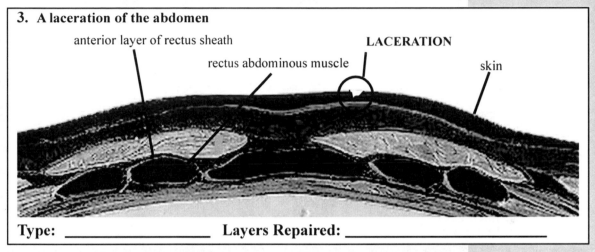

3. A laceration of the abdomen

anterior layer of rectus sheath

rectus abdominous muscle

LACERATION

skin

Type: _____   Layers Repaired: _____

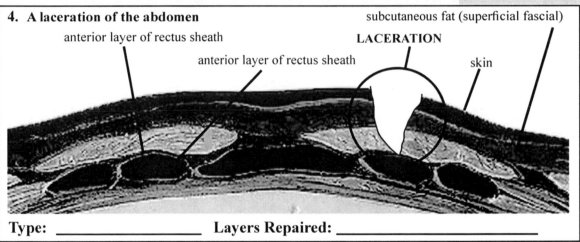

4. A laceration of the abdomen

subcutaneous fat (superficial fascial)

anterior layer of rectus sheath

anterior layer of rectus sheath

LACERATION

skin

Type: _____   Layers Repaired: _____

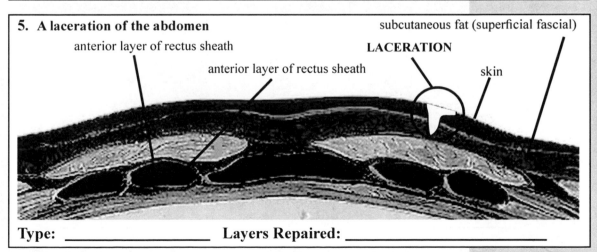

5. A laceration of the abdomen

subcutaneous fat (superficial fascial)

anterior layer of rectus sheath

anterior layer of rectus sheath

LACERATION

skin

Type: _____   Layers Repaired: _____

EXERCISE: 8.10

6. Laceration of the arm

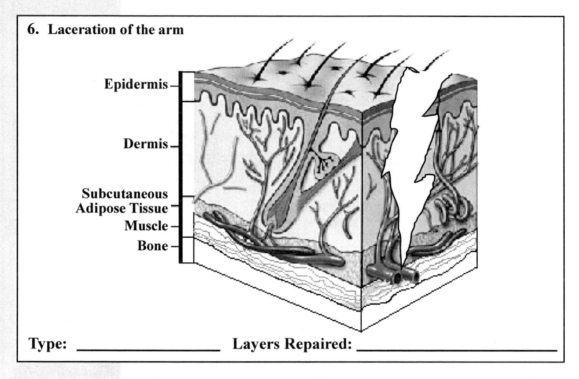

Epidermis

Dermis

Subcutaneous
Adipose Tissue

Muscle

Bone

Type: _____   Layers Repaired: _____

7. A laceration of the face

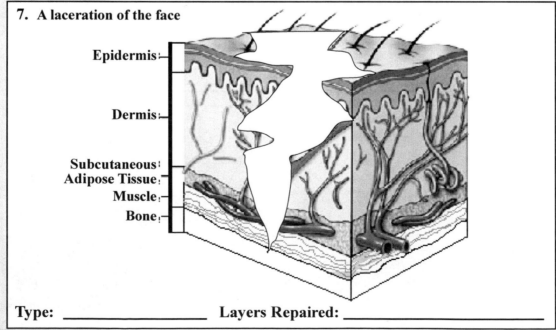

Epidermis

Dermis

Subcutaneous
Adipose Tissue

Muscle

Bone

Type: _____   Layers Repaired: _____

McGUFFEY

WORKBOOK

cpTeach
Expert Medical Coding Made Easy!

2012

Name:_____

Class/Section:_____

Date:_____

EXERCISE: 8.11

CHEEK REPAIR
2.5 cm complex repair

FOOT REPAIR
1.1 cm complex repair

Before You Begin:
Read Chapter 8 in cpTeach® on "Surgery." Follow along in CPT® with the points illustrated in cpTeach®.

Purpose of this Lesson:
To assist you in continuing your knowledge of the coding of repairs in a multiple procedure situation (i.e., more than one repair at one time).

Instructions:
1. Code the following repairs using the correct CPT® code. Write them up as you would on a CMS-1500 form (i.e., which one would be written first, second, etc.) located on the back of each exercise.

Notes: _____

_____

_____

_____

_____

_____

_____

Name:_____

Class/Section:_____

Date:_____

2012

EXERCISE: 8.11

1500

HEALTH INSURANCE CLAIM FORM

APPROVED BY NATIONAL UNIFORM CLAIM COMMITTEE 08/05

| | PICA | | | | | | | | PICA | |

1. MEDICARE	MEDICAID	TRICARE CHAMPUS	CHAMPVA	GROUP HEALTH PLAN	FECA BLK LUNG	OTHER	1a. INSURED'S I.D. NUMBER	(For Program in Item 1)
(Medicare #)	(Medicaid #)	(Sponsor's SSN)	(Member ID#)	(SSN or ID)	(SSN)	(ID)		

2. PATIENT'S NAME (Last Name, First Name, Middle Initial)

3. PATIENT'S BIRTH DATE MM DD YY   SEX   M   F

4. INSURED'S NAME (Last Name, First Name, Middle Initial)

5. PATIENT'S ADDRESS (No., Street)

6. PATIENT RELATIONSHIP TO INSURED   Self   Spouse   Child   Other

7. INSURED'S ADDRESS (No., Street)

CITY   STATE

8. PATIENT STATUS   Single   Married   Other

CITY   STATE

ZIP CODE   TELEPHONE (Include Area Code) ( )

Employed   Full-Time Student   Part-Time Student

ZIP CODE   TELEPHONE (Include Area Code) ( )

9. OTHER INSURED'S NAME (Last Name, First Name, Middle Initial)

10. IS PATIENT'S CONDITION RELATED TO:

11. INSURED'S POLICY GROUP OR FECA NUMBER

a. OTHER INSURED'S POLICY OR GROUP NUMBER

a. EMPLOYMENT? (Current or Previous)   YES   NO

a. INSURED'S DATE OF BIRTH MM DD YY   SEX   M   F

b. OTHER INSURED'S DATE OF BIRTH MM DD YY   SEX   M   F

b. AUTO ACCIDENT?   PLACE (State)   YES   NO

b. EMPLOYER'S NAME OR SCHOOL NAME

c. EMPLOYER'S NAME OR SCHOOL NAME

c. OTHER ACCIDENT?   YES   NO

c. INSURANCE PLAN NAME OR PROGRAM NAME

d. INSURANCE PLAN NAME OR PROGRAM NAME

10d. RESERVED FOR LOCAL USE

d. IS THERE ANOTHER HEALTH BENEFIT PLAN?   YES   NO   If yes, return to and complete item 9 a-d.

READ BACK OF FORM BEFORE COMPLETING & SIGNING THIS FORM.

12. PATIENT'S OR AUTHORIZED PERSON'S SIGNATURE   I authorize the release of any medical or other information necessary to process this claim. I also request payment of government benefits either to myself or to the party who accepts assignment below.

SIGNED_____   DATE_____

13. INSURED'S OR AUTHORIZED PERSON'S SIGNATURE   I authorize payment of medical benefits to the undersigned physician or supplier for services described below.

SIGNED_____

14. DATE OF CURRENT: MM DD YY   ILLNESS (First symptom) OR INJURY (Accident) OR PREGNANCY(LMP)

15. IF PATIENT HAS HAD SAME OR SIMILAR ILLNESS. GIVE FIRST DATE MM DD YY

16. DATES PATIENT UNABLE TO WORK IN CURRENT OCCUPATION   FROM MM DD YY   TO MM DD YY

17. NAME OF REFERRING PROVIDER OR OTHER SOURCE

17a.

17b. NPI

18. HOSPITALIZATION DATES RELATED TO CURRENT SERVICES   FROM MM DD YY   TO MM DD YY

19. RESERVED FOR LOCAL USE

20. OUTSIDE LAB?   YES   NO $ CHARGES

21. DIAGNOSIS OR NATURE OF ILLNESS OR INJURY (Relate Items 1, 2, 9 or 4 to Item 24E by Line)

1. |___.___   3. |___.___

2. |___.___   4. |___.___

22. MEDICAID RESUBMISSION CODE   ORIGINAL REF. NO.

23. PRIOR AUTHORIZATION NUMBER

24. A. DATE(S) OF SERVICE From MM DD YY To MM DD YY	B. PLACE OF SERVICE	C. EMG	D. PROCEDURES, SERVICES, OR SUPPLIES (Explain Unusual Circumstances) CPT/HCPCS MODIFIER	E. DIAGNOSIS POINTER	F. $ CHARGES	G. DAYS OR UNITS	H. EPSDT Family Plan	I. ID. QUAL.	J. RENDERING PROVIDER ID. #
1									NPI
2									NPI
3									NPI
4									NPI
5									NPI
6									NPI

25. FEDERAL TAX I.D. NUMBER   SSN   EIN

26. PATIENT'S ACCOUNT NO.

27. ACCEPT ASSIGNMENT? (For govt. claims, see back)   YES   NO

28. TOTAL CHARGE $

29. AMOUNT PAID $

30. BALANCE DUE $

31. SIGNATURE OF PHYSICIAN OR SUPPLIER INCLUDING DEGREES OR CREDENTIALS (I certify that the statements on the reverse apply to this bill and are made a part thereof.)

32. SERVICE FACILITY LOCATION INFORMATION

33. BILLING PROVIDER INFO & PH # ( )

CARRIER

PATIENT AND INSURED INFORMATION

PHYSICIAN OR SUPPLIER INFORMATION

EXERCISE 8.12

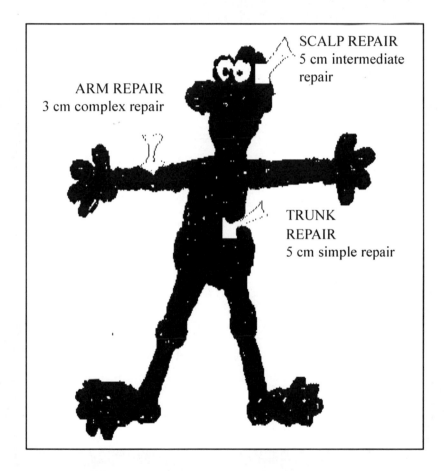

ARM REPAIR
3 cm complex repair

SCALP REPAIR
5 cm intermediate repair

TRUNK REPAIR
5 cm simple repair

Before You Begin:
Read Chapter 8 in cpTeach® on "Surgery." Follow along in CPT® with the points illustrated in cpTeach®.

Purpose of this Lesson:
To assist you in continuing your knowledge of the coding of repairs in a multiple procedure situation (i.e., more than one repair at one time).

Instructions:
1. Code the following repairs using the correct CPT® code. Write them up as you would on a CMS-1500 form (i.e., which one would be written first, second, etc.) located on the back of each exercise.

Notes: _____

_____

_____

_____

_____

_____

_____

_____

EXERCISE **8.12**

Name:_____

Class/Section:_____

Date:_____

cpTeach 2012

1500

HEALTH INSURANCE CLAIM FORM

APPROVED BY NATIONAL UNIFORM CLAIM COMMITTEE 08/05

CARRIER

| | PICA | | | | | | PICA | |

1. MEDICARE ☐ (Medicare #)	MEDICAID ☐ (Medicaid #)	TRICARE CHAMPUS ☐ (Sponsor's SSN)	CHAMPVA ☐ (Member ID#)	GROUP HEALTH PLAN ☐ (SSN or ID)	FECA BLK LUNG ☐ (SSN)	OTHER ☐ (ID)	1a. INSURED'S I.D. NUMBER (For Program in Item 1)

2. PATIENT'S NAME (Last Name, First Name, Middle Initial)

3. PATIENT'S BIRTH DATE MM | DD | YY   SEX M ☐ F ☐

4. INSURED'S NAME (Last Name, First Name, Middle Initial)

5. PATIENT'S ADDRESS (No., Street)

6. PATIENT RELATIONSHIP TO INSURED   Self ☐ Spouse ☐ Child ☐ Other ☐

7. INSURED'S ADDRESS (No., Street)

CITY   STATE

8. PATIENT STATUS   Single ☐ Married ☐ Other ☐

CITY   STATE

ZIP CODE   TELEPHONE (Include Area Code) ( )

Employed ☐ Full-Time Student ☐ Part-Time Student ☐

ZIP CODE   TELEPHONE (Include Area Code) ( )

9. OTHER INSURED'S NAME (Last Name, First Name, Middle Initial)

10. IS PATIENT'S CONDITION RELATED TO:

11. INSURED'S POLICY GROUP OR FECA NUMBER

a. OTHER INSURED'S POLICY OR GROUP NUMBER

a. EMPLOYMENT? (Current or Previous) ☐ YES ☐ NO

a. INSURED'S DATE OF BIRTH MM | DD | YY   SEX M ☐ F ☐

b. OTHER INSURED'S DATE OF BIRTH MM | DD | YY   SEX M ☐ F ☐

b. AUTO ACCIDENT?   PLACE (State) ☐ YES ☐ NO

b. EMPLOYER'S NAME OR SCHOOL NAME

c. EMPLOYER'S NAME OR SCHOOL NAME

c. OTHER ACCIDENT? ☐ YES ☐ NO

c. INSURANCE PLAN NAME OR PROGRAM NAME

d. INSURANCE PLAN NAME OR PROGRAM NAME

10d. RESERVED FOR LOCAL USE

d. IS THERE ANOTHER HEALTH BENEFIT PLAN? ☐ YES ☐ NO   If yes, return to and complete item 9 a-d.

READ BACK OF FORM BEFORE COMPLETING & SIGNING THIS FORM.

12. PATIENT'S OR AUTHORIZED PERSON'S SIGNATURE   I authorize the release of any medical or other information necessary to process this claim. I also request payment of government benefits either to myself or to the party who accepts assignment below.

SIGNED_____ DATE_____

13. INSURED'S OR AUTHORIZED PERSON'S SIGNATURE   I authorize payment of medical benefits to the undersigned physician or supplier for services described below.

SIGNED_____

PATIENT AND INSURED INFORMATION

14. DATE OF CURRENT: MM | DD | YY ◄ ILLNESS (First symptom) OR INJURY (Accident) OR PREGNANCY(LMP)

15. IF PATIENT HAS HAD SAME OR SIMILAR ILLNESS. GIVE FIRST DATE MM | DD | YY

16. DATES PATIENT UNABLE TO WORK IN CURRENT OCCUPATION FROM MM | DD | YY   TO MM | DD | YY

17. NAME OF REFERRING PROVIDER OR OTHER SOURCE

17a.
17b. NPI

18. HOSPITALIZATION DATES RELATED TO CURRENT SERVICES FROM MM | DD | YY   TO MM | DD | YY

19. RESERVED FOR LOCAL USE

20. OUTSIDE LAB? ☐ YES ☐ NO $ CHARGES

21. DIAGNOSIS OR NATURE OF ILLNESS OR INJURY (Relate Items 1, 2, 9 or 4 to Item 24E by Line)

1. |___.___   3. |___.___
2. |___.___   4. |___.___

22. MEDICAID RESUBMISSION CODE   ORIGINAL REF. NO.

23. PRIOR AUTHORIZATION NUMBER

24. A. DATE(S) OF SERVICE From MM DD YY	To MM DD YY	B. PLACE OF SERVICE	C. EMG	D. PROCEDURES, SERVICES, OR SUPPLIES (Explain Unusual Circumstances) CPT/HCPCS	MODIFIER	E. DIAGNOSIS POINTER	F. $ CHARGES	G. DAYS OR UNITS	H. EPSDT Family Plan	I. ID. QUAL.	J. RENDERING PROVIDER ID. #
1											NPI
2											NPI
3											NPI
4											NPI
5											NPI
6											NPI

25. FEDERAL TAX I.D. NUMBER   SSN ☐ EIN ☐

26. PATIENT'S ACCOUNT NO.

27. ACCEPT ASSIGNMENT? (For govt. claims, see back) ☐ YES ☐ NO

28. TOTAL CHARGE $

29. AMOUNT PAID $

30. BALANCE DUE $

31. SIGNATURE OF PHYSICIAN OR SUPPLIER INCLUDING DEGREES OR CREDENTIALS (I certify that the statements on the reverse apply to this bill and are made a part thereof.)

32. SERVICE FACILITY LOCATION INFORMATION

33. BILLING PROVIDER INFO & PH # ( )

PHYSICIAN OR SUPPLIER INFORMATION

Name:_____

Class/Section:_____

Date:_____

2012

EXERCISE 8.13

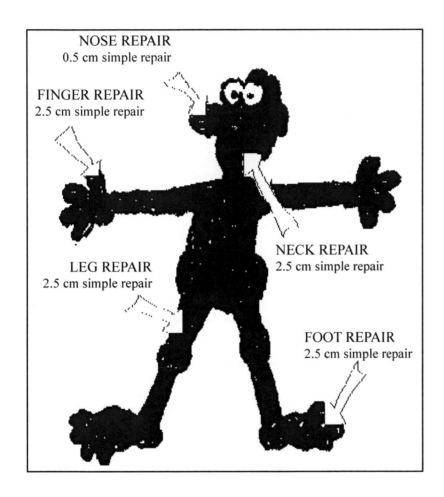

NOSE REPAIR
0.5 cm simple repair

FINGER REPAIR
2.5 cm simple repair

LEG REPAIR
2.5 cm simple repair

NECK REPAIR
2.5 cm simple repair

FOOT REPAIR
2.5 cm simple repair

Before You Begin:
Read Chapter 8 in cpTeach® on "Surgery." Follow along in CPT® with the points illustrated in cpTeach®.

Purpose of this Lesson:
To assist you in continuing your knowledge of the coding of repairs in a multiple procedure situation (i.e., more than one repair at one time).

Instructions:
1. Code the following repairs using the correct CPT® code. Write them up as you would on a CMS-1500 form (i.e., which one would be written first, second, etc.) located on the back of each exercise.

Notes: _____
_____
_____
_____
_____
_____
_____

Name:_____

Class/Section:_____

Date:_____

EXERCISE 8.13

1500

HEALTH INSURANCE CLAIM FORM

APPROVED BY NATIONAL UNIFORM CLAIM COMMITTEE 08/05

| | PICA | | | | | | | | PICA | | |

1. MEDICARE   MEDICAID   TRICARE   CHAMPVA   GROUP   FECA   OTHER   **1a.** INSURED'S I.D. NUMBER   (For Program in Item 1)
CHAMPUS   HEALTH PLAN   BLK LUNG
(Medicare #) (Medicaid #) (Sponsor's SSN) (Member ID#) (SSN or ID) (SSN) (ID)

2. PATIENT'S NAME (Last Name, First Name, Middle Initial)   **3.** PATIENT'S BIRTH DATE   SEX   **4.** INSURED'S NAME (Last Name, First Name, Middle Initial)
MM   DD   YY
M   F

5. PATIENT'S ADDRESS (No., Street)   **6.** PATIENT RELATIONSHIP TO INSURED   **7.** INSURED'S ADDRESS (No., Street)
Self   Spouse   Child   Other

CITY   STATE   **8.** PATIENT STATUS   CITY   STATE
Single   Married   Other

ZIP CODE   TELEPHONE (Include Area Code)   ZIP CODE   TELEPHONE (Include Area Code)
Employed   Full-Time   Part-Time
( )   Student   Student   ( )

9. OTHER INSURED'S NAME (Last Name, First Name, Middle Initial)   **10.** IS PATIENT'S CONDITION RELATED TO: **11.** INSURED'S POLICY GROUP OR FECA NUMBER

a. OTHER INSURED'S POLICY OR GROUP NUMBER   **a.** EMPLOYMENT? (Current or Previous)   **a.** INSURED'S DATE OF BIRTH   SEX
YES   NO   MM   DD   YY   M   F

b. OTHER INSURED'S DATE OF BIRTH   SEX   **b.** AUTO ACCIDENT?   PLACE (State)   **b.** EMPLOYER'S NAME OR SCHOOL NAME
MM   DD   YY   M   F   YES   NO

c. EMPLOYER'S NAME OR SCHOOL NAME   **c.** OTHER ACCIDENT?   **c.** INSURANCE PLAN NAME OR PROGRAM NAME
YES   NO

d. INSURANCE PLAN NAME OR PROGRAM NAME   **10d.** RESERVED FOR LOCAL USE   **d.** IS THERE ANOTHER HEALTH BENEFIT PLAN?
YES   NO   If yes, return to and complete item 9 a-d.

READ BACK OF FORM BEFORE COMPLETING & SIGNING THIS FORM.
12. PATIENT'S OR AUTHORIZED PERSON'S SIGNATURE I authorize the release of any medical or other information necessary to process this claim. I also request payment of government benefits either to myself or to the party who accepts assignment below.

SIGNED_____   DATE_____

13. INSURED'S OR AUTHORIZED PERSON'S SIGNATURE I authorize payment of medical benefits to the undersigned physician or supplier for services described below.

SIGNED_____

14. DATE OF CURRENT: ILLNESS (First symptom) OR   **15.** IF PATIENT HAS HAD SAME OR SIMILAR ILLNESS.   **16.** DATES PATIENT UNABLE TO WORK IN CURRENT OCCUPATION
MM   DD   YY   INJURY (Accident) OR   GIVE FIRST DATE MM   DD   YY   MM   DD   YY   MM   DD   YY
PREGNANCY(LMP)   FROM   TO

17. NAME OF REFERRING PROVIDER OR OTHER SOURCE   **17a.**   **18.** HOSPITALIZATION DATES RELATED TO CURRENT SERVICES
17b. NPI   MM   DD   YY   MM   DD   YY
FROM   TO

19. RESERVED FOR LOCAL USE   **20.** OUTSIDE LAB? $ CHARGES
YES   NO

21. DIAGNOSIS OR NATURE OF ILLNESS OR INJURY (Relate Items 1, 2, 9 or 4 to Item 24E by Line)   **22.** MEDICAID RESUBMISSION
CODE   ORIGINAL REF. NO.

1. |___.___| 3. |___.___|

2. |___.___| 4. |___.___| **23.** PRIOR AUTHORIZATION NUMBER

24. A. DATE(S) OF SERVICE						**B.** PLACE OF SERVICE	**C.** EMG	**D.** PROCEDURES, SERVICES, OR SUPPLIES (Explain Unusual Circumstances) CPT/HCPCS | MODIFIER	**E.** DIAGNOSIS POINTER	**F.** $ CHARGES	**G.** DAYS OR UNITS	**H.** EPSDT Family Plan	**I.** ID QUAL.	**J.** RENDERING PROVIDER ID. #
From		To												
MM	DD	YY	MM	DD	YY									
1													NPI	
2													NPI	
3													NPI	
4													NPI	
5													NPI	
6													NPI	

25. FEDERAL TAX I.D. NUMBER   SSN EIN   **26.** PATIENT'S ACCOUNT NO.   **27.** ACCEPT ASSIGNMENT? (For govt. claims, see back)   **28.** TOTAL CHARGE   **29.** AMOUNT PAID   **30.** BALANCE DUE
YES   NO $ $ $

31. SIGNATURE OF PHYSICIAN OR SUPPLIER INCLUDING DEGREES OR CREDENTIALS (I certify that the statements on the reverse apply to this bill and are made a part thereof.)   **32.** SERVICE FACILITY LOCATION INFORMATION   **33.** BILLING PROVIDER INFO & PH # ( )

Name:_____

Class/Section:_____

cpTeach
2012

Date:_____

EXERCISE 8.14

FOREHEAD REPAIR   **SCALP REPAIR**
2.5 cm complex repair   2.6 cm intermediate repair

Before You Begin:
Read Chapter 8 in cpTeach® on "Surgery." Follow along in CPT® with the points illustrated in cpTeach®.

Purpose of this Lesson:
To assist you in continuing your knowledge of the coding of repairs in a multiple procedure situation (i.e., more than one repair at one time).

Instructions:
1. Code the following repairs using the correct CPT® code. Write them up as you would on a CMS-1500 form (i.e., which one would be written first, second, etc.) located on the back of each exercise.

Notes: _____

_____

_____

_____

_____

_____

_____

WORKBOOK McGUFFEY

cpTeach

2012

Name:_____

Class/Section:_____

Date:_____

EXERCISE 8.14

1500

HEALTH INSURANCE CLAIM FORM

APPROVED BY NATIONAL UNIFORM CLAIM COMMITTEE 08/05

CARRIER

		PICA								PICA		

1. MEDICARE	MEDICAID	TRICARE CHAMPUS	CHAMPVA	GROUP HEALTH PLAN	FECA BLK LUNG	OTHER	1a. INSURED'S I.D. NUMBER (For Program in Item 1)
(Medicare #)	(Medicaid #)	(Sponsor's SSN)	(Member ID#)	(SSN or ID)	(SSN)	(ID)	

2. PATIENT'S NAME (Last Name, First Name, Middle Initial)

3. PATIENT'S BIRTH DATE MM DD YY   SEX M   F

4. INSURED'S NAME (Last Name, First Name, Middle Initial)

5. PATIENT'S ADDRESS (No., Street)

6. PATIENT RELATIONSHIP TO INSURED   Self   Spouse   Child   Other

7. INSURED'S ADDRESS (No., Street)

CITY   STATE

8. PATIENT STATUS   Single   Married   Other

CITY   STATE

ZIP CODE   TELEPHONE (Include Area Code) ( )

Employed   Full-Time Student   Part-Time Student

ZIP CODE   TELEPHONE (Include Area Code) ( )

9. OTHER INSURED'S NAME (Last Name, First Name, Middle Initial)

10. IS PATIENT'S CONDITION RELATED TO:

11. INSURED'S POLICY GROUP OR FECA NUMBER

a. OTHER INSURED'S POLICY OR GROUP NUMBER

a. EMPLOYMENT? (Current or Previous)   YES   NO

a. INSURED'S DATE OF BIRTH MM DD YY   SEX M   F

b. OTHER INSURED'S DATE OF BIRTH MM DD YY   SEX M   F

b. AUTO ACCIDENT?   PLACE (State)   YES   NO

b. EMPLOYER'S NAME OR SCHOOL NAME

c. EMPLOYER'S NAME OR SCHOOL NAME

c. OTHER ACCIDENT?   YES   NO

c. INSURANCE PLAN NAME OR PROGRAM NAME

d. INSURANCE PLAN NAME OR PROGRAM NAME

10d. RESERVED FOR LOCAL USE

d. IS THERE ANOTHER HEALTH BENEFIT PLAN?   YES   NO   If yes, return to and complete item 9 a-d.

READ BACK OF FORM BEFORE COMPLETING & SIGNING THIS FORM.

12. PATIENT'S OR AUTHORIZED PERSON'S SIGNATURE I authorize the release of any medical or other information necessary to process this claim. I also request payment of government benefits either to myself or to the party who accepts assignment below.

SIGNED_____ DATE_____

13. INSURED'S OR AUTHORIZED PERSON'S SIGNATURE I authorize payment of medical benefits to the undersigned physician or supplier for services described below.

SIGNED_____

14. DATE OF CURRENT: MM DD YY   ILLNESS (First symptom) OR INJURY (Accident) OR PREGNANCY(LMP)

15. IF PATIENT HAS HAD SAME OR SIMILAR ILLNESS. GIVE FIRST DATE MM DD YY

16. DATES PATIENT UNABLE TO WORK IN CURRENT OCCUPATION MM DD YY   FROM   TO

17. NAME OF REFERRING PROVIDER OR OTHER SOURCE

17a.
17b. NPI

18. HOSPITALIZATION DATES RELATED TO CURRENT SERVICES MM DD YY   FROM   TO

19. RESERVED FOR LOCAL USE

20. OUTSIDE LAB?   YES   NO $ CHARGES

21. DIAGNOSIS OR NATURE OF ILLNESS OR INJURY (Relate Items 1, 2, 9 or 4 to Item 24E by Line)

1. |___.___   3. |___.___
2. |___.___   4. |___.___

22. MEDICAID RESUBMISSION CODE   ORIGINAL REF. NO.

23. PRIOR AUTHORIZATION NUMBER

24. A. DATE(S) OF SERVICE From MM DD YY To MM DD YY	B. PLACE OF SERVICE	C. EMG	D. PROCEDURES, SERVICES, OR SUPPLIES (Explain Unusual Circumstances) CPT/HCPCS MODIFIER	E. DIAGNOSIS POINTER	F. $ CHARGES	G. DAYS OR UNITS	H. EPSDT Family Plan	I. ID. QUAL.	J. RENDERING PROVIDER ID. #
1								NPI	
2								NPI	
3								NPI	
4								NPI	
5								NPI	
6								NPI	

25. FEDERAL TAX I.D. NUMBER   SSN   EIN

26. PATIENT'S ACCOUNT NO.

27. ACCEPT ASSIGNMENT? (For govt. claims, see back)   YES   NO

28. TOTAL CHARGE $

29. AMOUNT PAID $

30. BALANCE DUE $

31. SIGNATURE OF PHYSICIAN OR SUPPLIER INCLUDING DEGREES OR CREDENTIALS (I certify that the statements on the reverse apply to this bill and are made a part thereof.)

32. SERVICE FACILITY LOCATION INFORMATION

33. BILLING PROVIDER INFO & PH # ( )

PATIENT AND INSURED INFORMATION

PHYSICIAN OR SUPPLIER INFORMATION

Name:_____

Class/Section:_____

cpTeach
Date:_____
2012

EXERCISE 8.15

New patient/first cast tibial shaft fracture - no manipulation, tissue closure or fixation required.

Before You Begin:
Read Chapter 8 in cpTeach® on "Surgery." Follow along in CPT® with the points illustrated in cpTeach®.

Purpose of this Lesson:
To assist you in understanding the correct usage of the casting codes and the differences between initial cast placement and subsequent (follow-up) casting as well as to develop an understanding of coding surgical packages.

Instructions:
1. Code the following examples. Assume that the surgical package includes pre-op, surgery and post-op. Complete the CPT® portion of the CMS-1500 form found on the back of each page.

Notes: _____
_____
_____
_____
_____
_____
_____

EXERCISE **8.15**

WORKBOOK

cpTeach
2012

Name:_____

Class/Section:_____

Date:_____

1500

HEALTH INSURANCE CLAIM FORM

APPROVED BY NATIONAL UNIFORM CLAIM COMMITTEE 08/05

| | PICA | | | | | | | | PICA | | |

1. MEDICARE	MEDICAID	TRICARE CHAMPUS	CHAMPVA	GROUP HEALTH PLAN	FECA BLK LUNG	OTHER	1a. INSURED'S I.D. NUMBER	(For Program in Item 1)
(Medicare #)	(Medicaid #)	(Sponsor's SSN)	(Member ID#)	(SSN or ID)	(SSN)	(ID)		

2. PATIENT'S NAME (Last Name, First Name, Middle Initial)	3. PATIENT'S BIRTH DATE MM DD YY SEX M F	4. INSURED'S NAME (Last Name, First Name, Middle Initial)
5. PATIENT'S ADDRESS (No., Street)	6. PATIENT RELATIONSHIP TO INSURED Self Spouse Child Other	7. INSURED'S ADDRESS (No., Street)
CITY STATE	8. PATIENT STATUS Single Married Other	CITY STATE
ZIP CODE TELEPHONE (Include Area Code) ( )	Employed Full-Time Student Part-Time Student	ZIP CODE TELEPHONE (Include Area Code) ( )
9. OTHER INSURED'S NAME (Last Name, First Name, Middle Initial)	10. IS PATIENT'S CONDITION RELATED TO:	11. INSURED'S POLICY GROUP OR FECA NUMBER
a. OTHER INSURED'S POLICY OR GROUP NUMBER	a. EMPLOYMENT? (Current or Previous) YES NO	a. INSURED'S DATE OF BIRTH MM DD YY SEX M F
b. OTHER INSURED'S DATE OF BIRTH MM DD YY SEX M F	b. AUTO ACCIDENT? PLACE (State) YES NO	b. EMPLOYER'S NAME OR SCHOOL NAME
c. EMPLOYER'S NAME OR SCHOOL NAME	c. OTHER ACCIDENT? YES NO	c. INSURANCE PLAN NAME OR PROGRAM NAME
d. INSURANCE PLAN NAME OR PROGRAM NAME	10d. RESERVED FOR LOCAL USE	d. IS THERE ANOTHER HEALTH BENEFIT PLAN? YES NO If yes, return to and complete item 9 a-d.

READ BACK OF FORM BEFORE COMPLETING & SIGNING THIS FORM.

12. PATIENT'S OR AUTHORIZED PERSON'S SIGNATURE I authorize the release of any medical or other information necessary to process this claim. I also request payment of government benefits either to myself or to the party who accepts assignment below. SIGNED_____ DATE_____	13. INSURED'S OR AUTHORIZED PERSON'S SIGNATURE I authorize payment of medical benefits to the undersigned physician or supplier for services described below. SIGNED_____

14. DATE OF CURRENT: MM DD YY ILLNESS (First symptom) OR INJURY (Accident) OR PREGNANCY(LMP)	15. IF PATIENT HAS HAD SAME OR SIMILAR ILLNESS. GIVE FIRST DATE MM DD YY	16. DATES PATIENT UNABLE TO WORK IN CURRENT OCCUPATION MM DD YY MM DD YY FROM TO
17. NAME OF REFERRING PROVIDER OR OTHER SOURCE	17a. 17b. NPI	18. HOSPITALIZATION DATES RELATED TO CURRENT SERVICES MM DD YY MM DD YY FROM TO
19. RESERVED FOR LOCAL USE		20. OUTSIDE LAB? YES NO $ CHARGES
21. DIAGNOSIS OR NATURE OF ILLNESS OR INJURY (Relate Items 1, 2, 9 or 4 to Item 24E by Line) 1. |___ . ___ 9. |___ . ___ 2. |___ . ___ 4. |___ . ___		22. MEDICAID RESUBMISSION CODE ORIGINAL REF. NO. 23. PRIOR AUTHORIZATION NUMBER

24. A. DATE(S) OF SERVICE From To MM DD YY MM DD YY	B. PLACE OF SERVICE	C. EMG	D. PROCEDURES, SERVICES, OR SUPPLIES (Explain Unusual Circumstances) CPT/HCPCS	MODIFIER	E. DIAGNOSIS POINTER	F. $ CHARGES	G. DAYS OR UNITS	H. EPSDT Family Plan	I. ID QUAL.	J. RENDERING PROVIDER ID. #
1										NPI
2										NPI
3										NPI
4										NPI
5										NPI
6										NPI

25. FEDERAL TAX I.D. NUMBER SSN EIN	26. PATIENT'S ACCOUNT NO.	27. ACCEPT ASSIGNMENT? (For govt. claims, see back) YES NO	28. TOTAL CHARGE $	29. AMOUNT PAID $	30. BALANCE DUE $
31. SIGNATURE OF PHYSICIAN OR SUPPLIER INCLUDING DEGREES OR CREDENTIALS (I certify that the statements on the reverse apply to this bill and are made a part thereof.)	32. SERVICE FACILITY LOCATION INFORMATION		33. BILLING PROVIDER INFO & PH # ( )		

CARRIER — *PATIENT AND INSURED INFORMATION* — *PHYSICIAN OR SUPPLIER INFORMATION*

Name:_____

Class/Section:_____

Date:_____

2012

EXERCISE 8.16

Established patient/second cast/forearm radial fracture - no manipulation, tissue closure or fixation was required. This is a closed fracture.

Notes: _____

_____

_____

_____

_____

_____

_____

Before You Begin:
Read Chapter 8 in cpTeach® on "Surgery." Follow along in CPT® with the points illustrated in cpTeach®.

Purpose of this Lesson:
To assist you in understanding the correct usage of the casting codes and the differences between initial cast placement and subsequent (follow-up) casting as well as to develop an understanding of coding surgical packages.

Instructions:
1. Code the following examples. Assume that the surgical package includes pre-op, surgery and post-op. Complete the CPT® portion of the CMS-1500 form found on the back of each page.

EXERCISE **8.16**

Name:_____

Class/Section:_____

Date:_____

cpTeach 2012

1500

HEALTH INSURANCE CLAIM FORM

APPROVED BY NATIONAL UNIFORM CLAIM COMMITTEE 08/05

CARRIER

☐☐ PICA   PICA ☐☐

| 1. MEDICARE ☐ (Medicare #) | MEDICAID ☐ (Medicaid #) | TRICARE CHAMPUS ☐ (Sponsor's SSN) | CHAMPVA ☐ (Member ID#) | GROUP HEALTH PLAN ☐ (SSN or ID) | FECA BLK LUNG ☐ (SSN) | OTHER ☐ (ID) | 1a. INSURED'S I.D. NUMBER (For Program in Item 1) |

| 2. PATIENT'S NAME (Last Name, First Name, Middle Initial) | 3. PATIENT'S BIRTH DATE MM DD YY SEX M☐ F☐ | 4. INSURED'S NAME (Last Name, First Name, Middle Initial) |

| 5. PATIENT'S ADDRESS (No., Street) | 6. PATIENT RELATIONSHIP TO INSURED Self☐ Spouse☐ Child☐ Other☐ | 7. INSURED'S ADDRESS (No., Street) |

| CITY | STATE | 8. PATIENT STATUS Single☐ Married☐ Other☐ | CITY | STATE |

| ZIP CODE | TELEPHONE (Include Area Code) ( ) | Employed☐ Full-Time Student☐ Part-Time Student☐ | ZIP CODE | TELEPHONE (Include Area Code) ( ) |

| 9. OTHER INSURED'S NAME (Last Name, First Name, Middle Initial) | 10. IS PATIENT'S CONDITION RELATED TO: | 11. INSURED'S POLICY GROUP OR FECA NUMBER |

| a. OTHER INSURED'S POLICY OR GROUP NUMBER | a. EMPLOYMENT? (Current or Previous) ☐YES ☐NO | a. INSURED'S DATE OF BIRTH MM DD YY SEX M☐ F☐ |

| b. OTHER INSURED'S DATE OF BIRTH MM DD YY SEX M☐ F☐ | b. AUTO ACCIDENT? PLACE (State) ☐YES ☐NO | b. EMPLOYER'S NAME OR SCHOOL NAME |

| c. EMPLOYER'S NAME OR SCHOOL NAME | c. OTHER ACCIDENT? ☐YES ☐NO | c. INSURANCE PLAN NAME OR PROGRAM NAME |

| d. INSURANCE PLAN NAME OR PROGRAM NAME | 10d. RESERVED FOR LOCAL USE | d. IS THERE ANOTHER HEALTH BENEFIT PLAN? ☐YES ☐NO If yes, return to and complete item 9 a-d. |

READ BACK OF FORM BEFORE COMPLETING & SIGNING THIS FORM.

12. PATIENT'S OR AUTHORIZED PERSON'S SIGNATURE I authorize the release of any medical or other information necessary to process this claim. I also request payment of government benefits either to myself or to the party who accepts assignment below.

SIGNED_____ DATE_____

13. INSURED'S OR AUTHORIZED PERSON'S SIGNATURE I authorize payment of medical benefits to the undersigned physician or supplier for services described below.

SIGNED_____

PATIENT AND INSURED INFORMATION

| 14. DATE OF CURRENT: MM DD YY ILLNESS (First symptom) OR INJURY (Accident) OR PREGNANCY(LMP) | 15. IF PATIENT HAS HAD SAME OR SIMILAR ILLNESS. GIVE FIRST DATE MM DD YY | 16. DATES PATIENT UNABLE TO WORK IN CURRENT OCCUPATION MM DD YY MM DD YY FROM TO |

| 17. NAME OF REFERRING PROVIDER OR OTHER SOURCE | 17a. 17b. NPI | 18. HOSPITALIZATION DATES RELATED TO CURRENT SERVICES MM DD YY MM DD YY FROM TO |

| 19. RESERVED FOR LOCAL USE | 20. OUTSIDE LAB? ☐YES ☐NO $ CHARGES |

21. DIAGNOSIS OR NATURE OF ILLNESS OR INJURY (Relate Items 1, 2, 9 or 4 to Item 24E by Line)

1. |____.____   3. |____.____

2. |____.____   4. |____.____

| 22. MEDICAID RESUBMISSION CODE ORIGINAL REF. NO. |
| 23. PRIOR AUTHORIZATION NUMBER |

24. A. DATE(S) OF SERVICE From To MM DD YY MM DD YY	B. PLACE OF SERVICE	C. EMG	D. PROCEDURES, SERVICES, OR SUPPLIES (Explain Unusual Circumstances) CPT/HCPCS MODIFIER	E. DIAGNOSIS POINTER	F. $ CHARGES	G. DAYS OR UNITS	H. EPSDT Family Plan	I. ID. QUAL.	J. RENDERING PROVIDER ID. #
1									NPI
2									NPI
3									NPI
4									NPI
5									NPI
6									NPI

PHYSICIAN OR SUPPLIER INFORMATION

| 25. FEDERAL TAX I.D. NUMBER SSN☐ EIN☐ | 26. PATIENT'S ACCOUNT NO. | 27. ACCEPT ASSIGNMENT? (For govt. claims, see back) ☐YES ☐NO | 28. TOTAL CHARGE $ | 29. AMOUNT PAID $ | 30. BALANCE DUE $ |

| 31. SIGNATURE OF PHYSICIAN OR SUPPLIER INCLUDING DEGREES OR CREDENTIALS (I certify that the statements on the reverse apply to this bill and are made a part thereof.) | 32. SERVICE FACILITY LOCATION INFORMATION | 33. BILLING PROVIDER INFO & PH # ( ) |

EXERCISE 8.17

Debra Caballo is a 12-year-old avid horseback rider. This past weekend while at her family's ranch, Debra was attacked by two pit bull dogs. While one of the dogs was scared away by the rearing horse, the other grabbed Debra's right leg and managed to pull her off of the horse. He proceeded to tear a huge chunk of the skin off of her calf before running off to catch the horse that was frightened away. When Debra came into the emergency room it was obvious that she required surgery. An orthopaedist was called to operate and a split graft encompassing about 200 sq. cm. was done on Debra's leg. Code for the surgery performed by the orthopaedist.

Before You Begin:
Read Chapter 8 in cpTeach® on "Surgery." Follow along in CPT® with the points illustrated in cpTeach®.

Purpose of this Lesson:
To assist you in understanding the correct usage of the casting codes and the differences between initial cast placement and subsequent (follow-up) casting as well as to develop an understanding of coding surgical packages.

Instructions:
1. Code the following examples. Assume that the surgical package includes pre-op, surgery and post-op. Complete the CPT® portion of the CMS-1500 form found on the back of each page.

Notes: _____
_____
_____
_____
_____
_____
_____

EXERCISE 8.17

WORKBOOK
cpTeach
2012

Name: _____

Class/Section: _____

Date: _____

1500

HEALTH INSURANCE CLAIM FORM

APPROVED BY NATIONAL UNIFORM CLAIM COMMITTEE 08/05

| | PICA | | | | | | | PICA | | |

CARRIER

1. MEDICARE (Medicare #) MEDICAID (Medicaid #) TRICARE CHAMPUS (Sponsor's SSN) CHAMPVA (Member ID#) GROUP HEALTH PLAN (SSN or ID) FECA BLK LUNG (SSN) OTHER (ID)   1a. INSURED'S I.D. NUMBER   (For Program in Item 1)

2. PATIENT'S NAME (Last Name, First Name, Middle Initial)

3. PATIENT'S BIRTH DATE MM DD YY   SEX M   F

4. INSURED'S NAME (Last Name, First Name, Middle Initial)

5. PATIENT'S ADDRESS (No., Street)

6. PATIENT RELATIONSHIP TO INSURED   Self   Spouse   Child   Other

7. INSURED'S ADDRESS (No., Street)

CITY   STATE

8. PATIENT STATUS   Single   Married   Other

CITY   STATE

ZIP CODE   TELEPHONE (Include Area Code) ( )

Employed   Full-Time Student   Part-Time Student

ZIP CODE   TELEPHONE (Include Area Code) ( )

9. OTHER INSURED'S NAME (Last Name, First Name, Middle Initial)

10. IS PATIENT'S CONDITION RELATED TO:

11. INSURED'S POLICY GROUP OR FECA NUMBER

a. OTHER INSURED'S POLICY OR GROUP NUMBER

a. EMPLOYMENT? (Current or Previous)   YES   NO

a. INSURED'S DATE OF BIRTH MM DD YY   SEX M   F

b. OTHER INSURED'S DATE OF BIRTH MM DD YY   SEX M   F

b. AUTO ACCIDENT?   YES   NO   PLACE (State)

b. EMPLOYER'S NAME OR SCHOOL NAME

c. EMPLOYER'S NAME OR SCHOOL NAME

c. OTHER ACCIDENT?   YES   NO

c. INSURANCE PLAN NAME OR PROGRAM NAME

d. INSURANCE PLAN NAME OR PROGRAM NAME

10d. RESERVED FOR LOCAL USE

d. IS THERE ANOTHER HEALTH BENEFIT PLAN?   YES   NO   If yes, return to and complete item 9 a-d.

READ BACK OF FORM BEFORE COMPLETING & SIGNING THIS FORM.

12. PATIENT'S OR AUTHORIZED PERSON'S SIGNATURE I authorize the release of any medical or other information necessary to process this claim. I also request payment of government benefits either to myself or to the party who accepts assignment below.

SIGNED_____   DATE_____

13. INSURED'S OR AUTHORIZED PERSON'S SIGNATURE I authorize payment of medical benefits to the undersigned physician or supplier for services described below.

SIGNED_____

PATIENT AND INSURED INFORMATION

14. DATE OF CURRENT: MM DD YY   ILLNESS (First symptom) OR INJURY (Accident) OR PREGNANCY(LMP)

15. IF PATIENT HAS HAD SAME OR SIMILAR ILLNESS. GIVE FIRST DATE MM DD YY

16. DATES PATIENT UNABLE TO WORK IN CURRENT OCCUPATION FROM MM DD YY TO MM DD YY

17. NAME OF REFERRING PROVIDER OR OTHER SOURCE

17a.
17b. NPI

18. HOSPITALIZATION DATES RELATED TO CURRENT SERVICES FROM MM DD YY TO MM DD YY

19. RESERVED FOR LOCAL USE

20. OUTSIDE LAB?   YES   NO $ CHARGES

21. DIAGNOSIS OR NATURE OF ILLNESS OR INJURY (Relate Items 1, 2, 9 or 4 to Item 24E by Line)

1. |____ . ____
2. |____ . ____
3. |____ . ____
4. |____ . ____

22. MEDICAID RESUBMISSION CODE   ORIGINAL REF. NO.

23. PRIOR AUTHORIZATION NUMBER

24. A. DATE(S) OF SERVICE						B. PLACE OF SERVICE	C. EMG	D. PROCEDURES, SERVICES, OR SUPPLIES (Explain Unusual Circumstances)		E. DIAGNOSIS POINTER	F. $ CHARGES	G. DAYS OR UNITS	H. EPSDT Family Plan	I. ID. QUAL.	J. RENDERING PROVIDER ID. #
From MM	DD	YY	To MM	DD	YY			CPT/HCPCS	MODIFIER						
1														NPI	
2														NPI	
3														NPI	
4														NPI	
5														NPI	
6														NPI	

PHYSICIAN OR SUPPLIER INFORMATION

25. FEDERAL TAX I.D. NUMBER   SSN EIN

26. PATIENT'S ACCOUNT NO.

27. ACCEPT ASSIGNMENT? (For govt. claims, see back)   YES   NO

28. TOTAL CHARGE $

29. AMOUNT PAID $

30. BALANCE DUE $

31. SIGNATURE OF PHYSICIAN OR SUPPLIER INCLUDING DEGREES OR CREDENTIALS (I certify that the statements on the reverse apply to this bill and are made a part thereof.)

32. SERVICE FACILITY LOCATION INFORMATION

33. BILLING PROVIDER INFO & PH # ( )

Name:_____

Class/Section:_____

Date:_____

EXERCISE 8.18

Your physician performs a knee arthroscopy on a patient named Beau Marrow for the treatment of an articular surface defect using osteochondral grafts (autografts) which are implanted in the patient's right knee. Code for this surgeon.

Before You Begin:
Read Chapter 8 in cpTeach® on "Surgery." Follow along in CPT® with the points illustrated in cpTeach®.

Purpose of this Lesson:
To assist you in understanding the correct usage of the casting codes and the differences between initial cast placement and subsequent (follow-up) casting as well as to develop an understanding of coding surgical packages.

Instructions:
1. Code the following examples. Assume that the surgical package includes pre-op, surgery and post-op. Complete the CPT® portion of the CMS-1500 form found on the back of each page.

Notes: _____

_____

_____

_____

_____

_____

_____

EXERCISE 8.18

Name: _____

Class/Section: _____

Date: _____

2012

1500

HEALTH INSURANCE CLAIM FORM

APPROVED BY NATIONAL UNIFORM CLAIM COMMITTEE 08/05

CARRIER

	PICA						PICA	

1. MEDICARE	MEDICAID	TRICARE CHAMPUS	CHAMPVA	GROUP HEALTH PLAN	FECA BLK LUNG	OTHER	1a. INSURED'S I.D. NUMBER (For Program in Item 1)
(Medicare #)	(Medicaid #)	(Sponsor's SSN)	(Member ID#)	(SSN or ID)	(SSN)	(ID)	

2. PATIENT'S NAME (Last Name, First Name, Middle Initial)

3. PATIENT'S BIRTH DATE MM | DD | YY   **SEX** M ☐ F ☐

4. INSURED'S NAME (Last Name, First Name, Middle Initial)

5. PATIENT'S ADDRESS (No., Street)

6. PATIENT RELATIONSHIP TO INSURED Self ☐ Spouse ☐ Child ☐ Other ☐

7. INSURED'S ADDRESS (No., Street)

CITY | STATE

8. PATIENT STATUS Single ☐ Married ☐ Other ☐

CITY | STATE

ZIP CODE | TELEPHONE (Include Area Code) ( )

Employed ☐ Full-Time Student ☐ Part-Time Student ☐

ZIP CODE | TELEPHONE (Include Area Code) ( )

9. OTHER INSURED'S NAME (Last Name, First Name, Middle Initial)

10. IS PATIENT'S CONDITION RELATED TO:

11. INSURED'S POLICY GROUP OR FECA NUMBER

a. OTHER INSURED'S POLICY OR GROUP NUMBER

a. EMPLOYMENT? (Current or Previous) YES ☐ NO ☐

a. INSURED'S DATE OF BIRTH MM | DD | YY   SEX M ☐ F ☐

b. OTHER INSURED'S DATE OF BIRTH MM | DD | YY   SEX M ☐ F ☐

b. AUTO ACCIDENT? PLACE (State) YES ☐ NO ☐

b. EMPLOYER'S NAME OR SCHOOL NAME

c. EMPLOYER'S NAME OR SCHOOL NAME

c. OTHER ACCIDENT? YES ☐ NO ☐

c. INSURANCE PLAN NAME OR PROGRAM NAME

d. INSURANCE PLAN NAME OR PROGRAM NAME

10d. RESERVED FOR LOCAL USE

d. IS THERE ANOTHER HEALTH BENEFIT PLAN? YES ☐ NO ☐ *If yes, return to and complete Item 9 a-d.*

READ BACK OF FORM BEFORE COMPLETING & SIGNING THIS FORM.

12. PATIENT'S OR AUTHORIZED PERSON'S SIGNATURE I authorize the release of any medical or other information necessary to process this claim. I also request payment of government benefits either to myself or to the party who accepts assignment below.

SIGNED _____ DATE _____

13. INSURED'S OR AUTHORIZED PERSON'S SIGNATURE I authorize payment of medical benefits to the undersigned physician or supplier for services described below.

SIGNED _____

14. DATE OF CURRENT: MM | DD | YY   ILLNESS (First symptom) OR INJURY (Accident) OR PREGNANCY (LMP)

15. IF PATIENT HAS HAD SAME OR SIMILAR ILLNESS. GIVE FIRST DATE MM | DD | YY

16. DATES PATIENT UNABLE TO WORK IN CURRENT OCCUPATION FROM MM | DD | YY TO MM | DD | YY

17. NAME OF REFERRING PROVIDER OR OTHER SOURCE

17a.

17b. NPI

18. HOSPITALIZATION DATES RELATED TO CURRENT SERVICES FROM MM | DD | YY TO MM | DD | YY

19. RESERVED FOR LOCAL USE

20. OUTSIDE LAB? YES ☐ NO ☐ $ CHARGES

21. DIAGNOSIS OR NATURE OF ILLNESS OR INJURY (Relate Items 1, 2, 3 or 4 to Item 24E by Line)

1. |___.___
2. |___.___
3. |___.___
4. |___.___

22. MEDICAID RESUBMISSION CODE ORIGINAL REF. NO.

23. PRIOR AUTHORIZATION NUMBER

24. A. DATE(S) OF SERVICE From MM DD YY To MM DD YY	B. PLACE OF SERVICE	C. EMG	D. PROCEDURES, SERVICES, OR SUPPLIES (Explain Unusual Circumstances) CPT/HCPCS	MODIFIER	E. DIAGNOSIS POINTER	F. $ CHARGES	G. DAYS OR UNITS	H. EPSDT Family Plan	I. ID. QUAL.	J. RENDERING PROVIDER ID. #
1										NPI
2										NPI
3										NPI
4										NPI
5										NPI
6										NPI

25. FEDERAL TAX I.D. NUMBER SSN ☐ EIN ☐

26. PATIENT'S ACCOUNT NO.

27. ACCEPT ASSIGNMENT? (For govt. claims, see back) YES ☐ NO ☐

28. TOTAL CHARGE $

29. AMOUNT PAID $

30. BALANCE DUE $

31. SIGNATURE OF PHYSICIAN OR SUPPLIER INCLUDING DEGREES OR CREDENTIALS (I certify that the statements on the reverse apply to this bill and are made a part thereof.)

32. SERVICE FACILITY LOCATION INFORMATION

33. BILLING PROVIDER INFO & PH # ( )

PATIENT AND INSURED INFORMATION

PHYSICIAN OR SUPPLIER INFORMATION

Name:_____

Class/Section:_____

Date:_____

2012

EXERCISE 8.19

Your physician performs a diagnostic, bilateral, nasal endoscopy on a patient named Brady Cardia. Code for your doctor.

Before You Begin:

Read Chapter 8 in cpTeach® on "Surgery." Follow along in CPT® with the points illustrated in cpTeach®.

Purpose of this Lesson:

To assist you in understanding the correct usage of the casting codes and the differences between initial cast placement and subsequent (follow-up) casting as well as to develop an understanding of coding surgical packages.

Instructions:

1. Code the following examples. Assume that the surgical package includes pre-op, surgery and post-op. Complete the CPT® portion of the CMS-1500 form found on the back of each page.

Notes: _____

_____

_____

_____

_____

_____

_____

EXERCISE **8.19**

Name:_____

Class/Section:_____

Date:_____

1500

HEALTH INSURANCE CLAIM FORM

APPROVED BY NATIONAL UNIFORM CLAIM COMMITTEE 08/05

☐☐ PICA   PICA ☐☐

1. MEDICARE MEDICAID TRICARE CHAMPVA GROUP FECA OTHER	1a. INSURED'S I.D. NUMBER (For Program in Item 1)
☐ (Medicare #) ☐ (Medicaid #) CHAMPUS ☐(Sponsor's SSN) ☐ (Member ID#) HEALTH PLAN ☐(SSN or ID) BLK LUNG ☐(SSN) ☐(ID)	

2. PATIENT'S NAME (Last Name, First Name, Middle Initial)	3. PATIENT'S BIRTH DATE SEX	4. INSURED'S NAME (Last Name, First Name, Middle Initial)
	MM DD YY M ☐ F ☐	

5. PATIENT'S ADDRESS (No., Street)	6. PATIENT RELATIONSHIP TO INSURED	7. INSURED'S ADDRESS (No., Street)
	Self ☐ Spouse ☐ Child ☐ Other ☐	
CITY STATE	8. PATIENT STATUS	CITY STATE
	Single ☐ Married ☐ Other ☐	
ZIP CODE TELEPHONE (Include Area Code) ( )	Employed ☐ Full-Time Student ☐ Part-Time Student ☐	ZIP CODE TELEPHONE (Include Area Code) ( )

9. OTHER INSURED'S NAME (Last Name, First Name, Middle Initial)	10. IS PATIENT'S CONDITION RELATED TO:	11. INSURED'S POLICY GROUP OR FECA NUMBER
a. OTHER INSURED'S POLICY OR GROUP NUMBER	a. EMPLOYMENT? (Current or Previous) ☐ YES ☐ NO	a. INSURED'S DATE OF BIRTH SEX MM DD YY M ☐ F ☐
b. OTHER INSURED'S DATE OF BIRTH SEX MM DD YY M ☐ F ☐	b. AUTO ACCIDENT? PLACE (State) ☐ YES ☐ NO	b. EMPLOYER'S NAME OR SCHOOL NAME
c. EMPLOYER'S NAME OR SCHOOL NAME	c. OTHER ACCIDENT? ☐ YES ☐ NO	c. INSURANCE PLAN NAME OR PROGRAM NAME
d. INSURANCE PLAN NAME OR PROGRAM NAME	10d. RESERVED FOR LOCAL USE	d. IS THERE ANOTHER HEALTH BENEFIT PLAN? ☐ YES ☐ NO If yes, return to and complete item 9 a-d.

READ BACK OF FORM BEFORE COMPLETING & SIGNING THIS FORM.

12. PATIENT'S OR AUTHORIZED PERSON'S SIGNATURE I authorize the release of any medical or other information necessary to process this claim. I also request payment of government benefits either to myself or to the party who accepts assignment below.

SIGNED_____   DATE_____

13. INSURED'S OR AUTHORIZED PERSON'S SIGNATURE I authorize payment of medical benefits to the undersigned physician or supplier for services described below.

SIGNED_____

14. DATE OF CURRENT: ILLNESS (First symptom) OR MM DD YY INJURY (Accident) OR PREGNANCY(LMP)	15. IF PATIENT HAS HAD SAME OR SIMILAR ILLNESS. GIVE FIRST DATE MM DD YY	16. DATES PATIENT UNABLE TO WORK IN CURRENT OCCUPATION MM DD YY MM DD YY FROM TO
17. NAME OF REFERRING PROVIDER OR OTHER SOURCE	17a. 17b. NPI	18. HOSPITALIZATION DATES RELATED TO CURRENT SERVICES MM DD YY MM DD YY FROM TO
19. RESERVED FOR LOCAL USE		20. OUTSIDE LAB? ☐ YES ☐ NO $ CHARGES

21. DIAGNOSIS OR NATURE OF ILLNESS OR INJURY (Relate Items 1, 2, 3 or 4 to Item 24E by Line)

1. |___.___   3. |___.___

2. |___.___   4. |___.___

22. MEDICAID RESUBMISSION CODE   ORIGINAL REF. NO.

23. PRIOR AUTHORIZATION NUMBER

24. A. DATE(S) OF SERVICE From To MM DD YY MM DD YY	B. PLACE OF SERVICE	C. EMG	D. PROCEDURES, SERVICES, OR SUPPLIES (Explain Unusual Circumstances) CPT/HCPCS MODIFIER	E. DIAGNOSIS POINTER	F. $ CHARGES	G. DAYS OR UNITS	H. EPSDT Family Plan	I. ID. QUAL.	J. RENDERING PROVIDER ID. #
1								NPI	
2								NPI	
3								NPI	
4								NPI	
5								NPI	
6								NPI	

25. FEDERAL TAX I.D. NUMBER SSN EIN ☐ ☐	26. PATIENT'S ACCOUNT NO.	27. ACCEPT ASSIGNMENT? (For govt. claims, see back) ☐ YES ☐ NO	28. TOTAL CHARGE $	29. AMOUNT PAID $	30. BALANCE DUE $

31. SIGNATURE OF PHYSICIAN OR SUPPLIER INCLUDING DEGREES OR CREDENTIALS (I certify that the statements on the reverse apply to this bill and are made a part thereof.)

32. SERVICE FACILITY LOCATION INFORMATION

33. BILLING PROVIDER INFO & PH # (   )

CARRIER ▸ PATIENT AND INSURED INFORMATION ▸ PHYSICIAN OR SUPPLIER INFORMATION

Name:_____

Class/Section:_____

cpTeach
2012   Date:_____

EXERCISE 8.20

Ms. Ima Snotty comes into the outpatient surgical center for her diagnostic laryngoscopy. Your surgeon discusses the surgery with Ms. Snotty and performs a brief exam to make sure she is still ready for the surgery. Code for all services rendered.

Before You Begin:
Read Chapter 8 in cpTeach® on "Surgery." Follow along in CPT® with the points illustrated in cpTeach®.

Purpose of this Lesson:
To assist you in understanding the correct usage of the casting codes and the differences between initial cast placement and subsequent (follow-up) casting as well as to develop an understanding of coding surgical packages.

Instructions:
1. Code the following examples. Assume that the surgical package includes pre-op, surgery and post-op. Complete the CPT® portion of the CMS-1500 form found on the back of each page.

Notes: _____
_____
_____
_____
_____
_____
_____
_____

EXERCISE 8.20

Name:_____

Class/Section:_____

Date:_____

cpTeach
2012

1500
HEALTH INSURANCE CLAIM FORM
APPROVED BY NATIONAL UNIFORM CLAIM COMMITTEE 08/05

PICA   PICA

1. MEDICARE MEDICAID TRICARE CHAMPUS CHAMPVA GROUP HEALTH PLAN FECA BLK LUNG OTHER	1a. INSURED'S I.D. NUMBER (For Program in Item 1)
(Medicare #) (Medicaid #) (Sponsor's SSN) (Member ID#) (SSN or ID) (SSN) (ID)	

2. PATIENT'S NAME (Last Name, First Name, Middle Initial) | 3. PATIENT'S BIRTH DATE   MM DD YY   SEX   M☐ F☐ | 4. INSURED'S NAME (Last Name, First Name, Middle Initial)

5. PATIENT'S ADDRESS (No., Street) | 6. PATIENT RELATIONSHIP TO INSURED   Self☐ Spouse☐ Child☐ Other☐ | 7. INSURED'S ADDRESS (No., Street)

CITY   STATE | 8. PATIENT STATUS   Single☐ Married☐ Other☐ | CITY   STATE

ZIP CODE   TELEPHONE (Include Area Code) ( ) | Employed☐ Full-Time Student☐ Part-Time Student☐ | ZIP CODE   TELEPHONE (Include Area Code) ( )

9. OTHER INSURED'S NAME (Last Name, First Name, Middle Initial) | 10. IS PATIENT'S CONDITION RELATED TO: | 11. INSURED'S POLICY GROUP OR FECA NUMBER

a. OTHER INSURED'S POLICY OR GROUP NUMBER | a. EMPLOYMENT? (Current or Previous)   YES☐ NO☐ | a. INSURED'S DATE OF BIRTH   MM DD YY   SEX   M☐ F☐

b. OTHER INSURED'S DATE OF BIRTH   MM DD YY   SEX   M☐ F☐ | b. AUTO ACCIDENT?   PLACE (State)   YES☐ NO☐ | b. EMPLOYER'S NAME OR SCHOOL NAME

c. EMPLOYER'S NAME OR SCHOOL NAME | c. OTHER ACCIDENT?   YES☐ NO☐ | c. INSURANCE PLAN NAME OR PROGRAM NAME

d. INSURANCE PLAN NAME OR PROGRAM NAME | 10d. RESERVED FOR LOCAL USE | d. IS THERE ANOTHER HEALTH BENEFIT PLAN?   YES☐ NO☐   If yes, return to and complete item 9 a-d.

READ BACK OF FORM BEFORE COMPLETING & SIGNING THIS FORM.
12. PATIENT'S OR AUTHORIZED PERSON'S SIGNATURE I authorize the release of any medical or other information necessary to process this claim. I also request payment of government benefits either to myself or to the party who accepts assignment below.

SIGNED_____   DATE_____

13. INSURED'S OR AUTHORIZED PERSON'S SIGNATURE I authorize payment of medical benefits to the undersigned physician or supplier for services described below.

SIGNED_____

14. DATE OF CURRENT: MM DD YY   ILLNESS (First symptom) OR INJURY (Accident) OR PREGNANCY(LMP) | 15. IF PATIENT HAS HAD SAME OR SIMILAR ILLNESS. GIVE FIRST DATE   MM DD YY | 16. DATES PATIENT UNABLE TO WORK IN CURRENT OCCUPATION   FROM MM DD YY TO MM DD YY

17. NAME OF REFERRING PROVIDER OR OTHER SOURCE | 17a.   17b. NPI | 18. HOSPITALIZATION DATES RELATED TO CURRENT SERVICES   FROM MM DD YY TO MM DD YY

19. RESERVED FOR LOCAL USE | 20. OUTSIDE LAB?   YES☐ NO☐ $ CHARGES

21. DIAGNOSIS OR NATURE OF ILLNESS OR INJURY (Relate Items 1, 2, 9 or 4 to Item 24E by Line)
1. |___.___   3. |___.___
2. |___.___   4. |___.___

22. MEDICAID RESUBMISSION CODE   ORIGINAL REF. NO.

23. PRIOR AUTHORIZATION NUMBER

24. A. DATE(S) OF SERVICE		B. PLACE OF SERVICE	C. EMG	D. PROCEDURES, SERVICES, OR SUPPLIES (Explain Unusual Circumstances)		E. DIAGNOSIS POINTER	F. $ CHARGES	G. DAYS OR UNITS	H. EPSDT Family Plan	I. ID. QUAL.	J. RENDERING PROVIDER ID. #
From MM DD YY	To MM DD YY			CPT/HCPCS	MODIFIER						
1										NPI	
2										NPI	
3										NPI	
4										NPI	
5										NPI	
6										NPI	

25. FEDERAL TAX I.D. NUMBER   SSN☐ EIN☐ | 26. PATIENT'S ACCOUNT NO. | 27. ACCEPT ASSIGNMENT? (For govt. claims, see back)   YES☐ NO☐ | 28. TOTAL CHARGE $ | 29. AMOUNT PAID $ | 30. BALANCE DUE $

31. SIGNATURE OF PHYSICIAN OR SUPPLIER INCLUDING DEGREES OR CREDENTIALS (I certify that the statements on the reverse apply to this bill and are made a part thereof.) | 32. SERVICE FACILITY LOCATION INFORMATION | 33. BILLING PROVIDER INFO & PH # ( )

EXERCISE 8.21

Mia Corazon is a 65-year-old Spanish immigrant who needs a replacement of her pacemaker pulse generator. Code for this service.

Notes: _____

_____

_____

_____

_____

_____

_____

Name:_____

Class/Section:_____

Date:_____

EXERCISE 8.21

CARRIER

1500

HEALTH INSURANCE CLAIM FORM

APPROVED BY NATIONAL UNIFORM CLAIM COMMITTEE 08/05

| | PICA | | | | | PICA | |

| 1. MEDICARE | MEDICAID | TRICARE CHAMPUS | CHAMPVA | GROUP HEALTH PLAN | FECA BLK LUNG | OTHER | 1a. INSURED'S I.D. NUMBER (For Program in Item 1) |
| (Medicare #) | (Medicaid #) | (Sponsor's SSN) | (Member ID#) | (SSN or ID) | (SSN) | (ID) | |

2. PATIENT'S NAME (Last Name, First Name, Middle Initial)

3. PATIENT'S BIRTH DATE MM | DD | YY   SEX   M☐ F☐

4. INSURED'S NAME (Last Name, First Name, Middle Initial)

5. PATIENT'S ADDRESS (No., Street)

6. PATIENT RELATIONSHIP TO INSURED   Self☐ Spouse☐ Child☐ Other☐

7. INSURED'S ADDRESS (No., Street)

CITY   STATE

8. PATIENT STATUS   Single☐ Married☐ Other☐

CITY   STATE

ZIP CODE   TELEPHONE (Include Area Code) (   )

Employed☐ Full-Time Student☐ Part-Time Student☐

ZIP CODE   TELEPHONE (Include Area Code) (   )

9. OTHER INSURED'S NAME (Last Name, First Name, Middle Initial)

10. IS PATIENT'S CONDITION RELATED TO:

11. INSURED'S POLICY GROUP OR FECA NUMBER

a. OTHER INSURED'S POLICY OR GROUP NUMBER

a. EMPLOYMENT? (Current or Previous) YES☐ NO☐

a. INSURED'S DATE OF BIRTH MM | DD | YY   SEX   M☐ F☐

b. OTHER INSURED'S DATE OF BIRTH MM | DD | YY   SEX   M☐ F☐

b. AUTO ACCIDENT?   PLACE (State) YES☐ NO☐

b. EMPLOYER'S NAME OR SCHOOL NAME

c. EMPLOYER'S NAME OR SCHOOL NAME

c. OTHER ACCIDENT? YES☐ NO☐

c. INSURANCE PLAN NAME OR PROGRAM NAME

d. INSURANCE PLAN NAME OR PROGRAM NAME

10d. RESERVED FOR LOCAL USE

d. IS THERE ANOTHER HEALTH BENEFIT PLAN? YES☐ NO☐ If yes, return to and complete item 9 a-d.

READ BACK OF FORM BEFORE COMPLETING & SIGNING THIS FORM.
12. PATIENT'S OR AUTHORIZED PERSON'S SIGNATURE I authorize the release of any medical or other information necessary to process this claim. I also request payment of government benefits either to myself or to the party who accepts assignment below.

SIGNED_____ DATE_____

13. INSURED'S OR AUTHORIZED PERSON'S SIGNATURE I authorize payment of medical benefits to the undersigned physician or supplier for services described below.

SIGNED_____

PATIENT AND INSURED INFORMATION

14. DATE OF CURRENT: MM | DD | YY   ILLNESS (First symptom) OR INJURY (Accident) OR PREGNANCY(LMP)

15. IF PATIENT HAS HAD SAME OR SIMILAR ILLNESS. GIVE FIRST DATE MM | DD | YY

16. DATES PATIENT UNABLE TO WORK IN CURRENT OCCUPATION MM | DD | YY   FROM   TO MM | DD | YY

17. NAME OF REFERRING PROVIDER OR OTHER SOURCE

17a.
17b. NPI

18. HOSPITALIZATION DATES RELATED TO CURRENT SERVICES MM | DD | YY   FROM   TO MM | DD | YY

19. RESERVED FOR LOCAL USE

20. OUTSIDE LAB? $ CHARGES   YES☐ NO☐

21. DIAGNOSIS OR NATURE OF ILLNESS OR INJURY (Relate Items 1, 2, 3 or 4 to Item 24E by Line)

1. |___.___   3. |___.___
2. |___.___   4. |___.___

22. MEDICAID RESUBMISSION CODE   ORIGINAL REF. NO.

23. PRIOR AUTHORIZATION NUMBER

24. A. DATE(S) OF SERVICE		B. PLACE OF SERVICE	C. EMG	D. PROCEDURES, SERVICES, OR SUPPLIES (Explain Unusual Circumstances)		E. DIAGNOSIS POINTER	F. $ CHARGES	G. DAYS OR UNITS	H. EPSDT Family Plan	I. ID QUAL.	J. RENDERING PROVIDER ID. #
From MM DD YY	To MM DD YY			CPT/HCPCS	MODIFIER						
1											NPI
2											NPI
3											NPI
4											NPI
5											NPI
6											NPI

25. FEDERAL TAX I.D. NUMBER   SSN☐ EIN☐

26. PATIENT'S ACCOUNT NO.

27. ACCEPT ASSIGNMENT? (For govt. claims, see back) YES☐ NO☐

28. TOTAL CHARGE $

29. AMOUNT PAID $

30. BALANCE DUE $

31. SIGNATURE OF PHYSICIAN OR SUPPLIER INCLUDING DEGREES OR CREDENTIALS (I certify that the statements on the reverse apply to this bill and are made a part thereof.)

32. SERVICE FACILITY LOCATION INFORMATION

33. BILLING PROVIDER INFO & PH # (   )

PHYSICIAN OR SUPPLIER INFORMATION

WORKBOOK

McGUFFEY

cpTeach

74th EDITION

2012

*Name:*_____

*Class/Section:*_____

*Date:*_____

Exercise 8.22

Ms. Carriage, a pregnant patient, presents to the hospital in her 7th month complaining of severe pelvic pain. Ms. Carriage lives on an Indian reservation with 50 other people, and there is no medical team within a 120 mile radius. Her doctor, an OB/GYN, is contacted via the internet to assess the patient and determine what the cause of her pelvic pain is. Your doctor provides an online E/M service in response to Ms. Carriage's request. Code for the online evaluation performed by your doctor.

Before You Begin:

Read Chapter 8 in cpTeach® on "Surgery." Follow along in CPT® with the points illustrated in cpTeach®.

Purpose of this Lesson:

To assist you in understanding the correct usage of the casting codes and the differences between initial cast placement and subsequent (follow-up) casting as well as to develop an understanding of coding surgical packages.

Instructions:

1. Code the following examples. Assume that the surgical package includes pre-op, surgery and post-op. Complete the CPT® portion of the CMS-1500 form found on the back of each page.

Notes: _____

_____

_____

_____

_____

_____

_____

EXERCISE 8.22

1500
HEALTH INSURANCE CLAIM FORM

APPROVED BY NATIONAL UNIFORM CLAIM COMMITTEE 08/05

CARRIER

| | PICA | | | | | | | | PICA | | |

| 1. MEDICARE | MEDICAID | TRICARE CHAMPUS | CHAMPVA | GROUP HEALTH PLAN | FECA BLK LUNG | OTHER | 1a. INSURED'S I.D. NUMBER | (For Program in Item 1) |
| (Medicare #) | (Medicaid #) | (Sponsor's SSN) | (Member ID#) | (SSN or ID) | (SSN) | (ID) | | |

2. PATIENT'S NAME (Last Name, First Name, Middle Initial)

3. PATIENT'S BIRTH DATE MM DD YY **SEX** M ☐ F ☐

4. INSURED'S NAME (Last Name, First Name, Middle Initial)

5. PATIENT'S ADDRESS (No., Street)

6. PATIENT RELATIONSHIP TO INSURED Self ☐ Spouse ☐ Child ☐ Other ☐

7. INSURED'S ADDRESS (No., Street)

CITY — STATE

8. PATIENT STATUS Single ☐ Married ☐ Other ☐

CITY — STATE

ZIP CODE — TELEPHONE (Include Area Code) ( )

Employed ☐ Full-Time Student ☐ Part-Time Student ☐

ZIP CODE — TELEPHONE (Include Area Code) ( )

9. OTHER INSURED'S NAME (Last Name, First Name, Middle Initial)

10. IS PATIENT'S CONDITION RELATED TO:

11. INSURED'S POLICY GROUP OR FECA NUMBER

a. OTHER INSURED'S POLICY OR GROUP NUMBER

a. EMPLOYMENT? (Current or Previous) ☐ YES ☐ NO

a. INSURED'S DATE OF BIRTH MM DD YY **SEX** M ☐ F ☐

b. OTHER INSURED'S DATE OF BIRTH MM DD YY SEX M ☐ F ☐

b. AUTO ACCIDENT? ☐ YES ☐ NO PLACE (State)

b. EMPLOYER'S NAME OR SCHOOL NAME

c. EMPLOYER'S NAME OR SCHOOL NAME

c. OTHER ACCIDENT? ☐ YES ☐ NO

c. INSURANCE PLAN NAME OR PROGRAM NAME

d. INSURANCE PLAN NAME OR PROGRAM NAME

10d. RESERVED FOR LOCAL USE

d. IS THERE ANOTHER HEALTH BENEFIT PLAN? ☐ YES ☐ NO *If yes, return to and complete item 9 a-d.*

READ BACK OF FORM BEFORE COMPLETING & SIGNING THIS FORM.
12. PATIENT'S OR AUTHORIZED PERSON'S SIGNATURE I authorize the release of any medical or other information necessary to process this claim. I also request payment of government benefits either to myself or to the party who accepts assignment below.

SIGNED_____ DATE_____

13. INSURED'S OR AUTHORIZED PERSON'S SIGNATURE I authorize payment of medical benefits to the undersigned physician or supplier for services described below.

SIGNED_____

PATIENT AND INSURED INFORMATION

14. DATE OF CURRENT: MM DD YY ILLNESS (First symptom) OR INJURY (Accident) OR PREGNANCY(LMP)

15. IF PATIENT HAS HAD SAME OR SIMILAR ILLNESS. GIVE FIRST DATE MM DD YY

16. DATES PATIENT UNABLE TO WORK IN CURRENT OCCUPATION MM DD YY FROM TO MM DD YY

17. NAME OF REFERRING PROVIDER OR OTHER SOURCE

17a.
17b. NPI

18. HOSPITALIZATION DATES RELATED TO CURRENT SERVICES MM DD YY FROM TO MM DD YY

19. RESERVED FOR LOCAL USE

20. OUTSIDE LAB? ☐ YES ☐ NO $ CHARGES

21. DIAGNOSIS OR NATURE OF ILLNESS OR INJURY (Relate Items 1, 2, 3 or 4 to Item 24E by Line)

1. ⌞___.___⌟ 3. ⌞___.___⌟
2. ⌞___.___⌟ 4. ⌞___.___⌟

22. MEDICAID RESUBMISSION CODE ORIGINAL REF. NO.

23. PRIOR AUTHORIZATION NUMBER

| 24. A. DATE(S) OF SERVICE | | | | | | B. PLACE OF SERVICE | C. EMG | D. PROCEDURES, SERVICES, OR SUPPLIES (Explain Unusual Circumstances) CPT/HCPCS MODIFIER | E. DIAGNOSIS POINTER | F. $ CHARGES | G. DAYS OR UNITS | H. EPSDT Family Plan | I. ID. QUAL. | J. RENDERING PROVIDER ID. # |
From MM	DD	YY	To MM	DD	YY									
1													NPI	
2													NPI	
3													NPI	
4													NPI	
5													NPI	
6													NPI	

PHYSICIAN OR SUPPLIER INFORMATION

25. FEDERAL TAX I.D. NUMBER SSN ☐ EIN ☐

26. PATIENT'S ACCOUNT NO.

27. ACCEPT ASSIGNMENT? (For govt. claims, see back) ☐ YES ☐ NO

28. TOTAL CHARGE $

29. AMOUNT PAID $

30. BALANCE DUE $

31. SIGNATURE OF PHYSICIAN OR SUPPLIER INCLUDING DEGREES OR CREDENTIALS (I certify that the statements on the reverse apply to this bill and are made a part thereof.)

32. SERVICE FACILITY LOCATION INFORMATION

33. BILLING PROVIDER INFO & PH # ( )

Name: _____

Class/Section: _____

cpTeach
2012

Date: _____

EXERCISE 8.23

A. Sid Ophilous, owner of a local Greek restaurant, receives a gastrotomy with removal of a foreign body (a seed) that got stuck recently in his stomach during an olive tasting party. Code for the surgery.

Before You Begin:
Read Chapter 8 in cpTeach® on "Surgery." Follow along in CPT® with the points illustrated in cpTeach®.

Purpose of this Lesson:
To assist you in understanding the correct usage of the casting codes and the differences between initial cast placement and subsequent (follow-up) casting as well as to develop an understanding of coding surgical packages.

Instructions:
1. Code the following examples. Assume that the surgical package includes pre-op, surgery and post-op. Complete the CPT® portion of the CMS-1500 form found on the back of each page.

Notes: _____

_____

_____

_____

_____

_____

_____

EXERCISE **8.23**

1500

HEALTH INSURANCE CLAIM FORM

APPROVED BY NATIONAL UNIFORM CLAIM COMMITTEE 08/05

CARRIER

| PICA | | | | | | | | | PICA | |

1. MEDICARE	MEDICAID	TRICARE CHAMPUS	CHAMPVA	GROUP HEALTH PLAN	FECA BLK LUNG	OTHER	1a. INSURED'S I.D. NUMBER	(For Program in Item 1)
(Medicare #)	(Medicaid #)	(Sponsor's SSN)	(Member ID#)	(SSN or ID)	(SSN)	(ID)		

2. PATIENT'S NAME (Last Name, First Name, Middle Initial)

3. PATIENT'S BIRTH DATE MM DD YY   SEX   M   F

4. INSURED'S NAME (Last Name, First Name, Middle Initial)

5. PATIENT'S ADDRESS (No., Street)

6. PATIENT RELATIONSHIP TO INSURED   Self   Spouse   Child   Other

7. INSURED'S ADDRESS (No., Street)

CITY   STATE

8. PATIENT STATUS   Single   Married   Other

Employed   Full-Time Student   Part-Time Student

CITY   STATE

ZIP CODE   TELEPHONE (Include Area Code) (   )

ZIP CODE   TELEPHONE (Include Area Code) (   )

9. OTHER INSURED'S NAME (Last Name, First Name, Middle Initial)

10. IS PATIENT'S CONDITION RELATED TO:

11. INSURED'S POLICY GROUP OR FECA NUMBER

a. OTHER INSURED'S POLICY OR GROUP NUMBER

a. EMPLOYMENT? (Current or Previous)   YES   NO

a. INSURED'S DATE OF BIRTH MM DD YY   SEX   M   F

b. OTHER INSURED'S DATE OF BIRTH MM DD YY   SEX   M   F

b. AUTO ACCIDENT?   PLACE (State)   YES   NO

b. EMPLOYER'S NAME OR SCHOOL NAME

c. EMPLOYER'S NAME OR SCHOOL NAME

c. OTHER ACCIDENT?   YES   NO

c. INSURANCE PLAN NAME OR PROGRAM NAME

d. INSURANCE PLAN NAME OR PROGRAM NAME

10d. RESERVED FOR LOCAL USE

d. IS THERE ANOTHER HEALTH BENEFIT PLAN?   YES   NO   If yes, return to and complete item 9 a-d.

READ BACK OF FORM BEFORE COMPLETING & SIGNING THIS FORM.

12. PATIENT'S OR AUTHORIZED PERSON'S SIGNATURE I authorize the release of any medical or other information necessary to process this claim. I also request payment of government benefits either to myself or to the party who accepts assignment below.

SIGNED_____ DATE_____

13. INSURED'S OR AUTHORIZED PERSON'S SIGNATURE I authorize payment of medical benefits to the undersigned physician or supplier for services described below.

SIGNED_____

14. DATE OF CURRENT: MM DD YY ILLNESS (First symptom) OR INJURY (Accident) OR PREGNANCY(LMP)

15. IF PATIENT HAS HAD SAME OR SIMILAR ILLNESS. GIVE FIRST DATE MM DD YY

16. DATES PATIENT UNABLE TO WORK IN CURRENT OCCUPATION MM DD YY FROM   TO MM DD YY

17. NAME OF REFERRING PROVIDER OR OTHER SOURCE

17a.

17b. NPI

18. HOSPITALIZATION DATES RELATED TO CURRENT SERVICES MM DD YY FROM   TO MM DD YY

19. RESERVED FOR LOCAL USE

20. OUTSIDE LAB?   YES   NO $ CHARGES

21. DIAGNOSIS OR NATURE OF ILLNESS OR INJURY (Relate Items 1, 2, 9 or 4 to Item 24E by Line)

1. |____.____

2. |____.____

3. |____.____

4. |____.____

22. MEDICAID RESUBMISSION CODE   ORIGINAL REF. NO.

23. PRIOR AUTHORIZATION NUMBER

24. A. DATE(S) OF SERVICE						B. PLACE OF SERVICE	C. EMG	D. PROCEDURES, SERVICES, OR SUPPLIES (Explain Unusual Circumstances) CPT/HCPCS	MODIFIER	E. DIAGNOSIS POINTER	F. $ CHARGES	G. DAYS OR UNITS	H. EPSDT Family Plan	I. ID. QUAL.	J. RENDERING PROVIDER ID. #
From MM	DD	YY	To MM	DD	YY										
1														NPI	
2														NPI	
3														NPI	
4														NPI	
5														NPI	
6														NPI	

25. FEDERAL TAX I.D. NUMBER   SSN EIN

26. PATIENT'S ACCOUNT NO.

27. ACCEPT ASSIGNMENT? (For govt. claims, see back)   YES   NO

28. TOTAL CHARGE $

29. AMOUNT PAID $

30. BALANCE DUE $

31. SIGNATURE OF PHYSICIAN OR SUPPLIER INCLUDING DEGREES OR CREDENTIALS (I certify that the statements on the reverse apply to this bill and are made a part thereof.)

32. SERVICE FACILITY LOCATION INFORMATION

33. BILLING PROVIDER INFO & PH # (   )

WORKBOOK

cpTeach

2012

Name:_____

Class/Section:_____

Date:_____

EXERCISE 8.24

Polly Up, an established patient of yours for the past five years, has come in for her annual exam. During that visit, you notice that she has developed some vaginal lesions that seem to be causing discomfort to her and that could continue to grow. You suggest that she have these removed which she agrees to. The surgery is scheduled for the following week. On the day of the surgery, you examine her briefly, talk with her regarding what she can expect post-operatively, and perform the surgery using a laser surgery technique to remove five lesions. Code for the surgery and not the original office visit.

Before You Begin:

Read Chapter 8 in cpTeach® on "Surgery." Follow along in CPT® with the points illustrated in cpTeach®.

Purpose of this Lesson:

To assist you in understanding the correct usage of the casting codes and the differences between initial cast placement and subsequent (follow-up) casting as well as to develop an understanding of coding surgical packages.

Instructions:

1. Code the following examples. Assume that the surgical package includes pre-op, surgery and post-op. Complete the CPT® portion of the CMS-1500 form found on the back of each page.

Notes: _____

_____

_____

_____

_____

_____

_____

EXERCISE **8.24**

1500

HEALTH INSURANCE CLAIM FORM

APPROVED BY NATIONAL UNIFORM CLAIM COMMITTEE 08/05

| | PICA | | | | | | PICA | |

| 1. MEDICARE | MEDICAID | TRICARE CHAMPUS | CHAMPVA | GROUP HEALTH PLAN | FECA BLK LUNG | OTHER | 1a. INSURED'S I.D. NUMBER | (For Program in Item 1) |
| (Medicare #) | (Medicaid #) | (Sponsor's SSN) | (Member ID#) | (SSN or ID) | (SSN) | (ID) | | |

2. PATIENT'S NAME (Last Name, First Name, Middle Initial)

3. PATIENT'S BIRTH DATE MM DD YY — SEX M □ F □

4. INSURED'S NAME (Last Name, First Name, Middle Initial)

5. PATIENT'S ADDRESS (No., Street)

6. PATIENT RELATIONSHIP TO INSURED — Self □ Spouse □ Child □ Other □

7. INSURED'S ADDRESS (No., Street)

CITY — STATE

8. PATIENT STATUS — Single □ Married □ Other □

CITY — STATE

ZIP CODE — TELEPHONE (Include Area Code) ( )

Employed □ Full-Time Student □ Part-Time Student □

ZIP CODE — TELEPHONE (Include Area Code) ( )

9. OTHER INSURED'S NAME (Last Name, First Name, Middle Initial)

10. IS PATIENT'S CONDITION RELATED TO:

11. INSURED'S POLICY GROUP OR FECA NUMBER

a. OTHER INSURED'S POLICY OR GROUP NUMBER

a. EMPLOYMENT? (Current or Previous) □ YES □ NO

a. INSURED'S DATE OF BIRTH MM DD YY — SEX M □ F □

b. OTHER INSURED'S DATE OF BIRTH MM DD YY — SEX M □ F □

b. AUTO ACCIDENT? □ YES □ NO — PLACE (State)

b. EMPLOYER'S NAME OR SCHOOL NAME

c. EMPLOYER'S NAME OR SCHOOL NAME

c. OTHER ACCIDENT? □ YES □ NO

c. INSURANCE PLAN NAME OR PROGRAM NAME

d. INSURANCE PLAN NAME OR PROGRAM NAME

10d. RESERVED FOR LOCAL USE

d. IS THERE ANOTHER HEALTH BENEFIT PLAN? □ YES □ NO _If yes, return to and complete item 9 a-d._

READ BACK OF FORM BEFORE COMPLETING & SIGNING THIS FORM.

12. PATIENT'S OR AUTHORIZED PERSON'S SIGNATURE I authorize the release of any medical or other information necessary to process this claim. I also request payment of government benefits either to myself or to the party who accepts assignment below.

SIGNED_____ DATE_____

13. INSURED'S OR AUTHORIZED PERSON'S SIGNATURE I authorize payment of medical benefits to the undersigned physician or supplier for services described below.

SIGNED_____

14. DATE OF CURRENT: MM DD YY ◄ ILLNESS (First symptom) OR INJURY (Accident) OR PREGNANCY(LMP)

15. IF PATIENT HAS HAD SAME OR SIMILAR ILLNESS. GIVE FIRST DATE MM DD YY

16. DATES PATIENT UNABLE TO WORK IN CURRENT OCCUPATION MM DD YY — MM DD YY — FROM — TO

17. NAME OF REFERRING PROVIDER OR OTHER SOURCE

17a.
17b. NPI

18. HOSPITALIZATION DATES RELATED TO CURRENT SERVICES MM DD YY — MM DD YY — FROM — TO

19. RESERVED FOR LOCAL USE

20. OUTSIDE LAB? □ YES □ NO — $ CHARGES

21. DIAGNOSIS OR NATURE OF ILLNESS OR INJURY (Relate Items 1, 2, 3 or 4 to Item 24E by Line)

1. |___.___   3. |___.___

2. |___.___   4. |___.___

22. MEDICAID RESUBMISSION CODE — ORIGINAL REF. NO.

23. PRIOR AUTHORIZATION NUMBER

24. A. DATE(S) OF SERVICE			B. PLACE OF SERVICE	C. EMG	D. PROCEDURES, SERVICES, OR SUPPLIES (Explain Unusual Circumstances)		E. DIAGNOSIS POINTER	F. $ CHARGES	G. DAYS OR UNITS	H. EPSDT Family Plan	I. ID. QUAL.	J. RENDERING PROVIDER ID. #
From		To			CPT/HCPCS	MODIFIER						
MM DD YY	MM DD YY											
1											NPI	
2											NPI	
3											NPI	
4											NPI	
5											NPI	
6											NPI	

25. FEDERAL TAX I.D. NUMBER □ SSN □ EIN

26. PATIENT'S ACCOUNT NO.

27. ACCEPT ASSIGNMENT? (For govt. claims, see back) □ YES □ NO

28. TOTAL CHARGE $

29. AMOUNT PAID $

30. BALANCE DUE $

31. SIGNATURE OF PHYSICIAN OR SUPPLIER INCLUDING DEGREES OR CREDENTIALS (I certify that the statements on the reverse apply to this bill and are made a part thereof.)

32. SERVICE FACILITY LOCATION INFORMATION

33. BILLING PROVIDER INFO & PH # ( )

CARRIER — PATIENT AND INSURED INFORMATION — PHYSICIAN OR SUPPLIER INFORMATION

EXERCISE 8.25

Ms. Dee Fective consults your office for the first time for pelvic pain. She claims during the office visit that she gets severe pain on her left side around the middle of the month of her cycle. Her abdominal exam shows a lump in her left side in the area of the ovaries. You decide to do an ultrasound and discover that she has a cyst of some kind in her left ovary. You explain this to Ms. Fective and schedule surgery on her the following day. When Ms. Fective comes in for her surgery, you perform another exam, look at the ultrasound again, and explain to Ms. Fective exactly what you will be doing and what she can expect both during surgery and postoperatively. Ms. Fective is taken into surgery and sedated. You perform the surgery, removing the cyst that is then sent to the pathology lab for analysis. Ms. Fective tolerates the surgery well and is sent home after the anesthesia wears off. Code for the surgery and not the office visit.

Before You Begin:
Read Chapter 8 in cpTeach® on "Surgery." Follow along in CPT® with the points illustrated in cpTeach®.

Purpose of this Lesson:
To assist you in understanding the correct usage of the casting codes and the differences between initial cast placement and subsequent (follow-up) casting as well as to develop an understanding of coding surgical packages.

Instructions:
1. Code the following examples. Assume that the surgical package includes pre-op, surgery and post-op. Complete the CPT® portion of the CMS-1500 form found on the back of each page.

Notes: _____
_____
_____
_____
_____
_____
_____

Name:_____

Class/Section:_____

Date:_____

EXERCISE **8.25**

1500

HEALTH INSURANCE CLAIM FORM

APPROVED BY NATIONAL UNIFORM CLAIM COMMITTEE 08/05

CARRIER

| | PICA | | | | | | | | PICA | | |

| 1. | MEDICARE | MEDICAID | TRICARE CHAMPUS | CHAMPVA | GROUP HEALTH PLAN | FECA BLK LUNG | OTHER | 1a. INSURED'S I.D. NUMBER | (For Program in Item 1) |
| | (Medicare #) | (Medicaid #) | (Sponsor's SSN) | (Member ID#) | (SSN or ID) | (SSN) | (ID) | | |

2. PATIENT'S NAME (Last Name, First Name, Middle Initial)

3. PATIENT'S BIRTH DATE   MM   DD   YY   SEX   M   F

4. INSURED'S NAME (Last Name, First Name, Middle Initial)

5. PATIENT'S ADDRESS (No., Street)

6. PATIENT RELATIONSHIP TO INSURED   Self   Spouse   Child   Other

7. INSURED'S ADDRESS (No., Street)

CITY   STATE

8. PATIENT STATUS   Single   Married   Other

CITY   STATE

ZIP CODE   TELEPHONE (Include Area Code) ( )

Employed   Full-Time Student   Part-Time Student

ZIP CODE   TELEPHONE (Include Area Code) ( )

9. OTHER INSURED'S NAME (Last Name, First Name, Middle Initial)

10. IS PATIENT'S CONDITION RELATED TO:

11. INSURED'S POLICY GROUP OR FECA NUMBER

a. OTHER INSURED'S POLICY OR GROUP NUMBER

a. EMPLOYMENT? (Current or Previous)   YES   NO

a. INSURED'S DATE OF BIRTH   MM   DD   YY   SEX   M   F

b. OTHER INSURED'S DATE OF BIRTH   MM   DD   YY   SEX   M   F

b. AUTO ACCIDENT?   YES   NO   PLACE (State)

b. EMPLOYER'S NAME OR SCHOOL NAME

c. EMPLOYER'S NAME OR SCHOOL NAME

c. OTHER ACCIDENT?   YES   NO

c. INSURANCE PLAN NAME OR PROGRAM NAME

d. INSURANCE PLAN NAME OR PROGRAM NAME

10d. RESERVED FOR LOCAL USE

d. IS THERE ANOTHER HEALTH BENEFIT PLAN?   YES   NO   If yes, return to and complete item 9 a-d.

READ BACK OF FORM BEFORE COMPLETING & SIGNING THIS FORM.

12. PATIENT'S OR AUTHORIZED PERSON'S SIGNATURE I authorize the release of any medical or other information necessary to process this claim. I also request payment of government benefits either to myself or to the party who accepts assignment below.

SIGNED_____ DATE_____

13. INSURED'S OR AUTHORIZED PERSON'S SIGNATURE I authorize payment of medical benefits to the undersigned physician or supplier for services described below.

SIGNED_____

PATIENT AND INSURED INFORMATION

14. DATE OF CURRENT: MM   DD   YY   ILLNESS (First symptom) OR INJURY (Accident) OR PREGNANCY(LMP)

15. IF PATIENT HAS HAD SAME OR SIMILAR ILLNESS. GIVE FIRST DATE   MM   DD   YY

16. DATES PATIENT UNABLE TO WORK IN CURRENT OCCUPATION   MM   DD   YY   FROM   TO   MM   DD   YY

17. NAME OF REFERRING PROVIDER OR OTHER SOURCE

17a.

17b. NPI

18. HOSPITALIZATION DATES RELATED TO CURRENT SERVICES   MM   DD   YY   FROM   TO   MM   DD   YY

19. RESERVED FOR LOCAL USE

20. OUTSIDE LAB?   YES   NO $ CHARGES

21. DIAGNOSIS OR NATURE OF ILLNESS OR INJURY (Relate Items 1, 2, 9 or 4 to Item 24E by Line)

1. |___ . ___| 3. |___ . ___|

2. |___ . ___| 4. |___ . ___|

22. MEDICAID RESUBMISSION CODE   ORIGINAL REF. NO.

23. PRIOR AUTHORIZATION NUMBER

24. A. DATE(S) OF SERVICE						B. PLACE OF SERVICE	C. EMG	D. PROCEDURES, SERVICES, OR SUPPLIES (Explain Unusual Circumstances)		E. DIAGNOSIS POINTER	F. $ CHARGES	G. DAYS OR UNITS	H. EPSDT Family Plan	I. ID QUAL.	J. RENDERING PROVIDER ID. #
From			To					CPT/HCPCS	MODIFIER						
MM	DD	YY	MM	DD	YY										
1															NPI
2															NPI
3															NPI
4															NPI
5															NPI
6															NPI

25. FEDERAL TAX I.D. NUMBER   SSN   EIN

26. PATIENT'S ACCOUNT NO.

27. ACCEPT ASSIGNMENT? (For govt. claims, see back)   YES   NO

28. TOTAL CHARGE $

29. AMOUNT PAID $

30. BALANCE DUE $

31. SIGNATURE OF PHYSICIAN OR SUPPLIER INCLUDING DEGREES OR CREDENTIALS (I certify that the statements on the reverse apply to this bill and are made a part thereof.)

32. SERVICE FACILITY LOCATION INFORMATION

33. BILLING PROVIDER INFO & PH # ( )

PHYSICIAN OR SUPPLIER INFORMATION

WORKBOOK

cpTeach

2012

*Name:*_____

*Class/Section:*_____

*Date:*_____

EXERCISE 8.26

Mr. Jarrot Tall is referred to your office by his primary care physician, because he is complaining of severe back pain that has not cleared up in the past 6 months. Mr. Tall is a 70-year-old male patient in good health. Your physician looks at the medical records that have been sent over by the primary care physician and decides to order some additional tests, e.g., a CAT scan and some lab work. During the exam, your physician, a neurologist, concludes that this patient probably has some intraspinal lesions (that could be confirmed by the scan) and that in all likelihood, surgery would be beneficial. All of this is explained to the patient who agrees that any relief would be helpful. Surgery is scheduled for the following week pending confirmation of the need for surgery from the scans. Three days later, your physician reviews the scans and decides that there are two lesions that are impacting Mr. Tall. One of these lesions is in the lumbar area and the other is in the sacral area. Mr. Tall is called and advised that the surgery should take place and is reminded that it will be on that Thursday. On the day of the surgery, Mr. Tall is briefed on the potential complications, the rewards, the postoperative management, etc., and he is examined. The physician also reviews the notes from the intake nurses on pulse, blood pressure, temperature, etc., making sure that Mr. Tall is still ready for surgery. The anesthesiologist begins the IV sedation and Mr. Tall is brought into the operating room. Once in, the patient is placed in the supine position and properly draped. An incision is made along the spinal column and a laminectomy for an extradural lumbar intraspinal lesion (non neoplasm) is performed. Additionally, another laminectomy for an intradural intraspinal lesion on the sacrum is provided. The patient tolerates the procedures well and is pulled from the operating room into recovery. Please code for the surgeon on the services that happened on the date of surgery.

Notes: _____

_____

_____

_____

_____

_____

_____

Before You Begin:
Read Chapter 8 in cpTeach® on "Surgery." Follow along in CPT® with the points illustrated in cpTeach®.

Purpose of this Lesson:
To assist you in understanding the correct usage of the casting codes and the differences between initial cast placement and subsequent (follow-up) casting as well as to develop an understanding of coding surgical packages.

Instructions:
1. Code the following examples. Assume that the surgical package includes pre-op, surgery and post-op. Complete the CPT® portion of the CMS-1500 form found on the back of each page.

EXERCISE **8.26**

1500

HEALTH INSURANCE CLAIM FORM

APPROVED BY NATIONAL UNIFORM CLAIM COMMITTEE 08/05

| | PICA | | | | | | | | PICA | |

CARRIER

1. MEDICARE	MEDICAID	TRICARE CHAMPUS	CHAMPVA	GROUP HEALTH PLAN	FECA BLK LUNG	OTHER	1a. INSURED'S I.D. NUMBER	(For Program in Item 1)
(Medicare #)	(Medicaid #)	(Sponsor's SSN)	(Member ID#)	(SSN or ID)	(SSN)	(ID)		

2. PATIENT'S NAME (Last Name, First Name, Middle Initial)	3. PATIENT'S BIRTH DATE MM DD YY	SEX M F	4. INSURED'S NAME (Last Name, First Name, Middle Initial)

5. PATIENT'S ADDRESS (No., Street)

6. PATIENT RELATIONSHIP TO INSURED
Self Spouse Child Other

7. INSURED'S ADDRESS (No., Street)

CITY | STATE

8. PATIENT STATUS
Single Married Other

CITY | STATE

ZIP CODE | TELEPHONE (Include Area Code) ( )

Employed Full-Time Student Part-Time Student

ZIP CODE | TELEPHONE (Include Area Code) ( )

PATIENT AND INSURED INFORMATION

9. OTHER INSURED'S NAME (Last Name, First Name, Middle Initial)

10. IS PATIENT'S CONDITION RELATED TO:

11. INSURED'S POLICY GROUP OR FECA NUMBER

a. OTHER INSURED'S POLICY OR GROUP NUMBER

a. EMPLOYMENT? (Current or Previous)
YES NO

a. INSURED'S DATE OF BIRTH MM DD YY SEX M F

b. OTHER INSURED'S DATE OF BIRTH MM DD YY SEX M F

b. AUTO ACCIDENT? PLACE (State)
YES NO

b. EMPLOYER'S NAME OR SCHOOL NAME

c. EMPLOYER'S NAME OR SCHOOL NAME

c. OTHER ACCIDENT?
YES NO

c. INSURANCE PLAN NAME OR PROGRAM NAME

d. INSURANCE PLAN NAME OR PROGRAM NAME

10d. RESERVED FOR LOCAL USE

d. IS THERE ANOTHER HEALTH BENEFIT PLAN?
YES NO If yes, return to and complete item 9 a-d.

READ BACK OF FORM BEFORE COMPLETING & SIGNING THIS FORM.
12. PATIENT'S OR AUTHORIZED PERSON'S SIGNATURE I authorize the release of any medical or other information necessary to process this claim. I also request payment of government benefits either to myself or to the party who accepts assignment below.

SIGNED_____ DATE_____

13. INSURED'S OR AUTHORIZED PERSON'S SIGNATURE I authorize payment of medical benefits to the undersigned physician or supplier for services described below.

SIGNED_____

14. DATE OF CURRENT: MM DD YY ILLNESS (First symptom) OR INJURY (Accident) OR PREGNANCY(LMP)

15. IF PATIENT HAS HAD SAME OR SIMILAR ILLNESS. GIVE FIRST DATE MM DD YY

16. DATES PATIENT UNABLE TO WORK IN CURRENT OCCUPATION MM DD YY TO MM DD YY
FROM

17. NAME OF REFERRING PROVIDER OR OTHER SOURCE

17a.
17b. NPI

18. HOSPITALIZATION DATES RELATED TO CURRENT SERVICES MM DD YY TO MM DD YY
FROM

19. RESERVED FOR LOCAL USE

20. OUTSIDE LAB? $ CHARGES
YES NO

21. DIAGNOSIS OR NATURE OF ILLNESS OR INJURY (Relate Items 1, 2, 3 or 4 to Item 24E by Line)

1. |____.____
2. |____.____
3. |____.____
4. |____.____

22. MEDICAID RESUBMISSION CODE ORIGINAL REF. NO.

23. PRIOR AUTHORIZATION NUMBER

24. A. DATE(S) OF SERVICE From MM DD YY To MM DD YY	B. PLACE OF SERVICE	C. EMG	D. PROCEDURES, SERVICES, OR SUPPLIES (Explain Unusual Circumstances) CPT/HCPCS MODIFIER	E. DIAGNOSIS POINTER	F. $ CHARGES	G. DAYS OR UNITS	H. EPSDT Family Plan	I. ID. QUAL.	J. RENDERING PROVIDER ID. #
1									NPI
2									NPI
3									NPI
4									NPI
5									NPI
6									NPI

PHYSICIAN OR SUPPLIER INFORMATION

25. FEDERAL TAX I.D. NUMBER SSN EIN

26. PATIENT'S ACCOUNT NO.

27. ACCEPT ASSIGNMENT? (For govt. claims, see back)
YES NO

28. TOTAL CHARGE $

29. AMOUNT PAID $

30. BALANCE DUE $

31. SIGNATURE OF PHYSICIAN OR SUPPLIER INCLUDING DEGREES OR CREDENTIALS (I certify that the statements on the reverse apply to this bill and are made a part thereof.)

32. SERVICE FACILITY LOCATION INFORMATION

33. BILLING PROVIDER INFO & PH # ( )

EXERCISE 8.27

Mr. E. Gomanic presents to your office with a lesion on his ear that seems to be on the ear lobe. It is readily viewable to the naked eye (albeit small) and seems to have grown rather rapidly (i.e., the onset was only about a month ago). Your physician decides that it would be best to take a biopsy of this lesion and does so at the time of the visit. The biopsy is sent to an outside lab for analysis. An intermediate repair of 1.0 cm is performed to close the biopsy site. Code for the surgical portion only.

Before You Begin:
Read Chapter 8 in cpTeach® on "Surgery." Follow along in CPT® with the points illustrated in cpTeach®.

Purpose of this Lesson:
To assist you in understanding the correct usage of the casting codes and the differences between initial cast placement and subsequent (follow-up) casting as well as to develop an understanding of coding surgical packages.

Instructions:
1. Code the following examples. Assume that the surgical package includes pre-op, surgery and post-op. Complete the CPT® portion of the CMS-1500 form found on the back of each page.

Notes: _____

_____

_____

_____

_____

_____

_____

EXERCISE 8.27

1500

HEALTH INSURANCE CLAIM FORM

APPROVED BY NATIONAL UNIFORM CLAIM COMMITTEE 08/05

| | PICA | | | | | | | | PICA | |

1. MEDICARE	MEDICAID	TRICARE CHAMPUS	CHAMPVA	GROUP HEALTH PLAN	FECA BLK LUNG	OTHER	1a. INSURED'S I.D. NUMBER	(For Program in Item 1)
(Medicare #)	(Medicaid #)	(Sponsor's SSN)	(Member ID#)	(SSN or ID)	(SSN)	(ID)		

2. PATIENT'S NAME (Last Name, First Name, Middle Initial)

3. PATIENT'S BIRTH DATE   MM   DD   YY   SEX   M   F

4. INSURED'S NAME (Last Name, First Name, Middle Initial)

5. PATIENT'S ADDRESS (No., Street)

6. PATIENT RELATIONSHIP TO INSURED   Self   Spouse   Child   Other

7. INSURED'S ADDRESS (No., Street)

CITY   STATE

8. PATIENT STATUS   Single   Married   Other   Employed   Full-Time Student   Part-Time Student

CITY   STATE

ZIP CODE   TELEPHONE (Include Area Code) (   )

ZIP CODE   TELEPHONE (Include Area Code) (   )

9. OTHER INSURED'S NAME (Last Name, First Name, Middle Initial)

10. IS PATIENT'S CONDITION RELATED TO:

11. INSURED'S POLICY GROUP OR FECA NUMBER

a. OTHER INSURED'S POLICY OR GROUP NUMBER

a. EMPLOYMENT? (Current or Previous)   YES   NO

a. INSURED'S DATE OF BIRTH   MM   DD   YY   SEX   M   F

b. OTHER INSURED'S DATE OF BIRTH   MM   DD   YY   SEX   M   F

b. AUTO ACCIDENT?   PLACE (State)   YES   NO

b. EMPLOYER'S NAME OR SCHOOL NAME

c. EMPLOYER'S NAME OR SCHOOL NAME

c. OTHER ACCIDENT?   YES   NO

c. INSURANCE PLAN NAME OR PROGRAM NAME

d. INSURANCE PLAN NAME OR PROGRAM NAME

10d. RESERVED FOR LOCAL USE

d. IS THERE ANOTHER HEALTH BENEFIT PLAN?   YES   NO   If yes, return to and complete item 9 a-d.

READ BACK OF FORM BEFORE COMPLETING & SIGNING THIS FORM.

12. PATIENT'S OR AUTHORIZED PERSON'S SIGNATURE I authorize the release of any medical or other information necessary to process this claim. I also request payment of government benefits either to myself or to the party who accepts assignment below.

SIGNED _____   DATE _____

13. INSURED'S OR AUTHORIZED PERSON'S SIGNATURE I authorize payment of medical benefits to the undersigned physician or supplier for services described below.

SIGNED _____

14. DATE OF CURRENT: MM   DD   YY   ILLNESS (First symptom) OR INJURY (Accident) OR PREGNANCY(LMP)

15. IF PATIENT HAS HAD SAME OR SIMILAR ILLNESS. GIVE FIRST DATE   MM   DD   YY

16. DATES PATIENT UNABLE TO WORK IN CURRENT OCCUPATION   MM   DD   YY   FROM   TO   MM   DD   YY

17. NAME OF REFERRING PROVIDER OR OTHER SOURCE

17a.   17b. NPI

18. HOSPITALIZATION DATES RELATED TO CURRENT SERVICES   MM   DD   YY   FROM   TO   MM   DD   YY

19. RESERVED FOR LOCAL USE

20. OUTSIDE LAB?   YES   NO $ CHARGES

21. DIAGNOSIS OR NATURE OF ILLNESS OR INJURY (Relate Items 1, 2, 9 or 4 to Item 24E by Line)

1. |___.___   3. |___.___

2. |___.___   4. |___.___

22. MEDICAID RESUBMISSION CODE   ORIGINAL REF. NO.

23. PRIOR AUTHORIZATION NUMBER

24. A. DATE(S) OF SERVICE						B. PLACE OF SERVICE	C. EMG	D. PROCEDURES, SERVICES, OR SUPPLIES (Explain Unusual Circumstances) CPT/HCPCS	MODIFIER	E. DIAGNOSIS POINTER	F. $ CHARGES	G. DAYS OR UNITS	H. EPSDT Family Plan	I. ID QUAL.	J. RENDERING PROVIDER ID. #
From MM	DD	YY	To MM	DD	YY										
1														NPI	
2														NPI	
3														NPI	
4														NPI	
5														NPI	
6														NPI	

25. FEDERAL TAX I.D. NUMBER   SSN   EIN

26. PATIENT'S ACCOUNT NO.

27. ACCEPT ASSIGNMENT? (For govt. claims, see back)   YES   NO

28. TOTAL CHARGE $

29. AMOUNT PAID $

30. BALANCE DUE $

31. SIGNATURE OF PHYSICIAN OR SUPPLIER INCLUDING DEGREES OR CREDENTIALS (I certify that the statements on the reverse apply to this bill and are made a part thereof.)

32. SERVICE FACILITY LOCATION INFORMATION

33. BILLING PROVIDER INFO & PH # (   )

Name:_____

Class/Section:_____

Date:_____

2012

EXERCISE 8.28

Hugh Phoric comes to your office complaining of multiple lesions all over his body. Upon examination, you discover that these lesions are benign (i.e., actinic keratoses) and are located mainly on his neck and back. You suggest to Mr. Phoric that these could be removed, and he asks you to do so. You remove a total of 12 lesions. Code for the lesion removals.

Before You Begin:
Read Chapter 8 in cpTeach® on "Surgery." Follow along in CPT® with the points illustrated in cpTeach®.

Purpose of this Lesson:
To assist you in understanding the correct usage of the casting codes and the differences between initial cast placement and subsequent (follow-up) casting as well as to develop an understanding of coding surgical packages.

Instructions:
1. Code the following examples. Assume that the surgical package includes pre-op, surgery and post-op. Complete the CPT® portion of the CMS-1500 form found on the back of each page.

Notes: _____

　_____

　_____

　_____

　_____

　_____

　_____

EXERCISE **8.28**

WORKBOOK

cpTeach

Name:_____

Class/Section:_____

Date:_____

2012

(1500)

HEALTH INSURANCE CLAIM FORM

APPROVED BY NATIONAL UNIFORM CLAIM COMMITTEE 08/05

| | PICA | | | | | | PICA | |

| 1. MEDICARE (Medicare #) | MEDICAID (Medicaid #) | TRICARE CHAMPUS (Sponsor's SSN) | CHAMPVA (Member ID#) | GROUP HEALTH PLAN (SSN or ID) | FECA BLK LUNG (SSN) | OTHER (ID) | 1a. INSURED'S I.D. NUMBER (For Program in Item 1) |

2. PATIENT'S NAME (Last Name, First Name, Middle Initial)

3. PATIENT'S BIRTH DATE MM DD YY   SEX M   F

4. INSURED'S NAME (Last Name, First Name, Middle Initial)

5. PATIENT'S ADDRESS (No., Street)

6. PATIENT RELATIONSHIP TO INSURED   Self   Spouse   Child   Other

7. INSURED'S ADDRESS (No., Street)

CITY   STATE

8. PATIENT STATUS   Single   Married   Other

CITY   STATE

ZIP CODE   TELEPHONE (Include Area Code) ( )

Employed   Full-Time Student   Part-Time Student

ZIP CODE   TELEPHONE (Include Area Code) ( )

9. OTHER INSURED'S NAME (Last Name, First Name, Middle Initial)

10. IS PATIENT'S CONDITION RELATED TO:

11. INSURED'S POLICY GROUP OR FECA NUMBER

a. OTHER INSURED'S POLICY OR GROUP NUMBER

a. EMPLOYMENT? (Current or Previous)   YES   NO

a. INSURED'S DATE OF BIRTH MM DD YY   SEX M   F

b. OTHER INSURED'S DATE OF BIRTH MM DD YY   SEX M   F

b. AUTO ACCIDENT?   PLACE (State)   YES   NO

b. EMPLOYER'S NAME OR SCHOOL NAME

c. EMPLOYER'S NAME OR SCHOOL NAME

c. OTHER ACCIDENT?   YES   NO

c. INSURANCE PLAN NAME OR PROGRAM NAME

d. INSURANCE PLAN NAME OR PROGRAM NAME

10d. RESERVED FOR LOCAL USE

d. IS THERE ANOTHER HEALTH BENEFIT PLAN?   YES   NO   If yes, return to and complete item 9 a-d.

READ BACK OF FORM BEFORE COMPLETING & SIGNING THIS FORM.

12. PATIENT'S OR AUTHORIZED PERSON'S SIGNATURE I authorize the release of any medical or other information necessary to process this claim. I also request payment of government benefits either to myself or to the party who accepts assignment below.

SIGNED_____   DATE_____

13. INSURED'S OR AUTHORIZED PERSON'S SIGNATURE I authorize payment of medical benefits to the undersigned physician or supplier for services described below.

SIGNED_____

14. DATE OF CURRENT: MM DD YY   ILLNESS (First symptom) OR INJURY (Accident) OR PREGNANCY(LMP)

15. IF PATIENT HAS HAD SAME OR SIMILAR ILLNESS. GIVE FIRST DATE MM DD YY

16. DATES PATIENT UNABLE TO WORK IN CURRENT OCCUPATION MM DD YY   FROM   TO   MM DD YY

17. NAME OF REFERRING PROVIDER OR OTHER SOURCE

17a.
17b. NPI

18. HOSPITALIZATION DATES RELATED TO CURRENT SERVICES MM DD YY   FROM   TO   MM DD YY

19. RESERVED FOR LOCAL USE

20. OUTSIDE LAB?   YES   NO $ CHARGES

21. DIAGNOSIS OR NATURE OF ILLNESS OR INJURY (Relate Items 1, 2, 9 or 4 to Item 24E by Line)

1. |____.____   3. |____.____
2. |____.____   4. |____.____

22. MEDICAID RESUBMISSION CODE   ORIGINAL REF. NO.

23. PRIOR AUTHORIZATION NUMBER

24. A. DATE(S) OF SERVICE						B. PLACE OF SERVICE	C. EMG	D. PROCEDURES, SERVICES, OR SUPPLIES (Explain Unusual Circumstances) CPT/HCPCS MODIFIER	E. DIAGNOSIS POINTER	F. $ CHARGES	G. DAYS OR UNITS	H. EPSDT Family Plan	I. ID. QUAL.	J. RENDERING PROVIDER ID. #
From MM DD YY	To MM DD YY													
1													NPI	
2													NPI	
3													NPI	
4													NPI	
5													NPI	
6													NPI	

25. FEDERAL TAX I.D. NUMBER   SSN EIN

26. PATIENT'S ACCOUNT NO.

27. ACCEPT ASSIGNMENT? (For govt. claims, see back)   YES   NO

28. TOTAL CHARGE $

29. AMOUNT PAID $

30. BALANCE DUE $

31. SIGNATURE OF PHYSICIAN OR SUPPLIER INCLUDING DEGREES OR CREDENTIALS (I certify that the statements on the reverse apply to this bill and are made a part thereof.)

32. SERVICE FACILITY LOCATION INFORMATION

33. BILLING PROVIDER INFO & PH # ( )

CARRIER

PATIENT AND INSURED INFORMATION

PHYSICIAN OR SUPPLIER INFORMATION

Name:_____

Class/Section:_____

Date:_____

2012

EXERCISE 8.29

Ms. Jen Der has noticed upon her regular self-administered breast exam that she has some lumps in her breast. She has received her mammogram and ultrasound, that both suggest that the lumps should be removed. (The mammogram shows two lumps in the right breast.) The radiologist has placed a radiological marker on the two lumps, and your job is to remove the lumps. You remove the first lump and the second one and send them to the pathologist to make sure that you have clear margins. When the pathology report comes back and shows that the margins are clear, you close the patient's wounds and she is brought to recovery. Code for the surgery only.

Before You Begin:
Read Chapter 8 in cpTeach® on "Surgery." Follow along in CPT® with the points illustrated in cpTeach®.

Purpose of this Lesson:
To assist you in understanding the correct usage of the casting codes and the differences between initial cast placement and subsequent (follow-up) casting as well as to develop an understanding of coding surgical packages.

Instructions:
1. Code the following examples. Assume that the surgical package includes pre-op, surgery and post-op. Complete the CPT® portion of the CMS-1500 form found on the back of each page.

Notes: _____

_____

_____

_____

_____

_____

_____

EXERCISE **8.29**

1500

HEALTH INSURANCE CLAIM FORM

APPROVED BY NATIONAL UNIFORM CLAIM COMMITTEE 08/05

| | PICA | | | | | | | | PICA | |

1. MEDICARE	MEDICAID	TRICARE CHAMPUS	CHAMPVA	GROUP HEALTH PLAN	FECA BLK LUNG	OTHER	1a. INSURED'S I.D. NUMBER	(For Program in Item 1)
(Medicare #)	(Medicaid #)	(Sponsor's SSN)	(Member ID#)	(SSN or ID)	(SSN)	(ID)		

2. PATIENT'S NAME (Last Name, First Name, Middle Initial)

3. PATIENT'S BIRTH DATE MM DD YY   SEX M F

4. INSURED'S NAME (Last Name, First Name, Middle Initial)

5. PATIENT'S ADDRESS (No., Street)

6. PATIENT RELATIONSHIP TO INSURED   Self   Spouse   Child   Other

7. INSURED'S ADDRESS (No., Street)

CITY   STATE

8. PATIENT STATUS   Single   Married   Other

CITY   STATE

ZIP CODE   TELEPHONE (Include Area Code) ( )

Employed   Full-Time Student   Part-Time Student

ZIP CODE   TELEPHONE (Include Area Code) ( )

9. OTHER INSURED'S NAME (Last Name, First Name, Middle Initial)

10. IS PATIENT'S CONDITION RELATED TO:

11. INSURED'S POLICY GROUP OR FECA NUMBER

a. OTHER INSURED'S POLICY OR GROUP NUMBER

a. EMPLOYMENT? (Current or Previous) YES NO

a. INSURED'S DATE OF BIRTH MM DD YY   SEX M F

b. OTHER INSURED'S DATE OF BIRTH MM DD YY   SEX M F

b. AUTO ACCIDENT?   PLACE (State) YES NO

b. EMPLOYER'S NAME OR SCHOOL NAME

c. EMPLOYER'S NAME OR SCHOOL NAME

c. OTHER ACCIDENT? YES NO

c. INSURANCE PLAN NAME OR PROGRAM NAME

d. INSURANCE PLAN NAME OR PROGRAM NAME

10d. RESERVED FOR LOCAL USE

d. IS THERE ANOTHER HEALTH BENEFIT PLAN? YES NO   If yes, return to and complete item 9 a-d.

READ BACK OF FORM BEFORE COMPLETING & SIGNING THIS FORM.

12. PATIENT'S OR AUTHORIZED PERSON'S SIGNATURE I authorize the release of any medical or other information necessary to process this claim. I also request payment of government benefits either to myself or to the party who accepts assignment below.

SIGNED_____ DATE_____

13. INSURED'S OR AUTHORIZED PERSON'S SIGNATURE I authorize payment of medical benefits to the undersigned physician or supplier for services described below.

SIGNED_____

14. DATE OF CURRENT: MM DD YY ILLNESS (First symptom) OR INJURY (Accident) OR PREGNANCY(LMP)

15. IF PATIENT HAS HAD SAME OR SIMILAR ILLNESS. GIVE FIRST DATE MM DD YY

16. DATES PATIENT UNABLE TO WORK IN CURRENT OCCUPATION FROM MM DD YY TO MM DD YY

17. NAME OF REFERRING PROVIDER OR OTHER SOURCE

17a.

17b. NPI

18. HOSPITALIZATION DATES RELATED TO CURRENT SERVICES FROM MM DD YY TO MM DD YY

19. RESERVED FOR LOCAL USE

20. OUTSIDE LAB? YES NO $ CHARGES

21. DIAGNOSIS OR NATURE OF ILLNESS OR INJURY (Relate Items 1, 2, 9 or 4 to Item 24E by Line)

1. |___.___ 3. |___.___
2. |___.___ 4. |___.___

22. MEDICAID RESUBMISSION CODE   ORIGINAL REF. NO.

23. PRIOR AUTHORIZATION NUMBER

24. A. DATE(S) OF SERVICE From MM DD YY To MM DD YY	B. PLACE OF SERVICE	C. EMG	D. PROCEDURES, SERVICES, OR SUPPLIES (Explain Unusual Circumstances) CPT/HCPCS MODIFIER	E. DIAGNOSIS POINTER	F. $ CHARGES	G. DAYS OR UNITS	H. EPSDT Family Plan	I. ID QUAL.	J. RENDERING PROVIDER ID. #
1									NPI
2									NPI
3									NPI
4									NPI
5									NPI
6									NPI

25. FEDERAL TAX I.D. NUMBER   SSN EIN

26. PATIENT'S ACCOUNT NO.

27. ACCEPT ASSIGNMENT? (For govt. claims, see back) YES NO

28. TOTAL CHARGE $

29. AMOUNT PAID $

30. BALANCE DUE $

31. SIGNATURE OF PHYSICIAN OR SUPPLIER INCLUDING DEGREES OR CREDENTIALS (I certify that the statements on the reverse apply to this bill and are made a part thereof.)

32. SERVICE FACILITY LOCATION INFORMATION

33. BILLING PROVIDER INFO & PH # ( )

EXERCISE 8.30

Mrs. Di Lacion has decided that she no longer wants any children and asks you to perform a hysterectomy. After careful consideration, you decide that the best course of action for Mrs. Lacion would be to carry out an abdominal hysterectomy. Mrs. Lacion comes to surgery where you open the abdominal cavity (laparotomy) and then perform the abdominal hysterectomy. Code for the surgeon's services on the day of surgery only.

Before You Begin:
Read Chapter 8 in cpTeach® on "Surgery." Follow along in CPT® with the points illustrated in cpTeach®.

Purpose of this Lesson:
To assist you in understanding the correct usage of the casting codes and the differences between initial cast placement and subsequent (follow-up) casting as well as to develop an understanding of coding surgical packages.

Instructions:
1. Code the following examples. Assume that the surgical package includes pre-op, surgery and post-op. Complete the CPT® portion of the CMS-1500 form found on the back of each page.

Notes: _____

_____

_____

_____

_____

_____

_____

EXERCISE 8.30

WORKBOOK

Name: _____

Class/Section: _____

cpTeach

Date: _____

2012

1500

HEALTH INSURANCE CLAIM FORM

APPROVED BY NATIONAL UNIFORM CLAIM COMMITTEE 08/05

| | PICA | | | | | | PICA | |

1. MEDICARE (Medicare #) **MEDICAID** (Medicaid #) **TRICARE CHAMPUS** (Sponsor's SSN) **CHAMPVA** (Member ID#) **GROUP HEALTH PLAN** (SSN or ID) **FECA BLK LUNG** (SSN) **OTHER** (ID) | **1a. INSURED'S I.D. NUMBER** (For Program in Item 1)

2. PATIENT'S NAME (Last Name, First Name, Middle Initial) | **3. PATIENT'S BIRTH DATE** MM DD YY **SEX** M ☐ F ☐ | **4. INSURED'S NAME** (Last Name, First Name, Middle Initial)

5. PATIENT'S ADDRESS (No., Street) | **6. PATIENT RELATIONSHIP TO INSURED** Self ☐ Spouse ☐ Child ☐ Other ☐ | **7. INSURED'S ADDRESS** (No., Street)

CITY | STATE | **8. PATIENT STATUS** Single ☐ Married ☐ Other ☐ | CITY | STATE

ZIP CODE | TELEPHONE (Include Area Code) ( ) | Employed ☐ Full-Time Student ☐ Part-Time Student ☐ | ZIP CODE | TELEPHONE (Include Area Code) ( )

9. OTHER INSURED'S NAME (Last Name, First Name, Middle Initial) | **10. IS PATIENT'S CONDITION RELATED TO:** | **11. INSURED'S POLICY GROUP OR FECA NUMBER**

a. OTHER INSURED'S POLICY OR GROUP NUMBER | **a. EMPLOYMENT?** (Current or Previous) ☐ YES ☐ NO | **a. INSURED'S DATE OF BIRTH** MM DD YY **SEX** M ☐ F ☐

b. OTHER INSURED'S DATE OF BIRTH MM DD YY **SEX** M ☐ F ☐ | **b. AUTO ACCIDENT?** PLACE (State) ☐ YES ☐ NO | **b. EMPLOYER'S NAME OR SCHOOL NAME**

c. EMPLOYER'S NAME OR SCHOOL NAME | **c. OTHER ACCIDENT?** ☐ YES ☐ NO | **c. INSURANCE PLAN NAME OR PROGRAM NAME**

d. INSURANCE PLAN NAME OR PROGRAM NAME | **10d. RESERVED FOR LOCAL USE** | **d. IS THERE ANOTHER HEALTH BENEFIT PLAN?** ☐ YES ☐ NO If yes, return to and complete item 9 a-d.

READ BACK OF FORM BEFORE COMPLETING & SIGNING THIS FORM.

12. PATIENT'S OR AUTHORIZED PERSON'S SIGNATURE I authorize the release of any medical or other information necessary to process this claim. I also request payment of government benefits either to myself or to the party who accepts assignment below.

SIGNED _____ DATE _____

13. INSURED'S OR AUTHORIZED PERSON'S SIGNATURE I authorize payment of medical benefits to the undersigned physician or supplier for services described below.

SIGNED _____

14. DATE OF CURRENT: MM DD YY ILLNESS (First symptom) OR INJURY (Accident) OR PREGNANCY(LMP) | **15. IF PATIENT HAS HAD SAME OR SIMILAR ILLNESS. GIVE FIRST DATE** MM DD YY | **16. DATES PATIENT UNABLE TO WORK IN CURRENT OCCUPATION** MM DD YY FROM TO MM DD YY

17. NAME OF REFERRING PROVIDER OR OTHER SOURCE | 17a. 17b. NPI | **18. HOSPITALIZATION DATES RELATED TO CURRENT SERVICES** MM DD YY FROM TO MM DD YY

19. RESERVED FOR LOCAL USE | **20. OUTSIDE LAB?** ☐ YES ☐ NO $ CHARGES

21. DIAGNOSIS OR NATURE OF ILLNESS OR INJURY (Relate Items 1, 2, 9 or 4 to Item 24E by Line)
1. |___.___ 3. |___.___
2. |___.___ 4. |___.___

22. MEDICAID RESUBMISSION CODE ORIGINAL REF. NO.

23. PRIOR AUTHORIZATION NUMBER

24. A. DATE(S) OF SERVICE				B. PLACE OF SERVICE	C. EMG	D. PROCEDURES, SERVICES, OR SUPPLIES (Explain Unusual Circumstances)		E. DIAGNOSIS POINTER	F. $ CHARGES	G. DAYS OR UNITS	H. EPSDT Family Plan	I. ID. QUAL.	J. RENDERING PROVIDER ID. #
From MM DD YY	To MM DD YY					CPT/HCPCS	MODIFIER						
1													NPI
2													NPI
3													NPI
4													NPI
5													NPI
6													NPI

25. FEDERAL TAX I.D. NUMBER SSN ☐ EIN ☐ | **26. PATIENT'S ACCOUNT NO.** | **27. ACCEPT ASSIGNMENT?** (For govt. claims, see back) ☐ YES ☐ NO | **28. TOTAL CHARGE** $ | **29. AMOUNT PAID** $ | **30. BALANCE DUE** $

31. SIGNATURE OF PHYSICIAN OR SUPPLIER INCLUDING DEGREES OR CREDENTIALS (I certify that the statements on the reverse apply to this bill and are made a part thereof.) | **32. SERVICE FACILITY LOCATION INFORMATION** | **33. BILLING PROVIDER INFO & PH #** ( )

EXERCISE 8.31

Ms. Polly Up is having difficulty with her sinuses. She presents to the office of an otorhinolaryngologist who suggests a sinusotomy of the sphenoid and frontal sinuses. Ms. Up receives both services. Code for the surgeries.

Before You Begin:
Read Chapter 8 in cpTeach® on "Surgery." Follow along in CPT® with the points illustrated in cpTeach®.

Purpose of this Lesson:
To assist you in understanding the correct usage of the casting codes and the differences between initial cast placement and subsequent (follow-up) casting as well as to develop an understanding of coding surgical packages.

Instructions:
1. Code the following examples. Assume that the surgical package includes pre-op, surgery and post-op. Complete the CPT® portion of the CMS-1500 form found on the back of each page.

Notes: _____

_____

_____

_____

_____

_____

_____

EXERCISE **8.31**

WORKBOOK

McGUFFEY

cpTeach

2012

Name:_____

Class/Section:_____

Date:_____

1500

HEALTH INSURANCE CLAIM FORM

APPROVED BY NATIONAL UNIFORM CLAIM COMMITTEE 08/05

| | PICA | | | | | | | PICA | |

| 1. MEDICARE | MEDICAID | TRICARE CHAMPUS | CHAMPVA | GROUP HEALTH PLAN | FECA BLK LUNG | OTHER | 1a. INSURED'S I.D. NUMBER | (For Program in Item 1) |
| (Medicare #) | (Medicaid #) | (Sponsor's SSN) | (Member ID#) | (SSN or ID) | (SSN) | (ID) | | |

2. PATIENT'S NAME (Last Name, First Name, Middle Initial)

3. PATIENT'S BIRTH DATE   MM DD YY   SEX   M   F

4. INSURED'S NAME (Last Name, First Name, Middle Initial)

5. PATIENT'S ADDRESS (No., Street)

6. PATIENT RELATIONSHIP TO INSURED   Self   Spouse   Child   Other

7. INSURED'S ADDRESS (No., Street)

CITY   STATE

8. PATIENT STATUS   Single   Married   Other

CITY   STATE

ZIP CODE   TELEPHONE (Include Area Code) (   )

Employed   Full-Time Student   Part-Time Student

ZIP CODE   TELEPHONE (Include Area Code) (   )

9. OTHER INSURED'S NAME (Last Name, First Name, Middle Initial)

10. IS PATIENT'S CONDITION RELATED TO:

11. INSURED'S POLICY GROUP OR FECA NUMBER

a. OTHER INSURED'S POLICY OR GROUP NUMBER

a. EMPLOYMENT? (Current or Previous)   YES   NO

a. INSURED'S DATE OF BIRTH   MM DD YY   SEX   M   F

b. OTHER INSURED'S DATE OF BIRTH   MM DD YY   SEX   M   F

b. AUTO ACCIDENT?   YES   NO   PLACE (State)

b. EMPLOYER'S NAME OR SCHOOL NAME

c. EMPLOYER'S NAME OR SCHOOL NAME

c. OTHER ACCIDENT?   YES   NO

c. INSURANCE PLAN NAME OR PROGRAM NAME

d. INSURANCE PLAN NAME OR PROGRAM NAME

10d. RESERVED FOR LOCAL USE

d. IS THERE ANOTHER HEALTH BENEFIT PLAN?   YES   NO   If yes, return to and complete item 9 a-d.

READ BACK OF FORM BEFORE COMPLETING & SIGNING THIS FORM.

12. PATIENT'S OR AUTHORIZED PERSON'S SIGNATURE I authorize the release of any medical or other information necessary to process this claim. I also request payment of government benefits either to myself or to the party who accepts assignment below.

SIGNED_____   DATE_____

13. INSURED'S OR AUTHORIZED PERSON'S SIGNATURE I authorize payment of medical benefits to the undersigned physician or supplier for services described below.

SIGNED_____

14. DATE OF CURRENT: MM DD YY   ILLNESS (First symptom) OR INJURY (Accident) OR PREGNANCY(LMP)

15. IF PATIENT HAS HAD SAME OR SIMILAR ILLNESS. GIVE FIRST DATE   MM DD YY

16. DATES PATIENT UNABLE TO WORK IN CURRENT OCCUPATION   MM DD YY   FROM   TO   MM DD YY

17. NAME OF REFERRING PROVIDER OR OTHER SOURCE

17a.

17b. NPI

18. HOSPITALIZATION DATES RELATED TO CURRENT SERVICES   MM DD YY   FROM   TO   MM DD YY

19. RESERVED FOR LOCAL USE

20. OUTSIDE LAB?   YES   NO $ CHARGES

21. DIAGNOSIS OR NATURE OF ILLNESS OR INJURY (Relate Items 1, 2, 9 or 4 to Item 24E by Line)

1. |___.___

2. |___.___

3. |___.___

4. |___.___

22. MEDICAID RESUBMISSION CODE   ORIGINAL REF. NO.

23. PRIOR AUTHORIZATION NUMBER

24. A. DATE(S) OF SERVICE						B. PLACE OF SERVICE	C. EMG	D. PROCEDURES, SERVICES, OR SUPPLIES (Explain Unusual Circumstances) CPT/HCPCS | MODIFIER	E. DIAGNOSIS POINTER	F. $ CHARGES	G. DAYS OR UNITS	H. EPSDT Family Plan	I. ID. QUAL.	J. RENDERING PROVIDER ID. #
From			To											
MM	DD	YY	MM	DD	YY									
1													NPI	
2													NPI	
3													NPI	
4													NPI	
5													NPI	
6													NPI	

25. FEDERAL TAX I.D. NUMBER   SSN   EIN

26. PATIENT'S ACCOUNT NO.

27. ACCEPT ASSIGNMENT? (For govt. claims, see back)   YES   NO

28. TOTAL CHARGE $

29. AMOUNT PAID $

30. BALANCE DUE $

31. SIGNATURE OF PHYSICIAN OR SUPPLIER INCLUDING DEGREES OR CREDENTIALS (I certify that the statements on the reverse apply to this bill and are made a part thereof.)

32. SERVICE FACILITY LOCATION INFORMATION

33. BILLING PROVIDER INFO & PH # (   )

CARRIER

PATIENT AND INSURED INFORMATION

PHYSICIAN OR SUPPLIER INFORMATION

WORKBOOK

McGUFFEY

cpTeach

2012

Name:_____

Class/Section:_____

Date:_____

EXERCISE 8.32

Nguyen Pipe comes in with some pain in his sinuses. He has been on a course of antibiotics for the prescribed amount of time, and the pain has not gotten any better. You decide that it would be best to perform a diagnostic surgery on him to examine the turbinates and the middle and superior meatus. Code for the surgery including the inspection of the turbinates and the middle and superior meatus.

Before You Begin:
Read Chapter 8 in cpTeach® on "Surgery." Follow along in CPT® with the points illustrated in cpTeach®.

Purpose of this Lesson:
To assist you in understanding the correct usage of the casting codes and the differences between initial cast placement and subsequent (follow-up) casting as well as to develop an understanding of coding surgical packages.

Instructions:
1. Code the following examples. Assume that the surgical package includes pre-op, surgery and post-op. Complete the CPT® portion of the CMS-1500 form found on the back of each page.

Notes: _____

_____

_____

_____

_____

_____

_____

WORKBOOK cpTeach 2012

Name: ____________________

Class/Section: ____________________

Date: ____________________

EXERCISE 8.32

1500

HEALTH INSURANCE CLAIM FORM

APPROVED BY NATIONAL UNIFORM CLAIM COMMITTEE 08/05

PICA PICA

CARRIER

1. MEDICARE (Medicare #) MEDICAID (Medicaid #) TRICARE CHAMPUS (Sponsor's SSN) CHAMPVA (Member ID#) GROUP HEALTH PLAN (SSN or ID) FECA BLK LUNG (SSN) OTHER (ID)

1a. INSURED'S I.D. NUMBER (For Program in Item 1)

2. PATIENT'S NAME (Last Name, First Name, Middle Initial)

3. PATIENT'S BIRTH DATE MM DD YY SEX M F

4. INSURED'S NAME (Last Name, First Name, Middle Initial)

5. PATIENT'S ADDRESS (No., Street)

6. PATIENT RELATIONSHIP TO INSURED Self Spouse Child Other

7. INSURED'S ADDRESS (No., Street)

CITY STATE

8. PATIENT STATUS Single Married Other

CITY STATE

ZIP CODE TELEPHONE (Include Area Code) ( )

Employed Full-Time Student Part-Time Student

ZIP CODE TELEPHONE (Include Area Code) ( )

9. OTHER INSURED'S NAME (Last Name, First Name, Middle Initial)

10. IS PATIENT'S CONDITION RELATED TO:

11. INSURED'S POLICY GROUP OR FECA NUMBER

a. OTHER INSURED'S POLICY OR GROUP NUMBER

a. EMPLOYMENT? (Current or Previous) YES NO

a. INSURED'S DATE OF BIRTH MM DD YY SEX M F

b. OTHER INSURED'S DATE OF BIRTH MM DD YY SEX M F

b. AUTO ACCIDENT? PLACE (State) YES NO

b. EMPLOYER'S NAME OR SCHOOL NAME

c. EMPLOYER'S NAME OR SCHOOL NAME

c. OTHER ACCIDENT? YES NO

c. INSURANCE PLAN NAME OR PROGRAM NAME

d. INSURANCE PLAN NAME OR PROGRAM NAME

10d. RESERVED FOR LOCAL USE

d. IS THERE ANOTHER HEALTH BENEFIT PLAN? YES NO *If yes*, return to and complete item 9 a-d.

READ BACK OF FORM BEFORE COMPLETING & SIGNING THIS FORM.

12. PATIENT'S OR AUTHORIZED PERSON'S SIGNATURE I authorize the release of any medical or other information necessary to process this claim. I also request payment of government benefits either to myself or to the party who accepts assignment below.

SIGNED ____________ DATE ____________

13. INSURED'S OR AUTHORIZED PERSON'S SIGNATURE I authorize payment of medical benefits to the undersigned physician or supplier for services described below.

SIGNED ____________

PATIENT AND INSURED INFORMATION

14. DATE OF CURRENT: MM DD YY ILLNESS (First symptom) OR INJURY (Accident) OR PREGNANCY(LMP)

15. IF PATIENT HAS HAD SAME OR SIMILAR ILLNESS. GIVE FIRST DATE MM DD YY

16. DATES PATIENT UNABLE TO WORK IN CURRENT OCCUPATION FROM MM DD YY TO MM DD YY

17. NAME OF REFERRING PROVIDER OR OTHER SOURCE

17a.

17b. NPI

18. HOSPITALIZATION DATES RELATED TO CURRENT SERVICES FROM MM DD YY TO MM DD YY

19. RESERVED FOR LOCAL USE

20. OUTSIDE LAB? YES NO $ CHARGES

21. DIAGNOSIS OR NATURE OF ILLNESS OR INJURY (Relate Items 1, 2, 3 or 4 to Item 24E by Line)

1. ___ . ___ 3. ___ . ___

2. ___ . ___ 4. ___ . ___

22. MEDICAID RESUBMISSION CODE ORIGINAL REF. NO.

23. PRIOR AUTHORIZATION NUMBER

24. A. DATE(S) OF SERVICE From MM DD YY To MM DD YY	B. PLACE OF SERVICE	C. EMG	D. PROCEDURES, SERVICES, OR SUPPLIES (Explain Unusual Circumstances) CPT/HCPCS MODIFIER	E. DIAGNOSIS POINTER	F. $ CHARGES	G. DAYS OR UNITS	H. EPSDT Family Plan	I. ID. QUAL.	J. RENDERING PROVIDER ID. #
1								NPI	
2								NPI	
3								NPI	
4								NPI	
5								NPI	
6								NPI	

25. FEDERAL TAX I.D. NUMBER SSN EIN

26. PATIENT'S ACCOUNT NO.

27. ACCEPT ASSIGNMENT? (For govt. claims, see back) YES NO

28. TOTAL CHARGE $

29. AMOUNT PAID $

30. BALANCE DUE $

31. SIGNATURE OF PHYSICIAN OR SUPPLIER INCLUDING DEGREES OR CREDENTIALS (I certify that the statements on the reverse apply to this bill and are made a part thereof.)

32. SERVICE FACILITY LOCATION INFORMATION

33. BILLING PROVIDER INFO & PH # ( )

PHYSICIAN OR SUPPLIER INFORMATION

WORKBOOK

McGUFFEY

*Name:*_____

*Class/Section:*_____

cpTeach
Expert Medical Coding Made Easy!

*Date:*_____

2012

EXERCISE 8.33

E. K. Gees is in need of two coronary venous bypass grafts. Your physician provides these to Mr. Gees. Code for the surgery(ies).

Before You Begin:

Read Chapter 8 in cpTeach® on "Surgery." Follow along in CPT® with the points illustrated in cpTeach®.

Purpose of this Lesson:

To assist you in understanding the correct usage of the casting codes and the differences between initial cast placement and subsequent (follow-up) casting as well as to develop an understanding of coding surgical packages.

Instructions:

1. Code the following examples. Assume that the surgical package includes pre-op, surgery and post-op. Complete the CPT® portion of the CMS-1500 form found on the back of each page.

Notes: _____
_____
_____
_____
_____
_____
_____

Name:_____

Class/Section:_____

Date:_____

EXERCISE 8.33

☐ 1500

HEALTH INSURANCE CLAIM FORM

APPROVED BY NATIONAL UNIFORM CLAIM COMMITTEE 08/05

CARRIER

☐☐ PICA			PICA ☐☐

1. MEDICARE MEDICAID TRICARE CHAMPVA GROUP FECA OTHER	1a. INSURED'S I.D. NUMBER (For Program in Item 1)
CHAMPUS HEALTH PLAN BLK LUNG	
☐ (Medicare #) ☐ (Medicaid #) ☐ (Sponsor's SSN) ☐ (Member ID#) ☐ (SSN or ID) ☐ (SSN) ☐ (ID)	

2. PATIENT'S NAME (Last Name, First Name, Middle Initial)	3. PATIENT'S BIRTH DATE SEX	4. INSURED'S NAME (Last Name, First Name, Middle Initial)
	MM DD YY M ☐ F ☐	

5. PATIENT'S ADDRESS (No., Street)	6. PATIENT RELATIONSHIP TO INSURED	7. INSURED'S ADDRESS (No., Street)
	Self ☐ Spouse ☐ Child ☐ Other ☐	

CITY STATE	8. PATIENT STATUS	CITY STATE
	Single ☐ Married ☐ Other ☐	
ZIP CODE TELEPHONE (Include Area Code) ( )	Employed ☐ Full-Time ☐ Part-Time ☐ Student Student	ZIP CODE TELEPHONE (Include Area Code) ( )

9. OTHER INSURED'S NAME (Last Name, First Name, Middle Initial)	10. IS PATIENT'S CONDITION RELATED TO:	11. INSURED'S POLICY GROUP OR FECA NUMBER
a. OTHER INSURED'S POLICY OR GROUP NUMBER	a. EMPLOYMENT? (Current or Previous) ☐ YES ☐ NO	a. INSURED'S DATE OF BIRTH SEX MM DD YY M ☐ F ☐
b. OTHER INSURED'S DATE OF BIRTH SEX MM DD YY M ☐ F ☐	b. AUTO ACCIDENT? PLACE (State) ☐ YES ☐ NO	b. EMPLOYER'S NAME OR SCHOOL NAME
c. EMPLOYER'S NAME OR SCHOOL NAME	c. OTHER ACCIDENT? ☐ YES ☐ NO	c. INSURANCE PLAN NAME OR PROGRAM NAME
d. INSURANCE PLAN NAME OR PROGRAM NAME	10d. RESERVED FOR LOCAL USE	d. IS THERE ANOTHER HEALTH BENEFIT PLAN? ☐ YES ☐ NO If yes, return to and complete item 9 a-d.

READ BACK OF FORM BEFORE COMPLETING & SIGNING THIS FORM.

12. PATIENT'S OR AUTHORIZED PERSON'S SIGNATURE I authorize the release of any medical or other information necessary to process this claim. I also request payment of government benefits either to myself or to the party who accepts assignment below.	13. INSURED'S OR AUTHORIZED PERSON'S SIGNATURE I authorize payment of medical benefits to the undersigned physician or supplier for services described below.
SIGNED_____ DATE_____	SIGNED_____

PATIENT AND INSURED INFORMATION

14. DATE OF CURRENT: ◄ ILLNESS (First symptom) OR MM DD YY INJURY (Accident) OR PREGNANCY(LMP)	15. IF PATIENT HAS HAD SAME OR SIMILAR ILLNESS. GIVE FIRST DATE MM DD YY	16. DATES PATIENT UNABLE TO WORK IN CURRENT OCCUPATION MM DD YY MM DD YY FROM TO
17. NAME OF REFERRING PROVIDER OR OTHER SOURCE	17a.	18. HOSPITALIZATION DATES RELATED TO CURRENT SERVICES MM DD YY MM DD YY
	17b. NPI	FROM TO
19. RESERVED FOR LOCAL USE		20. OUTSIDE LAB? $ CHARGES ☐ YES ☐ NO
21. DIAGNOSIS OR NATURE OF ILLNESS OR INJURY (Relate Items 1, 2, 9 or 4 to Item 24E by Line)		22. MEDICAID RESUBMISSION CODE ORIGINAL REF. NO.
1. |___.___| 3. |___.___|		23. PRIOR AUTHORIZATION NUMBER
2. |___.___| 4. |___.___|		

24. A. DATE(S) OF SERVICE   B.   C.   D. PROCEDURES, SERVICES, OR SUPPLIES   E.   F.   G.   H.   I.   J.
From   To   PLACE OF   (Explain Unusual Circumstances)   DIAGNOSIS   DAYS EPSDT ID.   RENDERING
MM DD YY   MM DD YY   SERVICE EMG   CPT/HCPCS   MODIFIER   POINTER $ CHARGES OR Family QUAL. PROVIDER ID. #
UNITS Plan

	From MM	DD	YY	To MM	DD	YY	B. PLACE OF SERVICE	C. EMG	D. CPT/HCPCS	MODIFIER	E. DIAGNOSIS POINTER	F. $ CHARGES	G. DAYS OR UNITS	H. EPSDT Family Plan	I. ID. QUAL.	J. RENDERING PROVIDER ID. #
1															NPI	
2															NPI	
3															NPI	
4															NPI	
5															NPI	
6															NPI	

25. FEDERAL TAX I.D. NUMBER SSN EIN	26. PATIENT'S ACCOUNT NO.	27. ACCEPT ASSIGNMENT? (For govt. claims, see back) ☐ YES ☐ NO	28. TOTAL CHARGE $	29. AMOUNT PAID $	30. BALANCE DUE $
☐ ☐					

31. SIGNATURE OF PHYSICIAN OR SUPPLIER INCLUDING DEGREES OR CREDENTIALS (I certify that the statements on the reverse apply to this bill and are made a part thereof.)	32. SERVICE FACILITY LOCATION INFORMATION	33. BILLING PROVIDER INFO & PH # ( )

PHYSICIAN OR SUPPLIER INFORMATION

Name:_____

Class/Section:_____

Date:_____

WORKBOOK

cpTeach
2012

EXERCISE 8.34

Another patient, Claude E. Cation, has a similar procedure as Mr. Gees, only Mr. Cation receives a coronary artery bypass graft using venous grafts and arterial grafts during the same procedure. Code for all surgeries.

Before You Begin:
Read Chapter 8 in cpTeach® on "Surgery." Follow along in CPT® with the points illustrated in cpTeach®.

Purpose of this Lesson:
To assist you in understanding the correct usage of the casting codes and the differences between initial cast placement and subsequent (follow-up) casting as well as to develop an understanding of coding surgical packages.

Instructions:
1. Code the following examples. Assume that the surgical package includes pre-op, surgery and post-op. Complete the CPT® portion of the CMS-1500 form found on the back of each page.

Notes: _____

_____

_____

_____

_____

_____

_____

EXERCISE **8.34**

┌─────┐
│1500 │
└─────┘

HEALTH INSURANCE CLAIM FORM

APPROVED BY NATIONAL UNIFORM CLAIM COMMITTEE 08/05

☐☐ PICA   PICA ☐☐☐

1. MEDICARE	MEDICAID	TRICARE CHAMPUS	CHAMPVA	GROUP HEALTH PLAN	FECA BLK LUNG	OTHER	1a. INSURED'S I.D. NUMBER (For Program in Item 1)
☐ (Medicare #)	☐ (Medicaid #)	☐ (Sponsor's SSN)	☐ (Member ID#)	☐ (SSN or ID)	☐ (SSN)	☐ (ID)	

2. PATIENT'S NAME (Last Name, First Name, Middle Initial)   3. PATIENT'S BIRTH DATE MM DD YY   SEX M☐ F☐   4. INSURED'S NAME (Last Name, First Name, Middle Initial)

5. PATIENT'S ADDRESS (No., Street)   6. PATIENT RELATIONSHIP TO INSURED   Self☐ Spouse☐ Child☐ Other☐   7. INSURED'S ADDRESS (No., Street)

CITY   STATE   9. PATIENT STATUS   Single☐ Married☐ Other☐   CITY   STATE

ZIP CODE   TELEPHONE (Include Area Code) (   )   Employed☐ Full-Time Student☐ Part-Time Student☐   ZIP CODE   TELEPHONE (Include Area Code) (   )

9. OTHER INSURED'S NAME (Last Name, First Name, Middle Initial)   10. IS PATIENT'S CONDITION RELATED TO: 11. INSURED'S POLICY GROUP OR FECA NUMBER

a. OTHER INSURED'S POLICY OR GROUP NUMBER   a. EMPLOYMENT? (Current or Previous) ☐YES ☐NO   a. INSURED'S DATE OF BIRTH MM DD YY   SEX M☐ F☐

b. OTHER INSURED'S DATE OF BIRTH MM DD YY   SEX M☐ F☐   b. AUTO ACCIDENT? ☐YES ☐NO   PLACE (State)   b. EMPLOYER'S NAME OR SCHOOL NAME

c. EMPLOYER'S NAME OR SCHOOL NAME   c. OTHER ACCIDENT? ☐YES ☐NO   c. INSURANCE PLAN NAME OR PROGRAM NAME

d. INSURANCE PLAN NAME OR PROGRAM NAME   10d. RESERVED FOR LOCAL USE   d. IS THERE ANOTHER HEALTH BENEFIT PLAN? ☐YES ☐NO   If yes, return to and complete item 9 a-d.

READ BACK OF FORM BEFORE COMPLETING & SIGNING THIS FORM.
12. PATIENT'S OR AUTHORIZED PERSON'S SIGNATURE I authorize the release of any medical or other information necessary to process this claim. I also request payment of government benefits either to myself or to the party who accepts assignment below.

SIGNED_____ DATE_____

13. INSURED'S OR AUTHORIZED PERSON'S SIGNATURE I authorize payment of medical benefits to the undersigned physician or supplier for services described below.

SIGNED_____

14. DATE OF CURRENT: MM DD YY   ILLNESS (First symptom) OR INJURY (Accident) OR PREGNANCY (LMP)   15. IF PATIENT HAS HAD SAME OR SIMILAR ILLNESS. GIVE FIRST DATE MM DD YY   16. DATES PATIENT UNABLE TO WORK IN CURRENT OCCUPATION FROM MM DD YY TO MM DD YY

17. NAME OF REFERRING PROVIDER OR OTHER SOURCE   17a.   17b. NPI   18. HOSPITALIZATION DATES RELATED TO CURRENT SERVICES FROM MM DD YY TO MM DD YY

19. RESERVED FOR LOCAL USE   20. OUTSIDE LAB? ☐YES ☐NO $ CHARGES

21. DIAGNOSIS OR NATURE OF ILLNESS OR INJURY (Relate Items 1, 2, 9 or 4 to Item 24E by Line)
1. |___.___   3. |___.___
2. |___.___   4. |___.___

22. MEDICAID RESUBMISSION CODE   ORIGINAL REF. NO.

23. PRIOR AUTHORIZATION NUMBER

24. A. DATE(S) OF SERVICE						B. PLACE OF SERVICE	C. EMG	D. PROCEDURES, SERVICES, OR SUPPLIES (Explain Unusual Circumstances) CPT/HCPCS MODIFIER	E. DIAGNOSIS POINTER	F. $ CHARGES	G. DAYS OR UNITS	H. EPSDT Family Plan	I. ID. QUAL.	J. RENDERING PROVIDER ID. #
From MM	DD	YY	To MM	DD	YY									
1													NPI	
2													NPI	
3													NPI	
4													NPI	
5													NPI	
6													NPI	

25. FEDERAL TAX I.D. NUMBER SSN☐ EIN☐   26. PATIENT'S ACCOUNT NO.   27. ACCEPT ASSIGNMENT? (For govt. claims, see back) ☐YES ☐NO   28. TOTAL CHARGE $ 29. AMOUNT PAID $ 30. BALANCE DUE $

31. SIGNATURE OF PHYSICIAN OR SUPPLIER INCLUDING DEGREES OR CREDENTIALS (I certify that the statements on the reverse apply to this bill and are made a part thereof.)   32. SERVICE FACILITY LOCATION INFORMATION   33. BILLING PROVIDER INFO & PH # (   )

CARRIER

PATIENT AND INSURED INFORMATION

PHYSICIAN OR SUPPLIER INFORMATION

Name:_____

Class/Section:_____

Date:_____

WORKBOOK

cpTeach
2012

EXERCISE 8.35

Yet another patient, Mr. Cliff Palate, has a coronary artery bypass using two coronary arterial grafts, where the grafting tissue came from the upper extremity. Code for this surgery.

Before You Begin:
Read Chapter 8 in cpTeach® on "Surgery." Follow along in CPT® with the points illustrated in cpTeach®.

Purpose of this Lesson:
To assist you in understanding the correct usage of the casting codes and the differences between initial cast placement and subsequent (follow-up) casting as well as to develop an understanding of coding surgical packages.

Instructions:
1. Code the following examples. Assume that the surgical package includes pre-op, surgery and post-op. Complete the CPT® portion of the CMS-1500 form found on the back of each page.

Notes: _____

_____

_____

_____

_____

_____

_____

EXERCISE 8.35

Name:_____

Class/Section:_____

Date:_____

2012

1500

HEALTH INSURANCE CLAIM FORM

APPROVED BY NATIONAL UNIFORM CLAIM COMMITTEE 08/05

| | PICA | | | | | | | PICA | |

| 1. MEDICARE | MEDICAID | TRICARE CHAMPUS | CHAMPVA | GROUP HEALTH PLAN | FECA BLK LUNG | OTHER | 1a. INSURED'S I.D. NUMBER | (For Program in Item 1) |
| (Medicare #) | (Medicaid #) | (Sponsor's SSN) | (Member ID#) | (SSN or ID) | (SSN) | (ID) | | |

2. PATIENT'S NAME (Last Name, First Name, Middle Initial)

3. PATIENT'S BIRTH DATE MM DD YY   SEX M ☐ F ☐

4. INSURED'S NAME (Last Name, First Name, Middle Initial)

5. PATIENT'S ADDRESS (No., Street)

6. PATIENT RELATIONSHIP TO INSURED   Self ☐ Spouse ☐ Child ☐ Other ☐

7. INSURED'S ADDRESS (No., Street)

CITY   STATE

8. PATIENT STATUS   Single ☐ Married ☐ Other ☐

Employed ☐ Full-Time Student ☐ Part-Time Student ☐

CITY   STATE

ZIP CODE   TELEPHONE (Include Area Code) (   )

ZIP CODE   TELEPHONE (Include Area Code) (   )

9. OTHER INSURED'S NAME (Last Name, First Name, Middle Initial)

10. IS PATIENT'S CONDITION RELATED TO:

11. INSURED'S POLICY GROUP OR FECA NUMBER

a. OTHER INSURED'S POLICY OR GROUP NUMBER

a. EMPLOYMENT? (Current or Previous) YES ☐ NO ☐

a. INSURED'S DATE OF BIRTH MM DD YY   SEX M ☐ F ☐

b. OTHER INSURED'S DATE OF BIRTH MM DD YY   SEX M ☐ F ☐

b. AUTO ACCIDENT? PLACE (State) YES ☐ NO ☐

b. EMPLOYER'S NAME OR SCHOOL NAME

c. EMPLOYER'S NAME OR SCHOOL NAME

c. OTHER ACCIDENT? YES ☐ NO ☐

c. INSURANCE PLAN NAME OR PROGRAM NAME

d. INSURANCE PLAN NAME OR PROGRAM NAME

10d. RESERVED FOR LOCAL USE

d. IS THERE ANOTHER HEALTH BENEFIT PLAN? YES ☐ NO ☐ If yes, return to and complete item 9 a-d.

READ BACK OF FORM BEFORE COMPLETING & SIGNING THIS FORM.

12. PATIENT'S OR AUTHORIZED PERSON'S SIGNATURE I authorize the release of any medical or other information necessary to process this claim. I also request payment of government benefits either to myself or to the party who accepts assignment below.

SIGNED_____ DATE_____

13. INSURED'S OR AUTHORIZED PERSON'S SIGNATURE I authorize payment of medical benefits to the undersigned physician or supplier for services described below.

SIGNED_____

14. DATE OF CURRENT: MM DD YY ◀ ILLNESS (First symptom) OR INJURY (Accident) OR PREGNANCY(LMP)

15. IF PATIENT HAS HAD SAME OR SIMILAR ILLNESS. GIVE FIRST DATE MM DD YY

16. DATES PATIENT UNABLE TO WORK IN CURRENT OCCUPATION FROM MM DD YY TO MM DD YY

17. NAME OF REFERRING PROVIDER OR OTHER SOURCE

17a.

17b. NPI

18. HOSPITALIZATION DATES RELATED TO CURRENT SERVICES FROM MM DD YY TO MM DD YY

19. RESERVED FOR LOCAL USE

20. OUTSIDE LAB? $ CHARGES   YES ☐ NO ☐

21. DIAGNOSIS OR NATURE OF ILLNESS OR INJURY (Relate Items 1, 2, 9 or 4 to Item 24E by Line)

1. |___.___   3. |___.___

2. |___.___   4. |___.___

22. MEDICAID RESUBMISSION CODE   ORIGINAL REF. NO.

23. PRIOR AUTHORIZATION NUMBER

24. A. DATE(S) OF SERVICE						B. PLACE OF SERVICE	C. EMG	D. PROCEDURES, SERVICES, OR SUPPLIES (Explain Unusual Circumstances) CPT/HCPCS	MODIFIER	E. DIAGNOSIS POINTER	F. $ CHARGES	G. DAYS OR UNITS	H. EPSDT Family Plan	I. ID. QUAL.	J. RENDERING PROVIDER ID. #
From			To												
MM	DD	YY	MM	DD	YY										
1														NPI	
2														NPI	
3														NPI	
4														NPI	
5														NPI	
6														NPI	

25. FEDERAL TAX I.D. NUMBER   SSN ☐ EIN ☐

26. PATIENT'S ACCOUNT NO.

27. ACCEPT ASSIGNMENT? (For govt. claims, see back) YES ☐ NO ☐

28. TOTAL CHARGE $

29. AMOUNT PAID $

30. BALANCE DUE $

31. SIGNATURE OF PHYSICIAN OR SUPPLIER INCLUDING DEGREES OR CREDENTIALS (I certify that the statements on the reverse apply to this bill and are made a part thereof.)

32. SERVICE FACILITY LOCATION INFORMATION

33. BILLING PROVIDER INFO & PH # (   )

CARRIER

PATIENT AND INSURED INFORMATION

PHYSICIAN OR SUPPLIER INFORMATION

*Name:*_____

*Class/Section:*_____

*Date:*_____

EXERCISE **8.36**

Sal Iva is a 12-year-old patient suffering from constantly swollen tonsils and adenoids. Your ENT physician suggests that he receive a tonsillectomy. Sal comes in on the day of the surgery and is very nervous, but when you tell him he will get to eat as much ice cream as he wants, he simmers down. Your doctor examines his throat by looking inside and by feeling the adenoids. The patient is briefed on what will happen, and the IV sedation is started. Once in the operating room, both the tonsils and the adenoids are removed. Code for all surgeries.

Before You Begin:
Read Chapter 8 in cpTeach® on "Surgery." Follow along in CPT® with the points illustrated in cpTeach®.

Purpose of this Lesson:
To assist you in understanding the correct usage of the casting codes and the differences between initial cast placement and subsequent (follow-up) casting as well as to develop an understanding of coding surgical packages.

Instructions:
1. Code the following examples. Assume that the surgical package includes pre-op, surgery and post-op. Complete the CPT® portion of the CMS-1500 form found on the back of each page.

Notes: _____

_____

_____

_____

_____

_____

_____

EXERCISE 8.36

1500

HEALTH INSURANCE CLAIM FORM

APPROVED BY NATIONAL UNIFORM CLAIM COMMITTEE 08/05

| | PICA | | | | | | | PICA | |

1. MEDICARE   MEDICAID   TRICARE CHAMPUS   CHAMPVA   GROUP HEALTH PLAN   FECA BLK LUNG   OTHER   1a. INSURED'S I.D. NUMBER   (For Program in Item 1)

(Medicare #)   (Medicaid #)   (Sponsor's SSN)   (Member ID#)   (SSN or ID)   (SSN)   (ID)

2. PATIENT'S NAME (Last Name, First Name, Middle Initial)   **3.** PATIENT'S BIRTH DATE   MM   DD   YY   SEX   M   F   **4.** INSURED'S NAME (Last Name, First Name, Middle Initial)

5. PATIENT'S ADDRESS (No., Street)   **6.** PATIENT RELATIONSHIP TO INSURED   Self   Spouse   Child   Other   **7.** INSURED'S ADDRESS (No., Street)

CITY   STATE   **8.** PATIENT STATUS   Single   Married   Other   CITY   STATE

ZIP CODE   TELEPHONE (Include Area Code)   ( )   Employed   Full-Time Student   Part-Time Student   ZIP CODE   TELEPHONE (Include Area Code)   ( )

9. OTHER INSURED'S NAME (Last Name, First Name, Middle Initial)   **10.** IS PATIENT'S CONDITION RELATED TO: **11.** INSURED'S POLICY GROUP OR FECA NUMBER

a. OTHER INSURED'S POLICY OR GROUP NUMBER   a. EMPLOYMENT? (Current or Previous)   YES   NO   a. INSURED'S DATE OF BIRTH   MM   DD   YY   SEX   M   F

b. OTHER INSURED'S DATE OF BIRTH   MM   DD   YY   SEX   M   F   b. AUTO ACCIDENT?   PLACE (State)   YES   NO   b. EMPLOYER'S NAME OR SCHOOL NAME

c. EMPLOYER'S NAME OR SCHOOL NAME   c. OTHER ACCIDENT?   YES   NO   c. INSURANCE PLAN NAME OR PROGRAM NAME

d. INSURANCE PLAN NAME OR PROGRAM NAME   10d. RESERVED FOR LOCAL USE   d. IS THERE ANOTHER HEALTH BENEFIT PLAN?   YES   NO   *If yes,* return to and complete item 9 a-d.

READ BACK OF FORM BEFORE COMPLETING & SIGNING THIS FORM.

12. PATIENT'S OR AUTHORIZED PERSON'S SIGNATURE   I authorize the release of any medical or other information necessary to process this claim. I also request payment of government benefits either to myself or to the party who accepts assignment below.

SIGNED_____ DATE_____

13. INSURED'S OR AUTHORIZED PERSON'S SIGNATURE   I authorize payment of medical benefits to the undersigned physician or supplier for services described below.

SIGNED_____

14. DATE OF CURRENT: MM   DD   YY   ILLNESS (First symptom) OR INJURY (Accident) OR PREGNANCY(LMP)   **15.** IF PATIENT HAS HAD SAME OR SIMILAR ILLNESS. GIVE FIRST DATE   MM   DD   YY   **16.** DATES PATIENT UNABLE TO WORK IN CURRENT OCCUPATION   MM   DD   YY   FROM   TO   MM   DD   YY

17. NAME OF REFERRING PROVIDER OR OTHER SOURCE   17a.   17b. NPI   **18.** HOSPITALIZATION DATES RELATED TO CURRENT SERVICES   MM   DD   YY   FROM   TO   MM   DD   YY

19. RESERVED FOR LOCAL USE   **20.** OUTSIDE LAB? $ CHARGES   YES   NO

21. DIAGNOSIS OR NATURE OF ILLNESS OR INJURY (Relate Items 1, 2, 9 or 4 to Item 24E by Line)

1. |____.____   3. |____.____

2. |____.____   4. |____.____

22. MEDICAID RESUBMISSION CODE   ORIGINAL REF. NO.

23. PRIOR AUTHORIZATION NUMBER

24. A. DATE(S) OF SERVICE From MM DD YY — To MM DD YY	**B.** PLACE OF SERVICE	**C.** EMG	**D.** PROCEDURES, SERVICES, OR SUPPLIES (Explain Unusual Circumstances) CPT/HCPCS — MODIFIER	**E.** DIAGNOSIS POINTER	**F.** $ CHARGES	**G.** DAYS OR UNITS	**H.** EPSDT Family Plan	**I.** ID. QUAL.	**J.** RENDERING PROVIDER ID. #
1									NPI
2									NPI
3									NPI
4									NPI
5									NPI
6									NPI

25. FEDERAL TAX I.D. NUMBER   SSN   EIN   **26.** PATIENT'S ACCOUNT NO.   **27.** ACCEPT ASSIGNMENT? (For govt. claims, see back)   YES   NO   **28.** TOTAL CHARGE $ **29.** AMOUNT PAID $ **30.** BALANCE DUE $

31. SIGNATURE OF PHYSICIAN OR SUPPLIER INCLUDING DEGREES OR CREDENTIALS (I certify that the statements on the reverse apply to this bill and are made a part thereof.)   **32.** SERVICE FACILITY LOCATION INFORMATION   **33.** BILLING PROVIDER INFO & PH # ( )

CARRIER   PATIENT AND INSURED INFORMATION   PHYSICIAN OR SUPPLIER INFORMATION

Name:_____

Class/Section:_____

cpTeach

Date:_____

2012

EXERCISE 8.37

Mrs. Dee Fibrillation comes in for the birth of her twins. She has been seeing you for her total OB care for the past nine months. You deliver the first baby vaginally (a bouncing baby boy, 4 lbs. 6 oz.) and then a few minutes later, you deliver a little girl (5 lbs. 2 oz) vaginally as well. Code for the deliveries.

Before You Begin:

Read Chapter 8 in cpTeach® on "Surgery." Follow along in CPT® with the points illustrated in cpTeach®.

Purpose of this Lesson:

To assist you in understanding the correct usage of the casting codes and the differences between initial cast placement and subsequent (follow-up) casting as well as to develop an understanding of coding surgical packages.

Instructions:

1. Code the following examples. Assume that the surgical package includes pre-op, surgery and post-op. Complete the CPT® portion of the CMS-1500 form found on the back of each page.

Notes: _____

_____

_____

_____

_____

_____

_____

EXERCISE 8.37

1500

HEALTH INSURANCE CLAIM FORM

APPROVED BY NATIONAL UNIFORM CLAIM COMMITTEE 08/05

| | PICA | | | | | | | | | PICA | |

1. MEDICARE   MEDICAID   TRICARE   CHAMPVA   GROUP   FECA   OTHER   1a. INSURED'S I.D. NUMBER   (For Program in Item 1)
   (Medicare #) (Medicaid #) CHAMPUS   (Member ID#) HEALTH PLAN BLK LUNG (ID)
                              (Sponsor's SSN)   (SSN or ID)   (SSN)

2. PATIENT'S NAME (Last Name, First Name, Middle Initial)   3. PATIENT'S BIRTH DATE   SEX   4. INSURED'S NAME (Last Name, First Name, Middle Initial)
                                                             MM   DD   YY   M   F

5. PATIENT'S ADDRESS (No., Street)   6. PATIENT RELATIONSHIP TO INSURED   7. INSURED'S ADDRESS (No., Street)
                                      Self   Spouse   Child   Other

CITY   STATE   8. PATIENT STATUS   CITY   STATE
                                     Single   Married   Other

ZIP CODE   TELEPHONE (Include Area Code)   ZIP CODE   TELEPHONE (Include Area Code)
            (   )   Employed   Full-Time   Part-Time   (   )
                                           Student   Student

9. OTHER INSURED'S NAME (Last Name, First Name, Middle Initial)   10. IS PATIENT'S CONDITION RELATED TO: 11. INSURED'S POLICY GROUP OR FECA NUMBER

a. OTHER INSURED'S POLICY OR GROUP NUMBER   a. EMPLOYMENT? (Current or Previous)   a. INSURED'S DATE OF BIRTH   SEX
                                                YES   NO   MM   DD   YY   M   F

b. OTHER INSURED'S DATE OF BIRTH   SEX   b. AUTO ACCIDENT?   PLACE (State)   b. EMPLOYER'S NAME OR SCHOOL NAME
   MM   DD   YY   M   F   YES   NO

c. EMPLOYER'S NAME OR SCHOOL NAME   c. OTHER ACCIDENT?   c. INSURANCE PLAN NAME OR PROGRAM NAME
                                        YES   NO

d. INSURANCE PLAN NAME OR PROGRAM NAME   10d. RESERVED FOR LOCAL USE   d. IS THERE ANOTHER HEALTH BENEFIT PLAN?
                                                                          YES   NO   If yes, return to and complete item 9 a-d.

READ BACK OF FORM BEFORE COMPLETING & SIGNING THIS FORM.
12. PATIENT'S OR AUTHORIZED PERSON'S SIGNATURE   I authorize the release of any medical or other information necessary to process this claim. I also request payment of government benefits either to myself or to the party who accepts assignment below.   13. INSURED'S OR AUTHORIZED PERSON'S SIGNATURE   I authorize payment of medical benefits to the undersigned physician or supplier for services described below.

SIGNED _____   DATE _____   SIGNED _____

14. DATE OF CURRENT: ILLNESS (First symptom) OR   15. IF PATIENT HAS HAD SAME OR SIMILAR ILLNESS.   16. DATES PATIENT UNABLE TO WORK IN CURRENT OCCUPATION
    MM   DD   YY   INJURY (Accident) OR   GIVE FIRST DATE   MM   DD   YY   MM   DD   YY   MM   DD   YY
                       PREGNANCY(LMP)   FROM   TO

17. NAME OF REFERRING PROVIDER OR OTHER SOURCE   17a.   18. HOSPITALIZATION DATES RELATED TO CURRENT SERVICES
                                                  17b. NPI   MM   DD   YY   MM   DD   YY
                                                                       FROM   TO

19. RESERVED FOR LOCAL USE   20. OUTSIDE LAB? $ CHARGES
                                                     YES   NO

21. DIAGNOSIS OR NATURE OF ILLNESS OR INJURY (Relate Items 1, 2, 9 or 4 to Item 24E by Line)   22. MEDICAID RESUBMISSION
                                                                                                CODE   ORIGINAL REF. NO.
1. ___.___   3. ___.___
                                                                                                23. PRIOR AUTHORIZATION NUMBER
2. ___.___   4. ___.___

24. A. DATE(S) OF SERVICE		B. PLACE OF SERVICE	C. EMG	D. PROCEDURES, SERVICES, OR SUPPLIES (Explain Unusual Circumstances)		E. DIAGNOSIS POINTER	F. $ CHARGES	G. DAYS OR UNITS	H. EPSDT Family Plan	I. ID QUAL.	J. RENDERING PROVIDER ID. #
From MM DD YY	To MM DD YY			CPT/HCPCS	MODIFIER						
1										NPI	
2										NPI	
3										NPI	
4										NPI	
5										NPI	
6										NPI	

25. FEDERAL TAX I.D. NUMBER   SSN EIN   26. PATIENT'S ACCOUNT NO.   27. ACCEPT ASSIGNMENT?   28. TOTAL CHARGE   29. AMOUNT PAID   30. BALANCE DUE
                                                                        (For govt. claims, see back) $ $ $
                                                                        YES   NO

31. SIGNATURE OF PHYSICIAN OR SUPPLIER INCLUDING DEGREES OR CREDENTIALS (I certify that the statements on the reverse apply to this bill and are made a part thereof.)   32. SERVICE FACILITY LOCATION INFORMATION   33. BILLING PROVIDER INFO & PH # (   )

WORKBOOK

Name:_____

Class/Section:_____

cpTeach
2012
Date:_____

EXERCISE 8.38

Sir Vix, a British professor here in the states and teaching at Harvard, has been experiencing severe problems with his back. You decide that he needs to have back surgery with decompression of the nerve root, including a partial facetectomy and excision of the herniated intervertebral disc in the cervical region including three interspaces. Code for the surgeries.

Before You Begin:
Read Chapter 8 in cpTeach® on "Surgery." Follow along in CPT® with the points illustrated in cpTeach®.

Purpose of this Lesson:
To assist you in understanding the correct usage of the casting codes and the differences between initial cast placement and subsequent (follow-up) casting as well as to develop an understanding of coding surgical packages.

Instructions:
1. Code the following examples. Assume that the surgical package includes pre-op, surgery and post-op. Complete the CPT® portion of the CMS-1500 form found on the back of each page.

Notes: _____

_____

_____

_____

_____

_____

_____

EXERCISE **8.38**

Name:_____

Class/Section:_____

cpTeach

Date:_____

2012

1500

HEALTH INSURANCE CLAIM FORM

APPROVED BY NATIONAL UNIFORM CLAIM COMMITTEE 08/05

CARRIER

PICA | | | | | | | | | PICA | |

| 1. MEDICARE   MEDICAID   TRICARE CHAMPUS   CHAMPVA   GROUP HEALTH PLAN   FECA BLK LUNG   OTHER | 1a. INSURED'S I.D. NUMBER (For Program in Item 1) |

(Medicare #) (Medicaid #) (Sponsor's SSN) (Member ID#) (SSN or ID) (SSN) (ID)

| 2. PATIENT'S NAME (Last Name, First Name, Middle Initial) | 3. PATIENT'S BIRTH DATE   SEX | 4. INSURED'S NAME (Last Name, First Name, Middle Initial) |

MM DD YY   M   F

| 5. PATIENT'S ADDRESS (No., Street) | 6. PATIENT RELATIONSHIP TO INSURED | 7. INSURED'S ADDRESS (No., Street) |

Self   Spouse   Child   Other

| CITY | STATE | 8. PATIENT STATUS | CITY | STATE |

Single   Married   Other

| ZIP CODE | TELEPHONE (Include Area Code) | | ZIP CODE | TELEPHONE (Include Area Code) |

( )   Employed   Full-Time Student   Part-Time Student   ( )

| 9. OTHER INSURED'S NAME (Last Name, First Name, Middle Initial) | 10. IS PATIENT'S CONDITION RELATED TO: | 11. INSURED'S POLICY GROUP OR FECA NUMBER |

| a. OTHER INSURED'S POLICY OR GROUP NUMBER | a. EMPLOYMENT? (Current or Previous)   YES   NO | a. INSURED'S DATE OF BIRTH   SEX   MM DD YY   M   F |

| b. OTHER INSURED'S DATE OF BIRTH   SEX   MM DD YY   M   F | b. AUTO ACCIDENT?   PLACE (State)   YES   NO | b. EMPLOYER'S NAME OR SCHOOL NAME |

| c. EMPLOYER'S NAME OR SCHOOL NAME | c. OTHER ACCIDENT?   YES   NO | c. INSURANCE PLAN NAME OR PROGRAM NAME |

| d. INSURANCE PLAN NAME OR PROGRAM NAME | 10d. RESERVED FOR LOCAL USE | d. IS THERE ANOTHER HEALTH BENEFIT PLAN?   YES   NO   If yes, return to and complete item 9 a-d. |

READ BACK OF FORM BEFORE COMPLETING & SIGNING THIS FORM.

12. PATIENT'S OR AUTHORIZED PERSON'S SIGNATURE I authorize the release of any medical or other information necessary to process this claim. I also request payment of government benefits either to myself or to the party who accepts assignment below.

SIGNED_____ DATE_____

13. INSURED'S OR AUTHORIZED PERSON'S SIGNATURE I authorize payment of medical benefits to the undersigned physician or supplier for services described below.

SIGNED_____

PATIENT AND INSURED INFORMATION

| 14. DATE OF CURRENT: ILLNESS (First symptom) OR   MM DD YY   INJURY (Accident) OR   PREGNANCY(LMP) | 15. IF PATIENT HAS HAD SAME OR SIMILAR ILLNESS.   GIVE FIRST DATE MM DD YY | 16. DATES PATIENT UNABLE TO WORK IN CURRENT OCCUPATION   MM DD YY   MM DD YY   FROM   TO |

| 17. NAME OF REFERRING PROVIDER OR OTHER SOURCE | 17a. | 18. HOSPITALIZATION DATES RELATED TO CURRENT SERVICES   MM DD YY   MM DD YY   FROM   TO |

17b. NPI

| 19. RESERVED FOR LOCAL USE | 20. OUTSIDE LAB? $ CHARGES   YES   NO |

21. DIAGNOSIS OR NATURE OF ILLNESS OR INJURY (Relate Items 1, 2, 3 or 4 to Item 24E by Line)

1. |___.___   3. |___.___

2. |___.___   4. |___.___

| 22. MEDICAID RESUBMISSION   CODE   ORIGINAL REF. NO. |

| 23. PRIOR AUTHORIZATION NUMBER |

24. A. DATE(S) OF SERVICE From To MM DD YY MM DD YY	B. PLACE OF SERVICE	C. EMG	D. PROCEDURES, SERVICES, OR SUPPLIES (Explain Unusual Circumstances) CPT/HCPCS MODIFIER	E. DIAGNOSIS POINTER	F. $ CHARGES	G. DAYS OR UNITS	H. EPSDT Family Plan	I. ID. QUAL.	J. RENDERING PROVIDER ID. #
1									NPI
2									NPI
3									NPI
4									NPI
5									NPI
6									NPI

| 25. FEDERAL TAX I.D. NUMBER   SSN EIN | 26. PATIENT'S ACCOUNT NO. | 27. ACCEPT ASSIGNMENT?   (For govt. claims, see back)   YES   NO | 28. TOTAL CHARGE $ | 29. AMOUNT PAID $ | 30. BALANCE DUE $ |

| 31. SIGNATURE OF PHYSICIAN OR SUPPLIER   INCLUDING DEGREES OR CREDENTIALS   (I certify that the statements on the reverse   apply to this bill and are made a part thereof.) | 32. SERVICE FACILITY LOCATION INFORMATION | 33. BILLING PROVIDER INFO & PH # ( ) |

PHYSICIAN OR SUPPLIER INFORMATION

WORKBOOK

*Name:*_____

*Class/Section:*_____

cpTeach *Date:*_____

2012

EXERCISE 8.39

Mr. Juan C. See comes into your office complaining of problems with his eyes. You review his past medical and surgical history and upon examination find that he has developed lesions on his cornea of both the right and left eyes. You suggest that Mr. See have surgery to remove the lesions and he agrees. During the surgery, you remove the first lesion from the left eye and then continue on to the next and remove the lesion from the right. Code for both removals only.

Before You Begin:

Read Chapter 8 in cpTeach® on "Surgery." Follow along in CPT® with the points illustrated in cpTeach®.

Purpose of this Lesson:

To assist you in understanding the correct usage of the casting codes and the differences between initial cast placement and subsequent (follow-up) casting as well as to develop an understanding of coding surgical packages.

Instructions:

1. Code the following examples. Assume that the surgical package includes pre-op, surgery and post-op. Complete the CPT® portion of the CMS-1500 form found on the back of each page.

Notes: _____

_____

_____

_____

_____

_____

_____

Name: _____

Class/Section: _____

Date: _____

EXERCISE 8.39

1500

HEALTH INSURANCE CLAIM FORM

APPROVED BY NATIONAL UNIFORM CLAIM COMMITTEE 08/05

CARRIER

| | | PICA | | | | | | | | | PICA | | |

1. MEDICARE	MEDICAID	TRICARE CHAMPUS	CHAMPVA	GROUP HEALTH PLAN	FECA BLK LUNG	OTHER	1a. INSURED'S I.D. NUMBER	(For Program in Item 1)
(Medicare #)	(Medicaid #)	(Sponsor's SSN)	(Member ID#)	(SSN or ID)	(SSN)	(ID)		

2. PATIENT'S NAME (Last Name, First Name, Middle Initial)

3. PATIENT'S BIRTH DATE MM DD YY SEX M F

4. INSURED'S NAME (Last Name, First Name, Middle Initial)

5. PATIENT'S ADDRESS (No., Street)

6. PATIENT RELATIONSHIP TO INSURED Self Spouse Child Other

7. INSURED'S ADDRESS (No., Street)

CITY STATE

8. PATIENT STATUS Single Married Other

Employed Full-Time Student Part-Time Student

CITY STATE

ZIP CODE TELEPHONE (Include Area Code) ( )

ZIP CODE TELEPHONE (Include Area Code) ( )

9. OTHER INSURED'S NAME (Last Name, First Name, Middle Initial)

10. IS PATIENT'S CONDITION RELATED TO:

11. INSURED'S POLICY GROUP OR FECA NUMBER

a. OTHER INSURED'S POLICY OR GROUP NUMBER

a. EMPLOYMENT? (Current or Previous) YES NO

a. INSURED'S DATE OF BIRTH MM DD YY SEX M F

b. OTHER INSURED'S DATE OF BIRTH MM DD YY SEX M F

b. AUTO ACCIDENT? PLACE (State) YES NO

b. EMPLOYER'S NAME OR SCHOOL NAME

c. EMPLOYER'S NAME OR SCHOOL NAME

c. OTHER ACCIDENT? YES NO

c. INSURANCE PLAN NAME OR PROGRAM NAME

d. INSURANCE PLAN NAME OR PROGRAM NAME

10d. RESERVED FOR LOCAL USE

d. IS THERE ANOTHER HEALTH BENEFIT PLAN? YES NO If yes, return to and complete item 9 a-d.

READ BACK OF FORM BEFORE COMPLETING & SIGNING THIS FORM.

12. PATIENT'S OR AUTHORIZED PERSON'S SIGNATURE I authorize the release of any medical or other information necessary to process this claim. I also request payment of government benefits either to myself or to the party who accepts assignment below.

SIGNED_____ DATE_____

13. INSURED'S OR AUTHORIZED PERSON'S SIGNATURE I authorize payment of medical benefits to the undersigned physician or supplier for services described below.

SIGNED_____

PATIENT AND INSURED INFORMATION

14. DATE OF CURRENT: ILLNESS (First symptom) OR INJURY (Accident) OR PREGNANCY(LMP) MM DD YY

15. IF PATIENT HAS HAD SAME OR SIMILAR ILLNESS. GIVE FIRST DATE MM DD YY

16. DATES PATIENT UNABLE TO WORK IN CURRENT OCCUPATION FROM MM DD YY TO MM DD YY

17. NAME OF REFERRING PROVIDER OR OTHER SOURCE

17a.

17b. NPI

18. HOSPITALIZATION DATES RELATED TO CURRENT SERVICES FROM MM DD YY TO MM DD YY

19. RESERVED FOR LOCAL USE

20. OUTSIDE LAB? YES NO $ CHARGES

21. DIAGNOSIS OR NATURE OF ILLNESS OR INJURY (Relate Items 1, 2, 9 or 4 to Item 24E by Line)

1. |___ . ___| 3. |___ . ___|

2. |___ . ___| 4. |___ . ___|

22. MEDICAID RESUBMISSION CODE ORIGINAL REF. NO.

23. PRIOR AUTHORIZATION NUMBER

24. A. DATE(S) OF SERVICE						B. PLACE OF SERVICE	C. EMG	D. PROCEDURES, SERVICES, OR SUPPLIES (Explain Unusual Circumstances) CPT/HCPCS	MODIFIER	E. DIAGNOSIS POINTER	F. $ CHARGES	G. DAYS OR UNITS	H. EPSDT Family Plan	I. ID QUAL.	J. RENDERING PROVIDER ID. #
From MM DD YY			To MM DD YY												
1														NPI	
2														NPI	
3														NPI	
4														NPI	
5														NPI	
6														NPI	

PHYSICIAN OR SUPPLIER INFORMATION

25. FEDERAL TAX I.D. NUMBER SSN EIN

26. PATIENT'S ACCOUNT NO.

27. ACCEPT ASSIGNMENT? (For govt. claims, see back) YES NO

28. TOTAL CHARGE $

29. AMOUNT PAID $

30. BALANCE DUE $

31. SIGNATURE OF PHYSICIAN OR SUPPLIER INCLUDING DEGREES OR CREDENTIALS (I certify that the statements on the reverse apply to this bill and are made a part thereof.)

32. SERVICE FACILITY LOCATION INFORMATION

33. BILLING PROVIDER INFO & PH # ( )

WORKBOOK

cpTeach
2012

Name:_____

Class/Section:_____

Date:_____

EXERCISE 8.40

After a thorough examination, your physician and Mr. Larry Nex agree that a trabeculoplasty should be performed in order to improve Mr. Nex's vision. The examination shows that three treatment sessions will be needed to completely fix the problem. Code for the surgeries.

Before You Begin:
Read Chapter 8 in cpTeach® on "Surgery." Follow along in CPT® with the points illustrated in cpTeach®.

Purpose of this Lesson:
To assist you in understanding the correct usage of the casting codes and the differences between initial cast placement and subsequent (follow-up) casting as well as to develop an understanding of coding surgical packages.

Instructions:
1. Code the following examples. Assume that the surgical package includes pre-op, surgery and post-op. Complete the CPT® portion of the CMS-1500 form found on the back of each page.

Notes: _____

_____

_____

_____

_____

_____

_____

EXERCISE **8.40**

Name:_____

Class/Section:_____

Date:_____

2012

1500

HEALTH INSURANCE CLAIM FORM

APPROVED BY NATIONAL UNIFORM CLAIM COMMITTEE 08/05

| | PICA | | | | | | | | | PICA | |

1. MEDICARE   MEDICAID   TRICARE   CHAMPVA   GROUP   FECA   OTHER   1a. INSURED'S I.D. NUMBER   (For Program in Item 1)
                            CHAMPUS   HEALTH PLAN   BLK LUNG
      (Medicare #)   (Medicaid #)   (Sponsor's SSN)   (Member ID#)   (SSN or ID)   (SSN)   (ID)

2. PATIENT'S NAME (Last Name, First Name, Middle Initial)   3. PATIENT'S BIRTH DATE   SEX   4. INSURED'S NAME (Last Name, First Name, Middle Initial)
                                                              MM   DD   YY   M   F

5. PATIENT'S ADDRESS (No., Street)   6. PATIENT RELATIONSHIP TO INSURED   7. INSURED'S ADDRESS (No., Street)
                                                              Self   Spouse   Child   Other

CITY   STATE   8. PATIENT STATUS   CITY   STATE
                                                              Single   Married   Other

ZIP CODE   TELEPHONE (Include Area Code)   ZIP CODE   TELEPHONE (Include Area Code)
                            (   )   Employed   Full-Time   Part-Time   (   )
                                                                    Student   Student

9. OTHER INSURED'S NAME (Last Name, First Name, Middle Initial)   10. IS PATIENT'S CONDITION RELATED TO: 11. INSURED'S POLICY GROUP OR FECA NUMBER

a. OTHER INSURED'S POLICY OR GROUP NUMBER   a. EMPLOYMENT? (Current or Previous)   a. INSURED'S DATE OF BIRTH   SEX
                                                                    YES   NO   MM   DD   YY   M   F

b. OTHER INSURED'S DATE OF BIRTH   SEX   b. AUTO ACCIDENT?   PLACE (State)   b. EMPLOYER'S NAME OR SCHOOL NAME
   MM   DD   YY   M   F   YES   NO

c. EMPLOYER'S NAME OR SCHOOL NAME   c. OTHER ACCIDENT?   c. INSURANCE PLAN NAME OR PROGRAM NAME
                                                                    YES   NO

d. INSURANCE PLAN NAME OR PROGRAM NAME   10d. RESERVED FOR LOCAL USE   d. IS THERE ANOTHER HEALTH BENEFIT PLAN?
                                                                                                              YES   NO   If yes, return to and complete item 9 a-d.

READ BACK OF FORM BEFORE COMPLETING & SIGNING THIS FORM.
12. PATIENT'S OR AUTHORIZED PERSON'S SIGNATURE I authorize the release of any medical or other information necessary   **13. INSURED'S OR AUTHORIZED PERSON'S SIGNATURE** I authorize
to process this claim. I also request payment of government benefits either to myself or to the party who accepts assignment   payment of medical benefits to the undersigned physician or supplier for
below.   services described below.

SIGNED_____   DATE_____   SIGNED_____

14. DATE OF CURRENT: ILLNESS (First symptom) OR   15. IF PATIENT HAS HAD SAME OR SIMILAR ILLNESS.   16. DATES PATIENT UNABLE TO WORK IN CURRENT OCCUPATION
   MM   DD   YY   INJURY (Accident) OR   GIVE FIRST DATE MM   DD   YY   MM   DD   YY   MM   DD   YY
                        PREGNANCY(LMP)   FROM   TO

17. NAME OF REFERRING PROVIDER OR OTHER SOURCE   17a.   **18. HOSPITALIZATION DATES RELATED TO CURRENT SERVICES**
                                                       17b. NPI   MM   DD   YY   MM   DD   YY
                                                                                                     FROM   TO

19. RESERVED FOR LOCAL USE   **20. OUTSIDE LAB? $ CHARGES**
                                                                                                        YES   NO

21. DIAGNOSIS OR NATURE OF ILLNESS OR INJURY (Relate Items 1, 2, 9 or 4 to Item 24E by Line)   **22. MEDICAID RESUBMISSION**
                                                                                                        CODE   ORIGINAL REF. NO.
1. |___.___   3. |___.___
                                                                                                     23. PRIOR AUTHORIZATION NUMBER
2. |___.___   4. |___.___

24. A. DATE(S) OF SERVICE		B. PLACE OF	C.	D. PROCEDURES, SERVICES, OR SUPPLIES	E.	F.	G. DAYS	H. EPSDT	I.	J.
From To		SERVICE	EMG	(Explain Unusual Circumstances)	DIAGNOSIS		OR	Family	ID.	RENDERING
MM DD YY MM DD YY				CPT/HCPCS MODIFIER	POINTER	$ CHARGES	UNITS	Plan	QUAL.	PROVIDER ID. #
1									NPI	
2									NPI	
3									NPI	
4									NPI	
5									NPI	
6									NPI	

25. FEDERAL TAX I.D. NUMBER   SSN EIN   26. PATIENT'S ACCOUNT NO.   27. ACCEPT ASSIGNMENT?   28. TOTAL CHARGE   29. AMOUNT PAID   30. BALANCE DUE
                                                                          (For govt. claims, see back)
                                                                          YES   NO $ $ $

31. SIGNATURE OF PHYSICIAN OR SUPPLIER   32. SERVICE FACILITY LOCATION INFORMATION   33. BILLING PROVIDER INFO & PH # (   )
    INCLUDING DEGREES OR CREDENTIALS
    (I certify that the statements on the reverse
    apply to this bill and are made a part thereof.)

Name:_____

Class/Section:_____

cpTeach   Date:_____

2012

EXERCISE 8.41

Another patient of yours, Mr. Max Illary, also needs a trabeculoplasty. Only for this patient, it seems as if the best course of treatment will be four treatment sessions. Code for these surgeries.

Before You Begin:
Read Chapter 8 in cpTeach® on "Surgery." Follow along in CPT® with the points illustrated in cpTeach®.

Purpose of this Lesson:
To assist you in understanding the correct usage of the casting codes and the differences between initial cast placement and subsequent (follow-up) casting as well as to develop an understanding of coding surgical packages.

Instructions:
1. Code the following examples. Assume that the surgical package includes pre-op, surgery and post-op. Complete the CPT® portion of the CMS-1500 form found on the back of each page.

Notes: _____

_____

_____

_____

_____

_____

_____

EXERCISE 8.41

Name: _____

Class/Section: _____

Date: _____

2012

1500

HEALTH INSURANCE CLAIM FORM

APPROVED BY NATIONAL UNIFORM CLAIM COMMITTEE 08/05

| | PICA | | | | | | | PICA | |

1. MEDICARE   MEDICAID   TRICARE CHAMPUS   CHAMPVA   GROUP HEALTH PLAN   FECA BLK LUNG   OTHER
(Medicare #)   (Medicaid #)   (Sponsor's SSN)   (Member ID#)   (SSN or ID)   (SSN)   (ID)

1a. INSURED'S I.D. NUMBER   (For Program in Item 1)

2. PATIENT'S NAME (Last Name, First Name, Middle Initial)

3. PATIENT'S BIRTH DATE   MM   DD   YY   SEX   M   F

4. INSURED'S NAME (Last Name, First Name, Middle Initial)

5. PATIENT'S ADDRESS (No., Street)

6. PATIENT RELATIONSHIP TO INSURED   Self   Spouse   Child   Other

7. INSURED'S ADDRESS (No., Street)

CITY   STATE

8. PATIENT STATUS   Single   Married   Other

CITY   STATE

ZIP CODE   TELEPHONE (Include Area Code) ( )

Employed   Full-Time Student   Part-Time Student

ZIP CODE   TELEPHONE (Include Area Code) ( )

9. OTHER INSURED'S NAME (Last Name, First Name, Middle Initial)

10. IS PATIENT'S CONDITION RELATED TO:

11. INSURED'S POLICY GROUP OR FECA NUMBER

a. OTHER INSURED'S POLICY OR GROUP NUMBER

a. EMPLOYMENT? (Current or Previous)   YES   NO

a. INSURED'S DATE OF BIRTH   MM   DD   YY   SEX   M   F

b. OTHER INSURED'S DATE OF BIRTH   MM   DD   YY   SEX   M   F

b. AUTO ACCIDENT?   YES   NO   PLACE (State)

b. EMPLOYER'S NAME OR SCHOOL NAME

c. EMPLOYER'S NAME OR SCHOOL NAME

c. OTHER ACCIDENT?   YES   NO

c. INSURANCE PLAN NAME OR PROGRAM NAME

d. INSURANCE PLAN NAME OR PROGRAM NAME

10d. RESERVED FOR LOCAL USE

d. IS THERE ANOTHER HEALTH BENEFIT PLAN?   YES   NO   If yes, return to and complete item 9 a-d.

READ BACK OF FORM BEFORE COMPLETING & SIGNING THIS FORM.
12. PATIENT'S OR AUTHORIZED PERSON'S SIGNATURE I authorize the release of any medical or other information necessary to process this claim. I also request payment of government benefits either to myself or to the party who accepts assignment below.

SIGNED _____ DATE _____

13. INSURED'S OR AUTHORIZED PERSON'S SIGNATURE I authorize payment of medical benefits to the undersigned physician or supplier for services described below.

SIGNED _____

14. DATE OF CURRENT: MM DD YY ILLNESS (First symptom) OR INJURY (Accident) OR PREGNANCY(LMP)

15. IF PATIENT HAS HAD SAME OR SIMILAR ILLNESS. GIVE FIRST DATE MM DD YY

16. DATES PATIENT UNABLE TO WORK IN CURRENT OCCUPATION MM DD YY FROM   TO MM DD YY

17. NAME OF REFERRING PROVIDER OR OTHER SOURCE   17a.   17b. NPI

18. HOSPITALIZATION DATES RELATED TO CURRENT SERVICES MM DD YY FROM   TO MM DD YY

19. RESERVED FOR LOCAL USE

20. OUTSIDE LAB?   YES   NO $ CHARGES

21. DIAGNOSIS OR NATURE OF ILLNESS OR INJURY (Relate Items 1, 2, 9 or 4 to Item 24E by Line)

1. _____   3. _____
2. _____   4. _____

22. MEDICAID RESUBMISSION CODE   ORIGINAL REF. NO.

23. PRIOR AUTHORIZATION NUMBER

24. A. DATE(S) OF SERVICE						B. PLACE OF SERVICE	C. EMG	D. PROCEDURES, SERVICES, OR SUPPLIES (Explain Unusual Circumstances) CPT/HCPCS	MODIFIER	E. DIAGNOSIS POINTER	F. $ CHARGES	G. DAYS OR UNITS	H. EPSDT Family Plan	I. ID. QUAL.	J. RENDERING PROVIDER ID. #
From MM	DD	YY	To MM	DD	YY										
1														NPI	
2														NPI	
3														NPI	
4														NPI	
5														NPI	
6														NPI	

25. FEDERAL TAX I.D. NUMBER   SSN   EIN

26. PATIENT'S ACCOUNT NO.

27. ACCEPT ASSIGNMENT? (For govt. claims, see back)   YES   NO

28. TOTAL CHARGE $

29. AMOUNT PAID $

30. BALANCE DUE $

31. SIGNATURE OF PHYSICIAN OR SUPPLIER INCLUDING DEGREES OR CREDENTIALS (I certify that the statements on the reverse apply to this bill and are made a part thereof.)

32. SERVICE FACILITY LOCATION INFORMATION

33. BILLING PROVIDER INFO & PH # ( )

Name:_____

Class/Section:_____

Date:_____

EXERCISE 8.42

You have placed ear tubes into the ears of a young patient, Phillip Ian Tube. It is time to remove them, and you do so. Code for the removal of the tubes.

Notes: _____
_____
_____
_____
_____
_____
_____

Exercise 8.42

1500

HEALTH INSURANCE CLAIM FORM

APPROVED BY NATIONAL UNIFORM CLAIM COMMITTEE 08/05

| | PICA | | | | | | | | | | | | PICA | |

1. MEDICARE (Medicare #) **MEDICAID** (Medicaid #) **TRICARE CHAMPUS** (Sponsor's SSN) **CHAMPVA** (Member ID#) **GROUP HEALTH PLAN** (SSN or ID) **FECA BLK LUNG** (SSN) **OTHER** (ID)   **1a. INSURED'S I.D. NUMBER**   (For Program in Item 1)

2. PATIENT'S NAME (Last Name, First Name, Middle Initial)   **3. PATIENT'S BIRTH DATE** MM DD YY   **SEX** M ☐ F ☐   **4. INSURED'S NAME** (Last Name, First Name, Middle Initial)

5. PATIENT'S ADDRESS (No., Street)   **6. PATIENT RELATIONSHIP TO INSURED** Self ☐ Spouse ☐ Child ☐ Other ☐   **7. INSURED'S ADDRESS** (No., Street)

CITY   STATE   **8. PATIENT STATUS** Single ☐ Married ☐ Other ☐   CITY   STATE

ZIP CODE   TELEPHONE (Include Area Code) (   )   Employed ☐ Full-Time Student ☐ Part-Time Student ☐   ZIP CODE   TELEPHONE (Include Area Code) (   )

9. OTHER INSURED'S NAME (Last Name, First Name, Middle Initial)   **10. IS PATIENT'S CONDITION RELATED TO:**   **11. INSURED'S POLICY GROUP OR FECA NUMBER**

a. OTHER INSURED'S POLICY OR GROUP NUMBER   **a. EMPLOYMENT?** (Current or Previous) ☐ YES ☐ NO   **a. INSURED'S DATE OF BIRTH** MM DD YY **SEX** M ☐ F ☐

b. OTHER INSURED'S DATE OF BIRTH MM DD YY **SEX** M ☐ F ☐   **b. AUTO ACCIDENT?** ☐ YES ☐ NO PLACE (State)   **b. EMPLOYER'S NAME OR SCHOOL NAME**

c. EMPLOYER'S NAME OR SCHOOL NAME   **c. OTHER ACCIDENT?** ☐ YES ☐ NO   **c. INSURANCE PLAN NAME OR PROGRAM NAME**

d. INSURANCE PLAN NAME OR PROGRAM NAME   **10d. RESERVED FOR LOCAL USE**   **d. IS THERE ANOTHER HEALTH BENEFIT PLAN?** ☐ YES ☐ NO If yes, return to and complete item 9 a-d.

READ BACK OF FORM BEFORE COMPLETING & SIGNING THIS FORM.
12. PATIENT'S OR AUTHORIZED PERSON'S SIGNATURE I authorize the release of any medical or other information necessary to process this claim. I also request payment of government benefits either to myself or to the party who accepts assignment below.

SIGNED_____   DATE_____

13. INSURED'S OR AUTHORIZED PERSON'S SIGNATURE I authorize payment of medical benefits to the undersigned physician or supplier for services described below.

SIGNED_____

14. DATE OF CURRENT: MM DD YY ILLNESS (First symptom) OR INJURY (Accident) OR PREGNANCY(LMP)   **15. IF PATIENT HAS HAD SAME OR SIMILAR ILLNESS.** GIVE FIRST DATE MM DD YY   **16. DATES PATIENT UNABLE TO WORK IN CURRENT OCCUPATION** FROM MM DD YY TO MM DD YY

17. NAME OF REFERRING PROVIDER OR OTHER SOURCE   17a.   17b. NPI   **18. HOSPITALIZATION DATES RELATED TO CURRENT SERVICES** FROM MM DD YY TO MM DD YY

19. RESERVED FOR LOCAL USE   **20. OUTSIDE LAB?** ☐ YES ☐ NO $ CHARGES

21. DIAGNOSIS OR NATURE OF ILLNESS OR INJURY (Relate Items 1, 2, 3 or 4 to Item 24E by Line)
1. |___.___   3. |___.___
2. |___.___   4. |___.___

22. MEDICAID RESUBMISSION CODE   ORIGINAL REF. NO.

23. PRIOR AUTHORIZATION NUMBER

24. A. DATE(S) OF SERVICE From MM DD YY To MM DD YY	B. PLACE OF SERVICE	C. EMG	D. PROCEDURES, SERVICES, OR SUPPLIES (Explain Unusual Circumstances) CPT/HCPCS MODIFIER	E. DIAGNOSIS POINTER	F. $ CHARGES	G. DAYS OR UNITS	H. EPSDT Family Plan	I. ID QUAL.	J. RENDERING PROVIDER ID. #
1								NPI	
2								NPI	
3								NPI	
4								NPI	
5								NPI	
6								NPI	

25. FEDERAL TAX I.D. NUMBER ☐ SSN ☐ EIN   **26. PATIENT'S ACCOUNT NO.**   **27. ACCEPT ASSIGNMENT?** (For govt. claims, see back) ☐ YES ☐ NO   **28. TOTAL CHARGE** $ **29. AMOUNT PAID** $ **30. BALANCE DUE** $

31. SIGNATURE OF PHYSICIAN OR SUPPLIER INCLUDING DEGREES OR CREDENTIALS (I certify that the statements on the reverse apply to this bill and are made a part thereof.)   **32. SERVICE FACILITY LOCATION INFORMATION**   **33. BILLING PROVIDER INFO & PH # (   )**

CARRIER

PATIENT AND INSURED INFORMATION

PHYSICIAN OR SUPPLIER INFORMATION

EXERCISE 8.43

Another young boy, Ian Continence, also needs his tubes removed. (These tubes were placed in Ian in the town where he used to live.) You remove the tubes. Code for the tube removals.

Before You Begin:

Read Chapter 8 in cpTeach® on "Surgery." Follow along in CPT® with the points illustrated in cpTeach®.

Purpose of this Lesson:

To assist you in understanding the correct usage of the casting codes and the differences between initial cast placement and subsequent (follow-up) casting as well as to develop an understanding of coding surgical packages.

Instructions:

1. Code the following examples. Assume that the surgical package includes pre-op, surgery and post-op. Complete the CPT® portion of the CMS-1500 form found on the back of each page.

Notes: _____

_____

_____

_____

_____

_____

_____

Name:_____

Class/Section:_____

Date:_____

cpTeach 2012

EXERCISE 8.43

1500

HEALTH INSURANCE CLAIM FORM

APPROVED BY NATIONAL UNIFORM CLAIM COMMITTEE 08/05

| | PICA | | | | | | | | | | | | PICA | | |

CARRIER

1. MEDICARE	MEDICAID	TRICARE CHAMPUS	CHAMPVA	GROUP HEALTH PLAN	FECA BLK LUNG	OTHER	1a. INSURED'S I.D. NUMBER (For Program in Item 1)
(Medicare #)	(Medicaid #)	(Sponsor's SSN)	(Member ID#)	(SSN or ID)	(SSN)	(ID)	

2. PATIENT'S NAME (Last Name, First Name, Middle Initial)

3. PATIENT'S BIRTH DATE MM DD YY   SEX   M   F

4. INSURED'S NAME (Last Name, First Name, Middle Initial)

5. PATIENT'S ADDRESS (No., Street)

6. PATIENT RELATIONSHIP TO INSURED   Self   Spouse   Child   Other

7. INSURED'S ADDRESS (No., Street)

CITY   STATE

8. PATIENT STATUS   Single   Married   Other

CITY   STATE

ZIP CODE   TELEPHONE (Include Area Code) ( )

Employed   Full-Time Student   Part-Time Student

ZIP CODE   TELEPHONE (Include Area Code) ( )

9. OTHER INSURED'S NAME (Last Name, First Name, Middle Initial)

10. IS PATIENT'S CONDITION RELATED TO:

11. INSURED'S POLICY GROUP OR FECA NUMBER

a. OTHER INSURED'S POLICY OR GROUP NUMBER

a. EMPLOYMENT? (Current or Previous)   YES   NO

a. INSURED'S DATE OF BIRTH MM DD YY   SEX   M   F

b. OTHER INSURED'S DATE OF BIRTH MM DD YY   SEX   M   F

b. AUTO ACCIDENT?   PLACE (State)   YES   NO

b. EMPLOYER'S NAME OR SCHOOL NAME

c. EMPLOYER'S NAME OR SCHOOL NAME

c. OTHER ACCIDENT?   YES   NO

c. INSURANCE PLAN NAME OR PROGRAM NAME

d. INSURANCE PLAN NAME OR PROGRAM NAME

10d. RESERVED FOR LOCAL USE

d. IS THERE ANOTHER HEALTH BENEFIT PLAN?   YES   NO   If yes, return to and complete item 9 a-d.

READ BACK OF FORM BEFORE COMPLETING & SIGNING THIS FORM.
12. PATIENT'S OR AUTHORIZED PERSON'S SIGNATURE I authorize the release of any medical or other information necessary to process this claim. I also request payment of government benefits either to myself or to the party who accepts assignment below.

SIGNED_____ DATE_____

13. INSURED'S OR AUTHORIZED PERSON'S SIGNATURE I authorize payment of medical benefits to the undersigned physician or supplier for services described below.

SIGNED_____

PATIENT AND INSURED INFORMATION

14. DATE OF CURRENT: MM DD YY   ILLNESS (First symptom) OR INJURY (Accident) OR PREGNANCY(LMP)

15. IF PATIENT HAS HAD SAME OR SIMILAR ILLNESS. GIVE FIRST DATE MM DD YY

16. DATES PATIENT UNABLE TO WORK IN CURRENT OCCUPATION MM DD YY   FROM   TO   MM DD YY

17. NAME OF REFERRING PROVIDER OR OTHER SOURCE

17a.

17b. NPI

18. HOSPITALIZATION DATES RELATED TO CURRENT SERVICES MM DD YY   FROM   TO   MM DD YY

19. RESERVED FOR LOCAL USE

20. OUTSIDE LAB?   YES   NO $ CHARGES

21. DIAGNOSIS OR NATURE OF ILLNESS OR INJURY (Relate Items 1, 2, 9 or 4 to Item 24E by Line)

1. |___.___   3. |___.___
2. |___.___   4. |___.___

22. MEDICAID RESUBMISSION CODE   ORIGINAL REF. NO.

23. PRIOR AUTHORIZATION NUMBER

24. A. DATE(S) OF SERVICE From	To	B. PLACE OF SERVICE	C. EMG	D. PROCEDURES, SERVICES, OR SUPPLIES (Explain Unusual Circumstances) CPT/HCPCS MODIFIER	E. DIAGNOSIS POINTER	F. $ CHARGES	G. DAYS OR UNITS	H. EPSDT Family Plan	I. ID. QUAL.	J. RENDERING PROVIDER ID. #
MM DD YY	MM DD YY									
1									NPI	
2									NPI	
3									NPI	
4									NPI	
5									NPI	
6									NPI	

PHYSICIAN OR SUPPLIER INFORMATION

25. FEDERAL TAX I.D. NUMBER   SSN   EIN

26. PATIENT'S ACCOUNT NO.

27. ACCEPT ASSIGNMENT? (For govt. claims, see back)   YES   NO

28. TOTAL CHARGE $

29. AMOUNT PAID $

30. BALANCE DUE $

31. SIGNATURE OF PHYSICIAN OR SUPPLIER INCLUDING DEGREES OR CREDENTIALS (I certify that the statements on the reverse apply to this bill and are made a part thereof.)

32. SERVICE FACILITY LOCATION INFORMATION

33. BILLING PROVIDER INFO & PH # ( )

EXERCISE 8.44

Ginger Vitis, a patient of yours for years, falls off of a scaffolding after painting the ceiling in her two-story living room to look like the Sistine Chapel. She feels that she may have hurt her ankle pretty badly, so she calls your office (around 2 p.m.) and explains what happened. You tell her to come in immediately so your doctor, Dr. Al Veolor, can examine her. Ms. Vitis comes in; Dr. Veolor examines her, orders some x-rays (A/P and lateral views) and evaluates them on the spot. The x-rays show that Ms. Vitis' ankle is, in fact, dislocated. Dr. Veolor treats the dislocation without anesthesia. Mrs. Vitis is not a Medicare patient.

Before You Begin:
Read Chapter 8 in cpTeach® on "Surgery." Follow along in CPT® with the points illustrated in cpTeach®.

Purpose of this Lesson:
To assist you in understanding the correct usage of the casting codes and the differences between initial cast placement and subsequent (follow-up) casting as well as to develop an understanding of coding surgical packages.

Instructions:
1. Code the following examples. Assume that the surgical package includes pre-op, surgery and post-op. Complete the CPT® portion of the CMS-1500 form found on the back of each page.

Notes: _____

_____

_____

_____

_____

_____

_____

EXERCISE 8.44

1500

HEALTH INSURANCE CLAIM FORM

APPROVED BY NATIONAL UNIFORM CLAIM COMMITTEE 08/05

| | PICA | | | | | | | | PICA | |

1. MEDICARE (Medicare #)   **MEDICAID** (Medicaid #)   **TRICARE CHAMPUS** (Sponsor's SSN)   **CHAMPVA** (Member ID#)   **GROUP HEALTH PLAN** (SSN or ID)   **FECA BLK LUNG** (SSN)   **OTHER** (ID)   **1a. INSURED'S I.D. NUMBER** (For Program in Item 1)

2. PATIENT'S NAME (Last Name, First Name, Middle Initial)   **3. PATIENT'S BIRTH DATE** MM DD YY   SEX M ☐ F ☐   **4. INSURED'S NAME** (Last Name, First Name, Middle Initial)

5. PATIENT'S ADDRESS (No., Street)   **6. PATIENT RELATIONSHIP TO INSURED**   Self ☐ Spouse ☐ Child ☐ Other ☐   **7. INSURED'S ADDRESS** (No., Street)

CITY   STATE   **8. PATIENT STATUS**   Single ☐ Married ☐ Other ☐   CITY   STATE

ZIP CODE   TELEPHONE (Include Area Code) ( )   Employed ☐ Full-Time Student ☐ Part-Time Student ☐   ZIP CODE   TELEPHONE (Include Area Code) ( )

9. OTHER INSURED'S NAME (Last Name, First Name, Middle Initial)   **10. IS PATIENT'S CONDITION RELATED TO:**   **11. INSURED'S POLICY GROUP OR FECA NUMBER**

a. OTHER INSURED'S POLICY OR GROUP NUMBER   **a. EMPLOYMENT?** (Current or Previous) ☐ YES ☐ NO   **a. INSURED'S DATE OF BIRTH** MM DD YY   SEX M ☐ F ☐

b. OTHER INSURED'S DATE OF BIRTH MM DD YY   SEX M ☐ F ☐   **b. AUTO ACCIDENT?** ☐ YES ☐ NO   PLACE (State)   **b. EMPLOYER'S NAME OR SCHOOL NAME**

c. EMPLOYER'S NAME OR SCHOOL NAME   **c. OTHER ACCIDENT?** ☐ YES ☐ NO   **c. INSURANCE PLAN NAME OR PROGRAM NAME**

d. INSURANCE PLAN NAME OR PROGRAM NAME   **10d. RESERVED FOR LOCAL USE**   **d. IS THERE ANOTHER HEALTH BENEFIT PLAN?** ☐ YES ☐ NO   If yes, return to and complete item 9 a-d.

READ BACK OF FORM BEFORE COMPLETING & SIGNING THIS FORM.
12. PATIENT'S OR AUTHORIZED PERSON'S SIGNATURE I authorize the release of any medical or other information necessary to process this claim. I also request payment of government benefits either to myself or to the party who accepts assignment below.

SIGNED_____ DATE_____

13. INSURED'S OR AUTHORIZED PERSON'S SIGNATURE I authorize payment of medical benefits to the undersigned physician or supplier for services described below.

SIGNED_____

14. DATE OF CURRENT: MM DD YY ◀ ILLNESS (First symptom) OR INJURY (Accident) OR PREGNANCY(LMP)   **15. IF PATIENT HAS HAD SAME OR SIMILAR ILLNESS.** GIVE FIRST DATE MM DD YY   **16. DATES PATIENT UNABLE TO WORK IN CURRENT OCCUPATION** MM DD YY FROM TO MM DD YY

17. NAME OF REFERRING PROVIDER OR OTHER SOURCE   17a.   17b. NPI   **18. HOSPITALIZATION DATES RELATED TO CURRENT SERVICES** MM DD YY FROM TO MM DD YY

19. RESERVED FOR LOCAL USE   **20. OUTSIDE LAB?** ☐ YES ☐ NO $ CHARGES

21. DIAGNOSIS OR NATURE OF ILLNESS OR INJURY (Relate Items 1, 2, 9 or 4 to Item 24E by Line)
1. ⌊___.___⌋   3. ⌊___.___⌋
2. ⌊___.___⌋   4. ⌊___.___⌋

22. MEDICAID RESUBMISSION CODE   ORIGINAL REF. NO.

23. PRIOR AUTHORIZATION NUMBER

24. A. DATE(S) OF SERVICE						B. PLACE OF SERVICE	C. EMG	D. PROCEDURES, SERVICES, OR SUPPLIES (Explain Unusual Circumstances)		E. DIAGNOSIS POINTER	F. $ CHARGES	G. DAYS OR UNITS	H. EPSDT Family Plan	I. ID. QUAL.	J. RENDERING PROVIDER ID. #
From MM	DD	YY	To MM	DD	YY			CPT/HCPCS	MODIFIER						
1														NPI	
2														NPI	
3														NPI	
4														NPI	
5														NPI	
6														NPI	

25. FEDERAL TAX I.D. NUMBER SSN ☐ EIN ☐   **26. PATIENT'S ACCOUNT NO.**   **27. ACCEPT ASSIGNMENT?** (For govt. claims, see back) ☐ YES ☐ NO   **28. TOTAL CHARGE** $ **29. AMOUNT PAID** $ **30. BALANCE DUE** $

31. SIGNATURE OF PHYSICIAN OR SUPPLIER INCLUDING DEGREES OR CREDENTIALS (I certify that the statements on the reverse apply to this bill and are made a part thereof.)   **32. SERVICE FACILITY LOCATION INFORMATION**   **33. BILLING PROVIDER INFO & PH #** ( )

Name:_____

Class/Section:_____

cpTeach Date:_____

2012

EXERCISE 8.45

Three weeks after Ms. Vitis' dislocation, she returns for one of her follow-up visits. At that visit she explains to Dr. Veolor that she will be going to a big gala benefit, and she would like her strapping to be replaced. Dr. Veolor agrees that the cast is dirty and could use replacement to assist in the promotion of Ms. Vitis' treatment, so he replaces it. Code for this strapping.

Before You Begin:
Read Chapter 8 in cpTeach® on "Surgery." Follow along in CPT® with the points illustrated in cpTeach®.

Purpose of this Lesson:
To assist you in understanding the correct usage of the casting codes and the differences between initial cast placement and subsequent (follow-up) casting as well as to develop an understanding of coding surgical packages.

Instructions:
1. Code the following examples. Assume that the surgical package includes pre-op, surgery and post-op. Complete the CPT® portion of the CMS-1500 form found on the back of each page.

Notes: _____
_____
_____
_____
_____
_____
_____

EXERCISE 8.45

Name: _____

Class/Section: _____

Date: _____

cpTeach 2012

1500

HEALTH INSURANCE CLAIM FORM

APPROVED BY NATIONAL UNIFORM CLAIM COMMITTEE 08/05

| | PICA | | | | | | | | | | PICA | |

1. MEDICARE (Medicare #)   MEDICAID (Medicaid #)   TRICARE CHAMPUS (Sponsor's SSN)   CHAMPVA (Member ID#)   GROUP HEALTH PLAN (SSN or ID)   FECA BLK LUNG (SSN)   OTHER (ID)   **1a.** INSURED'S I.D. NUMBER   (For Program in Item 1)

2. PATIENT'S NAME (Last Name, First Name, Middle Initial)   **3.** PATIENT'S BIRTH DATE MM | DD | YY   SEX M   F   **4.** INSURED'S NAME (Last Name, First Name, Middle Initial)

5. PATIENT'S ADDRESS (No., Street)   **6.** PATIENT RELATIONSHIP TO INSURED Self   Spouse   Child   Other   **7.** INSURED'S ADDRESS (No., Street)

CITY   STATE   **8.** PATIENT STATUS Single   Married   Other   CITY   STATE

ZIP CODE   TELEPHONE (Include Area Code) (   )   Employed   Full-Time Student   Part-Time Student   ZIP CODE   TELEPHONE (Include Area Code) (   )

9. OTHER INSURED'S NAME (Last Name, First Name, Middle Initial)   **10.** IS PATIENT'S CONDITION RELATED TO: **11.** INSURED'S POLICY GROUP OR FECA NUMBER

a. OTHER INSURED'S POLICY OR GROUP NUMBER   **a.** EMPLOYMENT? (Current or Previous) YES   NO   **a.** INSURED'S DATE OF BIRTH MM | DD | YY   SEX M   F

b. OTHER INSURED'S DATE OF BIRTH MM | DD | YY   SEX M   F   **b.** AUTO ACCIDENT? YES   NO   PLACE (State)   **b.** EMPLOYER'S NAME OR SCHOOL NAME

c. EMPLOYER'S NAME OR SCHOOL NAME   **c.** OTHER ACCIDENT? YES   NO   **c.** INSURANCE PLAN NAME OR PROGRAM NAME

d. INSURANCE PLAN NAME OR PROGRAM NAME   **10d.** RESERVED FOR LOCAL USE   **d.** IS THERE ANOTHER HEALTH BENEFIT PLAN? YES   NO   If yes, return to and complete item 9 a-d.

READ BACK OF FORM BEFORE COMPLETING & SIGNING THIS FORM.
12. PATIENT'S OR AUTHORIZED PERSON'S SIGNATURE I authorize the release of any medical or other information necessary to process this claim. I also request payment of government benefits either to myself or to the party who accepts assignment below.

SIGNED_____   DATE_____

13. INSURED'S OR AUTHORIZED PERSON'S SIGNATURE I authorize payment of medical benefits to the undersigned physician or supplier for services described below.

SIGNED_____

14. DATE OF CURRENT: MM | DD | YY   ILLNESS (First symptom) OR INJURY (Accident) OR PREGNANCY(LMP)   **15.** IF PATIENT HAS HAD SAME OR SIMILAR ILLNESS. GIVE FIRST DATE MM | DD | YY   **16.** DATES PATIENT UNABLE TO WORK IN CURRENT OCCUPATION MM | DD | YY   FROM   TO MM | DD | YY

17. NAME OF REFERRING PROVIDER OR OTHER SOURCE   **17a.**   **17b.** NPI   **18.** HOSPITALIZATION DATES RELATED TO CURRENT SERVICES MM | DD | YY   FROM   TO MM | DD | YY

19. RESERVED FOR LOCAL USE   **20.** OUTSIDE LAB? YES   NO $ CHARGES

21. DIAGNOSIS OR NATURE OF ILLNESS OR INJURY (Relate Items 1, 2, 9 or 4 to Item 24E by Line)
1. ___ . ___   3. ___ . ___
2. ___ . ___   4. ___ . ___

22. MEDICAID RESUBMISSION CODE   ORIGINAL REF. NO.

23. PRIOR AUTHORIZATION NUMBER

| 24. A. DATE(S) OF SERVICE | | | | | | B. PLACE OF SERVICE | C. EMG | D. PROCEDURES, SERVICES, OR SUPPLIES (Explain Unusual Circumstances) CPT/HCPCS | MODIFIER | E. DIAGNOSIS POINTER | F. $ CHARGES | G. DAYS OR UNITS | H. EPSDT Family Plan | I. ID. QUAL. | J. RENDERING PROVIDER ID. # |
From MM	DD	YY	To MM	DD	YY										
1														NPI	
2														NPI	
3														NPI	
4														NPI	
5														NPI	
6														NPI	

25. FEDERAL TAX I.D. NUMBER   SSN   EIN   **26.** PATIENT'S ACCOUNT NO.   **27.** ACCEPT ASSIGNMENT? (For govt. claims, see back) YES   NO   **28.** TOTAL CHARGE $ **29.** AMOUNT PAID $ **30.** BALANCE DUE $

31. SIGNATURE OF PHYSICIAN OR SUPPLIER INCLUDING DEGREES OR CREDENTIALS (I certify that the statements on the reverse apply to this bill and are made a part thereof.)   **32.** SERVICE FACILITY LOCATION INFORMATION   **33.** BILLING PROVIDER INFO & PH # (   )

CARRIER

PATIENT AND INSURED INFORMATION

PHYSICIAN OR SUPPLIER INFORMATION

EXERCISE 8.46

Al Cohol, an established patient of yours, calls your office one day complaining about pain in his right leg. He says that he has recently fallen from a scaffold (within the hour) and would like to be seen as he is "hurting real bad." You agree for him to come in. He presents himself to your office approximately 15 minutes later. Your physician examines Mr. Cohol's leg, checking for any visible signs of fracture, finds out how the injury occurred, and orders some x-rays. When the films come back, your physician sees that there is a hairline fracture of the tibia and decides to place an ambulatory type cast on the leg to immobilize it for healing. Code for Mr. Cohol.

Before You Begin:
Read Chapter 8 in cpTeach® on "Surgery." Follow along in CPT® with the points illustrated in cpTeach®.

Purpose of this Lesson:
To assist you in understanding the correct usage of the casting codes and the differences between initial cast placement and subsequent (follow-up) casting as well as to develop an understanding of coding surgical packages.

Instructions:
1. Code the following examples. Assume that the surgical package includes pre-op, surgery and post-op. Complete the CPT® portion of the CMS-1500 form found on the back of each page.

Notes: _____
_____
_____
_____
_____
_____
_____

EXERCISE 8.46

Name: _____

Class/Section: _____

Date: _____

2012

1500

HEALTH INSURANCE CLAIM FORM

APPROVED BY NATIONAL UNIFORM CLAIM COMMITTEE 08/05

| | PICA | | | | | | | | | PICA | |

1. MEDICARE	MEDICAID	TRICARE CHAMPUS	CHAMPVA	GROUP HEALTH PLAN	FECA BLK LUNG	OTHER	1a. INSURED'S I.D. NUMBER	(For Program In Item 1)
(Medicare #)	(Medicaid #)	(Sponsor's SSN)	(Member ID#)	(SSN or ID)	(SSN)	(ID)		

2. PATIENT'S NAME (Last Name, First Name, Middle Initial)

3. PATIENT'S BIRTH DATE MM | DD | YY   SEX M ☐ F ☐

4. INSURED'S NAME (Last Name, First Name, Middle Initial)

5. PATIENT'S ADDRESS (No., Street)

6. PATIENT RELATIONSHIP TO INSURED Self ☐ Spouse ☐ Child ☐ Other ☐

7. INSURED'S ADDRESS (No., Street)

CITY   STATE

8. PATIENT STATUS Single ☐ Married ☐ Other ☐

CITY   STATE

ZIP CODE   TELEPHONE (Include Area Code) (   )

Employed ☐ Full-Time Student ☐ Part-Time Student ☐

ZIP CODE   TELEPHONE (Include Area Code) (   )

9. OTHER INSURED'S NAME (Last Name, First Name, Middle Initial)

10. IS PATIENT'S CONDITION RELATED TO:

11. INSURED'S POLICY GROUP OR FECA NUMBER

a. OTHER INSURED'S POLICY OR GROUP NUMBER

a. EMPLOYMENT? (Current or Previous) ☐ YES ☐ NO

a. INSURED'S DATE OF BIRTH MM | DD | YY   SEX M ☐ F ☐

b. OTHER INSURED'S DATE OF BIRTH MM | DD | YY   SEX M ☐ F ☐

b. AUTO ACCIDENT? ☐ YES ☐ NO   PLACE (State)

b. EMPLOYER'S NAME OR SCHOOL NAME

c. EMPLOYER'S NAME OR SCHOOL NAME

c. OTHER ACCIDENT? ☐ YES ☐ NO

c. INSURANCE PLAN NAME OR PROGRAM NAME

d. INSURANCE PLAN NAME OR PROGRAM NAME

10d. RESERVED FOR LOCAL USE

d. IS THERE ANOTHER HEALTH BENEFIT PLAN? ☐ YES ☐ NO   *If yes*, return to and complete item 9 a-d.

READ BACK OF FORM BEFORE COMPLETING & SIGNING THIS FORM.

12. PATIENT'S OR AUTHORIZED PERSON'S SIGNATURE I authorize the release of any medical or other information necessary to process this claim. I also request payment of government benefits either to myself or to the party who accepts assignment below.

SIGNED _____   DATE _____

13. INSURED'S OR AUTHORIZED PERSON'S SIGNATURE I authorize payment of medical benefits to the undersigned physician or supplier for services described below.

SIGNED _____

14. DATE OF CURRENT: MM | DD | YY   ILLNESS (First symptom) OR INJURY (Accident) OR PREGNANCY(LMP)

15. IF PATIENT HAS HAD SAME OR SIMILAR ILLNESS. GIVE FIRST DATE MM | DD | YY

16. DATES PATIENT UNABLE TO WORK IN CURRENT OCCUPATION FROM MM | DD | YY TO MM | DD | YY

17. NAME OF REFERRING PROVIDER OR OTHER SOURCE

17a. | 17b. NPI |

18. HOSPITALIZATION DATES RELATED TO CURRENT SERVICES FROM MM | DD | YY TO MM | DD | YY

19. RESERVED FOR LOCAL USE

20. OUTSIDE LAB? ☐ YES ☐ NO $ CHARGES

21. DIAGNOSIS OR NATURE OF ILLNESS OR INJURY (Relate Items 1, 2, 9 or 4 to Item 24E by Line)

1. |____.____| 3. |____.____|

2. |____.____| 4. |____.____|

22. MEDICAID RESUBMISSION CODE   ORIGINAL REF. NO.

23. PRIOR AUTHORIZATION NUMBER

24. A. DATE(S) OF SERVICE					B. PLACE OF SERVICE	C. EMG	D. PROCEDURES, SERVICES, OR SUPPLIES (Explain Unusual Circumstances)		E. DIAGNOSIS POINTER	F. $ CHARGES	G. DAYS OR UNITS	H. EPSDT Family Plan	I. ID. QUAL.	J. RENDERING PROVIDER ID. #
From MM DD YY		To MM DD YY					CPT/HCPCS	MODIFIER						
1													NPI	
2													NPI	
3													NPI	
4													NPI	
5													NPI	
6													NPI	

25. FEDERAL TAX I.D. NUMBER SSN ☐ EIN ☐

26. PATIENT'S ACCOUNT NO.

27. ACCEPT ASSIGNMENT? *(For govt. claims, see back)* ☐ YES ☐ NO

28. TOTAL CHARGE $

29. AMOUNT PAID $

30. BALANCE DUE $

31. SIGNATURE OF PHYSICIAN OR SUPPLIER INCLUDING DEGREES OR CREDENTIALS (I certify that the statements on the reverse apply to this bill and are made a part thereof.)

32. SERVICE FACILITY LOCATION INFORMATION

33. BILLING PROVIDER INFO & PH # (   )

CARRIER

PATIENT AND INSURED INFORMATION

PHYSICIAN OR SUPPLIER INFORMATION

EXERCISE 8.47

Lise T. Vall, a new patient, comes to your office because she is complaining of pain in her knee. You perform the history on her finding out that she is active in sports and has been involved in sports since the age of five. Her father, a coach at a local high school, got her interested. He was actively involved in sports as a youngster, as was her mother. No one in the family smokes or drinks regularly, although her dad has an occasional beer. Her grandmother was one of the first athletes in her town (unusual for a woman who is now in her nineties), but suffered from severe arthritis when she turned 53. Lise has been captain of the school volleyball team and has been very active in track. She is 18 years old. She has had a steady boyfriend for 2 years and they are sexually active. She is on the pill but does not use any other medications. You examine the knee and find out that she has difficulty in rotating it properly. She also has some problems with flexion and extension. You order some x-rays and discover that there appear to be some calcifications in her knee joint. You suggest an arthroscopy to get a better handle on her condition and schedule the surgery for the next day. During the surgery, which started off as a diagnostic arthroscopy of the knee, you discover that you need to remove some loose bodies. You also need to do a major synovectomy. Code for the surgery(ies).

Before You Begin:
Read Chapter 8 in cpTeach® on "Surgery." Follow along in CPT® with the points illustrated in cpTeach®.

Purpose of this Lesson:
To assist you in understanding the correct usage of the casting codes and the differences between initial cast placement and subsequent (follow-up) casting as well as to develop an understanding of coding surgical packages.

Instructions:
1. Code the following examples. Assume that the surgical package includes pre-op, surgery and post-op. Complete the CPT® portion of the CMS-1500 form found on the back of each page.

Notes: _____

_____

_____

_____

_____

_____

_____

EXERCISE 8.47

1500

HEALTH INSURANCE CLAIM FORM

APPROVED BY NATIONAL UNIFORM CLAIM COMMITTEE 08/05

CARRIER

		PICA							PICA		

1. MEDICARE	MEDICAID	TRICARE CHAMPUS	CHAMPVA	GROUP HEALTH PLAN	FECA BLK LUNG	OTHER	1a. INSURED'S I.D. NUMBER (For Program in Item 1)
(Medicare #)	(Medicaid #)	(Sponsor's SSN)	(Member ID#)	(SSN or ID)	(SSN)	(ID)	

2. PATIENT'S NAME (Last Name, First Name, Middle Initial)	3. PATIENT'S BIRTH DATE MM DD YY SEX M F	4. INSURED'S NAME (Last Name, First Name, Middle Initial)

5. PATIENT'S ADDRESS (No., Street)	6. PATIENT RELATIONSHIP TO INSURED Self Spouse Child Other	7. INSURED'S ADDRESS (No., Street)

CITY	STATE	8. PATIENT STATUS Single Married Other	CITY	STATE

ZIP CODE	TELEPHONE (Include Area Code) ( )	Employed Full-Time Student Part-Time Student	ZIP CODE	TELEPHONE (Include Area Code) ( )

9. OTHER INSURED'S NAME (Last Name, First Name, Middle Initial)	10. IS PATIENT'S CONDITION RELATED TO:	11. INSURED'S POLICY GROUP OR FECA NUMBER

a. OTHER INSURED'S POLICY OR GROUP NUMBER	a. EMPLOYMENT? (Current or Previous) YES NO	a. INSURED'S DATE OF BIRTH MM DD YY SEX M F

b. OTHER INSURED'S DATE OF BIRTH MM DD YY SEX M F	b. AUTO ACCIDENT? PLACE (State) YES NO	b. EMPLOYER'S NAME OR SCHOOL NAME

c. EMPLOYER'S NAME OR SCHOOL NAME	c. OTHER ACCIDENT? YES NO	c. INSURANCE PLAN NAME OR PROGRAM NAME

d. INSURANCE PLAN NAME OR PROGRAM NAME	10d. RESERVED FOR LOCAL USE	d. IS THERE ANOTHER HEALTH BENEFIT PLAN? YES NO If yes, return to and complete Item 9 a-d.

READ BACK OF FORM BEFORE COMPLETING & SIGNING THIS FORM.

12. PATIENT'S OR AUTHORIZED PERSON'S SIGNATURE I authorize the release of any medical or other information necessary to process this claim. I also request payment of government benefits either to myself or to the party who accepts assignment below. SIGNED_____ DATE_____	13. INSURED'S OR AUTHORIZED PERSON'S SIGNATURE I authorize payment of medical benefits to the undersigned physician or supplier for services described below. SIGNED_____

PATIENT AND INSURED INFORMATION

14. DATE OF CURRENT: MM DD YY ◄ ILLNESS (First symptom) OR INJURY (Accident) OR PREGNANCY(LMP)	15. IF PATIENT HAS HAD SAME OR SIMILAR ILLNESS. GIVE FIRST DATE MM DD YY	16. DATES PATIENT UNABLE TO WORK IN CURRENT OCCUPATION MM DD YY MM DD YY FROM TO

17. NAME OF REFERRING PROVIDER OR OTHER SOURCE	17a. 17b. NPI	18. HOSPITALIZATION DATES RELATED TO CURRENT SERVICES MM DD YY MM DD YY FROM TO

19. RESERVED FOR LOCAL USE		20. OUTSIDE LAB? YES NO $ CHARGES

21. DIAGNOSIS OR NATURE OF ILLNESS OR INJURY (Relate Items 1, 2, 9 or 4 to Item 24E by Line) 1. |____.____ 3. |____.____ 2. |____.____ 4. |____.____	22. MEDICAID RESUBMISSION CODE ORIGINAL REF. NO. 23. PRIOR AUTHORIZATION NUMBER

24. A. DATE(S) OF SERVICE		B. PLACE OF SERVICE	C. EMG	D. PROCEDURES, SERVICES, OR SUPPLIES (Explain Unusual Circumstances)		E. DIAGNOSIS POINTER	F. $ CHARGES	G. DAYS OR UNITS	H. EPSDT Family Plan	I. ID. QUAL.	J. RENDERING PROVIDER ID. #
From MM DD YY	To MM DD YY			CPT/HCPCS	MODIFIER						
1										NPI	
2										NPI	
3										NPI	
4										NPI	
5										NPI	
6										NPI	

25. FEDERAL TAX I.D. NUMBER SSN EIN	26. PATIENT'S ACCOUNT NO.	27. ACCEPT ASSIGNMENT? (For govt. claims, see back) YES NO	28. TOTAL CHARGE $	29. AMOUNT PAID $	30. BALANCE DUE $

31. SIGNATURE OF PHYSICIAN OR SUPPLIER INCLUDING DEGREES OR CREDENTIALS (I certify that the statements on the reverse apply to this bill and are made a part thereof.)	32. SERVICE FACILITY LOCATION INFORMATION	33. BILLING PROVIDER INFO & PH # ( )

PHYSICIAN OR SUPPLIER INFORMATION

Name:_____

Class/Section:_____

cpTeach   Date:_____
2012

EXERCISE 8.48

Mr. C. Breeze comes to your office having been referred by his family practitioner. He is complaining of not being able to breathe properly and of feeling like he has something stuck up his nose. In spite of how many times he "blows" or uses nose drops, it just feels "thick" up there and he is afraid that he has a terrible cancer and will die. Mr. Breeze used to smoke when he was in his twenties (he is now 53). You examine his nasal passage and find that there appears to be some blockage but suggest that an endoscopy is probably in order. Mr. Breeze agrees. You send a letter to the primary physician and explain that you have scheduled Mr. Breeze for surgery. You perform the procedure a few days later which begins as a diagnostic service, and then once you are in, realize that there are polyps and that you need to remove them. Code for the surgeries. What kind of Evaluation and Management service would you have chosen for the initial visit in the office? Why?

Before You Begin:
Read Chapter 8 in cpTeach® on "Surgery." Follow along in CPT® with the points illustrated in cpTeach®.

Purpose of this Lesson:
To assist you in understanding the correct usage of the casting codes and the differences between initial cast placement and subsequent (follow-up) casting as well as to develop an understanding of coding surgical packages.

Instructions:
1. Code the following examples. Assume that the surgical package includes pre-op, surgery and post-op. Complete the CPT® portion of the CMS-1500 form found on the back of each page.

Notes: _____

_____

_____

_____

_____

_____

_____

EXERCISE 8.48

Name:_____

Class/Section:_____

Date:_____

2012

1500

HEALTH INSURANCE CLAIM FORM

APPROVED BY NATIONAL UNIFORM CLAIM COMMITTEE 08/05

| | PICA | | | | | | | PICA | |

1. MEDICARE	MEDICAID	TRICARE CHAMPUS	CHAMPVA	GROUP HEALTH PLAN	FECA BLK LUNG	OTHER	1a. INSURED'S I.D. NUMBER	(For Program In Item 1)
(Medicare #)	(Medicaid #)	(Sponsor's SSN)	(Member ID#)	(SSN or ID)	(SSN)	(ID)		

2. PATIENT'S NAME (Last Name, First Name, Middle Initial)

3. PATIENT'S BIRTH DATE MM DD YY   SEX   M ☐ F ☐

4. INSURED'S NAME (Last Name, First Name, Middle Initial)

5. PATIENT'S ADDRESS (No., Street)

6. PATIENT RELATIONSHIP TO INSURED   Self ☐ Spouse ☐ Child ☐ Other ☐

7. INSURED'S ADDRESS (No., Street)

CITY   STATE

8. PATIENT STATUS   Single ☐ Married ☐ Other ☐

CITY   STATE

ZIP CODE   TELEPHONE (Include Area Code) (   )

Employed ☐   Full-Time Student ☐   Part-Time Student ☐

ZIP CODE   TELEPHONE (Include Area Code) (   )

9. OTHER INSURED'S NAME (Last Name, First Name, Middle Initial)

10. IS PATIENT'S CONDITION RELATED TO:

11. INSURED'S POLICY GROUP OR FECA NUMBER

a. OTHER INSURED'S POLICY OR GROUP NUMBER

a. EMPLOYMENT? (Current or Previous)   YES ☐ NO ☐

a. INSURED'S DATE OF BIRTH MM DD YY   SEX   M ☐ F ☐

b. OTHER INSURED'S DATE OF BIRTH MM DD YY   SEX   M ☐ F ☐

b. AUTO ACCIDENT?   PLACE (State)   YES ☐ NO ☐

b. EMPLOYER'S NAME OR SCHOOL NAME

c. EMPLOYER'S NAME OR SCHOOL NAME

c. OTHER ACCIDENT?   YES ☐ NO ☐

c. INSURANCE PLAN NAME OR PROGRAM NAME

d. INSURANCE PLAN NAME OR PROGRAM NAME

10d. RESERVED FOR LOCAL USE

d. IS THERE ANOTHER HEALTH BENEFIT PLAN?   YES ☐ NO ☐   If yes, return to and complete item 9 a-d.

READ BACK OF FORM BEFORE COMPLETING & SIGNING THIS FORM.
12. PATIENT'S OR AUTHORIZED PERSON'S SIGNATURE I authorize the release of any medical or other information necessary to process this claim. I also request payment of government benefits either to myself or to the party who accepts assignment below.

SIGNED_____   DATE_____

13. INSURED'S OR AUTHORIZED PERSON'S SIGNATURE I authorize payment of medical benefits to the undersigned physician or supplier for services described below.

SIGNED_____

14. DATE OF CURRENT: MM DD YY ILLNESS (First symptom) OR INJURY (Accident) OR PREGNANCY(LMP)

15. IF PATIENT HAS HAD SAME OR SIMILAR ILLNESS. GIVE FIRST DATE MM DD YY

16. DATES PATIENT UNABLE TO WORK IN CURRENT OCCUPATION MM DD YY FROM   TO MM DD YY

17. NAME OF REFERRING PROVIDER OR OTHER SOURCE

17a.
17b. NPI

18. HOSPITALIZATION DATES RELATED TO CURRENT SERVICES MM DD YY FROM   TO MM DD YY

19. RESERVED FOR LOCAL USE

20. OUTSIDE LAB?   YES ☐ NO ☐ $ CHARGES

21. DIAGNOSIS OR NATURE OF ILLNESS OR INJURY (Relate Items 1, 2, 3 or 4 to Item 24E by Line)

1. |___.___   3. |___.___
2. |___.___   4. |___.___

22. MEDICAID RESUBMISSION CODE   ORIGINAL REF. NO.

23. PRIOR AUTHORIZATION NUMBER

24. A. DATE(S) OF SERVICE						B. PLACE OF SERVICE	C. EMG	D. PROCEDURES, SERVICES, OR SUPPLIES (Explain Unusual Circumstances) CPT/HCPCS MODIFIER	E. DIAGNOSIS POINTER	F. $ CHARGES	G. DAYS OR UNITS	H. EPSDT Family Plan	I. ID. QUAL.	J. RENDERING PROVIDER ID. #
From MM	DD	YY	To MM	DD	YY									
1													NPI	
2													NPI	
3													NPI	
4													NPI	
5													NPI	
6													NPI	

25. FEDERAL TAX I.D. NUMBER   SSN ☐ EIN ☐

26. PATIENT'S ACCOUNT NO.

27. ACCEPT ASSIGNMENT? (For govt. claims, see back)   YES ☐ NO ☐

28. TOTAL CHARGE $

29. AMOUNT PAID $

30. BALANCE DUE $

31. SIGNATURE OF PHYSICIAN OR SUPPLIER INCLUDING DEGREES OR CREDENTIALS (I certify that the statements on the reverse apply to this bill and are made a part thereof.)

32. SERVICE FACILITY LOCATION INFORMATION

33. BILLING PROVIDER INFO & PH # (   )

Name:_____

Class/Section:_____

Date:_____

cpTeach
2012

EXERCISE 8.49

Ms. Jones presents to your office with her child that she has just adopted from South America. The child, a little girl, suffers from a unilateral cleft lip. Now that the child is 2 years old, the mother would like for you to fix it and achieve the best cosmetic result possible. You take a complete history on the patient (as much as you can knowing that past family and social history are basically unavailable), and you are able to find out what she is allergic to, how much she weighs, and what past surgeries she has had. At the same time you perform an exam on her lip and palate making sure that the palate has not been affected. Since this is a first child for this mother and since she is apprehensive, you spend the balance of your session (approximately one hour) talking with the mother about the surgery, the anesthesia, the risks, and what she might be able to expect from the surgery. You then schedule the surgery for the next week. You do the surgery, completing a plastic repair of the lip, but due to the patient's age, you re-create the defect so that you can obtain a better cosmetic result. Code for both the office visit and the surgery.

Before You Begin:
Read Chapter 8 in cpTeach® on "Surgery." Follow along in CPT® with the points illustrated in cpTeach®.

Purpose of this Lesson:
To assist you in understanding the correct usage of the casting codes and the differences between initial cast placement and subsequent (follow-up) casting as well as to develop an understanding of coding surgical packages.

Instructions:
1. Code the following examples. Assume that the surgical package includes pre-op, surgery and post-op. Complete the CPT® portion of the CMS-1500 form found on the back of each page.

Notes: _____

_____

_____

_____

_____

_____

_____

WORKBOOK

Name:_____

Class/Section:_____

cpTeach

Date:_____

2012

EXERCISE 8.49

1500

HEALTH INSURANCE CLAIM FORM

APPROVED BY NATIONAL UNIFORM CLAIM COMMITTEE 08/05

CARRIER

| | PICA | | | | | | | | | | PICA | |

1. MEDICARE (Medicare #)   **MEDICAID** (Medicaid #)   **TRICARE CHAMPUS** (Sponsor's SSN)   **CHAMPVA** (Member ID#)   **GROUP HEALTH PLAN** (SSN or ID)   **FECA BLK LUNG** (SSN)   **OTHER** (ID)   **1a. INSURED'S I.D. NUMBER**   (For Program in Item 1)

2. PATIENT'S NAME (Last Name, First Name, Middle Initial)

3. PATIENT'S BIRTH DATE MM | DD | YY   **SEX** M [ ] F [ ]

4. INSURED'S NAME (Last Name, First Name, Middle Initial)

5. PATIENT'S ADDRESS (No., Street)

6. PATIENT RELATIONSHIP TO INSURED
Self [ ]   Spouse [ ]   Child [ ]   Other [ ]

7. INSURED'S ADDRESS (No., Street)

CITY   STATE

8. PATIENT STATUS
Single [ ]   Married [ ]   Other [ ]

CITY   STATE

ZIP CODE   TELEPHONE (Include Area Code)
                  (   )

Employed [ ]   Full-Time Student [ ]   Part-Time Student [ ]

ZIP CODE   TELEPHONE (Include Area Code)
                  (   )

9. OTHER INSURED'S NAME (Last Name, First Name, Middle Initial)

10. IS PATIENT'S CONDITION RELATED TO:

11. INSURED'S POLICY GROUP OR FECA NUMBER

a. OTHER INSURED'S POLICY OR GROUP NUMBER

a. EMPLOYMENT? (Current or Previous)
YES [ ]   NO [ ]

a. INSURED'S DATE OF BIRTH MM | DD | YY   **SEX** M [ ] F [ ]

b. OTHER INSURED'S DATE OF BIRTH MM | DD | YY   **SEX** M [ ] F [ ]

b. AUTO ACCIDENT?   PLACE (State)
YES [ ]   NO [ ]

b. EMPLOYER'S NAME OR SCHOOL NAME

c. EMPLOYER'S NAME OR SCHOOL NAME

c. OTHER ACCIDENT?
YES [ ]   NO [ ]

c. INSURANCE PLAN NAME OR PROGRAM NAME

d. INSURANCE PLAN NAME OR PROGRAM NAME

10d. RESERVED FOR LOCAL USE

d. IS THERE ANOTHER HEALTH BENEFIT PLAN?
YES [ ]   NO [ ]   If yes, return to and complete item 9 a-d.

READ BACK OF FORM BEFORE COMPLETING & SIGNING THIS FORM.
12. PATIENT'S OR AUTHORIZED PERSON'S SIGNATURE I authorize the release of any medical or other information necessary to process this claim. I also request payment of government benefits either to myself or to the party who accepts assignment below.

SIGNED_____   DATE_____

13. INSURED'S OR AUTHORIZED PERSON'S SIGNATURE I authorize payment of medical benefits to the undersigned physician or supplier for services described below.

SIGNED_____

PATIENT AND INSURED INFORMATION

14. DATE OF CURRENT: MM | DD | YY   ILLNESS (First symptom) OR INJURY (Accident) OR PREGNANCY(LMP)

15. IF PATIENT HAS HAD SAME OR SIMILAR ILLNESS. GIVE FIRST DATE MM | DD | YY

16. DATES PATIENT UNABLE TO WORK IN CURRENT OCCUPATION FROM MM | DD | YY   TO MM | DD | YY

17. NAME OF REFERRING PROVIDER OR OTHER SOURCE

17a.
17b. NPI

18. HOSPITALIZATION DATES RELATED TO CURRENT SERVICES FROM MM | DD | YY   TO MM | DD | YY

19. RESERVED FOR LOCAL USE

20. OUTSIDE LAB? $ CHARGES
YES [ ]   NO [ ]

21. DIAGNOSIS OR NATURE OF ILLNESS OR INJURY (Relate Items 1, 2, 9 or 4 to Item 24E by Line)

1. |___.___| 3. |___.___|

2. |___.___| 4. |___.___|

22. MEDICAID RESUBMISSION CODE   ORIGINAL REF. NO.

23. PRIOR AUTHORIZATION NUMBER

24. A. DATE(S) OF SERVICE						B. PLACE OF SERVICE	C. EMG	D. PROCEDURES, SERVICES, OR SUPPLIES (Explain Unusual Circumstances)		E. DIAGNOSIS POINTER	F. $ CHARGES	G. DAYS OR UNITS	H. EPSDT Family Plan	I. ID. QUAL.	J. RENDERING PROVIDER ID. #
From			To					CPT/HCPCS	MODIFIER						
MM	DD	YY	MM	DD	YY										
1														NPI	
2														NPI	
3														NPI	
4														NPI	
5														NPI	
6														NPI	

25. FEDERAL TAX I.D. NUMBER   SSN [ ] EIN [ ]

26. PATIENT'S ACCOUNT NO.

27. ACCEPT ASSIGNMENT? (For govt. claims, see back)
YES [ ]   NO [ ]

28. TOTAL CHARGE
$

29. AMOUNT PAID
$

30. BALANCE DUE
$

31. SIGNATURE OF PHYSICIAN OR SUPPLIER INCLUDING DEGREES OR CREDENTIALS (I certify that the statements on the reverse apply to this bill and are made a part thereof.)

32. SERVICE FACILITY LOCATION INFORMATION

33. BILLING PROVIDER INFO & PH # (   )

PHYSICIAN OR SUPPLIER INFORMATION

Name: _____

Class/Section: _____

Date: _____

cpTeach
2012

EXERCISE 8.50

Ms. Emma Hogge presents to the emergency room having had a beer bottle break in her mouth. She is bleeding extensively and, upon examination, you discover that she has cut her tongue. You find out that she is a heavy drinker and smoker and that she has a history of bouts with the law and drunk driving. You also discover through the blood work that you do that she has a low WBC and that she is on medication for high blood pressure. (You are told by a friend, who happens to be with her, that Ms. Hogge had passed out due to the amount of alcohol she had ingested.) Upon examination of the mouth, you see the cut and notice that it can be repaired and that there are no other significant problems. You repair the laceration of 2.1cm and send her home with instructions to her friend, requesting that they go to see both a counselor and a family physician within a week to check on the repair. Code for this (these) services explaining not the specific E/M, but the kind of E/M code that would be used.

Before You Begin:
Read Chapter 8 in cpTeach® on "Surgery." Follow along in CPT® with the points illustrated in cpTeach®.

Purpose of this Lesson:
To assist you in understanding the correct usage of the casting codes and the differences between initial cast placement and subsequent (follow-up) casting as well as to develop an understanding of coding surgical packages.

Instructions:
1. Code the following examples. Assume that the surgical package includes pre-op, surgery and post-op. Complete the CPT® portion of the CMS-1500 form found on the back of each page.

Notes: _____

_____

_____

_____

_____

_____

_____

EXERCISE **8.50**

Name:_____

Class/Section:_____

Date:_____

cpTeach 2012

1500

HEALTH INSURANCE CLAIM FORM

APPROVED BY NATIONAL UNIFORM CLAIM COMMITTEE 08/05

	PICA								PICA	

1. MEDICARE	MEDICAID	TRICARE CHAMPUS	CHAMPVA	GROUP HEALTH PLAN	FECA BLK LUNG	OTHER	1a. INSURED'S I.D. NUMBER (For Program in Item 1)
(Medicare #)	(Medicaid #)	(Sponsor's SSN)	(Member ID#)	(SSN or ID)	(SSN)	(ID)	

2. PATIENT'S NAME (Last Name, First Name, Middle Initial)

3. PATIENT'S BIRTH DATE MM DD YY   SEX   M   F

4. INSURED'S NAME (Last Name, First Name, Middle Initial)

5. PATIENT'S ADDRESS (No., Street)

6. PATIENT RELATIONSHIP TO INSURED   Self   Spouse   Child   Other

7. INSURED'S ADDRESS (No., Street)

CITY   STATE

8. PATIENT STATUS   Single   Married   Other

CITY   STATE

ZIP CODE   TELEPHONE (Include Area Code) (   )

Employed   Full-Time Student   Part-Time Student

ZIP CODE   TELEPHONE (Include Area Code) (   )

9. OTHER INSURED'S NAME (Last Name, First Name, Middle Initial)

10. IS PATIENT'S CONDITION RELATED TO:

11. INSURED'S POLICY GROUP OR FECA NUMBER

a. OTHER INSURED'S POLICY OR GROUP NUMBER

a. EMPLOYMENT? (Current or Previous)   YES   NO

a. INSURED'S DATE OF BIRTH MM DD YY   SEX   M   F

b. OTHER INSURED'S DATE OF BIRTH MM DD YY   SEX   M   F

b. AUTO ACCIDENT?   PLACE (State)   YES   NO

b. EMPLOYER'S NAME OR SCHOOL NAME

c. EMPLOYER'S NAME OR SCHOOL NAME

c. OTHER ACCIDENT?   YES   NO

c. INSURANCE PLAN NAME OR PROGRAM NAME

d. INSURANCE PLAN NAME OR PROGRAM NAME

10d. RESERVED FOR LOCAL USE

d. IS THERE ANOTHER HEALTH BENEFIT PLAN?   YES   NO   If yes, return to and complete item 9 a-d.

READ BACK OF FORM BEFORE COMPLETING & SIGNING THIS FORM.

12. PATIENT'S OR AUTHORIZED PERSON'S SIGNATURE I authorize the release of any medical or other information necessary to process this claim. I also request payment of government benefits either to myself or to the party who accepts assignment below.

SIGNED_____   DATE_____

13. INSURED'S OR AUTHORIZED PERSON'S SIGNATURE I authorize payment of medical benefits to the undersigned physician or supplier for services described below.

SIGNED_____

14. DATE OF CURRENT: MM DD YY   ILLNESS (First symptom) OR INJURY (Accident) OR PREGNANCY(LMP)

15. IF PATIENT HAS HAD SAME OR SIMILAR ILLNESS. GIVE FIRST DATE MM DD YY

16. DATES PATIENT UNABLE TO WORK IN CURRENT OCCUPATION MM DD YY   FROM   TO   MM DD YY

17. NAME OF REFERRING PROVIDER OR OTHER SOURCE

17a.

17b. NPI

18. HOSPITALIZATION DATES RELATED TO CURRENT SERVICES MM DD YY   FROM   TO   MM DD YY

19. RESERVED FOR LOCAL USE

20. OUTSIDE LAB?   YES   NO $ CHARGES

21. DIAGNOSIS OR NATURE OF ILLNESS OR INJURY (Relate Items 1, 2, 9 or 4 to Item 24E by Line)

1. |___.___| 3. |___.___|

2. |___.___| 4. |___.___|

22. MEDICAID RESUBMISSION CODE   ORIGINAL REF. NO.

23. PRIOR AUTHORIZATION NUMBER

24. A. DATE(S) OF SERVICE From MM DD YY To MM DD YY	B. PLACE OF SERVICE	C. EMG	D. PROCEDURES, SERVICES, OR SUPPLIES (Explain Unusual Circumstances) CPT/HCPCS	MODIFIER	E. DIAGNOSIS POINTER	F. $ CHARGES	G. DAYS OR UNITS	H. EPSDT Family Plan	I. ID. QUAL.	J. RENDERING PROVIDER ID. #
1									NPI	
2									NPI	
3									NPI	
4									NPI	
5									NPI	
6									NPI	

25. FEDERAL TAX I.D. NUMBER   SSN   EIN

26. PATIENT'S ACCOUNT NO.

27. ACCEPT ASSIGNMENT? (For govt. claims, see back)   YES   NO

28. TOTAL CHARGE $

29. AMOUNT PAID $

30. BALANCE DUE $

31. SIGNATURE OF PHYSICIAN OR SUPPLIER INCLUDING DEGREES OR CREDENTIALS (I certify that the statements on the reverse apply to this bill and are made a part thereof.)

32. SERVICE FACILITY LOCATION INFORMATION

33. BILLING PROVIDER INFO & PH # (   )

EXERCISE 8.51

Code the previous example but pretend that Ms. Hogge also had a 1.5 cm laceration of her palate. Would this impact your coding at all? How?

Before You Begin:
Read Chapter 8 in cpTeach® on "Surgery." Follow along in CPT® with the points illustrated in cpTeach®.

Purpose of this Lesson:
To assist you in understanding the correct usage of the casting codes and the differences between initial cast placement and subsequent (follow-up) casting as well as to develop an understanding of coding surgical packages.

Instructions:
1. Code the following examples. Assume that the surgical package includes pre-op, surgery and post-op. Complete the CPT® portion of the CMS-1500 form found on the back of each page.

Notes: _____
_____
_____
_____
_____
_____
_____

EXERCISE **8.51**

Name:_____

Class/Section:_____

Date:_____

2012

1500

HEALTH INSURANCE CLAIM FORM

APPROVED BY NATIONAL UNIFORM CLAIM COMMITTEE 08/05

| | PICA | | | | | | | | PICA | |

1. MEDICARE	MEDICAID	TRICARE CHAMPUS	CHAMPVA	GROUP HEALTH PLAN	FECA BLK LUNG	OTHER	1a. INSURED'S I.D. NUMBER	(For Program in Item 1)
(Medicare #)	(Medicaid #)	(Sponsor's SSN)	(Member ID#)	(SSN or ID)	(SSN)	(ID)		

2. PATIENT'S NAME (Last Name, First Name, Middle Initial)

3. PATIENT'S BIRTH DATE   MM   DD   YY   SEX   M   F

4. INSURED'S NAME (Last Name, First Name, Middle Initial)

5. PATIENT'S ADDRESS (No., Street)

6. PATIENT RELATIONSHIP TO INSURED   Self   Spouse   Child   Other

7. INSURED'S ADDRESS (No., Street)

CITY   STATE

8. PATIENT STATUS   Single   Married   Other

CITY   STATE

ZIP CODE   TELEPHONE (Include Area Code) (   )

Employed   Full-Time Student   Part-Time Student

ZIP CODE   TELEPHONE (Include Area Code) (   )

9. OTHER INSURED'S NAME (Last Name, First Name, Middle Initial)

10. IS PATIENT'S CONDITION RELATED TO:

11. INSURED'S POLICY GROUP OR FECA NUMBER

a. OTHER INSURED'S POLICY OR GROUP NUMBER

a. EMPLOYMENT? (Current or Previous)   YES   NO

a. INSURED'S DATE OF BIRTH   MM   DD   YY   SEX   M   F

b. OTHER INSURED'S DATE OF BIRTH   MM   DD   YY   SEX   M   F

b. AUTO ACCIDENT?   PLACE (State)   YES   NO

b. EMPLOYER'S NAME OR SCHOOL NAME

c. EMPLOYER'S NAME OR SCHOOL NAME

c. OTHER ACCIDENT?   YES   NO

c. INSURANCE PLAN NAME OR PROGRAM NAME

d. INSURANCE PLAN NAME OR PROGRAM NAME

10d. RESERVED FOR LOCAL USE

d. IS THERE ANOTHER HEALTH BENEFIT PLAN?   YES   NO   If yes, return to and complete item 9 a-d.

READ BACK OF FORM BEFORE COMPLETING & SIGNING THIS FORM.

12. PATIENT'S OR AUTHORIZED PERSON'S SIGNATURE I authorize the release of any medical or other information necessary to process this claim. I also request payment of government benefits either to myself or to the party who accepts assignment below.

SIGNED _____   DATE _____

19. INSURED'S OR AUTHORIZED PERSON'S SIGNATURE I authorize payment of medical benefits to the undersigned physician or supplier for services described below.

SIGNED _____

14. DATE OF CURRENT: MM   DD   YY   ILLNESS (First symptom) OR INJURY (Accident) OR PREGNANCY(LMP)

15. IF PATIENT HAS HAD SAME OR SIMILAR ILLNESS. GIVE FIRST DATE   MM   DD   YY

16. DATES PATIENT UNABLE TO WORK IN CURRENT OCCUPATION   MM   DD   YY   FROM   TO   MM   DD   YY

17. NAME OF REFERRING PROVIDER OR OTHER SOURCE

17a.

17b. NPI

18. HOSPITALIZATION DATES RELATED TO CURRENT SERVICES   MM   DD   YY   FROM   TO   MM   DD   YY

19. RESERVED FOR LOCAL USE

20. OUTSIDE LAB?   YES   NO $ CHARGES

21. DIAGNOSIS OR NATURE OF ILLNESS OR INJURY (Relate Items 1, 2, 9 or 4 to Item 24E by Line)

1. |___.___   3. |___.___

2. |___.___   4. |___.___

22. MEDICAID RESUBMISSION CODE   ORIGINAL REF. NO.

23. PRIOR AUTHORIZATION NUMBER

24. A. DATE(S) OF SERVICE						B. PLACE OF SERVICE	C. EMG	D. PROCEDURES, SERVICES, OR SUPPLIES (Explain Unusual Circumstances) CPT/HCPCS MODIFIER	E. DIAGNOSIS POINTER	F. $ CHARGES	G. DAYS OR UNITS	H. EPSDT Family Plan	I. ID QUAL.	J. RENDERING PROVIDER ID. #
From			To											
MM	DD	YY	MM	DD	YY									
1													NPI	
2													NPI	
3													NPI	
4													NPI	
5													NPI	
6													NPI	

25. FEDERAL TAX I.D. NUMBER   SSN   EIN

26. PATIENT'S ACCOUNT NO.

27. ACCEPT ASSIGNMENT? (For govt. claims, see back)   YES   NO

28. TOTAL CHARGE $

29. AMOUNT PAID $

30. BALANCE DUE $

31. SIGNATURE OF PHYSICIAN OR SUPPLIER INCLUDING DEGREES OR CREDENTIALS (I certify that the statements on the reverse apply to this bill and are made a part thereof.)

32. SERVICE FACILITY LOCATION INFORMATION

33. BILLING PROVIDER INFO & PH # (   )

CARRIER

PATIENT AND INSURED INFORMATION

PHYSICIAN OR SUPPLIER INFORMATION

Radiology

Codes in the Radiology section begin with the number 7.

The four major subsections in the Radiology section include:

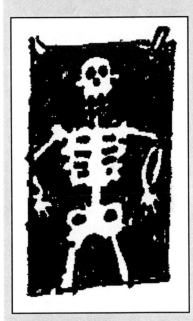

1. Diagnostic Radiology/Diagnostic Imaging
2. Diagnostic Ultrasound
3. Radiologic Guidance
4. Breast Mammography
5. Bone/Joint Studies
6. Radiation Oncology
7. Nuclear Medicine

The codes in each of the subsections are generally arranged by anatomic site, from the top of the body to the bottom.

"Complete" procedures are those that include all views of a certain area. If a physician provides supervision and interpretation of a procedure as well as the procedure itself (e.g., endoscopy, injection of contrast medium), two codes should be used: one for the procedure itself and the other for the supervision and interpretation of the procedure. Codes for the procedures such as injection of contrast media for endoscopy are found in other sections of the CPT® codebook, usually the Surgery section. Codes for supervision and interpretation of the procedures are found in the Radiology section.

It is important to read all of the notes in each subsection, as they give important information about accurate coding of the procedures found in that subsection.

Tip

Within each of the subsections (e.g., Diagnostic Radiology), codes are arranged, for the most part, in anatomical order, from the top of the body to the bottom (i.e., head and neck, chest, spine, and pelvis).

Name:_____

Class/Section:_____

cpTeach

Date:_____

2012

EXERCISE 9.1

Nuclear Medicine	Diagnostic Radiology
Radiation Oncology	Diagnostic Ultrasound
Radiologic Guidance	Breast Mammography
Bone/Joint Studies	

1. _____

2. _____

3. _____

4. _____

5. _____

6. _____

7. _____

Before You Begin:
Read Chapter 9 in cpTeach®
on "Radiology." Follow
along in CPT® with the points
illustrated in cpTeach®.

Purpose of this Lesson:
To familiarize the student
with the different sections in
the Radiology chapter..

Instructions:
1. Look at the following
    subsections of the
    Radiology chapter.

2. Place these subsections
    in order as they appear
    in the CPT® codebook.

In Radiology the codes in the subsections have been arranged in anatomical
order from top to bottom, i.e., head and
neck, chest, spine and pelvis.

Before You Begin:

Read Chapter 9 in cpTeach® on "Radiology." Follow along in your CPT® codebook with the points illustrated in cpTeach®.

Purpose of this Lesson:

To familiarize the student with the Radiology section and show how to code for a complete procedure.

Instructions:

1. Read the following descriptions of service. Code as if the same physician provided both the injection, if necessary, the interpretation of the film and the technical component.

EXERCISE 9.2

1. Transluminal artherectomy, visceral, radiological supervision and interpretation.

   _____

   _____

2. Radiologic examination, hip; complete with injection for arthrography, no anesthesia.

   _____

   _____

3. Radiologic examination wrist with injection for arthrography.

   _____

   _____

4. Radiologic examination, foot; complete, minimum of three views.

   _____

   _____

5. Myelography, cervical (C1-C2); complete with injection procedure.

   _____

   _____

	Name:_____
WORKBOOK	Class/Section:_____
cpTeach 2012	Date:_____

EXERCISE 9.3

Dr. Perry Neum, a world renowned radiologist, receives some films that were prepared by a small family practice group in Texas. He is reviewing the films because the family practition-cr wants to confirm his diagnosis. The film reviews consist of x-rays of the foot (four views). Code for this review and the report.

Before You Begin:
Read Chapter 9 in cpTeach® on "Radiology." Follow along in your CPT® codebook with the points illustrated in cpTeach®.

Purpose of this Lesson:
To familiarize the student with the Radiology section and show how to code for a complete procedure.

Instructions:
1. Code the following using the correct CPT® code. Write them up as you would on a CMS-1500 form located on the back of each exercise.

Notes: _____

_____

_____

_____

_____

_____

_____

EXERCISE 9.3

1500

HEALTH INSURANCE CLAIM FORM

APPROVED BY NATIONAL UNIFORM CLAIM COMMITTEE 08/05

[ ][ ][ ] PICA

1. MEDICARE	MEDICAID	TRICARE CHAMPUS	CHAMPVA	GROUP HEALTH PLAN	FECA BLK LUNG	OTHER	1a. INSURED'S I.D. NUMBER (For Program in Item 1)
(Medicare #)	(Medicaid #)	(Sponsor's SSN)	(Member ID#)	(SSN or ID)	(SSN)	(ID)	

2. PATIENT'S NAME (Last Name, First Name, Middle Initial)

3. PATIENT'S BIRTH DATE MM DD YY   SEX M ☐ F ☐

4. INSURED'S NAME (Last Name, First Name, Middle Initial)

5. PATIENT'S ADDRESS (No., Street)

6. PATIENT RELATIONSHIP TO INSURED
Self ☐ Spouse ☐ Child ☐ Other ☐

7. INSURED'S ADDRESS (No., Street)

CITY   STATE

8. PATIENT STATUS
Single ☐ Married ☐ Other ☐
Employed ☐ Full-Time Student ☐ Part-Time Student ☐

CITY   STATE

ZIP CODE   TELEPHONE (Include Area Code) (   )

ZIP CODE   TELEPHONE (Include Area Code) (   )

9. OTHER INSURED'S NAME (Last Name, First Name, Middle Initial)

10. IS PATIENT'S CONDITION RELATED TO:

11. INSURED'S POLICY GROUP OR FECA NUMBER

a. OTHER INSURED'S POLICY OR GROUP NUMBER

a. EMPLOYMENT? (Current or Previous) YES ☐ NO ☐

a. INSURED'S DATE OF BIRTH MM DD YY   SEX M ☐ F ☐

b. OTHER INSURED'S DATE OF BIRTH MM DD YY   SEX M ☐ F ☐

b. AUTO ACCIDENT? PLACE (State) YES ☐ NO ☐

b. EMPLOYER'S NAME OR SCHOOL NAME

c. EMPLOYER'S NAME OR SCHOOL NAME

c. OTHER ACCIDENT? YES ☐ NO ☐

c. INSURANCE PLAN NAME OR PROGRAM NAME

d. INSURANCE PLAN NAME OR PROGRAM NAME

10d. RESERVED FOR LOCAL USE

d. IS THERE ANOTHER HEALTH BENEFIT PLAN?
YES ☐ NO ☐ If yes, return to and complete item 9 a-d.

READ BACK OF FORM BEFORE COMPLETING & SIGNING THIS FORM.
12. PATIENT'S OR AUTHORIZED PERSON'S SIGNATURE I authorize the release of any medical or other information necessary to process this claim. I also request payment of government benefits either to myself or to the party who accepts assignment below.

SIGNED_____   DATE_____

13. INSURED'S OR AUTHORIZED PERSON'S SIGNATURE I authorize payment of medical benefits to the undersigned physician or supplier for services described below.

SIGNED_____

14. DATE OF CURRENT: MM DD YY ILLNESS (First symptom) OR INJURY (Accident) OR PREGNANCY(LMP)

15. IF PATIENT HAS HAD SAME OR SIMILAR ILLNESS. GIVE FIRST DATE MM DD YY

16. DATES PATIENT UNABLE TO WORK IN CURRENT OCCUPATION MM DD YY FROM TO MM DD YY

17. NAME OF REFERRING PROVIDER OR OTHER SOURCE

17a.

17b. NPI

18. HOSPITALIZATION DATES RELATED TO CURRENT SERVICES MM DD YY FROM TO MM DD YY

19. RESERVED FOR LOCAL USE

20. OUTSIDE LAB? YES ☐ NO ☐ $ CHARGES

21. DIAGNOSIS OR NATURE OF ILLNESS OR INJURY (Relate Items 1, 2, 3 or 4 to Item 24E by Line)

1. |___.___| 3. |___.___|

2. |___.___| 4. |___.___|

22. MEDICAID RESUBMISSION CODE   ORIGINAL REF. NO.

23. PRIOR AUTHORIZATION NUMBER

24. A. DATE(S) OF SERVICE						B. PLACE OF SERVICE	C. EMG	D. PROCEDURES, SERVICES, OR SUPPLIES (Explain Unusual Circumstances) CPT/HCPCS MODIFIER	E. DIAGNOSIS POINTER	F. $ CHARGES	G. DAYS OR UNITS	H. EPSDT Family Plan	I. ID. QUAL.	J. RENDERING PROVIDER ID. #
From MM	DD	YY	To MM	DD	YY									
1													NPI	
2													NPI	
3													NPI	
4													NPI	
5													NPI	
6													NPI	

25. FEDERAL TAX I.D. NUMBER   SSN ☐ EIN ☐

26. PATIENT'S ACCOUNT NO.

27. ACCEPT ASSIGNMENT? (For govt. claims, see back) YES ☐ NO ☐

28. TOTAL CHARGE $

29. AMOUNT PAID $

30. BALANCE DUE $

31. SIGNATURE OF PHYSICIAN OR SUPPLIER INCLUDING DEGREES OR CREDENTIALS (I certify that the statements on the reverse apply to this bill and are made a part thereof.)

32. SERVICE FACILITY LOCATION INFORMATION

33. BILLING PROVIDER INFO & PH # (   )

WORKBOOK

cpTeach
Expert Medical Coding Made Easy!
2012

Name:_____

Class/Section:_____

Date:_____

EXERCISE 9.4

Your patient, Ms. Di Lacion, presents herself to your OB/GYN clinic for her annual exam. Your PA performs the history, getting updates on the past year and also completes the exam. During the cxam, she notices that Ms. Lacion seems to have a mass in her abdomen that is located in her lower left quadrant. You are asked to come in to examine the patient, and when you do, you find the same mass. You ask your technician to take Ms. Lacion down the hall to your ultrasound room where she receives an abdominal ultrasound of the lower left quadrant. Code for the ultrasound only.

Before You Begin:
Read Chapter 9 in cpTeach® on "Radiology." Follow along in your CPT® codebook with the points illustrated in cpTeach®.

Purpose of this Lesson:
To familiarize the student with the Radiology section and show how to code for a complete procedure.

Instructions:
1. Code the following using the correct CPT® code. Write them up as you would on a CMS-1500 form located on the back of each exercise.

Notes: _____
_____
_____
_____
_____
_____
_____

Exercise 9.4

1500

HEALTH INSURANCE CLAIM FORM

APPROVED BY NATIONAL UNIFORM CLAIM COMMITTEE 08/05

	PICA								PICA	

1. MEDICARE ☐ (Medicare #)   MEDICAID ☐ (Medicaid #)   TRICARE CHAMPUS ☐ (Sponsor's SSN)   CHAMPVA ☐ (Member ID#)   GROUP HEALTH PLAN ☐ (SSN or ID)   FECA BLK LUNG ☐ (SSN)   OTHER ☐ (ID)   **1a.** INSURED'S I.D. NUMBER   (For Program in Item 1)

2. PATIENT'S NAME (Last Name, First Name, Middle Initial)

3. PATIENT'S BIRTH DATE   MM | DD | YY   SEX   M ☐   F ☐

4. INSURED'S NAME (Last Name, First Name, Middle Initial)

5. PATIENT'S ADDRESS (No., Street)

6. PATIENT RELATIONSHIP TO INSURED   Self ☐   Spouse ☐   Child ☐   Other ☐

7. INSURED'S ADDRESS (No., Street)

CITY   STATE

8. PATIENT STATUS   Single ☐   Married ☐   Other ☐

Employed ☐   Full-Time Student ☐   Part-Time Student ☐

CITY   STATE

ZIP CODE   TELEPHONE (Include Area Code) ( )

ZIP CODE   TELEPHONE (Include Area Code) ( )

9. OTHER INSURED'S NAME (Last Name, First Name, Middle Initial)

10. IS PATIENT'S CONDITION RELATED TO:

11. INSURED'S POLICY GROUP OR FECA NUMBER

a. OTHER INSURED'S POLICY OR GROUP NUMBER

a. EMPLOYMENT? (Current or Previous)   YES ☐   NO ☐

a. INSURED'S DATE OF BIRTH   MM | DD | YY   SEX   M ☐   F ☐

b. OTHER INSURED'S DATE OF BIRTH   MM | DD | YY   SEX   M ☐   F ☐

b. AUTO ACCIDENT?   YES ☐   NO ☐   PLACE (State)

b. EMPLOYER'S NAME OR SCHOOL NAME

c. EMPLOYER'S NAME OR SCHOOL NAME

c. OTHER ACCIDENT?   YES ☐   NO ☐

c. INSURANCE PLAN NAME OR PROGRAM NAME

d. INSURANCE PLAN NAME OR PROGRAM NAME

10d. RESERVED FOR LOCAL USE

d. IS THERE ANOTHER HEALTH BENEFIT PLAN?   YES ☐   NO ☐   If yes, return to and complete item 9 a-d.

READ BACK OF FORM BEFORE COMPLETING & SIGNING THIS FORM.

12. PATIENT'S OR AUTHORIZED PERSON'S SIGNATURE I authorize the release of any medical or other information necessary to process this claim. I also request payment of government benefits either to myself or to the party who accepts assignment below.

SIGNED _____ DATE _____

13. INSURED'S OR AUTHORIZED PERSON'S SIGNATURE I authorize payment of medical benefits to the undersigned physician or supplier for services described below.

SIGNED _____

14. DATE OF CURRENT: MM | DD | YY   ILLNESS (First symptom) OR INJURY (Accident) OR PREGNANCY(LMP)

15. IF PATIENT HAS HAD SAME OR SIMILAR ILLNESS. GIVE FIRST DATE   MM | DD | YY

16. DATES PATIENT UNABLE TO WORK IN CURRENT OCCUPATION   MM | DD | YY   FROM   TO   MM | DD | YY

17. NAME OF REFERRING PROVIDER OR OTHER SOURCE

17a.

17b. NPI

18. HOSPITALIZATION DATES RELATED TO CURRENT SERVICES   MM | DD | YY   FROM   TO   MM | DD | YY

19. RESERVED FOR LOCAL USE

20. OUTSIDE LAB?   YES ☐   NO ☐ $ CHARGES

21. DIAGNOSIS OR NATURE OF ILLNESS OR INJURY (Relate items 1, 2, 3 or 4 to item 24E by Line)

1. |___.___   3. |___.___

2. |___.___   4. |___.___

22. MEDICAID RESUBMISSION CODE   ORIGINAL REF. NO.

23. PRIOR AUTHORIZATION NUMBER

24. A. DATE(S) OF SERVICE						B. PLACE OF SERVICE	C. EMG	D. PROCEDURES, SERVICES, OR SUPPLIES (Explain Unusual Circumstances)		E. DIAGNOSIS POINTER	F. $ CHARGES	G. DAYS OR UNITS	H. EPSDT Family Plan	I. ID QUAL.	J. RENDERING PROVIDER ID. #
From MM	DD	YY	To MM	DD	YY			CPT/HCPCS	MODIFIER						
1														NPI	
2														NPI	
3														NPI	
4														NPI	
5														NPI	
6														NPI	

25. FEDERAL TAX I.D. NUMBER   SSN ☐ EIN ☐

26. PATIENT'S ACCOUNT NO.

27. ACCEPT ASSIGNMENT? (For govt. claims, see back) YES ☐ NO ☐

28. TOTAL CHARGE $

29. AMOUNT PAID $

30. BALANCE DUE $

31. SIGNATURE OF PHYSICIAN OR SUPPLIER INCLUDING DEGREES OR CREDENTIALS (I certify that the statements on the reverse apply to this bill and are made a part thereof.)

32. SERVICE FACILITY LOCATION INFORMATION

33. BILLING PROVIDER INFO & PH # ( )

WORKBOOK

cpTeach

2012

Name:_____

Class/Section:_____

Date:_____

EXERCISE 9.5

Ms. Mam A. Grams, a 76-year-old southern lady from Atlanta, GA, is in today for her screening mammograms. The physician has ordered that both breasts are to be x-rayed. Code for the mammogram done on each side.

Before You Begin:
Read Chapter 9 in cpTeach® on "Radiology." Follow along in your CPT® codebook with the points illustrated in cpTeach®.

Purpose of this Lesson:
To familiarize the student with the Radiology section and show how to code for a complete procedure.

Instructions:
1. Code the following using the correct CPT® code. Write them up as you would on a CMS-1500 form located on the back of each exercise.

Notes: _____

_____

_____

_____

_____

_____

_____

EXERCISE 9.5

1500

HEALTH INSURANCE CLAIM FORM

APPROVED BY NATIONAL UNIFORM CLAIM COMMITTEE 08/05

	PICA						PICA	

1. MEDICARE ☐ (Medicare #) MEDICAID ☐ (Medicaid #) TRICARE CHAMPUS ☐ (Sponsor's SSN) CHAMPVA ☐ (Member ID#) GROUP HEALTH PLAN ☐ (SSN or ID) FECA BLK LUNG ☐ (SSN) OTHER ☐ (ID) **1a. INSURED'S I.D. NUMBER** (For Program in Item 1)

2. PATIENT'S NAME (Last Name, First Name, Middle Initial)

3. PATIENT'S BIRTH DATE MM DD YY   SEX   M ☐ F ☐

4. INSURED'S NAME (Last Name, First Name, Middle Initial)

5. PATIENT'S ADDRESS (No., Street)

6. PATIENT RELATIONSHIP TO INSURED Self ☐ Spouse ☐ Child ☐ Other ☐

7. INSURED'S ADDRESS (No., Street)

CITY   STATE

8. PATIENT STATUS Single ☐ Married ☐ Other ☐

CITY   STATE

ZIP CODE   TELEPHONE (Include Area Code) ( )

Employed ☐ Full-Time Student ☐ Part-Time Student ☐

ZIP CODE   TELEPHONE (Include Area Code) ( )

9. OTHER INSURED'S NAME (Last Name, First Name, Middle Initial)

10. IS PATIENT'S CONDITION RELATED TO:

11. INSURED'S POLICY GROUP OR FECA NUMBER

a. OTHER INSURED'S POLICY OR GROUP NUMBER

a. EMPLOYMENT? (Current or Previous) ☐ YES ☐ NO

a. INSURED'S DATE OF BIRTH MM DD YY   SEX   M ☐ F ☐

b. OTHER INSURED'S DATE OF BIRTH MM DD YY   SEX   M ☐ F ☐

b. AUTO ACCIDENT? PLACE (State) ☐ YES ☐ NO

b. EMPLOYER'S NAME OR SCHOOL NAME

c. EMPLOYER'S NAME OR SCHOOL NAME

c. OTHER ACCIDENT? ☐ YES ☐ NO

c. INSURANCE PLAN NAME OR PROGRAM NAME

d. INSURANCE PLAN NAME OR PROGRAM NAME

10d. RESERVED FOR LOCAL USE

d. IS THERE ANOTHER HEALTH BENEFIT PLAN? ☐ YES ☐ NO   If yes, return to and complete item 9 a-d.

READ BACK OF FORM BEFORE COMPLETING & SIGNING THIS FORM.

12. PATIENT'S OR AUTHORIZED PERSON'S SIGNATURE I authorize the release of any medical or other information necessary to process this claim. I also request payment of government benefits either to myself or to the party who accepts assignment below.

SIGNED _____ DATE _____

13. INSURED'S OR AUTHORIZED PERSON'S SIGNATURE I authorize payment of medical benefits to the undersigned physician or supplier for services described below.

SIGNED _____

14. DATE OF CURRENT: MM DD YY   ILLNESS (First symptom) OR INJURY (Accident) OR PREGNANCY(LMP)

15. IF PATIENT HAS HAD SAME OR SIMILAR ILLNESS. GIVE FIRST DATE MM DD YY

16. DATES PATIENT UNABLE TO WORK IN CURRENT OCCUPATION MM DD YY   FROM   TO   MM DD YY

17. NAME OF REFERRING PROVIDER OR OTHER SOURCE

17a.

17b. NPI

18. HOSPITALIZATION DATES RELATED TO CURRENT SERVICES MM DD YY   FROM   TO   MM DD YY

19. RESERVED FOR LOCAL USE

20. OUTSIDE LAB? ☐ YES ☐ NO $ CHARGES

21. DIAGNOSIS OR NATURE OF ILLNESS OR INJURY (Relate Items 1, 2, 9 or 4 to Item 24E by Line)

1. |___.___   3. |___.___
2. |___.___   4. |___.___

22. MEDICAID RESUBMISSION CODE   ORIGINAL REF. NO.

23. PRIOR AUTHORIZATION NUMBER

24. A. DATE(S) OF SERVICE						B. PLACE OF SERVICE	C. EMG	D. PROCEDURES, SERVICES, OR SUPPLIES (Explain Unusual Circumstances) CPT/HCPCS MODIFIER	E. DIAGNOSIS POINTER	F. $ CHARGES	G. DAYS OR UNITS	H. EPSDT Family Plan	I. ID. QUAL.	J. RENDERING PROVIDER ID. #
From MM	DD	YY	To MM	DD	YY									
1													NPI	
2													NPI	
3													NPI	
4													NPI	
5													NPI	
6													NPI	

25. FEDERAL TAX I.D. NUMBER SSN ☐ EIN ☐

26. PATIENT'S ACCOUNT NO.

27. ACCEPT ASSIGNMENT? (For govt. claims, see back) ☐ YES ☐ NO

28. TOTAL CHARGE $

29. AMOUNT PAID $

30. BALANCE DUE $

31. SIGNATURE OF PHYSICIAN OR SUPPLIER INCLUDING DEGREES OR CREDENTIALS (I certify that the statements on the reverse apply to this bill and are made a part thereof.)

32. SERVICE FACILITY LOCATION INFORMATION

33. BILLING PROVIDER INFO & PH # ( )

Name:_____

Class/Section:_____

Date:_____

2012

EXERCISE 9.6

Tim C. Seas has cancer. His oncologist says that he needs to receive radiation treatment. Your doctor, a radiologist, determines that Mr. Seas should have a regimen of treatment consisting of seven courses of treatment. This treatment spans the period of 21 days.   Code for all courses.

Before You Begin:
Read Chapter 9 in cpTeach® on "Radiology." Follow along in your CPT® codebook with the points illustrated in cpTeach®.

Purpose of this Lesson:
To familiarize the student with the Radiology section and show how to code for a complete procedure.

Instructions:
1. Code the following using the correct CPT® code. Write them up as you would on a CMS-1500 form located on the back of each exercise.

Notes: _____

_____

_____

_____

_____

_____

_____

Name:_____

Class/Section:_____

Date:_____

cpTeach
2012

EXERCISE 9.6

1500

HEALTH INSURANCE CLAIM FORM

APPROVED BY NATIONAL UNIFORM CLAIM COMMITTEE 08/05

| | PICA | | | | | | | PICA | |

1. MEDICARE   MEDICAID   TRICARE CHAMPUS   CHAMPVA   GROUP HEALTH PLAN   FECA BLK LUNG   OTHER   1a. INSURED'S I.D. NUMBER   (For Program in Item 1)

(Medicare #)   (Medicaid #)   (Sponsor's SSN)   (Member ID#)   (SSN or ID)   (SSN)   (ID)

2. PATIENT'S NAME (Last Name, First Name, Middle Initial)   3. PATIENT'S BIRTH DATE   MM   DD   YY   SEX   M   F   4. INSURED'S NAME (Last Name, First Name, Middle Initial)

5. PATIENT'S ADDRESS (No., Street)   6. PATIENT RELATIONSHIP TO INSURED   Self   Spouse   Child   Other   7. INSURED'S ADDRESS (No., Street)

CITY   STATE   8. PATIENT STATUS   Single   Married   Other   CITY   STATE

ZIP CODE   TELEPHONE (Include Area Code) ( )   Employed   Full-Time Student   Part-Time Student   ZIP CODE   TELEPHONE (Include Area Code) ( )

9. OTHER INSURED'S NAME (Last Name, First Name, Middle Initial)   10. IS PATIENT'S CONDITION RELATED TO: 11. INSURED'S POLICY GROUP OR FECA NUMBER

a. OTHER INSURED'S POLICY OR GROUP NUMBER   a. EMPLOYMENT? (Current or Previous)   YES   NO   a. INSURED'S DATE OF BIRTH   MM   DD   YY   SEX   M   F

b. OTHER INSURED'S DATE OF BIRTH   MM   DD   YY   SEX   M   F   b. AUTO ACCIDENT?   PLACE (State)   YES   NO   b. EMPLOYER'S NAME OR SCHOOL NAME

c. EMPLOYER'S NAME OR SCHOOL NAME   c. OTHER ACCIDENT?   YES   NO   c. INSURANCE PLAN NAME OR PROGRAM NAME

d. INSURANCE PLAN NAME OR PROGRAM NAME   10d. RESERVED FOR LOCAL USE   d. IS THERE ANOTHER HEALTH BENEFIT PLAN?   YES   NO   If yes, return to and complete item 9 a-d.

READ BACK OF FORM BEFORE COMPLETING & SIGNING THIS FORM.
12. PATIENT'S OR AUTHORIZED PERSON'S SIGNATURE I authorize the release of any medical or other information necessary to process this claim. I also request payment of government benefits either to myself or to the party who accepts assignment below.

SIGNED _____   DATE _____

13. INSURED'S OR AUTHORIZED PERSON'S SIGNATURE I authorize payment of medical benefits to the undersigned physician or supplier for services described below.

SIGNED _____

14. DATE OF CURRENT: MM   DD   YY   ILLNESS (First symptom) OR INJURY (Accident) OR PREGNANCY(LMP)   15. IF PATIENT HAS HAD SAME OR SIMILAR ILLNESS. GIVE FIRST DATE   MM   DD   YY   16. DATES PATIENT UNABLE TO WORK IN CURRENT OCCUPATION   MM   DD   YY   FROM   TO   MM   DD   YY

17. NAME OF REFERRING PROVIDER OR OTHER SOURCE   17a.   17b. NPI   18. HOSPITALIZATION DATES RELATED TO CURRENT SERVICES   MM   DD   YY   FROM   TO   MM   DD   YY

19. RESERVED FOR LOCAL USE   20. OUTSIDE LAB?   YES   NO $ CHARGES

21. DIAGNOSIS OR NATURE OF ILLNESS OR INJURY (Relate Items 1, 2, 3 or 4 to Item 24E by Line)
1. |___.___   3. |___.___
2. |___.___   4. |___.___

22. MEDICAID RESUBMISSION CODE   ORIGINAL REF. NO.

23. PRIOR AUTHORIZATION NUMBER

24. A. DATE(S) OF SERVICE						B. PLACE OF SERVICE	C. EMG	D. PROCEDURES, SERVICES, OR SUPPLIES (Explain Unusual Circumstances) CPT/HCPCS MODIFIER	E. DIAGNOSIS POINTER	F. $ CHARGES	G. DAYS OR UNITS	H. EPSDT Family Plan	I. ID QUAL.	J. RENDERING PROVIDER ID. #
From MM	DD	YY	To MM	DD	YY									
1													NPI	
2													NPI	
3													NPI	
4													NPI	
5													NPI	
6													NPI	

25. FEDERAL TAX I.D. NUMBER   SSN   EIN   26. PATIENT'S ACCOUNT NO.   27. ACCEPT ASSIGNMENT? (For govt. claims, see back)   YES   NO   28. TOTAL CHARGE $ 29. AMOUNT PAID $ 30. BALANCE DUE $

31. SIGNATURE OF PHYSICIAN OR SUPPLIER INCLUDING DEGREES OR CREDENTIALS (I certify that the statements on the reverse apply to this bill and are made a part thereof.)   32. SERVICE FACILITY LOCATION INFORMATION   33. BILLING PROVIDER INFO & PH # ( )

CARRIER

PATIENT AND INSURED INFORMATION

PHYSICIAN OR SUPPLIER INFORMATION

Pathology & Laboratory

Codes found in the Pathology and Laboratory section begin with the number 8. It is important to read and understand all information found in the subsection "notes," as well as any other information in parentheses.

As with all other sections of the CPT® codebook, if you are trying to code for something which has no existing code, try looking for your service in the Category III section of the CPT® codebook. If you are unable to locate a code there, you can use an Unlisted Procedure code.

In submitting an unlisted procedure or a procedure with an Unusual Service (modifier-22), it is important that you include a special report that is written so that it can be understood by the average layperson.

In coding for tests in the Organ or Disease Oriented Panels, you must make sure that the panels include the lists of tests described under each description. Any tests not included in the lists of tests for each panel should be reported separately and in addition to the code for the other service(s). For example, a basic metabolic panel (80048) must include the following tests in order to be coded as the 80048:

1   **Calcium; total (82310)**

2   **Carbon dioxide (bicarbonate) (82374)**

3   **Chloride; blood (82435)**

4   **Creatinine; blood (82565)**

5   **Glucose; quantitative, blood (except reagent strip) (82947)**

Tip

It is very important that you understand the information contained in the notes before you begin to code the procedures and services found in each subsection.

6   Potassium; serum plasma or whole blood (84132)

7   Sodium; serum plasma or whole blood (84295)

8   Urea nitrogen; quantitative (BUN) (84520)

If one or more of these tests were not provided as part of the basic metabolic panel, do not code the number 80048.

Some Surgical Pathology codes are divided into "levels." The level of a given service depends on the degree of difficulty involved in the physician's evaluation of that specimen (e.g., higher levels are associated with greater degrees of pathology), as well as where the specimen came from (for example, cervix versus colon).

Be sure to read the different specimen listings under each code in the Surgical Pathology section. The specimen you may think is part of one code may actually be part of another.

EXERCISE 10.1

1. _____   Urinalysis

2. _____   Organ or Disease Panels

3. _____   Consultations (Clinical Pathology)

4. _____   Microbiology

5. _____   Cytopathology

6. _____   Drug Testing

7. _____   Therapeutic Drug Assays

8. _____   Surgical Pathology

9. _____   Evocative/Suppression Testing

10. _____   Chemistry

11. _____   Cytogenetic Studies

Before You Begin:
Read Chapter 10 in cpTeach® on "Pathology." Follow along in your CPT® with the points illustrated in cpTeach®.

Purpose of this Lesson:
To familiarize the student with the Radiology section and show how to code for a complete procedure.

Instructions:
1. To familiarize the student with the overall arrangement of the Pathology chapter.

2. Place the subsections in the order in which they appear in your CPT® codebook by writing a 1, 2, 3, etc., in the space to the left of each.

WORKBOOK

cpTeach
2012

Name:_____

Class/Section:_____

Date:_____

Before You Begin:

Read Chapter 10 in cpTeach® on "Pathology." Follow along in your CPT® with the points illustrated in cpTeach®.

Purpose of this Lesson:

To familiarize the student with the overall arrangement of the Pathology chapter

Instructions:

1. Read each of the statements below.

2. Write a "T" if the statement you read is true and an "F" if the statement you read is false.

EXERCISE 10.2

1. _____   Within a particular subsection of the Pathology section (e.g., Chemistry), the tests are listed alphabetically.

2. _____   There are Consultation codes found in the Pathology section.

3. _____   The Pathology codes include both a physician and technical component. Listing the code by itself with no modifier means that both components are included in the one global charge.

4. _____   There are codes in the Pathology section that describe an autopsy.

5. _____   The codes found in the Surgical Pathology subsection represent levels of difficulty of the particular specimen examined.

6. _____   In order to code for a procedure in the Surgical Pathology subsection, you must locate the kind of tissue examined and code accordingly.

Name:_____

Class/Section:_____

cpTeach

2012   Date:_____

Exercise 10.3

Clint Ical is a druggie and everyone knows it. He is currently employed at John's Records and Tapes, where it has been reported that lots of inventory is missing and where all employees are to receive drug testing. Mr. Ical is sent to your lab. After obtaining the appropriate sample, you find cocaine. You perform another test to confirm this result. You also have been asked (in advance) to provide any testing on the amount of cocaine present, if you have in fact found some in your initial trials. Since you have found cocaine, you provide a quantitative analysis. Code for all testing done on Mr. Ical.

Before You Begin:
Read Chapter 10 in cpTeach® on "Pathology and Laboratory." Follow along in your CPT® codebook with the points illustrated in cpTeach®.

Purpose of this Lesson:
To familiarize the student with the Pathology and Laboratory section.

Instructions:
1. Code the following using the correct CPT® code. Write them up as you would on a CMS-1500 form located on the back of each exercise.

Notes: _____

_____

_____

_____

_____

_____

_____

EXERCISE 10.3

Name:_____

Class/Section:_____

Date:_____

cpTeach 2012

1500
HEALTH INSURANCE CLAIM FORM
APPROVED BY NATIONAL UNIFORM CLAIM COMMITTEE 08/05

☐☐☐ PICA   PICA ☐☐☐

| 1. MEDICARE ☐ (Medicare #)   MEDICAID ☐ (Medicaid #)   TRICARE CHAMPUS ☐ (Sponsor's SSN)   CHAMPVA ☐ (Member ID#)   GROUP HEALTH PLAN ☐ (SSN or ID)   FECA BLK LUNG ☐ (SSN)   OTHER ☐ (ID) | 1a. INSURED'S I.D. NUMBER   (For Program in Item 1) |

2. PATIENT'S NAME (Last Name, First Name, Middle Initial)

3. PATIENT'S BIRTH DATE MM DD YY   SEX M ☐ F ☐

4. INSURED'S NAME (Last Name, First Name, Middle Initial)

5. PATIENT'S ADDRESS (No., Street)

6. PATIENT RELATIONSHIP TO INSURED Self ☐ Spouse ☐ Child ☐ Other ☐

7. INSURED'S ADDRESS (No., Street)

CITY   STATE

8. PATIENT STATUS Single ☐ Married ☐ Other ☐

CITY   STATE

ZIP CODE   TELEPHONE (Include Area Code) (   )

Employed ☐ Full-Time Student ☐ Part-Time Student ☐

ZIP CODE   TELEPHONE (Include Area Code) (   )

9. OTHER INSURED'S NAME (Last Name, First Name, Middle Initial)

10. IS PATIENT'S CONDITION RELATED TO:

11. INSURED'S POLICY GROUP OR FECA NUMBER

a. OTHER INSURED'S POLICY OR GROUP NUMBER

a. EMPLOYMENT? (Current or Previous) YES ☐ NO ☐

a. INSURED'S DATE OF BIRTH MM DD YY   SEX M ☐ F ☐

b. OTHER INSURED'S DATE OF BIRTH MM DD YY   SEX M ☐ F ☐

b. AUTO ACCIDENT? YES ☐ NO ☐ PLACE (State)

b. EMPLOYER'S NAME OR SCHOOL NAME

c. EMPLOYER'S NAME OR SCHOOL NAME

c. OTHER ACCIDENT? YES ☐ NO ☐

c. INSURANCE PLAN NAME OR PROGRAM NAME

d. INSURANCE PLAN NAME OR PROGRAM NAME

10d. RESERVED FOR LOCAL USE

d. IS THERE ANOTHER HEALTH BENEFIT PLAN? YES ☐ NO ☐ If yes, return to and complete item 9 a-d.

READ BACK OF FORM BEFORE COMPLETING & SIGNING THIS FORM.
12. PATIENT'S OR AUTHORIZED PERSON'S SIGNATURE I authorize the release of any medical or other information necessary to process this claim. I also request payment of government benefits either to myself or to the party who accepts assignment below.

SIGNED_____   DATE_____

13. INSURED'S OR AUTHORIZED PERSON'S SIGNATURE I authorize payment of medical benefits to the undersigned physician or supplier for services described below.

SIGNED_____

14. DATE OF CURRENT: MM DD YY ILLNESS (First symptom) OR INJURY (Accident) OR PREGNANCY(LMP)

15. IF PATIENT HAS HAD SAME OR SIMILAR ILLNESS. GIVE FIRST DATE MM DD YY

16. DATES PATIENT UNABLE TO WORK IN CURRENT OCCUPATION MM DD YY FROM   TO MM DD YY

17. NAME OF REFERRING PROVIDER OR OTHER SOURCE

17a.
17b. NPI

18. HOSPITALIZATION DATES RELATED TO CURRENT SERVICES MM DD YY FROM   TO MM DD YY

19. RESERVED FOR LOCAL USE

20. OUTSIDE LAB? YES ☐ NO ☐ $ CHARGES

21. DIAGNOSIS OR NATURE OF ILLNESS OR INJURY (Relate Items 1, 2, 9 or 4 to Item 24E by Line)

1. |___.___   3. |___.___
2. |___.___   4. |___.___

22. MEDICAID RESUBMISSION CODE   ORIGINAL REF. NO.

23. PRIOR AUTHORIZATION NUMBER

24. A. DATE(S) OF SERVICE From MM DD YY To MM DD YY	B. PLACE OF SERVICE	C. EMG	D. PROCEDURES, SERVICES, OR SUPPLIES (Explain Unusual Circumstances) CPT/HCPCS MODIFIER	E. DIAGNOSIS POINTER	F. $ CHARGES	G. DAYS OR UNITS	H. EPSDT Family Plan	I. ID. QUAL.	J. RENDERING PROVIDER ID. #
1									NPI
2									NPI
3									NPI
4									NPI
5									NPI
6									NPI

25. FEDERAL TAX I.D. NUMBER   SSN ☐ EIN ☐

26. PATIENT'S ACCOUNT NO.

27. ACCEPT ASSIGNMENT? (For govt. claims, see back) YES ☐ NO ☐

28. TOTAL CHARGE $

29. AMOUNT PAID $

30. BALANCE DUE $

31. SIGNATURE OF PHYSICIAN OR SUPPLIER INCLUDING DEGREES OR CREDENTIALS (I certify that the statements on the reverse apply to this bill and are made a part thereof.)

32. SERVICE FACILITY LOCATION INFORMATION

33. BILLING PROVIDER INFO & PH # (   )

Name:_____

Class/Section:_____

Date:_____

2012

EXERCISE 10.4

Sir Ringe, a British knight here for an extended holiday, has been experiencing some problems with his adrenal glands. Your physician determines that Sir Ringe should receive some lab tests which would find out about any adrenal insufficiency. These tests include two tests for total cortisol as well as an ACTH stimulation panel. Code for all tests.

Before You Begin:
Read Chapter 10 in cpTeach® on "Pathology and Laboratory." Follow along in your CPT® codebook with the points illustrated in cpTeach®.

Purpose of this Lesson:
To familiarize the student with the Pathology and Laboratory section.

Instructions:
1. Code the following using the correct CPT® code. Write them up as you would on a CMS-1500 form located on the back of each exercise.

Notes: _____
_____
_____
_____
_____
_____
_____

EXERCISE 10.4

WORKBOOK
cpTeach
2012

Name:_____

Class/Section:_____

Date:_____

1500

HEALTH INSURANCE CLAIM FORM

APPROVED BY NATIONAL UNIFORM CLAIM COMMITTEE 08/05

| | PICA | | | | | | | | PICA | |

1. MEDICARE	MEDICAID	TRICARE CHAMPUS	CHAMPVA	GROUP HEALTH PLAN	FECA BLK LUNG	OTHER	1a. INSURED'S I.D. NUMBER	(For Program in Item 1)
(Medicare #)	(Medicaid #)	(Sponsor's SSN)	(Member ID#)	(SSN or ID)	(SSN)	(ID)		

2. PATIENT'S NAME (Last Name, First Name, Middle Initial)

3. PATIENT'S BIRTH DATE MM DD YY   SEX   M   F

4. INSURED'S NAME (Last Name, First Name, Middle Initial)

5. PATIENT'S ADDRESS (No., Street)

6. PATIENT RELATIONSHIP TO INSURED   Self   Spouse   Child   Other

7. INSURED'S ADDRESS (No., Street)

CITY   STATE

8. PATIENT STATUS   Single   Married   Other

CITY   STATE

ZIP CODE   TELEPHONE (Include Area Code) (   )

Employed   Full-Time Student   Part-Time Student

ZIP CODE   TELEPHONE (Include Area Code) (   )

9. OTHER INSURED'S NAME (Last Name, First Name, Middle Initial)

10. IS PATIENT'S CONDITION RELATED TO:

11. INSURED'S POLICY GROUP OR FECA NUMBER

a. OTHER INSURED'S POLICY OR GROUP NUMBER

a. EMPLOYMENT? (Current or Previous)   YES   NO

a. INSURED'S DATE OF BIRTH MM DD YY   SEX   M   F

b. OTHER INSURED'S DATE OF BIRTH MM DD YY   SEX   M   F

b. AUTO ACCIDENT?   YES   NO   PLACE (State)

b. EMPLOYER'S NAME OR SCHOOL NAME

c. EMPLOYER'S NAME OR SCHOOL NAME

c. OTHER ACCIDENT?   YES   NO

c. INSURANCE PLAN NAME OR PROGRAM NAME

d. INSURANCE PLAN NAME OR PROGRAM NAME

10d. RESERVED FOR LOCAL USE

d. IS THERE ANOTHER HEALTH BENEFIT PLAN?   YES   NO   If yes, return to and complete item 9 a-d.

READ BACK OF FORM BEFORE COMPLETING & SIGNING THIS FORM.

12. PATIENT'S OR AUTHORIZED PERSON'S SIGNATURE I authorize the release of any medical or other information necessary to process this claim. I also request payment of government benefits either to myself or to the party who accepts assignment below.

SIGNED _____ DATE _____

13. INSURED'S OR AUTHORIZED PERSON'S SIGNATURE I authorize payment of medical benefits to the undersigned physician or supplier for services described below.

SIGNED _____

14. DATE OF CURRENT: MM DD YY   ILLNESS (First symptom) OR INJURY (Accident) OR PREGNANCY(LMP)

15. IF PATIENT HAS HAD SAME OR SIMILAR ILLNESS. GIVE FIRST DATE MM DD YY

16. DATES PATIENT UNABLE TO WORK IN CURRENT OCCUPATION MM DD YY   FROM   TO MM DD YY

17. NAME OF REFERRING PROVIDER OR OTHER SOURCE

17a.

17b. NPI

18. HOSPITALIZATION DATES RELATED TO CURRENT SERVICES MM DD YY   FROM   TO MM DD YY

19. RESERVED FOR LOCAL USE

20. OUTSIDE LAB?   YES   NO $ CHARGES

21. DIAGNOSIS OR NATURE OF ILLNESS OR INJURY (Relate Items 1, 2, 9 or 4 to item 24E by Line)

1. _____._____   3. _____._____

2. _____._____   4. _____._____

22. MEDICAID RESUBMISSION CODE   ORIGINAL REF. NO.

23. PRIOR AUTHORIZATION NUMBER

24. A. DATE(S) OF SERVICE From MM DD YY To MM DD YY	B. PLACE OF SERVICE	C. EMG	D. PROCEDURES, SERVICES, OR SUPPLIES (Explain Unusual Circumstances) CPT/HCPCS MODIFIER	E. DIAGNOSIS POINTER	F. $ CHARGES	G. DAYS OR UNITS	H. EPSDT Family Plan	I. ID. QUAL.	J. RENDERING PROVIDER ID. #
1								NPI	
2								NPI	
3								NPI	
4								NPI	
5								NPI	
6								NPI	

25. FEDERAL TAX I.D. NUMBER   SSN   EIN

26. PATIENT'S ACCOUNT NO.

27. ACCEPT ASSIGNMENT? (For govt. claims, see back)   YES   NO

28. TOTAL CHARGE $

29. AMOUNT PAID $

30. BALANCE DUE $

31. SIGNATURE OF PHYSICIAN OR SUPPLIER INCLUDING DEGREES OR CREDENTIALS (I certify that the statements on the reverse apply to this bill and are made a part thereof.)

32. SERVICE FACILITY LOCATION INFORMATION

33. BILLING PROVIDER INFO & PH # (   )

Name:_____

Class/Section:_____

Date:_____

2012

EXERCISE 10.5

You have a patient who has missed a period. You decide to perform a test on her urine for pregnancy (i.e., you want to see if there is any human chorionic gonadotropin). What code should you use to report this test?

Before You Begin:
Read Chapter 10 in cpTeach® on "Pathology and Laboratory." Follow along in your CPT® codebook with the points illustrated in cpTeach®.

Purpose of this Lesson:
To familiarize the student with the Pathology and Laboratory section.

Instructions:
1. Code the following using the correct CPT® code. Write them up as you would on a CMS-1500 form located on the back of each exercise.

Notes: _____

_____

_____

_____

_____

_____

_____

EXERCISE 10.5

1500

HEALTH INSURANCE CLAIM FORM

APPROVED BY NATIONAL UNIFORM CLAIM COMMITTEE 08/05

CARRIER

| | PICA | | | | | | PICA | |

1. MEDICARE (Medicare #) | MEDICAID (Medicaid #) | TRICARE CHAMPUS (Sponsor's SSN) | CHAMPVA (Member ID#) | GROUP HEALTH PLAN (SSN or ID) | FECA BLK LUNG (SSN) | OTHER (ID) | 1a. INSURED'S I.D. NUMBER (For Program in Item 1)

2. PATIENT'S NAME (Last Name, First Name, Middle Initial)

3. PATIENT'S BIRTH DATE   MM   DD   YY   SEX   M [ ]   F [ ]

4. INSURED'S NAME (Last Name, First Name, Middle Initial)

5. PATIENT'S ADDRESS (No., Street)

6. PATIENT RELATIONSHIP TO INSURED   Self [ ]   Spouse [ ]   Child [ ]   Other [ ]

7. INSURED'S ADDRESS (No., Street)

CITY   STATE

8. PATIENT STATUS   Single [ ]   Married [ ]   Other [ ]

CITY   STATE

ZIP CODE   TELEPHONE (Include Area Code) ( )

Employed [ ]   Full-Time Student [ ]   Part-Time Student [ ]

ZIP CODE   TELEPHONE (Include Area Code) ( )

9. OTHER INSURED'S NAME (Last Name, First Name, Middle Initial)

10. IS PATIENT'S CONDITION RELATED TO:

11. INSURED'S POLICY GROUP OR FECA NUMBER

a. OTHER INSURED'S POLICY OR GROUP NUMBER

a. EMPLOYMENT? (Current or Previous)   YES [ ]   NO [ ]

a. INSURED'S DATE OF BIRTH   MM   DD   YY   SEX   M [ ]   F [ ]

b. OTHER INSURED'S DATE OF BIRTH   MM   DD   YY   SEX   M [ ]   F [ ]

b. AUTO ACCIDENT?   PLACE (State)   YES [ ]   NO [ ]

b. EMPLOYER'S NAME OR SCHOOL NAME

c. EMPLOYER'S NAME OR SCHOOL NAME

c. OTHER ACCIDENT?   YES [ ]   NO [ ]

c. INSURANCE PLAN NAME OR PROGRAM NAME

d. INSURANCE PLAN NAME OR PROGRAM NAME

10d. RESERVED FOR LOCAL USE

d. IS THERE ANOTHER HEALTH BENEFIT PLAN?   YES [ ]   NO [ ]   If yes, return to and complete item 9 a-d.

READ BACK OF FORM BEFORE COMPLETING & SIGNING THIS FORM.

12. PATIENT'S OR AUTHORIZED PERSON'S SIGNATURE I authorize the release of any medical or other information necessary to process this claim. I also request payment of government benefits either to myself or to the party who accepts assignment below.

SIGNED_____   DATE_____

13. INSURED'S OR AUTHORIZED PERSON'S SIGNATURE I authorize payment of medical benefits to the undersigned physician or supplier for services described below.

SIGNED_____

14. DATE OF CURRENT: MM   DD   YY   ILLNESS (First symptom) OR INJURY (Accident) OR PREGNANCY (LMP)

15. IF PATIENT HAS HAD SAME OR SIMILAR ILLNESS. GIVE FIRST DATE   MM   DD   YY

16. DATES PATIENT UNABLE TO WORK IN CURRENT OCCUPATION   MM   DD   YY   FROM   TO   MM   DD   YY

17. NAME OF REFERRING PROVIDER OR OTHER SOURCE

17a. |
17b. NPI |

18. HOSPITALIZATION DATES RELATED TO CURRENT SERVICES   MM   DD   YY   FROM   TO   MM   DD   YY

19. RESERVED FOR LOCAL USE

20. OUTSIDE LAB?   YES [ ]   NO [ ] $ CHARGES

21. DIAGNOSIS OR NATURE OF ILLNESS OR INJURY (Relate Items 1, 2, 3 or 4 to Item 24E by Line)

1. |___.___| 3. |___.___|

2. |___.___| 4. |___.___|

22. MEDICAID RESUBMISSION CODE   ORIGINAL REF. NO.

23. PRIOR AUTHORIZATION NUMBER

24. A. DATE(S) OF SERVICE						B. PLACE OF SERVICE	C. EMG	D. PROCEDURES, SERVICES, OR SUPPLIES (Explain Unusual Circumstances)		E. DIAGNOSIS POINTER	F. $ CHARGES	G. DAYS OR UNITS	H. EPSDT Family Plan	I. ID. QUAL.	J. RENDERING PROVIDER ID. #
From			To					CPT/HCPCS	MODIFIER						
MM	DD	YY	MM	DD	YY										
1															NPI
2															NPI
3															NPI
4															NPI
5															NPI
6															NPI

25. FEDERAL TAX I.D. NUMBER   SSN [ ] EIN [ ]

26. PATIENT'S ACCOUNT NO.

27. ACCEPT ASSIGNMENT? (For govt. claims, see back)   YES [ ]   NO [ ]

28. TOTAL CHARGE $

29. AMOUNT PAID $

30. BALANCE DUE $

31. SIGNATURE OF PHYSICIAN OR SUPPLIER INCLUDING DEGREES OR CREDENTIALS (I certify that the statements on the reverse apply to this bill and are made a part thereof.)

32. SERVICE FACILITY LOCATION INFORMATION

33. BILLING PROVIDER INFO & PH # ( )

Name:_____

Class/Section:_____

cpTeach
2012
Date:_____

EXERCISE 10.6

During a surgery that is occurring downstairs in the operating room, you receive a specimen that you are supposed to analyze. The patient is being operated on to remove some lumps that were located in her breast and the surgeon just wants to make sure that the lumps have been completely removed and that there are clear margins. As the pathologist, you provide that analysis and prepare three tissue blocks with frozen sections. Code for your services.

Before You Begin:

Read Chapter 10 in cpTeach® on "Pathology and Laboratory." Follow along in your CPT® codebook with the points illustrated in cpTeach®.

Purpose of this Lesson:

To familiarize the student with the Pathology and Laboratory section.

Instructions:

1. Code the following using the correct CPT® code. Write them up as you would on a CMS-1500 form located on the back of each exercise.

Notes: _____

_____

_____

_____

_____

_____

_____

Name:_____

Class/Section:_____

cpTeach

Date:_____

2012

EXERCISE 10.6

1500

HEALTH INSURANCE CLAIM FORM

APPROVED BY NATIONAL UNIFORM CLAIM COMMITTEE 08/05

| | | PICA | | | | | | | | | | PICA | | |

1. MEDICARE	MEDICAID	TRICARE CHAMPUS	CHAMPVA	GROUP HEALTH PLAN	FECA BLK LUNG	OTHER	1a. INSURED'S I.D. NUMBER	(For Program in Item 1)
(Medicare #)	(Medicaid #)	(Sponsor's SSN)	(Member ID#)	(SSN or ID)	(SSN)	(ID)		

2. PATIENT'S NAME (Last Name, First Name, Middle Initial)	3. PATIENT'S BIRTH DATE MM DD YY SEX M F	4. INSURED'S NAME (Last Name, First Name, Middle Initial)

5. PATIENT'S ADDRESS (No., Street)	6. PATIENT RELATIONSHIP TO INSURED Self Spouse Child Other	7. INSURED'S ADDRESS (No., Street)

CITY	STATE	8. PATIENT STATUS Single Married Other	CITY	STATE

ZIP CODE	TELEPHONE (Include Area Code) ( )	Employed Full-Time Student Part-Time Student	ZIP CODE	TELEPHONE (Include Area Code) ( )

9. OTHER INSURED'S NAME (Last Name, First Name, Middle Initial)	10. IS PATIENT'S CONDITION RELATED TO:	11. INSURED'S POLICY GROUP OR FECA NUMBER

a. OTHER INSURED'S POLICY OR GROUP NUMBER	a. EMPLOYMENT? (Current or Previous) YES NO	a. INSURED'S DATE OF BIRTH MM DD YY SEX M F

b. OTHER INSURED'S DATE OF BIRTH MM DD YY SEX M F	b. AUTO ACCIDENT? PLACE (State) YES NO	b. EMPLOYER'S NAME OR SCHOOL NAME

c. EMPLOYER'S NAME OR SCHOOL NAME	c. OTHER ACCIDENT? YES NO	c. INSURANCE PLAN NAME OR PROGRAM NAME

d. INSURANCE PLAN NAME OR PROGRAM NAME	10d. RESERVED FOR LOCAL USE	d. IS THERE ANOTHER HEALTH BENEFIT PLAN? YES NO If yes, return to and complete item 9 a-d.

READ BACK OF FORM BEFORE COMPLETING & SIGNING THIS FORM.

12. PATIENT'S OR AUTHORIZED PERSON'S SIGNATURE I authorize the release of any medical or other information necessary to process this claim. I also request payment of government benefits either to myself or to the party who accepts assignment below.

SIGNED _____   DATE _____

13. INSURED'S OR AUTHORIZED PERSON'S SIGNATURE I authorize payment of medical benefits to the undersigned physician or supplier for services described below.

SIGNED _____

14. DATE OF CURRENT: MM DD YY ILLNESS (First symptom) OR INJURY (Accident) OR PREGNANCY(LMP)	15. IF PATIENT HAS HAD SAME OR SIMILAR ILLNESS. GIVE FIRST DATE MM DD YY	16. DATES PATIENT UNABLE TO WORK IN CURRENT OCCUPATION MM DD YY MM DD YY FROM TO

17. NAME OF REFERRING PROVIDER OR OTHER SOURCE	17a. 17b. NPI	18. HOSPITALIZATION DATES RELATED TO CURRENT SERVICES MM DD YY MM DD YY FROM TO

19. RESERVED FOR LOCAL USE	20. OUTSIDE LAB? $ CHARGES YES NO

21. DIAGNOSIS OR NATURE OF ILLNESS OR INJURY (Relate Items 1, 2, 3 or 4 to Item 24E by Line)

1. |___.___| 3. |___.___|

2. |___.___| 4. |___.___|

22. MEDICAID RESUBMISSION CODE   ORIGINAL REF. NO.
23. PRIOR AUTHORIZATION NUMBER

24. A. DATE(S) OF SERVICE From To MM DD YY MM DD YY	B. PLACE OF SERVICE	C. EMG	D. PROCEDURES, SERVICES, OR SUPPLIES (Explain Unusual Circumstances) CPT/HCPCS MODIFIER	E. DIAGNOSIS POINTER	F. $ CHARGES	G. DAYS OR UNITS	H. EPSDT Family Plan	I. ID QUAL.	J. RENDERING PROVIDER ID. #
1									NPI
2									NPI
3									NPI
4									NPI
5									NPI
6									NPI

25. FEDERAL TAX I.D. NUMBER SSN EIN	26. PATIENT'S ACCOUNT NO.	27. ACCEPT ASSIGNMENT? (For govt. claims, see back) YES NO	28. TOTAL CHARGE $	29. AMOUNT PAID $	30. BALANCE DUE $

31. SIGNATURE OF PHYSICIAN OR SUPPLIER INCLUDING DEGREES OR CREDENTIALS (I certify that the statements on the reverse apply to this bill and are made a part thereof.)	32. SERVICE FACILITY LOCATION INFORMATION	33. BILLING PROVIDER INFO & PH # ( )

CARRIER

PATIENT AND INSURED INFORMATION

PHYSICIAN OR SUPPLIER INFORMATION

Name:_____

Class/Section:_____

Date:_____

2012

EXERCISE 10.7

As one of the leaders on neuroblastomas in pediatric patients, you receive some slides from a hospital in Dallas, Texas. You are asked to review these slides and consult on them providing the attending physician with your opinion as to the diagnosis. You review five slides and prepare your report for the attending physician. Code for all five reviews.

Notes: _____

_____

_____

_____

_____

_____

_____

EXERCISE 10.7

1500

HEALTH INSURANCE CLAIM FORM

APPROVED BY NATIONAL UNIFORM CLAIM COMMITTEE 08/05

PICA			PICA

1. MEDICARE (Medicare #) **MEDICAID** (Medicaid #) **TRICARE CHAMPUS** (Sponsor's SSN) **CHAMPVA** (Member ID#) **GROUP HEALTH PLAN** (SSN or ID) **FECA BLK LUNG** (SSN) **OTHER** (ID) | **1a. INSURED'S I.D. NUMBER** (For Program in Item 1)

2. PATIENT'S NAME (Last Name, First Name, Middle Initial) | **3. PATIENT'S BIRTH DATE** MM DD YY **SEX** M ☐ F ☐ | **4. INSURED'S NAME** (Last Name, First Name, Middle Initial)

5. PATIENT'S ADDRESS (No., Street) | **6. PATIENT RELATIONSHIP TO INSURED** Self ☐ Spouse ☐ Child ☐ Other ☐ | **7. INSURED'S ADDRESS** (No., Street)

CITY **STATE** | **8. PATIENT STATUS** Single ☐ Married ☐ Other ☐ | **CITY** **STATE**

ZIP CODE **TELEPHONE (Include Area Code)** ( ) | Employed ☐ Full-Time Student ☐ Part-Time Student ☐ | **ZIP CODE** **TELEPHONE (Include Area Code)** ( )

9. OTHER INSURED'S NAME (Last Name, First Name, Middle Initial) | **10. IS PATIENT'S CONDITION RELATED TO:** | **11. INSURED'S POLICY GROUP OR FECA NUMBER**

a. OTHER INSURED'S POLICY OR GROUP NUMBER | **a. EMPLOYMENT? (Current or Previous)** YES ☐ NO ☐ | **a. INSURED'S DATE OF BIRTH** MM DD YY **SEX** M ☐ F ☐

b. OTHER INSURED'S DATE OF BIRTH MM DD YY **SEX** M ☐ F ☐ | **b. AUTO ACCIDENT?** YES ☐ NO ☐ **PLACE (State)** | **b. EMPLOYER'S NAME OR SCHOOL NAME**

c. EMPLOYER'S NAME OR SCHOOL NAME | **c. OTHER ACCIDENT?** YES ☐ NO ☐ | **c. INSURANCE PLAN NAME OR PROGRAM NAME**

d. INSURANCE PLAN NAME OR PROGRAM NAME | **10d. RESERVED FOR LOCAL USE** | **d. IS THERE ANOTHER HEALTH BENEFIT PLAN?** YES ☐ NO ☐ If yes, return to and complete item 9 a-d.

READ BACK OF FORM BEFORE COMPLETING & SIGNING THIS FORM.

12. PATIENT'S OR AUTHORIZED PERSON'S SIGNATURE I authorize the release of any medical or other information necessary to process this claim. I also request payment of government benefits either to myself or to the party who accepts assignment below.

SIGNED_____ DATE_____

13. INSURED'S OR AUTHORIZED PERSON'S SIGNATURE I authorize payment of medical benefits to the undersigned physician or supplier for services described below.

SIGNED_____

14. DATE OF CURRENT: MM DD YY **ILLNESS (First symptom) OR INJURY (Accident) OR PREGNANCY(LMP)** | **15. IF PATIENT HAS HAD SAME OR SIMILAR ILLNESS. GIVE FIRST DATE** MM DD YY | **16. DATES PATIENT UNABLE TO WORK IN CURRENT OCCUPATION** MM DD YY FROM TO MM DD YY

17. NAME OF REFERRING PROVIDER OR OTHER SOURCE | **17a.** **17b. NPI** | **18. HOSPITALIZATION DATES RELATED TO CURRENT SERVICES** MM DD YY FROM TO MM DD YY

19. RESERVED FOR LOCAL USE | **20. OUTSIDE LAB?** YES ☐ NO ☐ **$ CHARGES**

21. DIAGNOSIS OR NATURE OF ILLNESS OR INJURY (Relate Items 1, 2, 9 or 4 to Item 24E by Line)
1. ____.____   3. ____.____
2. ____.____   4. ____.____
| **22. MEDICAID RESUBMISSION CODE** **ORIGINAL REF. NO.**

23. PRIOR AUTHORIZATION NUMBER

24. A. DATE(S) OF SERVICE		B. PLACE OF SERVICE	C. EMG	D. PROCEDURES, SERVICES, OR SUPPLIES (Explain Unusual Circumstances)		E. DIAGNOSIS POINTER	F. $ CHARGES	G. DAYS OR UNITS	H. EPSDT Family Plan	I. ID. QUAL.	J. RENDERING PROVIDER ID. #
From MM DD YY	To MM DD YY			CPT/HCPCS	MODIFIER						
1										NPI	
2										NPI	
3										NPI	
4										NPI	
5										NPI	
6										NPI	

25. FEDERAL TAX I.D. NUMBER SSN ☐ EIN ☐ | **26. PATIENT'S ACCOUNT NO.** | **27. ACCEPT ASSIGNMENT?** (For govt. claims, see back) YES ☐ NO ☐ | **28. TOTAL CHARGE** $ | **29. AMOUNT PAID** $ | **30. BALANCE DUE** $

31. SIGNATURE OF PHYSICIAN OR SUPPLIER INCLUDING DEGREES OR CREDENTIALS (I certify that the statements on the reverse apply to this bill and are made a part thereof.) | **32. SERVICE FACILITY LOCATION INFORMATION** | **33. BILLING PROVIDER INFO & PH #** ( )

Name:_____

Class/Section:_____

cpTeach

Date:_____

2012

EXERCISE 10.8

As the head pathologist you are asked to do things that you sometimes wish you did not have to do. Today, you are asked to provide an autopsy on a patient who was stillborn. Since the pregnancy had gone so well and was full term and even up until yesterday the patient was reportedly fine in utero, the OB/GYN has requested on behalf of the family that you provide both a gross examination of the stillborn baby and a microscopic examination. Code for your services.

Before You Begin:
Read Chapter 10 in cpTeach® on "Pathology and Laboratory." Follow along in your CPT® codebook with the points illustrated in cpTeach®.

Purpose of this Lesson:
To familiarize the student with the Pathology and Laboratory section.

Instructions:
1. Code the following using the correct CPT® code. Write them up as you would on a CMS-1500 form located on the back of each exercise.

Notes: _____

_____

_____

_____

_____

_____

_____

EXERCISE 10.8

Name: _____

Class/Section: _____

Date: _____

cpTeach 2012

1500

HEALTH INSURANCE CLAIM FORM

APPROVED BY NATIONAL UNIFORM CLAIM COMMITTEE 08/05

| | PICA | | | | | | | | | | PICA | |

1. MEDICARE	MEDICAID	TRICARE CHAMPUS	CHAMPVA	GROUP HEALTH PLAN	FECA BLK LUNG	OTHER	1a. INSURED'S I.D. NUMBER	(For Program in Item 1)
(Medicare #)	(Medicaid #)	(Sponsor's SSN)	(Member ID#)	(SSN or ID)	(SSN)	(ID)		

2. PATIENT'S NAME (Last Name, First Name, Middle Initial)

3. PATIENT'S BIRTH DATE MM DD YY   SEX   M   F

4. INSURED'S NAME (Last Name, First Name, Middle Initial)

5. PATIENT'S ADDRESS (No., Street)

6. PATIENT RELATIONSHIP TO INSURED   Self   Spouse   Child   Other

7. INSURED'S ADDRESS (No., Street)

CITY   STATE

8. PATIENT STATUS   Single   Married   Other

CITY   STATE

ZIP CODE   TELEPHONE (Include Area Code) (   )

Employed   Full-Time Student   Part-Time Student

ZIP CODE   TELEPHONE (Include Area Code) (   )

9. OTHER INSURED'S NAME (Last Name, First Name, Middle Initial)

10. IS PATIENT'S CONDITION RELATED TO:

11. INSURED'S POLICY GROUP OR FECA NUMBER

a. OTHER INSURED'S POLICY OR GROUP NUMBER

a. EMPLOYMENT? (Current or Previous)   YES   NO

a. INSURED'S DATE OF BIRTH MM DD YY   SEX   M   F

b. OTHER INSURED'S DATE OF BIRTH MM DD YY   SEX   M   F

b. AUTO ACCIDENT?   YES   NO   PLACE (State)

b. EMPLOYER'S NAME OR SCHOOL NAME

c. EMPLOYER'S NAME OR SCHOOL NAME

c. OTHER ACCIDENT?   YES   NO

c. INSURANCE PLAN NAME OR PROGRAM NAME

d. INSURANCE PLAN NAME OR PROGRAM NAME

10d. RESERVED FOR LOCAL USE

d. IS THERE ANOTHER HEALTH BENEFIT PLAN?   YES   NO   If yes, return to and complete item 9 a-d.

READ BACK OF FORM BEFORE COMPLETING & SIGNING THIS FORM.

12. PATIENT'S OR AUTHORIZED PERSON'S SIGNATURE I authorize the release of any medical or other information necessary to process this claim. I also request payment of government benefits either to myself or to the party who accepts assignment below.

SIGNED _____ DATE _____

13. INSURED'S OR AUTHORIZED PERSON'S SIGNATURE I authorize payment of medical benefits to the undersigned physician or supplier for services described below.

SIGNED _____

14. DATE OF CURRENT: MM DD YY   ILLNESS (First symptom) OR INJURY (Accident) OR PREGNANCY(LMP)

15. IF PATIENT HAS HAD SAME OR SIMILAR ILLNESS. GIVE FIRST DATE MM DD YY

16. DATES PATIENT UNABLE TO WORK IN CURRENT OCCUPATION MM DD YY FROM   TO   MM DD YY

17. NAME OF REFERRING PROVIDER OR OTHER SOURCE

17a.

17b. NPI

18. HOSPITALIZATION DATES RELATED TO CURRENT SERVICES MM DD YY FROM   TO   MM DD YY

19. RESERVED FOR LOCAL USE

20. OUTSIDE LAB?   YES   NO $ CHARGES

21. DIAGNOSIS OR NATURE OF ILLNESS OR INJURY (Relate Items 1, 2, 9 or 4 to Item 24E by Line)

1. |___.___   3. |___.___

2. |___.___   4. |___.___

22. MEDICAID RESUBMISSION CODE   ORIGINAL REF. NO.

23. PRIOR AUTHORIZATION NUMBER

24. A. DATE(S) OF SERVICE						B. PLACE OF SERVICE	C. EMG	D. PROCEDURES, SERVICES, OR SUPPLIES (Explain Unusual Circumstances)		E. DIAGNOSIS POINTER	F. $ CHARGES	G. DAYS OR UNITS	H. EPSDT Family Plan	I. ID. QUAL.	J. RENDERING PROVIDER ID. #
From MM DD YY			To MM DD YY					CPT/HCPCS	MODIFIER						
1														NPI	
2														NPI	
3														NPI	
4														NPI	
5														NPI	
6														NPI	

25. FEDERAL TAX I.D. NUMBER   SSN EIN

26. PATIENT'S ACCOUNT NO.

27. ACCEPT ASSIGNMENT? (For govt. claims, see back)   YES   NO

28. TOTAL CHARGE $

29. AMOUNT PAID $

30. BALANCE DUE $

31. SIGNATURE OF PHYSICIAN OR SUPPLIER INCLUDING DEGREES OR CREDENTIALS (I certify that the statements on the reverse apply to this bill and are made a part thereof.)

32. SERVICE FACILITY LOCATION INFORMATION

33. BILLING PROVIDER INFO & PH # (   )

CARRIER — PATIENT AND INSURED INFORMATION — PHYSICIAN OR SUPPLIER INFORMATION

EXERCISE 10.9

You are called to the crime scene to see and provide a necropsy on the victim of a brutal rape and murder. Code for the service of making that visit to the scene.

Before You Begin:

Read Chapter 10 in cpTeach® on "Pathology and Laboratory." Follow along in your CPT® codebook with the points illustrated in cpTeach®.

Purpose of this Lesson:

To familiarize the student with the Pathology and Laboratory section.

Instructions:

1. Code the following using the correct CPT® code. Write them up as you would on a CMS-1500 form located on the back of each exercise.

Notes: _____

_____

_____

_____

_____

_____

_____

EXERCISE 10.9

Name:_____

Class/Section:_____

Date:_____

2012

1500
HEALTH INSURANCE CLAIM FORM
APPROVED BY NATIONAL UNIFORM CLAIM COMMITTEE 08/05

CARRIER

| | PICA | | | | | | | PICA | |

1. MEDICARE ☐ (Medicare #)   MEDICAID ☐ (Medicaid #)   TRICARE CHAMPUS ☐ (Sponsor's SSN)   CHAMPVA ☐ (Member ID#)   GROUP HEALTH PLAN ☐ (SSN or ID)   FECA BLK LUNG ☐ (SSN)   OTHER ☐ (ID)

1a. INSURED'S I.D. NUMBER   (For Program in Item 1)

2. PATIENT'S NAME (Last Name, First Name, Middle Initial)

3. PATIENT'S BIRTH DATE MM DD YY   SEX M ☐ F ☐

4. INSURED'S NAME (Last Name, First Name, Middle Initial)

5. PATIENT'S ADDRESS (No., Street)

6. PATIENT RELATIONSHIP TO INSURED   Self ☐ Spouse ☐ Child ☐ Other ☐

7. INSURED'S ADDRESS (No., Street)

CITY   STATE

8. PATIENT STATUS   Single ☐ Married ☐ Other ☐

CITY   STATE

ZIP CODE   TELEPHONE (Include Area Code) ( )

Employed ☐ Full-Time Student ☐ Part-Time Student ☐

ZIP CODE   TELEPHONE (Include Area Code) ( )

9. OTHER INSURED'S NAME (Last Name, First Name, Middle Initial)

10. IS PATIENT'S CONDITION RELATED TO:

11. INSURED'S POLICY GROUP OR FECA NUMBER

a. OTHER INSURED'S POLICY OR GROUP NUMBER

a. EMPLOYMENT? (Current or Previous) ☐ YES ☐ NO

a. INSURED'S DATE OF BIRTH MM DD YY   SEX M ☐ F ☐

b. OTHER INSURED'S DATE OF BIRTH MM DD YY   SEX M ☐ F ☐

b. AUTO ACCIDENT? ☐ YES ☐ NO   PLACE (State)

b. EMPLOYER'S NAME OR SCHOOL NAME

c. EMPLOYER'S NAME OR SCHOOL NAME

c. OTHER ACCIDENT? ☐ YES ☐ NO

c. INSURANCE PLAN NAME OR PROGRAM NAME

d. INSURANCE PLAN NAME OR PROGRAM NAME

10d. RESERVED FOR LOCAL USE

d. IS THERE ANOTHER HEALTH BENEFIT PLAN? ☐ YES ☐ NO   If yes, return to and complete item 9 a-d.

READ BACK OF FORM BEFORE COMPLETING & SIGNING THIS FORM.

12. PATIENT'S OR AUTHORIZED PERSON'S SIGNATURE I authorize the release of any medical or other information necessary to process this claim. I also request payment of government benefits either to myself or to the party who accepts assignment below.

SIGNED_____ DATE_____

13. INSURED'S OR AUTHORIZED PERSON'S SIGNATURE I authorize payment of medical benefits to the undersigned physician or supplier for services described below.

SIGNED_____

PATIENT AND INSURED INFORMATION

14. DATE OF CURRENT: MM DD YY ILLNESS (First symptom) OR INJURY (Accident) OR PREGNANCY(LMP)

15. IF PATIENT HAS HAD SAME OR SIMILAR ILLNESS. GIVE FIRST DATE MM DD YY

16. DATES PATIENT UNABLE TO WORK IN CURRENT OCCUPATION FROM MM DD YY TO MM DD YY

17. NAME OF REFERRING PROVIDER OR OTHER SOURCE

17a.
17b. NPI

18. HOSPITALIZATION DATES RELATED TO CURRENT SERVICES FROM MM DD YY TO MM DD YY

19. RESERVED FOR LOCAL USE

20. OUTSIDE LAB? ☐ YES ☐ NO $ CHARGES

21. DIAGNOSIS OR NATURE OF ILLNESS OR INJURY (Relate Items 1, 2, 9 or 4 to Item 24E by Line)

1. |___._____
2. |___._____
3. |___._____
4. |___._____

22. MEDICAID RESUBMISSION CODE   ORIGINAL REF. NO.

23. PRIOR AUTHORIZATION NUMBER

24. A. DATE(S) OF SERVICE						B. PLACE OF SERVICE	C. EMG	D. PROCEDURES, SERVICES, OR SUPPLIES (Explain Unusual Circumstances) CPT/HCPCS MODIFIER	E. DIAGNOSIS POINTER	F. $ CHARGES	G. DAYS OR UNITS	H. EPSDT Family Plan	I. ID. QUAL.	J. RENDERING PROVIDER ID. #
From MM	DD	YY	To MM	DD	YY									
1													NPI	
2													NPI	
3													NPI	
4													NPI	
5													NPI	
6													NPI	

25. FEDERAL TAX I.D. NUMBER   SSN ☐ EIN ☐

26. PATIENT'S ACCOUNT NO.

27. ACCEPT ASSIGNMENT? (For govt. claims, see back) ☐ YES ☐ NO

28. TOTAL CHARGE $

29. AMOUNT PAID $

30. BALANCE DUE $

31. SIGNATURE OF PHYSICIAN OR SUPPLIER INCLUDING DEGREES OR CREDENTIALS (I certify that the statements on the reverse apply to this bill and are made a part thereof.)

32. SERVICE FACILITY LOCATION INFORMATION

33. BILLING PROVIDER INFO & PH # ( )

PHYSICIAN OR SUPPLIER INFORMATION

Medicine

The Medicine section is the last major section of the CPT® codebook. All codes found in the Medicine section begin with the number 9 and the services found here are generally non-invasive, meaning you won't generally find incisions or excisions.

The codes found in the immunization subsection include the immune globulin product only. You must use an additional code (see 96365-96368, 96372, 96374-96375) to code for the administration of the components. Likewise, the codes found under the Vaccines, Toxoids subsection include the vaccine product only and need to be reported in addition to the code for the actual administration of the product (see 90476 through 90749).

Concerning therapeutic or diagnostic injections, many carriers allow the coder to bill for the actual administration of the drug using the code 96360 through 96379 *and* the supply of the drug using the HCPCS National Coding Manual. It is helpful to use the most specific codes for different injectables and supplies. This protects your physician's profile by locking in a specific dollar amount for a particular code. If you are coding an office visit on the same day as you provide an injection, Medicare will only allow you to be paid on the supply of the drug and the E/M service.

The Special Services, Procedures and Reports subsection of the Medicine section consists of codes 99000 through 99091. Examples of some of these codes are ones used to report inconvenience of services done after hours, on an emergency basis, or the handling and/or conveyance of specimens or devices. These codes are considered to be adjunct codes and go in addition to the codes for the basic services you provide.

Tip

Use of modifier -51 (Multiple Procedures) is not always necessary as some codes include both the supply and the procedure of administration (of the supply).

Remember to code for both the supply and the administration.

Tip

Remember that if you are also supplying any other medications (e.g., analgesics or antibiotics) to the patient at the time of the chemotherapy, you will need to get the codes from the hydration/therapeutic injections subsection (see codes 96360 through 96379) to code for this, as well as the codes for the supply of any medications.

Key

Supervised services do not require that the therapist be one-on-one with the patient for the entire time. In contrast, "constant attendance" that the therapist be with the patient one-on-one for the entire visit.

Tip

Remember: Make sure that you read and re-read all of the information in and around the codes so that you can pick the most accurate code possible.

CATEGORY II CODES

Added to the CPT® codebook in the 2004 version, the Category II codes are five-digit alphanumeric codes that have the last digit of the code as a letter of the alphabet. An example of a Category II code is shown below.

2000F   Blood pressure, measured (CKD, DM)

Copyright AMA, 2011

As you can see by looking at this code, the first digit begins with a number and the last digit ends with a letter. The use of the number and letter combination is helpful in distinguishing this code from a "regular" CPT® code that only contains numbers and a HCPCS National code (Level II code) that contains both alpha and numeric characters, but whose first digit begins with an alpha character.

The importance of the Category II codes found in CPT® is to help researchers identify certain procedures that take place during a normal Evaluation and Management visit, but which are normally inherent parts of the visit. Category II codes give the coder a way to identify some of the individual components of the office visit by providing a separate number that describes some of these components.

Currently there are no relative values established for these codes due to the facts described above: that is, because these codes are inherent parts of the Evaluation and Management codes, no separate relative values are necessary. Because there are no separate relative values (weighed measures used to determine the value and hence the price of a service or procedure) for these Category II codes, payment on them is highly unlikely. Additionally, the use of these codes is not required to "code correctly." One can code the regular Evaluation and Management codes and not code the Category II codes (even if the use of some of these would apply as in the example above) and still "code correctly."

CATEGORY III CODES

Category III codes are temporary codes that can be used by a variety of entities (e.g., insurance carriers, AMA, etc.) to measure usage of particular services. These codes are to be used in place of the unlisted procedure codes (usually found at the end of a section), if available. For example, if you provide a service for which there is no regular CPT® code but there is a Category III code, you should use the Category III code instead of the Unlisted Procedure code.

Category III codes may change every year if it is noticed that their usage by physicians is low, or if it is recognized that they are widely used and should be adopted within the regular text portion of the CPT® codebook. You will find a listing of the Category III codes at the end of the regular text of CPT® and right before the Appendices.

EXERCISE 11.1

Mr. Aurthur Pedic feels some strong radiating pain in his left arm and some severe shortness of breath. He also feels like someone is stepping on his chest. He relates this to his wife who suggests that they go to the emergency room. They get in the car, and just as they get to the hospital, Mr. Pedic stops breathing. The nurses come with the on-call physician and begin CPR on Mr. Pedic. The cardiac output measurements are interpreted and the blood gases are measured.

Before You Begin:
Read Chapter 11 in cpTeach® on "Medicine." Follow along in CPT® with the points illustrated in cpTeach®.

Purpose of this Lesson:
To help the student practice the concepts learned thus far and, in particular, to concentrate on those learned in the Medicine section.

Instructions:
1. Read each of the case studies below.

2. Select the correct codes needed for each. NOTE: Some of the cases may require more than one code.

3. Complete the CPT® portion of the CMS-1500 form located on the back of each exercise.

Notes: _____

_____

_____

_____

_____

_____

_____

EXERCISE **11.1**

WORKBOOK
cpTeach
Name:_____
Class/Section:_____
Date:_____
2012

1500

HEALTH INSURANCE CLAIM FORM

APPROVED BY NATIONAL UNIFORM CLAIM COMMITTEE 08/05

☐☐☐ PICA | PICA ☐☐☐

| 1. MEDICARE ☐ (Medicare #) | MEDICAID ☐ (Medicaid #) | TRICARE CHAMPUS ☐ (Sponsor's SSN) | CHAMPVA ☐ (Member ID#) | GROUP HEALTH PLAN ☐ (SSN or ID) | FECA BLK LUNG ☐ (SSN) | OTHER ☐ (ID) | 1a. INSURED'S I.D. NUMBER (For Program in Item 1) |

2. PATIENT'S NAME (Last Name, First Name, Middle Initial)

3. PATIENT'S BIRTH DATE MM DD YY   SEX M ☐ F ☐

4. INSURED'S NAME (Last Name, First Name, Middle Initial)

5. PATIENT'S ADDRESS (No., Street)

6. PATIENT RELATIONSHIP TO INSURED
Self ☐ Spouse ☐ Child ☐ Other ☐

7. INSURED'S ADDRESS (No., Street)

CITY | STATE

8. PATIENT STATUS
Single ☐ Married ☐ Other ☐
Employed ☐ Full-Time Student ☐ Part-Time Student ☐

CITY | STATE

ZIP CODE | TELEPHONE (Include Area Code) ( )

ZIP CODE | TELEPHONE (Include Area Code) ( )

9. OTHER INSURED'S NAME (Last Name, First Name, Middle Initial)

10. IS PATIENT'S CONDITION RELATED TO:

11. INSURED'S POLICY GROUP OR FECA NUMBER

a. OTHER INSURED'S POLICY OR GROUP NUMBER

a. EMPLOYMENT? (Current or Previous)
YES ☐ NO ☐

a. INSURED'S DATE OF BIRTH MM DD YY SEX M ☐ F ☐

b. OTHER INSURED'S DATE OF BIRTH MM DD YY SEX M ☐ F ☐

b. AUTO ACCIDENT? PLACE (State)
YES ☐ NO ☐

b. EMPLOYER'S NAME OR SCHOOL NAME

c. EMPLOYER'S NAME OR SCHOOL NAME

c. OTHER ACCIDENT?
YES ☐ NO ☐

c. INSURANCE PLAN NAME OR PROGRAM NAME

d. INSURANCE PLAN NAME OR PROGRAM NAME

10d. RESERVED FOR LOCAL USE

d. IS THERE ANOTHER HEALTH BENEFIT PLAN?
YES ☐ NO ☐ If yes, return to and complete item 9 a-d.

READ BACK OF FORM BEFORE COMPLETING & SIGNING THIS FORM.

12. PATIENT'S OR AUTHORIZED PERSON'S SIGNATURE I authorize the release of any medical or other information necessary to process this claim. I also request payment of government benefits either to myself or to the party who accepts assignment below.

SIGNED_____ DATE_____

13. INSURED'S OR AUTHORIZED PERSON'S SIGNATURE I authorize payment of medical benefits to the undersigned physician or supplier for services described below.

SIGNED_____

14. DATE OF CURRENT: MM DD YY ◄ ILLNESS (First symptom) OR INJURY (Accident) OR PREGNANCY(LMP)

15. IF PATIENT HAS HAD SAME OR SIMILAR ILLNESS. GIVE FIRST DATE MM DD YY

16. DATES PATIENT UNABLE TO WORK IN CURRENT OCCUPATION MM DD YY FROM   TO MM DD YY

17. NAME OF REFERRING PROVIDER OR OTHER SOURCE

17a. | 17b. NPI

18. HOSPITALIZATION DATES RELATED TO CURRENT SERVICES MM DD YY FROM   TO MM DD YY

19. RESERVED FOR LOCAL USE

20. OUTSIDE LAB? $ CHARGES
YES ☐ NO ☐

21. DIAGNOSIS OR NATURE OF ILLNESS OR INJURY (Relate Items 1, 2, 9 or 4 to Item 24E by Line)
1. |___.___
2. |___.___
3. |___.___
4. |___.___

22. MEDICAID RESUBMISSION CODE | ORIGINAL REF. NO.

23. PRIOR AUTHORIZATION NUMBER

24. A. DATE(S) OF SERVICE From MM DD YY To MM DD YY	B. PLACE OF SERVICE	C. EMG	D. PROCEDURES, SERVICES, OR SUPPLIES (Explain Unusual Circumstances) CPT/HCPCS MODIFIER	E. DIAGNOSIS POINTER	F. $ CHARGES	G. DAYS OR UNITS	H. EPSDT Family Plan	I. ID. QUAL.	J. RENDERING PROVIDER ID. #
1									NPI
2									NPI
3									NPI
4									NPI
5									NPI
6									NPI

25. FEDERAL TAX I.D. NUMBER SSN ☐ EIN ☐

26. PATIENT'S ACCOUNT NO.

27. ACCEPT ASSIGNMENT? (For govt. claims, see back) YES ☐ NO ☐

28. TOTAL CHARGE $

29. AMOUNT PAID $

30. BALANCE DUE $

31. SIGNATURE OF PHYSICIAN OR SUPPLIER INCLUDING DEGREES OR CREDENTIALS (I certify that the statements on the reverse apply to this bill and are made a part thereof.)

32. SERVICE FACILITY LOCATION INFORMATION

33. BILLING PROVIDER INFO & PH # ( )

CARRIER | PATIENT AND INSURED INFORMATION | PHYSICIAN OR SUPPLIER INFORMATION

Name:_____

Class/Section:_____

Date:_____

2012

EXERCISE 11.2

Mr. Mort Ality has been experiencing bouts of deep depression since his wife passed away in a recent car accident. He is sent to your office (a psychiatry office) for treatment. Today is the first day that you get to visit with Mr. Ality. During the visit, you spend 75-80 minutes with the patient and also provide medical evaluation and management services. Code for all services rendered.

Before You Begin:
Read Chapter 11 in cpTeach® on "Medicine." Follow along in CPT® with the points illustrated in cpTeach®.

Purpose of this Lesson:
To help the student practice the concepts learned thus far and, in particular, to concentrate on those learned in the Medicine section.

Instructions:

1. Read each of the case studies below.

2. Select the correct codes needed for each. NOTE: Some of the cases may require more than one code.

3. Complete the CPT® portion of the CMS-1500 form located on the back of each exercise.

Notes: _____

_____

_____

_____

_____

_____

_____

Name:_____

Class/Section:_____

cpTeach
2012

Date:_____

EXERCISE 11.2

1500

HEALTH INSURANCE CLAIM FORM

APPROVED BY NATIONAL UNIFORM CLAIM COMMITTEE 08/05

CARRIER

| PICA | | | | | | | | PICA | |

1. MEDICARE MEDICAID TRICARE CHAMPUS CHAMPVA GROUP HEALTH PLAN FECA BLK LUNG OTHER	1a. INSURED'S I.D. NUMBER (For Program in Item 1)
(Medicare #) (Medicaid #) (Sponsor's SSN) (Member ID#) (SSN or ID) (SSN) (ID)	

2. PATIENT'S NAME (Last Name, First Name, Middle Initial)	3. PATIENT'S BIRTH DATE MM DD YY SEX M F	4. INSURED'S NAME (Last Name, First Name, Middle Initial)

5. PATIENT'S ADDRESS (No., Street)	6. PATIENT RELATIONSHIP TO INSURED Self Spouse Child Other	7. INSURED'S ADDRESS (No., Street)
CITY STATE	8. PATIENT STATUS Single Married Other	CITY STATE
ZIP CODE TELEPHONE (Include Area Code) ( )	Employed Full-Time Student Part-Time Student	ZIP CODE TELEPHONE (Include Area Code) ( )

9. OTHER INSURED'S NAME (Last Name, First Name, Middle Initial)	10. IS PATIENT'S CONDITION RELATED TO:	11. INSURED'S POLICY GROUP OR FECA NUMBER
a. OTHER INSURED'S POLICY OR GROUP NUMBER	a. EMPLOYMENT? (Current or Previous) YES NO	a. INSURED'S DATE OF BIRTH MM DD YY SEX M F
b. OTHER INSURED'S DATE OF BIRTH MM DD YY SEX M F	b. AUTO ACCIDENT? PLACE (State) YES NO	b. EMPLOYER'S NAME OR SCHOOL NAME
c. EMPLOYER'S NAME OR SCHOOL NAME	c. OTHER ACCIDENT? YES NO	c. INSURANCE PLAN NAME OR PROGRAM NAME
d. INSURANCE PLAN NAME OR PROGRAM NAME	10d. RESERVED FOR LOCAL USE	d. IS THERE ANOTHER HEALTH BENEFIT PLAN? YES NO If yes, return to and complete item 9 a-d.

READ BACK OF FORM BEFORE COMPLETING & SIGNING THIS FORM.

12. PATIENT'S OR AUTHORIZED PERSON'S SIGNATURE I authorize the release of any medical or other information necessary to process this claim. I also request payment of government benefits either to myself or to the party who accepts assignment below. SIGNED _____ DATE _____	13. INSURED'S OR AUTHORIZED PERSON'S SIGNATURE I authorize payment of medical benefits to the undersigned physician or supplier for services described below. SIGNED _____

PATIENT AND INSURED INFORMATION

14. DATE OF CURRENT: MM DD YY ILLNESS (First symptom) OR INJURY (Accident) OR PREGNANCY(LMP)	15. IF PATIENT HAS HAD SAME OR SIMILAR ILLNESS. GIVE FIRST DATE MM DD YY	16. DATES PATIENT UNABLE TO WORK IN CURRENT OCCUPATION MM DD YY FROM TO MM DD YY
17. NAME OF REFERRING PROVIDER OR OTHER SOURCE	17a. 17b. NPI	18. HOSPITALIZATION DATES RELATED TO CURRENT SERVICES MM DD YY FROM TO MM DD YY
19. RESERVED FOR LOCAL USE		20. OUTSIDE LAB? YES NO $ CHARGES
21. DIAGNOSIS OR NATURE OF ILLNESS OR INJURY (Relate Items 1, 2, 9 or 4 to Item 24E by Line) 1. |____.____ 3. |____.____ 2. |____.____ 4. |____.____		22. MEDICAID RESUBMISSION CODE ORIGINAL REF. NO. 23. PRIOR AUTHORIZATION NUMBER

24. A. DATE(S) OF SERVICE						B. PLACE OF SERVICE	C. EMG	D. PROCEDURES, SERVICES, OR SUPPLIES (Explain Unusual Circumstances) CPT/HCPCS MODIFIER	E. DIAGNOSIS POINTER	F. $ CHARGES	G. DAYS OR UNITS	H. EPSDT Family Plan	I. ID QUAL.	J. RENDERING PROVIDER ID. #
From MM	DD	YY	To MM	DD	YY									
1													NPI	
2													NPI	
3													NPI	
4													NPI	
5													NPI	
6													NPI	

PHYSICIAN OR SUPPLIER INFORMATION

25. FEDERAL TAX I.D. NUMBER SSN EIN	26. PATIENT'S ACCOUNT NO.	27. ACCEPT ASSIGNMENT? (For govt. claims, see back) YES NO	28. TOTAL CHARGE $	29. AMOUNT PAID $	30. BALANCE DUE $
31. SIGNATURE OF PHYSICIAN OR SUPPLIER INCLUDING DEGREES OR CREDENTIALS (I certify that the statements on the reverse apply to this bill and are made a part thereof.)	32. SERVICE FACILITY LOCATION INFORMATION		33. BILLING PROVIDER INFO & PH # ( )		

WORKBOOK

cpTeach.

2012

Name:_____

Class/Section:_____

Date:_____

EXERCISE 11.3

Herb Ivor is complaining to his wife that he can no longer see as well as he used to. Since Mrs. Ivor is concerned about her husband, she decides to make an appointment with the local ophthalmologist. A new patient appointment is set and Mr. Ivor goes to see you. During the first visit, you determine his refractive state, provide a comprehensive history and exam, a general medical observation, external ophthalmological exams and some biomicroscopy. Code for all of these services.

Before You Begin:
Read Chapter 11 in cpTeach® on "Medicine." Follow along in CPT® with the points illustrated in cpTeach®.

Purpose of this Lesson:
To help the student practice the concepts learned thus far and, in particular, to concentrate on those learned in the Medicine section.

Instructions:
1. Read each of the case studies below.

2. Select the correct codes needed for each. NOTE: Some of the cases may require more than one code.

3. Complete the CPT® portion of the CMS-1500 form located on the back of each exercise.

Notes: _____

_____

_____

_____

_____

_____

_____

EXERCISE 11.3

Name:_____

Class/Section:_____

Date:_____

2012

1500

HEALTH INSURANCE CLAIM FORM

APPROVED BY NATIONAL UNIFORM CLAIM COMMITTEE 08/05

| | PICA | | | | | | PICA | | |

| 1. MEDICARE | MEDICAID | TRICARE CHAMPUS | CHAMPVA | GROUP HEALTH PLAN | FECA BLK LUNG | OTHER | 1a. INSURED'S I.D. NUMBER | (For Program in Item 1) |

(Medicare #) (Medicaid #) (Sponsor's SSN) (Member ID#) (SSN or ID) (SSN) (ID)

2. PATIENT'S NAME (Last Name, First Name, Middle Initial)

3. PATIENT'S BIRTH DATE MM DD YY SEX M F

4. INSURED'S NAME (Last Name, First Name, Middle Initial)

5. PATIENT'S ADDRESS (No., Street)

6. PATIENT RELATIONSHIP TO INSURED Self Spouse Child Other

7. INSURED'S ADDRESS (No., Street)

CITY STATE

8. PATIENT STATUS Single Married Other

CITY STATE

ZIP CODE TELEPHONE (Include Area Code) ( )

Employed Full-Time Student Part-Time Student

ZIP CODE TELEPHONE (Include Area Code) ( )

9. OTHER INSURED'S NAME (Last Name, First Name, Middle Initial)

10. IS PATIENT'S CONDITION RELATED TO:

11. INSURED'S POLICY GROUP OR FECA NUMBER

a. OTHER INSURED'S POLICY OR GROUP NUMBER

a. EMPLOYMENT? (Current or Previous) YES NO

a. INSURED'S DATE OF BIRTH MM DD YY SEX M F

b. OTHER INSURED'S DATE OF BIRTH MM DD YY SEX M F

b. AUTO ACCIDENT? PLACE (State) YES NO

b. EMPLOYER'S NAME OR SCHOOL NAME

c. EMPLOYER'S NAME OR SCHOOL NAME

c. OTHER ACCIDENT? YES NO

c. INSURANCE PLAN NAME OR PROGRAM NAME

d. INSURANCE PLAN NAME OR PROGRAM NAME

10d. RESERVED FOR LOCAL USE

d. IS THERE ANOTHER HEALTH BENEFIT PLAN? YES NO If yes, return to and complete item 9 a-d.

READ BACK OF FORM BEFORE COMPLETING & SIGNING THIS FORM.

12. PATIENT'S OR AUTHORIZED PERSON'S SIGNATURE I authorize the release of any medical or other information necessary to process this claim. I also request payment of government benefits either to myself or to the party who accepts assignment below.

SIGNED_____ DATE_____

13. INSURED'S OR AUTHORIZED PERSON'S SIGNATURE I authorize payment of medical benefits to the undersigned physician or supplier for services described below.

SIGNED_____

14. DATE OF CURRENT: MM DD YY ILLNESS (First symptom) OR INJURY (Accident) OR PREGNANCY(LMP)

15. IF PATIENT HAS HAD SAME OR SIMILAR ILLNESS. GIVE FIRST DATE MM DD YY

16. DATES PATIENT UNABLE TO WORK IN CURRENT OCCUPATION MM DD YY FROM TO MM DD YY

17. NAME OF REFERRING PROVIDER OR OTHER SOURCE

17a.

17b. NPI

18. HOSPITALIZATION DATES RELATED TO CURRENT SERVICES MM DD YY FROM TO MM DD YY

19. RESERVED FOR LOCAL USE

20. OUTSIDE LAB? YES NO $ CHARGES

21. DIAGNOSIS OR NATURE OF ILLNESS OR INJURY (Relate Items 1, 2, 3 or 4 to Item 24E by Line)

1. |___.___| 3. |___.___|

2. |___.___| 4. |___.___|

22. MEDICAID RESUBMISSION CODE ORIGINAL REF. NO.

23. PRIOR AUTHORIZATION NUMBER

24. A	DATE(S) OF SERVICE			B.	C.	D. PROCEDURES, SERVICES, OR SUPPLIES	E.	F.	G.	H.	I.	J.
	From		To	PLACE OF	EMG	(Explain Unusual Circumstances)	DIAGNOSIS		DAYS OR	EPSDT Family	ID.	RENDERING
MM DD YY		MM DD YY		SERVICE		CPT/HCPCS MODIFIER	POINTER	$ CHARGES	UNITS	Plan	QUAL.	PROVIDER ID. #
1											NPI	
2											NPI	
3											NPI	
4											NPI	
5											NPI	
6											NPI	

25. FEDERAL TAX I.D. NUMBER SSN EIN

26. PATIENT'S ACCOUNT NO.

27. ACCEPT ASSIGNMENT? (For govt. claims, see back) YES NO

28. TOTAL CHARGE $

29. AMOUNT PAID $

30. BALANCE DUE $

31. SIGNATURE OF PHYSICIAN OR SUPPLIER INCLUDING DEGREES OR CREDENTIALS (I certify that the statements on the reverse apply to this bill and are made a part thereof.)

32. SERVICE FACILITY LOCATION INFORMATION

33. BILLING PROVIDER INFO & PH # ( )

WORKBOOK	McGUFFEY	*Name:* _____
		Class/Section: _____
	cpTeach	*Date:* _____
	2012	

EXERCISE 11.4

Steff Noid is another patient who comes to your office. Steff is a 27-year-old male patient who is quickly climbing the corporate ladder. Steff is here to see you today, because he has been to see a personal coach who thinks that it would be good for him to update his image. In doing so, Steff wants to get contacts and also update his prescription as he has been using the computer a lot and is noticing that he can't see as well as he used to. Since Steff is an established patient, you provide a comprehensive history and exam, determine the refractive state and prescribe contacts and glasses. Code for all services.

Before You Begin:
Read Chapter 11 in cpTeach® on "Medicine." Follow along in CPT® with the points illustrated in cpTeach®.

Purpose of this Lesson:
To help the student practice the concepts learned thus far and, in particular, to concentrate on those learned in the Medicine section.

Instructions:
1. Read each of the case studies below.

2. Select the correct codes needed for each. NOTE: Some of the cases may require more than one code.

3. Complete the CPT® portion of the CMS-1500 form located on the back of each exercise.

Notes: _____
_____
_____
_____
_____
_____
_____

Name: _____

Class/Section: _____

Date: _____

2012

EXERCISE 11.4

1500
HEALTH INSURANCE CLAIM FORM
APPROVED BY NATIONAL UNIFORM CLAIM COMMITTEE 08/05

| | PICA | | | | | | | | | PICA | |

1. MEDICARE	MEDICAID	TRICARE CHAMPUS	CHAMPVA	GROUP HEALTH PLAN	FECA BLK LUNG	OTHER	1a. INSURED'S I.D. NUMBER	(For Program in Item 1)
(Medicare #)	(Medicaid #)	(Sponsor's SSN)	(Member ID#)	(SSN or ID)	(SSN)	(ID)		

2. PATIENT'S NAME (Last Name, First Name, Middle Initial)

3. PATIENT'S BIRTH DATE MM | DD | YY   **SEX**   M ☐ F ☐

4. INSURED'S NAME (Last Name, First Name, Middle Initial)

5. PATIENT'S ADDRESS (No., Street)

6. PATIENT RELATIONSHIP TO INSURED   Self ☐ Spouse ☐ Child ☐ Other ☐

7. INSURED'S ADDRESS (No., Street)

CITY   STATE

8. PATIENT STATUS   Single ☐ Married ☐ Other ☐

CITY   STATE

ZIP CODE   TELEPHONE (Include Area Code) (   )

Employed ☐ Full-Time Student ☐ Part-Time Student ☐

ZIP CODE   TELEPHONE (Include Area Code) (   )

9. OTHER INSURED'S NAME (Last Name, First Name, Middle Initial)

10. IS PATIENT'S CONDITION RELATED TO:

11. INSURED'S POLICY GROUP OR FECA NUMBER

a. OTHER INSURED'S POLICY OR GROUP NUMBER

a. EMPLOYMENT? (Current or Previous)   YES ☐ NO ☐

a. INSURED'S DATE OF BIRTH MM | DD | YY   SEX   M ☐ F ☐

b. OTHER INSURED'S DATE OF BIRTH MM | DD | YY   SEX   M ☐ F ☐

b. AUTO ACCIDENT?   PLACE (State)   YES ☐ NO ☐

b. EMPLOYER'S NAME OR SCHOOL NAME

c. EMPLOYER'S NAME OR SCHOOL NAME

c. OTHER ACCIDENT?   YES ☐ NO ☐

c. INSURANCE PLAN NAME OR PROGRAM NAME

d. INSURANCE PLAN NAME OR PROGRAM NAME

10d. RESERVED FOR LOCAL USE

d. IS THERE ANOTHER HEALTH BENEFIT PLAN?   YES ☐ NO ☐ If yes, return to and complete item 9 a-d.

READ BACK OF FORM BEFORE COMPLETING & SIGNING THIS FORM.
12. PATIENT'S OR AUTHORIZED PERSON'S SIGNATURE I authorize the release of any medical or other information necessary to process this claim. I also request payment of government benefits either to myself or to the party who accepts assignment below.

SIGNED _____   DATE _____

13. INSURED'S OR AUTHORIZED PERSON'S SIGNATURE I authorize payment of medical benefits to the undersigned physician or supplier for services described below.

SIGNED _____

14. DATE OF CURRENT: MM | DD | YY   ◄ ILLNESS (First symptom) OR INJURY (Accident) OR PREGNANCY(LMP)

15. IF PATIENT HAS HAD SAME OR SIMILAR ILLNESS. GIVE FIRST DATE MM | DD | YY

16. DATES PATIENT UNABLE TO WORK IN CURRENT OCCUPATION FROM MM | DD | YY TO MM | DD | YY

17. NAME OF REFERRING PROVIDER OR OTHER SOURCE

17a.
17b. NPI

18. HOSPITALIZATION DATES RELATED TO CURRENT SERVICES FROM MM | DD | YY TO MM | DD | YY

19. RESERVED FOR LOCAL USE

20. OUTSIDE LAB?   YES ☐ NO ☐ $ CHARGES

21. DIAGNOSIS OR NATURE OF ILLNESS OR INJURY (Relate Items 1, 2, 9 or 4 to Item 24E by Line)

1. |___.___| 3. |___.___|
2. |___.___| 4. |___.___|

22. MEDICAID RESUBMISSION CODE   ORIGINAL REF. NO.

23. PRIOR AUTHORIZATION NUMBER

24. A. DATE(S) OF SERVICE						B. PLACE OF SERVICE	C. EMG	D. PROCEDURES, SERVICES, OR SUPPLIES (Explain Unusual Circumstances)		E. DIAGNOSIS POINTER	F. $ CHARGES	G. DAYS OR UNITS	H. EPSDT Family Plan	I. ID. QUAL.	J. RENDERING PROVIDER ID. #
From MM	DD	YY	To MM	DD	YY			CPT/HCPCS	MODIFIER						
1														NPI	
2														NPI	
3														NPI	
4														NPI	
5														NPI	
6														NPI	

25. FEDERAL TAX I.D. NUMBER SSN ☐ EIN ☐

26. PATIENT'S ACCOUNT NO.

27. ACCEPT ASSIGNMENT? (For govt. claims, see back) YES ☐ NO ☐

28. TOTAL CHARGE $

29. AMOUNT PAID $

30. BALANCE DUE $

31. SIGNATURE OF PHYSICIAN OR SUPPLIER INCLUDING DEGREES OR CREDENTIALS (I certify that the statements on the reverse apply to this bill and are made a part thereof.)

32. SERVICE FACILITY LOCATION INFORMATION

33. BILLING PROVIDER INFO & PH # (   )

CARRIER

PATIENT AND INSURED INFORMATION

PHYSICIAN OR SUPPLIER INFORMATION

EXERCISE 11.5

Lance Sets is a 45-year-old patient who has been experiencing intermittent chest pain. His internist decides that Mr. Sets should receive an ECG. Your doctor places the 12 leads on Mr. Sets and provides a full interpretation and report. Code for the cardiography.

Before You Begin:
Read Chapter 11 in cpTeach® on "Medicine." Follow along in CPT® with the points illustrated in cpTeach®.

Purpose of this Lesson:
To help the student practice the concepts learned thus far and, in particular, to concentrate on those learned in the Medicine section.

Instructions:
1. Read each of the case studies below.

2. Select the correct codes needed for each. NOTE: Some of the cases may require more than one code.

3. Complete the CPT® portion of the CMS-1500 form located on the back of each exercise.

Notes: _____
_____
_____
_____
_____
_____
_____

EXERCISE 11.5

Name: _____

Class/Section: _____

cpTeach

Date: _____

2012

1500

HEALTH INSURANCE CLAIM FORM

APPROVED BY NATIONAL UNIFORM CLAIM COMMITTEE 08/05

| | PICA | | | | | | PICA | | |

1. MEDICARE MEDICAID TRICARE CHAMPUS CHAMPVA GROUP HEALTH PLAN FECA BLK LUNG OTHER
(Medicare #) (Medicaid #) (Sponsor's SSN) (Member ID#) (SSN or ID) (SSN) (ID)

1a. INSURED'S I.D. NUMBER (For Program in Item 1)

2. PATIENT'S NAME (Last Name, First Name, Middle Initial)

3. PATIENT'S BIRTH DATE MM DD YY **SEX** M F

4. INSURED'S NAME (Last Name, First Name, Middle Initial)

5. PATIENT'S ADDRESS (No., Street)

6. PATIENT RELATIONSHIP TO INSURED Self Spouse Child Other

7. INSURED'S ADDRESS (No., Street)

CITY   **STATE**

8. PATIENT STATUS Single Married Other

CITY   **STATE**

ZIP CODE   **TELEPHONE (Include Area Code)** ( )

Employed Full-Time Student Part-Time Student

ZIP CODE   **TELEPHONE (Include Area Code)** ( )

9. OTHER INSURED'S NAME (Last Name, First Name, Middle Initial)

10. IS PATIENT'S CONDITION RELATED TO:

11. INSURED'S POLICY GROUP OR FECA NUMBER

a. OTHER INSURED'S POLICY OR GROUP NUMBER

a. EMPLOYMENT? (Current or Previous) YES NO

a. INSURED'S DATE OF BIRTH MM DD YY **SEX** M F

b. OTHER INSURED'S DATE OF BIRTH MM DD YY **SEX** M F

b. AUTO ACCIDENT? YES NO **PLACE (State)**

b. EMPLOYER'S NAME OR SCHOOL NAME

c. EMPLOYER'S NAME OR SCHOOL NAME

c. OTHER ACCIDENT? YES NO

c. INSURANCE PLAN NAME OR PROGRAM NAME

d. INSURANCE PLAN NAME OR PROGRAM NAME

10d. RESERVED FOR LOCAL USE

d. IS THERE ANOTHER HEALTH BENEFIT PLAN? YES NO *If yes, return to and complete item 9 a-d.*

READ BACK OF FORM BEFORE COMPLETING & SIGNING THIS FORM.
12. PATIENT'S OR AUTHORIZED PERSON'S SIGNATURE I authorize the release of any medical or other information necessary to process this claim. I also request payment of government benefits either to myself or to the party who accepts assignment below.

SIGNED_____ DATE_____

13. INSURED'S OR AUTHORIZED PERSON'S SIGNATURE I authorize payment of medical benefits to the undersigned physician or supplier for services described below.

SIGNED_____

14. DATE OF CURRENT: MM DD YY **ILLNESS (First symptom) OR INJURY (Accident) OR PREGNANCY(LMP)**

15. IF PATIENT HAS HAD SAME OR SIMILAR ILLNESS. GIVE FIRST DATE MM DD YY

16. DATES PATIENT UNABLE TO WORK IN CURRENT OCCUPATION MM DD YY FROM TO MM DD YY

17. NAME OF REFERRING PROVIDER OR OTHER SOURCE

17a.
17b. NPI

18. HOSPITALIZATION DATES RELATED TO CURRENT SERVICES MM DD YY FROM TO MM DD YY

19. RESERVED FOR LOCAL USE

20. OUTSIDE LAB? YES NO **$ CHARGES**

21. DIAGNOSIS OR NATURE OF ILLNESS OR INJURY (Relate Items 1, 2, 9 or 4 to Item 24E by Line)

1. |___.___
2. |___.___
3. |___.___
4. |___.___

22. MEDICAID RESUBMISSION CODE   **ORIGINAL REF. NO.**

23. PRIOR AUTHORIZATION NUMBER

24. A. DATE(S) OF SERVICE						B. PLACE OF SERVICE	C. EMG	D. PROCEDURES, SERVICES, OR SUPPLIES (Explain Unusual Circumstances) CPT/HCPCS MODIFIER	E. DIAGNOSIS POINTER	F. $ CHARGES	G. DAYS OR UNITS	H. EPSDT Family Plan	I. ID. QUAL.	J. RENDERING PROVIDER ID. #
From MM	DD	YY	To MM	DD	YY									
1													NPI	
2													NPI	
3													NPI	
4													NPI	
5													NPI	
6													NPI	

25. FEDERAL TAX I.D. NUMBER SSN EIN

26. PATIENT'S ACCOUNT NO.

27. ACCEPT ASSIGNMENT? *(For govt. claims, see back)* YES NO

28. TOTAL CHARGE $

29. AMOUNT PAID $

30. BALANCE DUE $

31. SIGNATURE OF PHYSICIAN OR SUPPLIER INCLUDING DEGREES OR CREDENTIALS (I certify that the statements on the reverse apply to this bill and are made a part thereof.)

32. SERVICE FACILITY LOCATION INFORMATION

33. BILLING PROVIDER INFO & PH # ( )

CARRIER

PATIENT AND INSURED INFORMATION

PHYSICIAN OR SUPPLIER INFORMATION

Name:_____

Class/Section:_____

cpTeach
2012   Date:_____

EXERCISE 11.6

Mr. Pickett has really been feeling the allergies this year! He sneezes, coughs, has watery eyes, and seems to go crazy every time there is a cat around. His wife suggests that he get tested so that he can get some help with what she says are "allergies." Although a bit reluctant, Mr. Pickett comes to your office for the first time to receive a full workup. While there, your physician completes a comprehensive history finding out about Mr. Pickett's past, social, medical and family history, and a detailed exam by looking at Mr. Pickett's eyes, ears, nose and throat and examining his skin. Your doctor makes a decision of low complexity, and decides to run some allergy tests on Mr. Pickett. The nurse is summoned to run eight intradermal tests with allergenic extracts and to get the results back to the physician immediately. She reports back to the physician that Mr. Pickett tested positive to all eight tests. The results are explained to Mr. Pickett who is asked to come back in one week and begin receiving his allergen immunotherapy. Code for all of the services that were provided today.

Before You Begin:
Read Chapter 11 in cpTeach® on "Medicine." Follow along in CPT® with the points illustrated in cpTeach®.

Purpose of this Lesson:
To help the student practice the concepts learned thus far and, in particular, to concentrate on those learned in the Medicine section.

Instructions:
1. Read each of the case studies below.

2. Select the correct codes needed for each. NOTE: Some of the cases may require more than one code.

3. Complete the CPT® portion of the CMS-1500 form located on the back of each exercise.

Notes: _____

_____

_____

_____

_____

_____

_____

EXERCISE 11.6

1500

HEALTH INSURANCE CLAIM FORM

APPROVED BY NATIONAL UNIFORM CLAIM COMMITTEE 08/05

| | PICA | | | | | | | | | | PICA | |

1. MEDICARE	MEDICAID	TRICARE CHAMPUS	CHAMPVA	GROUP HEALTH PLAN	FECA BLK LUNG	OTHER	1a. INSURED'S I.D. NUMBER	(For Program in Item 1)
☐ (Medicare #)	☐ (Medicaid #)	☐ (Sponsor's SSN)	☐ (Member ID#)	☐ (SSN or ID)	☐ (SSN)	☐ (ID)		

2. PATIENT'S NAME (Last Name, First Name, Middle Initial)	3. PATIENT'S BIRTH DATE SEX	4. INSURED'S NAME (Last Name, First Name, Middle Initial)
	MM DD YY M ☐ F ☐	

5. PATIENT'S ADDRESS (No., Street)	6. PATIENT RELATIONSHIP TO INSURED	7. INSURED'S ADDRESS (No., Street)
	Self ☐ Spouse ☐ Child ☐ Other ☐	

CITY	STATE	8. PATIENT STATUS	CITY	STATE
		Single ☐ Married ☐ Other ☐		

ZIP CODE	TELEPHONE (Include Area Code) ( )	Employed ☐ Full-Time Student ☐ Part-Time Student ☐	ZIP CODE	TELEPHONE (Include Area Code) ( )

9. OTHER INSURED'S NAME (Last Name, First Name, Middle Initial)	10. IS PATIENT'S CONDITION RELATED TO:	11. INSURED'S POLICY GROUP OR FECA NUMBER

a. OTHER INSURED'S POLICY OR GROUP NUMBER	a. EMPLOYMENT? (Current or Previous) ☐ YES ☐ NO	a. INSURED'S DATE OF BIRTH MM DD YY SEX M ☐ F ☐

b. OTHER INSURED'S DATE OF BIRTH MM DD YY SEX M ☐ F ☐	b. AUTO ACCIDENT? PLACE (State) ☐ YES ☐ NO	b. EMPLOYER'S NAME OR SCHOOL NAME

c. EMPLOYER'S NAME OR SCHOOL NAME	c. OTHER ACCIDENT? ☐ YES ☐ NO	c. INSURANCE PLAN NAME OR PROGRAM NAME

d. INSURANCE PLAN NAME OR PROGRAM NAME	10d. RESERVED FOR LOCAL USE	d. IS THERE ANOTHER HEALTH BENEFIT PLAN? ☐ YES ☐ NO If yes, return to and complete item 9 a-d.

READ BACK OF FORM BEFORE COMPLETING & SIGNING THIS FORM.

12. PATIENT'S OR AUTHORIZED PERSON'S SIGNATURE I authorize the release of any medical or other information necessary to process this claim. I also request payment of government benefits either to myself or to the party who accepts assignment below.

SIGNED_____   DATE_____

13. INSURED'S OR AUTHORIZED PERSON'S SIGNATURE I authorize payment of medical benefits to the undersigned physician or supplier for services described below.

SIGNED_____

14. DATE OF CURRENT: MM DD YY ◄ ILLNESS (First symptom) OR INJURY (Accident) OR PREGNANCY(LMP)	15. IF PATIENT HAS HAD SAME OR SIMILAR ILLNESS. GIVE FIRST DATE MM DD YY	16. DATES PATIENT UNABLE TO WORK IN CURRENT OCCUPATION MM DD YY MM DD YY FROM TO

17. NAME OF REFERRING PROVIDER OR OTHER SOURCE	17a.	18. HOSPITALIZATION DATES RELATED TO CURRENT SERVICES MM DD YY MM DD YY
	17b. NPI	FROM TO

19. RESERVED FOR LOCAL USE	20. OUTSIDE LAB? $ CHARGES ☐ YES ☐ NO

21. DIAGNOSIS OR NATURE OF ILLNESS OR INJURY (Relate Items 1, 2, 9 or 4 to Item 24E by Line)	22. MEDICAID RESUBMISSION CODE ORIGINAL REF. NO.
1. |____.____ 3. |____.____	
2. |____.____ 4. |____.____	23. PRIOR AUTHORIZATION NUMBER

24. A. DATE(S) OF SERVICE From To MM DD YY MM DD YY	B. PLACE OF SERVICE	C. EMG	D. PROCEDURES, SERVICES, OR SUPPLIES (Explain Unusual Circumstances) CPT/HCPCS	MODIFIER	E. DIAGNOSIS POINTER	F. $ CHARGES	G. DAYS OR UNITS	H. EPSDT Family Plan	I. ID QUAL.	J. RENDERING PROVIDER ID. #
1										NPI
2										NPI
3										NPI
4										NPI
5										NPI
6										NPI

25. FEDERAL TAX I.D. NUMBER SSN EIN ☐ ☐	26. PATIENT'S ACCOUNT NO.	27. ACCEPT ASSIGNMENT? (For govt. claims, see back) ☐ YES ☐ NO	28. TOTAL CHARGE $	29. AMOUNT PAID $	30. BALANCE DUE $

31. SIGNATURE OF PHYSICIAN OR SUPPLIER INCLUDING DEGREES OR CREDENTIALS (I certify that the statements on the reverse apply to this bill and are made a part thereof.)	32. SERVICE FACILITY LOCATION INFORMATION	33. BILLING PROVIDER INFO & PH # ( )

CARRIER

PATIENT AND INSURED INFORMATION

PHYSICIAN OR SUPPLIER INFORMATION

Name:_____

Class/Section:_____

Date:_____

Workbook

cpTeach
2012

EXERCISE 11.7

The next week, Mr. Pickett returns for his immunotherapy. The nurse administers all eight injections that have been prepared in your office and sends Mr. Pickett home. None of these are stinging venoms.   Code for the services rendered today.

Before You Begin:
Read Chapter 11 in cpTeach® on "Medicine." Follow along in CPT® with the points illustrated in cpTeach®.

Purpose of this Lesson:
To help the student practice the concepts learned thus far and, in particular, to concentrate on those learned in the Medicine section.

Instructions:
1. Read each of the case studies below.

2. Select the correct codes needed for each. NOTE: Some of the cases may require more than one code.

3. Complete the CPT® portion of the CMS-1500 form located on the back of each exercise.

Notes: _____

_____

_____

_____

_____

_____

_____

EXERCISE 11.7

1500

HEALTH INSURANCE CLAIM FORM

APPROVED BY NATIONAL UNIFORM CLAIM COMMITTEE 08/05

| | PICA | | | | | | PICA | |

1. MEDICARE (Medicare #)   **MEDICAID** (Medicaid #)   **TRICARE CHAMPUS** (Sponsor's SSN)   **CHAMPVA** (Member ID#)   **GROUP HEALTH PLAN** (SSN or ID)   **FECA BLK LUNG** (SSN)   **OTHER** (ID)   **1a. INSURED'S I.D. NUMBER**   (For Program in Item 1)

2. PATIENT'S NAME (Last Name, First Name, Middle Initial)

3. PATIENT'S BIRTH DATE MM DD YY   **SEX** M ☐ F ☐

4. INSURED'S NAME (Last Name, First Name, Middle Initial)

5. PATIENT'S ADDRESS (No., Street)

6. PATIENT RELATIONSHIP TO INSURED   Self ☐ Spouse ☐ Child ☐ Other ☐

7. INSURED'S ADDRESS (No., Street)

CITY   **STATE**

8. PATIENT STATUS   Single ☐ Married ☐ Other ☐

CITY   **STATE**

ZIP CODE   **TELEPHONE (Include Area Code)** ( )

Employed ☐ Full-Time Student ☐ Part-Time Student ☐

ZIP CODE   **TELEPHONE (Include Area Code)** ( )

9. OTHER INSURED'S NAME (Last Name, First Name, Middle Initial)

10. IS PATIENT'S CONDITION RELATED TO:

11. INSURED'S POLICY GROUP OR FECA NUMBER

a. OTHER INSURED'S POLICY OR GROUP NUMBER

a. EMPLOYMENT? (Current or Previous) ☐ YES ☐ NO

a. INSURED'S DATE OF BIRTH MM DD YY   **SEX** M ☐ F ☐

b. OTHER INSURED'S DATE OF BIRTH MM DD YY   **SEX** M ☐ F ☐

b. AUTO ACCIDENT?   PLACE (State) ☐ YES ☐ NO

b. EMPLOYER'S NAME OR SCHOOL NAME

c. EMPLOYER'S NAME OR SCHOOL NAME

c. OTHER ACCIDENT? ☐ YES ☐ NO

c. INSURANCE PLAN NAME OR PROGRAM NAME

d. INSURANCE PLAN NAME OR PROGRAM NAME

10d. RESERVED FOR LOCAL USE

d. IS THERE ANOTHER HEALTH BENEFIT PLAN? ☐ YES ☐ NO   If yes, return to and complete item 9 a-d.

READ BACK OF FORM BEFORE COMPLETING & SIGNING THIS FORM.

12. PATIENT'S OR AUTHORIZED PERSON'S SIGNATURE I authorize the release of any medical or other information necessary to process this claim. I also request payment of government benefits either to myself or to the party who accepts assignment below.

SIGNED_____ DATE_____

13. INSURED'S OR AUTHORIZED PERSON'S SIGNATURE I authorize payment of medical benefits to the undersigned physician or supplier for services described below.

SIGNED_____

14. DATE OF CURRENT: MM DD YY   ILLNESS (First symptom) OR INJURY (Accident) OR PREGNANCY(LMP)

15. IF PATIENT HAS HAD SAME OR SIMILAR ILLNESS. GIVE FIRST DATE MM DD YY

16. DATES PATIENT UNABLE TO WORK IN CURRENT OCCUPATION FROM MM DD YY TO MM DD YY

17. NAME OF REFERRING PROVIDER OR OTHER SOURCE

17a.   17b. NPI

18. HOSPITALIZATION DATES RELATED TO CURRENT SERVICES FROM MM DD YY TO MM DD YY

19. RESERVED FOR LOCAL USE

20. OUTSIDE LAB? ☐ YES ☐ NO $ CHARGES

21. DIAGNOSIS OR NATURE OF ILLNESS OR INJURY (Relate Items 1, 2, 3 or 4 to Item 24E by Line)

1. |___.___   3. |___.___

2. |___.___   4. |___.___

22. MEDICAID RESUBMISSION CODE   ORIGINAL REF. NO.

23. PRIOR AUTHORIZATION NUMBER

24. A. DATE(S) OF SERVICE From MM DD YY — To MM DD YY	B. PLACE OF SERVICE	C. EMG	D. PROCEDURES, SERVICES, OR SUPPLIES (Explain Unusual Circumstances) CPT/HCPCS MODIFIER	E. DIAGNOSIS POINTER	F. $ CHARGES	G. DAYS OR UNITS	H. EPSDT Family Plan	I. ID. QUAL.	J. RENDERING PROVIDER ID. #
1									NPI
2									NPI
3									NPI
4									NPI
5									NPI
6									NPI

25. FEDERAL TAX I.D. NUMBER SSN ☐ EIN ☐

26. PATIENT'S ACCOUNT NO.

27. ACCEPT ASSIGNMENT? (For govt. claims, see back) ☐ YES ☐ NO

28. TOTAL CHARGE $

29. AMOUNT PAID $

30. BALANCE DUE $

31. SIGNATURE OF PHYSICIAN OR SUPPLIER INCLUDING DEGREES OR CREDENTIALS (I certify that the statements on the reverse apply to this bill and are made a part thereof.)

32. SERVICE FACILITY LOCATION INFORMATION

33. BILLING PROVIDER INFO & PH # ( )

CARRIER   PATIENT AND INSURED INFORMATION   PHYSICIAN OR SUPPLIER INFORMATION

Name:_____

Class/Section:_____

Date:_____

2012

EXERCISE 11.8

Pappy S. Mears has been receiving physical therapy for his back from your office for years. (Mr. Mears is really more of a hypochondriac than anything.) Anyway, upon orders from the physician, you are providing whirlpool treatment to Mr. Mears in one 1minute interval. Code for the service.

Before You Begin:
Read Chapter 11 in cpTeach® on "Medicine." Follow along in CPT® with the points illustrated in cpTeach®.

Purpose of this Lesson:
To help the student practice the concepts learned thus far and, in particular, to concentrate on those learned in the Medicine section.

Instructions:
1. Read each of the case studies below.

2. Select the correct codes needed for each. NOTE: Some of the cases may require more than one code.

3. Complete the CPT® portion of the CMS-1500 form located on the back of each exercise.

Notes: _____

_____

_____

_____

_____

_____

_____

Name: _____

Class/Section: _____

cpTeach

Date: _____

2012

EXERCISE 11.8

1500

HEALTH INSURANCE CLAIM FORM

APPROVED BY NATIONAL UNIFORM CLAIM COMMITTEE 08/05

CARRIER

| | PICA | | | | | | | PICA | | |

1. MEDICARE MEDICAID TRICARE CHAMPUS CHAMPVA GROUP HEALTH PLAN FECA BLK LUNG OTHER   1a. INSURED'S I.D. NUMBER (For Program in Item 1)

(Medicare #) (Medicaid #) (Sponsor's SSN) (Member ID#) (SSN or ID) (SSN) (ID)

2. PATIENT'S NAME (Last Name, First Name, Middle Initial)   3. PATIENT'S BIRTH DATE SEX   4. INSURED'S NAME (Last Name, First Name, Middle Initial)
MM   DD   YY   M   F

5. PATIENT'S ADDRESS (No., Street)   6. PATIENT RELATIONSHIP TO INSURED   7. INSURED'S ADDRESS (No., Street)

Self   Spouse   Child   Other

CITY   STATE   8. PATIENT STATUS   CITY   STATE

Single   Married   Other

ZIP CODE   TELEPHONE (Include Area Code)   ZIP CODE   TELEPHONE (Include Area Code)

(   )   Employed   Full-Time Student   Part-Time Student   (   )

9. OTHER INSURED'S NAME (Last Name, First Name, Middle Initial)   10. IS PATIENT'S CONDITION RELATED TO: 11. INSURED'S POLICY GROUP OR FECA NUMBER

a. OTHER INSURED'S POLICY OR GROUP NUMBER   a. EMPLOYMENT? (Current or Previous)   a. INSURED'S DATE OF BIRTH   SEX
MM   DD   YY   M   F
YES   NO

b. OTHER INSURED'S DATE OF BIRTH   SEX   b. AUTO ACCIDENT?   PLACE (State)   b. EMPLOYER'S NAME OR SCHOOL NAME
MM   DD   YY   M   F   YES   NO

c. EMPLOYER'S NAME OR SCHOOL NAME   c. OTHER ACCIDENT?   c. INSURANCE PLAN NAME OR PROGRAM NAME
YES   NO

d. INSURANCE PLAN NAME OR PROGRAM NAME   10d. RESERVED FOR LOCAL USE   d. IS THERE ANOTHER HEALTH BENEFIT PLAN?
YES   NO   If yes, return to and complete item 9 a-d.

READ BACK OF FORM BEFORE COMPLETING & SIGNING THIS FORM.
12. PATIENT'S OR AUTHORIZED PERSON'S SIGNATURE I authorize the release of any medical or other information necessary to process this claim. I also request payment of government benefits either to myself or to the party who accepts assignment below.   13. INSURED'S OR AUTHORIZED PERSON'S SIGNATURE I authorize payment of medical benefits to the undersigned physician or supplier for services described below.

SIGNED _____   DATE _____   SIGNED _____

PATIENT AND INSURED INFORMATION

14. DATE OF CURRENT: ILLNESS (First symptom) OR   15. IF PATIENT HAS HAD SAME OR SIMILAR ILLNESS.   16. DATES PATIENT UNABLE TO WORK IN CURRENT OCCUPATION
MM   DD   YY   INJURY (Accident) OR PREGNANCY(LMP)   GIVE FIRST DATE   MM   DD   YY   MM   DD   YY   MM   DD   YY
FROM   TO

17. NAME OF REFERRING PROVIDER OR OTHER SOURCE   17a.   18. HOSPITALIZATION DATES RELATED TO CURRENT SERVICES
MM   DD   YY   MM   DD   YY
17b. NPI   FROM   TO

19. RESERVED FOR LOCAL USE   20. OUTSIDE LAB? $ CHARGES
YES   NO

21. DIAGNOSIS OR NATURE OF ILLNESS OR INJURY (Relate Items 1, 2, 9 or 4 to Item 24E by Line)   22. MEDICAID RESUBMISSION CODE   ORIGINAL REF. NO.

1. |___.___| 3. |___.___|

23. PRIOR AUTHORIZATION NUMBER

2. |___.___| 4. |___.___|

24. A. DATE(S) OF SERVICE						B. PLACE OF SERVICE	C. EMG	D. PROCEDURES, SERVICES, OR SUPPLIES (Explain Unusual Circumstances)		E. DIAGNOSIS POINTER	F. $ CHARGES	G. DAYS OR UNITS	H. EPSDT Family Plan	I. ID. QUAL.	J. RENDERING PROVIDER ID. #
From			To					CPT/HCPCS	MODIFIER						
MM	DD	YY	MM	DD	YY										
1														NPI	
2														NPI	
3														NPI	
4														NPI	
5														NPI	
6														NPI	

25. FEDERAL TAX I.D. NUMBER   SSN EIN   26. PATIENT'S ACCOUNT NO.   27. ACCEPT ASSIGNMENT? (For govt. claims, see back)   28. TOTAL CHARGE   29. AMOUNT PAID   30. BALANCE DUE
YES   NO $ $ $

31. SIGNATURE OF PHYSICIAN OR SUPPLIER INCLUDING DEGREES OR CREDENTIALS (I certify that the statements on the reverse apply to this bill and are made a part thereof.)   32. SERVICE FACILITY LOCATION INFORMATION   33. BILLING PROVIDER INFO & PH # (   )

PHYSICIAN OR SUPPLIER INFORMATION

WORKBOOK

*Name:*_____

*Class/Section:*_____

cpTeach

*Date:*_____

2012

EXERCISE 11.9

Sandy Beach, a diabetic patient, is pregnant again. However, she is not tolerating this pregnancy as well as her last one, and she has been ordered to maintain strict bed rest and to monitor her contractions every 2 hours. As a home health nurse, you have been asked to provide her home-visit prenatal monitoring and assessment. Code for your services.

Before You Begin:
Read Chapter 11 in cpTeach® on "Medicine." Follow along in CPT® with the points illustrated in cpTeach®.

Purpose of this Lesson:
To help the student practice the concepts learned thus far and, in particular, to concentrate on those learned in the Medicine section.

Instructions:
1. Read each of the case studies below.

2. Select the correct codes needed for each. NOTE: Some of the cases may require more than one code.

3. Complete the CPT® portion of the CMS-1500 form located on the back of each exercise.

Notes: _____
_____
_____
_____
_____
_____
_____

EXERCISE 11.9

Name:_____

Class/Section:_____

Date:_____

WORKBOOK

cpTeach

2012

1500

HEALTH INSURANCE CLAIM FORM

APPROVED BY NATIONAL UNIFORM CLAIM COMMITTEE 08/05

CARRIER

	PICA							PICA	

1. MEDICARE   MEDICAID   TRICARE CHAMPUS   CHAMPVA   GROUP HEALTH PLAN   FECA BLK LUNG   OTHER   **1a.** INSURED'S I.D. NUMBER   (For Program in Item 1)

☐ (Medicare #) ☐ (Medicaid #) ☐ (Sponsor's SSN) ☐ (Member ID#) ☐ (SSN or ID) ☐ (SSN) ☐ (ID)

2. PATIENT'S NAME (Last Name, First Name, Middle Initial)   **3.** PATIENT'S BIRTH DATE   SEX   **4.** INSURED'S NAME (Last Name, First Name, Middle Initial)
MM   DD   YY   M ☐   F ☐

5. PATIENT'S ADDRESS (No., Street)   **6.** PATIENT RELATIONSHIP TO INSURED   **7.** INSURED'S ADDRESS (No., Street)
Self ☐   Spouse ☐   Child ☐   Other ☐

CITY   STATE   **8.** PATIENT STATUS   CITY   STATE
                                        Single ☐   Married ☐   Other ☐

ZIP CODE   TELEPHONE (Include Area Code)   ZIP CODE   TELEPHONE (Include Area Code)
                  (   )   Employed ☐ Full-Time Student ☐ Part-Time Student ☐   (   )

9. OTHER INSURED'S NAME (Last Name, First Name, Middle Initial)   **10.** IS PATIENT'S CONDITION RELATED TO: **11.** INSURED'S POLICY GROUP OR FECA NUMBER

a. OTHER INSURED'S POLICY OR GROUP NUMBER   **a.** EMPLOYMENT? (Current or Previous)   **a.** INSURED'S DATE OF BIRTH   SEX
                                                  ☐ YES   ☐ NO   MM   DD   YY   M ☐   F ☐

b. OTHER INSURED'S DATE OF BIRTH   SEX   **b.** AUTO ACCIDENT?   PLACE (State)   **b.** EMPLOYER'S NAME OR SCHOOL NAME
MM   DD   YY   M ☐   F ☐   ☐ YES   ☐ NO

c. EMPLOYER'S NAME OR SCHOOL NAME   **c.** OTHER ACCIDENT?   **c.** INSURANCE PLAN NAME OR PROGRAM NAME
                                          ☐ YES   ☐ NO

d. INSURANCE PLAN NAME OR PROGRAM NAME   **10d.** RESERVED FOR LOCAL USE   **d.** IS THERE ANOTHER HEALTH BENEFIT PLAN?
                                              ☐ YES   ☐ NO   If yes, return to and complete item 9 a-d.

READ BACK OF FORM BEFORE COMPLETING & SIGNING THIS FORM.

12. PATIENT'S OR AUTHORIZED PERSON'S SIGNATURE I authorize the release of any medical or other information necessary to process this claim. I also request payment of government benefits either to myself or to the party who accepts assignment below.

SIGNED_____   DATE_____

13. INSURED'S OR AUTHORIZED PERSON'S SIGNATURE I authorize payment of medical benefits to the undersigned physician or supplier for services described below.

SIGNED_____

PATIENT AND INSURED INFORMATION

14. DATE OF CURRENT: ILLNESS (First symptom) OR   **15.** IF PATIENT HAS HAD SAME OR SIMILAR ILLNESS.   **16.** DATES PATIENT UNABLE TO WORK IN CURRENT OCCUPATION
MM   DD   YY   INJURY (Accident) OR   GIVE FIRST DATE MM   DD   YY   MM   DD   YY   MM   DD   YY
              PREGNANCY(LMP)   FROM   TO

17. NAME OF REFERRING PROVIDER OR OTHER SOURCE   17a.   **18.** HOSPITALIZATION DATES RELATED TO CURRENT SERVICES
                                                     17b. NPI   MM   DD   YY   MM   DD   YY
                                                                 FROM   TO

19. RESERVED FOR LOCAL USE   **20.** OUTSIDE LAB? $ CHARGES
                                   ☐ YES   ☐ NO

21. DIAGNOSIS OR NATURE OF ILLNESS OR INJURY (Relate Items 1, 2, 3 or 4 to Item 24E by Line)
1. |___.___| 3. |___.___| **22.** MEDICAID RESUBMISSION CODE   ORIGINAL REF. NO.
2. |___.___| 4. |___.___| **23.** PRIOR AUTHORIZATION NUMBER

24. A. DATE(S) OF SERVICE						**B.** PLACE OF SERVICE	**C.** EMG	**D.** PROCEDURES, SERVICES, OR SUPPLIES (Explain Unusual Circumstances)		**E.** DIAGNOSIS POINTER	**F.** $ CHARGES	**G.** DAYS OR UNITS	**H.** EPSDT Family Plan	**I.** ID. QUAL.	**J.** RENDERING PROVIDER ID. #
From			To					CPT/HCPCS	MODIFIER						
MM	DD	YY	MM	DD	YY										
1														NPI	
2														NPI	
3														NPI	
4														NPI	
5														NPI	
6														NPI	

PHYSICIAN OR SUPPLIER INFORMATION

25. FEDERAL TAX I.D. NUMBER   SSN EIN   **26.** PATIENT'S ACCOUNT NO.   **27.** ACCEPT ASSIGNMENT? (For govt. claims, see back)   **28.** TOTAL CHARGE   **29.** AMOUNT PAID   **30.** BALANCE DUE
                              ☐ ☐   ☐ YES   ☐ NO $ $ $

31. SIGNATURE OF PHYSICIAN OR SUPPLIER INCLUDING DEGREES OR CREDENTIALS (I certify that the statements on the reverse apply to this bill and are made a part thereof.)   **32.** SERVICE FACILITY LOCATION INFORMATION   **33.** BILLING PROVIDER INFO & PH # (   )

WORKBOOK

*Name:*_____

*Class/Section:*_____

cpTeach

*Date:*_____

2012

EXERCISE 11.10

Ms. I. Sea wakes up one morning (after having a complete makeover the day before) and is unable to see clearly. Her vision is very cloudy, and she is obviously very concerned. She phones her ophthalmologist who asks her to come in immediately. Ms. Sea goes to the office where her doctor performs an expanded problem focused history and exam, reviews Ms. Sea's past medical history, prescribes some cortisone drops, and discusses Ms. Sea's condition with her. Ms. Sea is an established patient of this ophthalmologist.

Before You Begin:
Read Chapter 11 in cpTeach® on "Medicine." Follow along in CPT® with the points illustrated in cpTeach®.

Purpose of this Lesson:
To help the student practice the concepts learned thus far and, in particular, to concentrate on those learned in the Medicine section.

Instructions:
1. Read each of the case studies below.

2. Select the correct codes needed for each. NOTE: Some of the cases may require more than one code.

3. Complete the CPT® portion of the CMS-1500 form located on the back of each exercise.

Notes: _____

_____

_____

_____

_____

_____

_____

EXERCISE 11.10

Name:_____

Class/Section:_____

Date:_____

2012

1500

HEALTH INSURANCE CLAIM FORM

APPROVED BY NATIONAL UNIFORM CLAIM COMMITTEE 08/05

CARRIER

| | PICA | | | | | | PICA | |

1. MEDICARE	MEDICAID	TRICARE CHAMPUS	CHAMPVA	GROUP HEALTH PLAN	FECA BLK LUNG	OTHER	1a. INSURED'S I.D. NUMBER	(For Program in Item 1)
(Medicare #)	(Medicaid #)	(Sponsor's SSN)	(Member ID#)	(SSN or ID)	(SSN)	(ID)		

2. PATIENT'S NAME (Last Name, First Name, Middle Initial)

3. PATIENT'S BIRTH DATE   MM   DD   YY   SEX   M   F

4. INSURED'S NAME (Last Name, First Name, Middle Initial)

5. PATIENT'S ADDRESS (No., Street)

6. PATIENT RELATIONSHIP TO INSURED   Self   Spouse   Child   Other

7. INSURED'S ADDRESS (No., Street)

CITY   STATE

8. PATIENT STATUS   Single   Married   Other

CITY   STATE

ZIP CODE   TELEPHONE (Include Area Code) (   )

Employed   Full-Time Student   Part-Time Student

ZIP CODE   TELEPHONE (Include Area Code) (   )

9. OTHER INSURED'S NAME (Last Name, First Name, Middle Initial)

10. IS PATIENT'S CONDITION RELATED TO:

11. INSURED'S POLICY GROUP OR FECA NUMBER

a. OTHER INSURED'S POLICY OR GROUP NUMBER

a. EMPLOYMENT? (Current or Previous)   YES   NO

a. INSURED'S DATE OF BIRTH   MM   DD   YY   SEX   M   F

b. OTHER INSURED'S DATE OF BIRTH   MM   DD   YY   SEX   M   F

b. AUTO ACCIDENT?   YES   NO   PLACE (State)

b. EMPLOYER'S NAME OR SCHOOL NAME

c. EMPLOYER'S NAME OR SCHOOL NAME

c. OTHER ACCIDENT?   YES   NO

c. INSURANCE PLAN NAME OR PROGRAM NAME

d. INSURANCE PLAN NAME OR PROGRAM NAME

10d. RESERVED FOR LOCAL USE

d. IS THERE ANOTHER HEALTH BENEFIT PLAN?   YES   NO   If yes, return to and complete item 9 a-d.

READ BACK OF FORM BEFORE COMPLETING & SIGNING THIS FORM.

12. PATIENT'S OR AUTHORIZED PERSON'S SIGNATURE I authorize the release of any medical or other information necessary to process this claim. I also request payment of government benefits either to myself or to the party who accepts assignment below.

SIGNED_____   DATE_____

13. INSURED'S OR AUTHORIZED PERSON'S SIGNATURE I authorize payment of medical benefits to the undersigned physician or supplier for services described below.

SIGNED_____

14. DATE OF CURRENT: MM   DD   YY   ILLNESS (First symptom) OR INJURY (Accident) OR PREGNANCY(LMP)

15. IF PATIENT HAS HAD SAME OR SIMILAR ILLNESS. GIVE FIRST DATE   MM   DD   YY

16. DATES PATIENT UNABLE TO WORK IN CURRENT OCCUPATION   MM   DD   YY   TO   MM   DD   YY   FROM

17. NAME OF REFERRING PROVIDER OR OTHER SOURCE

17a.

17b. NPI

18. HOSPITALIZATION DATES RELATED TO CURRENT SERVICES   MM   DD   YY   TO   MM   DD   YY   FROM

19. RESERVED FOR LOCAL USE

20. OUTSIDE LAB?   YES   NO $ CHARGES

21. DIAGNOSIS OR NATURE OF ILLNESS OR INJURY (Relate Items 1, 2, 9 or 4 to Item 24E by Line)

1. |____.____   3. |____.____

2. |____.____   4. |____.____

22. MEDICAID RESUBMISSION CODE   ORIGINAL REF. NO.

23. PRIOR AUTHORIZATION NUMBER

24. A. DATE(S) OF SERVICE From			To			B. PLACE OF SERVICE	C. EMG	D. PROCEDURES, SERVICES, OR SUPPLIES (Explain Unusual Circumstances) CPT/HCPCS	MODIFIER	E. DIAGNOSIS POINTER	F. $ CHARGES	G. DAYS OR UNITS	H. EPSDT Family Plan	I. ID. QUAL.	J. RENDERING PROVIDER ID. #
MM	DD	YY	MM	DD	YY										
1														NPI	
2														NPI	
3														NPI	
4														NPI	
5														NPI	
6														NPI	

25. FEDERAL TAX I.D. NUMBER   SSN EIN

26. PATIENT'S ACCOUNT NO.

27. ACCEPT ASSIGNMENT? (For govt. claims, see back)   YES   NO

28. TOTAL CHARGE $

29. AMOUNT PAID $

30. BALANCE DUE $

31. SIGNATURE OF PHYSICIAN OR SUPPLIER INCLUDING DEGREES OR CREDENTIALS (I certify that the statements on the reverse apply to this bill and are made a part thereof.)

32. SERVICE FACILITY LOCATION INFORMATION

33. BILLING PROVIDER INFO & PH # (   )

PATIENT AND INSURED INFORMATION

PHYSICIAN OR SUPPLIER INFORMATION

Name:_____

Class/Section:_____

Date:_____

2012

EXERCISE 11.11

After three months, when Ms. Sea's condition is not better, Dr. I. M. Skinney decides that he should get another opinion. He sends Ms. Sea over to the university where one of the specialists takes a look. During the visit, the specialist evaluates the records sent by Dr. Skinney, examines Ms. Sea's eyes, records her chief complaint, and completes a brief history of Ms. Sea's illness. He makes a low complexity decision regarding Ms. Sea's probable diagnoses, prescribes a different kind of drops which will assist him in defining his diagnosis, and makes his recommendations to Dr. Skinney through preparation of a report. The specialist also requests that Ms. Sea come back in one week.

Before You Begin:
Read Chapter 11 in cpTeach® on "Medicine." Follow along in CPT® with the points illustrated in cpTeach®.

Purpose of this Lesson:
To help the student practice the concepts learned thus far and, in particular, to concentrate on those learned in the Medicine section.

Instructions:
1. Read each of the case studies below.

2. Select the correct codes needed for each. NOTE: Some of the cases may require more than one code.

3. Complete the CPT® portion of the CMS-1500 form located on the back of each exercise.

Notes: _____
_____
_____
_____
_____
_____
_____

EXERCISE 11.11

WORKBOOK

Name:_____

Class/Section:_____

cpTeach

Date:_____

2012

1500

HEALTH INSURANCE CLAIM FORM

APPROVED BY NATIONAL UNIFORM CLAIM COMMITTEE 08/05

CARRIER

| | PICA | | | | | | | PICA | |

| 1. MEDICARE (Medicare #) | MEDICAID (Medicaid #) | TRICARE CHAMPUS (Sponsor's SSN) | CHAMPVA (Member ID#) | GROUP HEALTH PLAN (SSN or ID) | FECA BLK LUNG (SSN) | OTHER (ID) | 1a. INSURED'S I.D. NUMBER (For Program in Item 1) |

| 2. PATIENT'S NAME (Last Name, First Name, Middle Initial) | 3. PATIENT'S BIRTH DATE MM DD YY SEX M ☐ F ☐ | 4. INSURED'S NAME (Last Name, First Name, Middle Initial) |

| 5. PATIENT'S ADDRESS (No., Street) | 6. PATIENT RELATIONSHIP TO INSURED Self ☐ Spouse ☐ Child ☐ Other ☐ | 7. INSURED'S ADDRESS (No., Street) |

| CITY   STATE | 8. PATIENT STATUS Single ☐ Married ☐ Other ☐ | CITY   STATE |

| ZIP CODE   TELEPHONE (Include Area Code) ( ) | Employed ☐ Full-Time Student ☐ Part-Time Student ☐ | ZIP CODE   TELEPHONE (Include Area Code) ( ) |

| 9. OTHER INSURED'S NAME (Last Name, First Name, Middle Initial) | 10. IS PATIENT'S CONDITION RELATED TO: | 11. INSURED'S POLICY GROUP OR FECA NUMBER |

| a. OTHER INSURED'S POLICY OR GROUP NUMBER | a. EMPLOYMENT? (Current or Previous) ☐ YES ☐ NO | a. INSURED'S DATE OF BIRTH MM DD YY SEX M ☐ F ☐ |

| b. OTHER INSURED'S DATE OF BIRTH MM DD YY SEX M ☐ F ☐ | b. AUTO ACCIDENT? PLACE (State) ☐ YES ☐ NO | b. EMPLOYER'S NAME OR SCHOOL NAME |

| c. EMPLOYER'S NAME OR SCHOOL NAME | c. OTHER ACCIDENT? ☐ YES ☐ NO | c. INSURANCE PLAN NAME OR PROGRAM NAME |

| d. INSURANCE PLAN NAME OR PROGRAM NAME | 10d. RESERVED FOR LOCAL USE | d. IS THERE ANOTHER HEALTH BENEFIT PLAN? ☐ YES ☐ NO If yes, return to and complete item 9 a-d. |

READ BACK OF FORM BEFORE COMPLETING & SIGNING THIS FORM.

PATIENT AND INSURED INFORMATION

12. PATIENT'S OR AUTHORIZED PERSON'S SIGNATURE I authorize the release of any medical or other information necessary to process this claim. I also request payment of government benefits either to myself or to the party who accepts assignment below.

SIGNED_____ DATE_____

13. INSURED'S OR AUTHORIZED PERSON'S SIGNATURE I authorize payment of medical benefits to the undersigned physician or supplier for services described below.

SIGNED_____

| 14. DATE OF CURRENT: MM DD YY ILLNESS (First symptom) OR INJURY (Accident) OR PREGNANCY(LMP) | 15. IF PATIENT HAS HAD SAME OR SIMILAR ILLNESS. GIVE FIRST DATE MM DD YY | 16. DATES PATIENT UNABLE TO WORK IN CURRENT OCCUPATION MM DD YY MM DD YY FROM TO |

| 17. NAME OF REFERRING PROVIDER OR OTHER SOURCE | 17a. 17b. NPI | 18. HOSPITALIZATION DATES RELATED TO CURRENT SERVICES MM DD YY MM DD YY FROM TO |

| 19. RESERVED FOR LOCAL USE | | 20. OUTSIDE LAB? ☐ YES ☐ NO $ CHARGES |

21. DIAGNOSIS OR NATURE OF ILLNESS OR INJURY (Relate Items 1, 2, 9 or 4 to Item 24E by Line)

1. |___.___   3. |___.___

2. |___.___   4. |___.___

| 22. MEDICAID RESUBMISSION CODE ORIGINAL REF. NO. |
| 23. PRIOR AUTHORIZATION NUMBER |

PHYSICIAN OR SUPPLIER INFORMATION

24. A. DATE(S) OF SERVICE From MM DD YY To MM DD YY	B. PLACE OF SERVICE	C. EMG	D. PROCEDURES, SERVICES, OR SUPPLIES (Explain Unusual Circumstances) CPT/HCPCS MODIFIER	E. DIAGNOSIS POINTER	F. $ CHARGES	G. DAYS OR UNITS	H. EPSDT Family Plan	I. ID. QUAL.	J. RENDERING PROVIDER ID. #
1								NPI	
2								NPI	
3								NPI	
4								NPI	
5								NPI	
6								NPI	

| 25. FEDERAL TAX I.D. NUMBER SSN ☐ EIN ☐ | 26. PATIENT'S ACCOUNT NO. | 27. ACCEPT ASSIGNMENT? (For govt. claims, see back) ☐ YES ☐ NO | 28. TOTAL CHARGE $ | 29. AMOUNT PAID $ | 30. BALANCE DUE $ |

| 31. SIGNATURE OF PHYSICIAN OR SUPPLIER INCLUDING DEGREES OR CREDENTIALS (I certify that the statements on the reverse apply to this bill and are made a part thereof.) | 32. SERVICE FACILITY LOCATION INFORMATION | 33. BILLING PROVIDER INFO & PH # ( ) |

WORKBOOK

McGUFFEY

cpTeach
Expert Medical Coding Made Easy!

Name:_____

Class/Section:_____

Date:_____

2012

EXERCISE 11.12

One week later, Ms. Sea returns. Upon examination, the specialist concludes (in a straightforward decision) that Ms. Sea does have iritis. The specialist prescribes some therapeutic drugs and sends Ms. Sea on her way.

Before You Begin:
Read Chapter 11 in cpTeach® on "Medicine." Follow along in CPT® with the points illustrated in cpTeach®.

Purpose of this Lesson:
To help the student practice the concepts learned thus far and, in particular, to concentrate on those learned in the Medicine section.

Instructions:
1. Read each of the case studies below.

2. Select the correct codes needed for each. NOTE: Some of the cases may require more than one code.

3. Complete the CPT® portion of the CMS-1500 form located on the back of each exercise.

Notes: _____
_____
_____
_____
_____
_____
_____

WORKBOOK

McGUFFEY

cpTeach
2012

Name:_____

Class/Section:_____

Date:_____

EXERCISE 11.12

1500

HEALTH INSURANCE CLAIM FORM

APPROVED BY NATIONAL UNIFORM CLAIM COMMITTEE 08/05

| | PICA | | | | | | | | PICA | | |

1. MEDICARE	MEDICAID	TRICARE CHAMPUS	CHAMPVA	GROUP HEALTH PLAN	FECA BLK LUNG	OTHER	1a. INSURED'S I.D. NUMBER	(For Program in Item 1)
(Medicare #)	(Medicaid #)	(Sponsor's SSN)	(Member ID#)	(SSN or ID)	(SSN)	(ID)		

2. PATIENT'S NAME (Last Name, First Name, Middle Initial)

3. PATIENT'S BIRTH DATE   MM   DD   YY   SEX   M   F

4. INSURED'S NAME (Last Name, First Name, Middle Initial)

5. PATIENT'S ADDRESS (No., Street)

6. PATIENT RELATIONSHIP TO INSURED   Self   Spouse   Child   Other

7. INSURED'S ADDRESS (No., Street)

CITY   STATE

8. PATIENT STATUS   Single   Married   Other

CITY   STATE

ZIP CODE   TELEPHONE (Include Area Code) (   )

Employed   Full-Time Student   Part-Time Student

ZIP CODE   TELEPHONE (Include Area Code) (   )

9. OTHER INSURED'S NAME (Last Name, First Name, Middle Initial)

10. IS PATIENT'S CONDITION RELATED TO:

11. INSURED'S POLICY GROUP OR FECA NUMBER

a. OTHER INSURED'S POLICY OR GROUP NUMBER

a. EMPLOYMENT? (Current or Previous)   YES   NO

a. INSURED'S DATE OF BIRTH   MM   DD   YY   SEX   M   F

b. OTHER INSURED'S DATE OF BIRTH   MM   DD   YY   SEX   M   F

b. AUTO ACCIDENT?   PLACE (State)   YES   NO

b. EMPLOYER'S NAME OR SCHOOL NAME

c. EMPLOYER'S NAME OR SCHOOL NAME

c. OTHER ACCIDENT?   YES   NO

c. INSURANCE PLAN NAME OR PROGRAM NAME

d. INSURANCE PLAN NAME OR PROGRAM NAME

10d. RESERVED FOR LOCAL USE

d. IS THERE ANOTHER HEALTH BENEFIT PLAN?   YES   NO   If yes, return to and complete item 9 a-d.

READ BACK OF FORM BEFORE COMPLETING & SIGNING THIS FORM.
12. PATIENT'S OR AUTHORIZED PERSON'S SIGNATURE I authorize the release of any medical or other information necessary to process this claim. I also request payment of government benefits either to myself or to the party who accepts assignment below.

SIGNED_____   DATE_____

13. INSURED'S OR AUTHORIZED PERSON'S SIGNATURE I authorize payment of medical benefits to the undersigned physician or supplier for services described below.

SIGNED_____

14. DATE OF CURRENT: MM   DD   YY   ILLNESS (First symptom) OR INJURY (Accident) OR PREGNANCY (LMP)

15. IF PATIENT HAS HAD SAME OR SIMILAR ILLNESS. GIVE FIRST DATE   MM   DD   YY

16. DATES PATIENT UNABLE TO WORK IN CURRENT OCCUPATION   FROM   MM   DD   YY   TO   MM   DD   YY

17. NAME OF REFERRING PROVIDER OR OTHER SOURCE

17a.
17b. NPI

18. HOSPITALIZATION DATES RELATED TO CURRENT SERVICES   FROM   MM   DD   YY   TO   MM   DD   YY

19. RESERVED FOR LOCAL USE

20. OUTSIDE LAB?   YES   NO $ CHARGES

21. DIAGNOSIS OR NATURE OF ILLNESS OR INJURY (Relate Items 1, 2, 9 or 4 to Item 24E by Line)

1. |___.___   3. |___.___
2. |___.___   4. |___.___

22. MEDICAID RESUBMISSION CODE   ORIGINAL REF. NO.

23. PRIOR AUTHORIZATION NUMBER

24. A. DATE(S) OF SERVICE						B. PLACE OF SERVICE	C. EMG	D. PROCEDURES, SERVICES, OR SUPPLIES (Explain Unusual Circumstances) CPT/HCPCS	MODIFIER	E. DIAGNOSIS POINTER	F. $ CHARGES	G. DAYS OR UNITS	H. EPSDT Family Plan	I. ID. QUAL.	J. RENDERING PROVIDER ID. #
From MM	DD	YY	To MM	DD	YY										
1														NPI	
2														NPI	
3														NPI	
4														NPI	
5														NPI	
6														NPI	

25. FEDERAL TAX I.D. NUMBER   SSN   EIN

26. PATIENT'S ACCOUNT NO.

27. ACCEPT ASSIGNMENT? (For govt. claims, see back)   YES   NO

28. TOTAL CHARGE $

29. AMOUNT PAID $

30. BALANCE DUE $

31. SIGNATURE OF PHYSICIAN OR SUPPLIER INCLUDING DEGREES OR CREDENTIALS (I certify that the statements on the reverse apply to this bill and are made a part thereof.)

32. SERVICE FACILITY LOCATION INFORMATION

33. BILLING PROVIDER INFO & PH # (   )

Name:_____

Class/Section:_____

cpTeach
2012   Date:_____

EXERCISE 11.13

Ms.Sea decides to continue her treatment with the specialist and returns to his office 2 weeks later. The specialist reevaluates Ms. Sea's condition, and completes an expanded problem focused history and exam to see if she has any other eye problems (e.g., poor vision, cataracts). He reviews her past records, makes a straightforward medical decision regarding her treatment, and discusses Ms. Sea's progress with her. Ms. Sea proves to be an inquisitive patient and has many questions. The doctor finds he has spent 40 minutes making sure that his diagnosis and instructions have been understood.

Before You Begin:
Read Chapter 11 in cpTeach® on "Medicine." Follow along in CPT® with the points illustrated in cpTeach®.

Purpose of this Lesson:
To help the student practice the concepts learned thus far and, in particular, to concentrate on those learned in the Medicine section.

Instructions:
1. Read each of the case studies below.

2. Select the correct codes needed for each. NOTE: Some of the cases may require more than one code.

3. Complete the CPT® portion of the CMS-1500 form located on the back of each exercise.

Notes: _____

_____

_____

_____

_____

_____

_____

EXERCISE 11.13

Name:_____

Class/Section:_____

Date:_____

2012

1500
HEALTH INSURANCE CLAIM FORM
APPROVED BY NATIONAL UNIFORM CLAIM COMMITTEE 08/05

| | PICA | PICA | |

1. MEDICARE   MEDICAID   TRICARE   CHAMPVA   GROUP   FECA   OTHER
CHAMPUS   HEALTH PLAN   BLK LUNG
(Medicare #) (Medicaid #) (Sponsor's SSN) (Member ID#) (SSN or ID) (SSN) (ID)

1a. INSURED'S I.D. NUMBER   (For Program in Item 1)

2. PATIENT'S NAME (Last Name, First Name, Middle Initial)

3. PATIENT'S BIRTH DATE   SEX
MM   DD   YY   M   F

4. INSURED'S NAME (Last Name, First Name, Middle Initial)

5. PATIENT'S ADDRESS (No., Street)

6. PATIENT RELATIONSHIP TO INSURED
Self   Spouse   Child   Other

7. INSURED'S ADDRESS (No., Street)

CITY   STATE

8. PATIENT STATUS
Single   Married   Other

CITY   STATE

ZIP CODE   TELEPHONE (Include Area Code)
(   )

Employed   Full-Time   Part-Time
Student   Student

ZIP CODE   TELEPHONE (Include Area Code)
(   )

9. OTHER INSURED'S NAME (Last Name, First Name, Middle Initial)

10. IS PATIENT'S CONDITION RELATED TO:

11. INSURED'S POLICY GROUP OR FECA NUMBER

a. OTHER INSURED'S POLICY OR GROUP NUMBER

a. EMPLOYMENT? (Current or Previous)
YES   NO

a. INSURED'S DATE OF BIRTH   SEX
MM   DD   YY   M   F

b. OTHER INSURED'S DATE OF BIRTH   SEX
MM   DD   YY   M   F

b. AUTO ACCIDENT?   PLACE (State)
YES   NO

b. EMPLOYER'S NAME OR SCHOOL NAME

c. EMPLOYER'S NAME OR SCHOOL NAME

c. OTHER ACCIDENT?
YES   NO

c. INSURANCE PLAN NAME OR PROGRAM NAME

d. INSURANCE PLAN NAME OR PROGRAM NAME

10d. RESERVED FOR LOCAL USE

d. IS THERE ANOTHER HEALTH BENEFIT PLAN?
YES   NO   If yes, return to and complete item 9 a-d.

READ BACK OF FORM BEFORE COMPLETING & SIGNING THIS FORM.
12. PATIENT'S OR AUTHORIZED PERSON'S SIGNATURE I authorize the release of any medical or other information necessary to process this claim. I also request payment of government benefits either to myself or to the party who accepts assignment below.

SIGNED_____ DATE_____

13. INSURED'S OR AUTHORIZED PERSON'S SIGNATURE I authorize payment of medical benefits to the undersigned physician or supplier for services described below.

SIGNED_____

14. DATE OF CURRENT: ILLNESS (First symptom) OR
MM   DD   YY   INJURY (Accident) OR
PREGNANCY(LMP)

15. IF PATIENT HAS HAD SAME OR SIMILAR ILLNESS.
GIVE FIRST DATE   MM   DD   YY

16. DATES PATIENT UNABLE TO WORK IN CURRENT OCCUPATION
MM   DD   YY   MM   DD   YY
FROM   TO

17. NAME OF REFERRING PROVIDER OR OTHER SOURCE

17a.

17b. NPI

18. HOSPITALIZATION DATES RELATED TO CURRENT SERVICES
MM   DD   YY   MM   DD   YY
FROM   TO

19. RESERVED FOR LOCAL USE

20. OUTSIDE LAB? $ CHARGES
YES   NO

21. DIAGNOSIS OR NATURE OF ILLNESS OR INJURY (Relate Items 1, 2, 3 or 4 to Item 24E by Line)

1. |____.____   3. |____.____

2. |____.____   4. |____.____

22. MEDICAID RESUBMISSION
CODE   ORIGINAL REF. NO.

23. PRIOR AUTHORIZATION NUMBER

24. A. DATE(S) OF SERVICE		B.	C.	D. PROCEDURES, SERVICES, OR SUPPLIES	E.	F.	G.	H.	I.	J.
From To		PLACE OF		(Explain Unusual Circumstances)	DIAGNOSIS		DAYS	EPSDT	ID.	RENDERING
MM DD YY MM DD YY		SERVICE	EMG	CPT/HCPCS MODIFIER	POINTER	$ CHARGES	OR UNITS	Family Plan	QUAL.	PROVIDER ID. #
1									NPI	
2									NPI	
3									NPI	
4									NPI	
5									NPI	
6									NPI	

25. FEDERAL TAX I.D. NUMBER   SSN EIN

26. PATIENT'S ACCOUNT NO.

27. ACCEPT ASSIGNMENT?
(For govt. claims, see back)
YES   NO

28. TOTAL CHARGE
$

29. AMOUNT PAID
$

30. BALANCE DUE
$

31. SIGNATURE OF PHYSICIAN OR SUPPLIER
INCLUDING DEGREES OR CREDENTIALS
(I certify that the statements on the reverse apply to this bill and are made a part thereof.)

32. SERVICE FACILITY LOCATION INFORMATION

33. BILLING PROVIDER INFO & PH # (   )

CARRIER

PATIENT AND INSURED INFORMATION

PHYSICIAN OR SUPPLIER INFORMATION

WORKBOOK

cpTeach
Expert Medical Coding Made Easy!
2012

Name:_____

Class/Section:_____

Date:_____

EXERCISE 11.14

Mrs. Tally brings her grandson, Tanner, to Dr. Primeaux's office for his second tetanus immunization. The nurse administers the immunization under Dr. Primeaux's supervision.

Before You Begin:
Read Chapter 11 in cpTeach® on "Medicine." Follow along in CPT® with the points illustrated in cpTeach®.

Purpose of this Lesson:
To help the student practice the concepts learned thus far and, in particular, to concentrate on those learned in the Medicine section.

Instructions:
1. Read each of the case studies below.

2. Select the correct codes needed for each. NOTE: Some of the cases may require more than one code.

3. Complete the CPT® portion of the CMS-1500 form located on the back of each exercise.

Notes: _____
_____
_____
_____
_____
_____
_____

EXERCISE 11.14

WORKBOOK

cpTeach

2012

Name:_____

Class/Section:_____

Date:_____

CARRIER

1500

HEALTH INSURANCE CLAIM FORM

APPROVED BY NATIONAL UNIFORM CLAIM COMMITTEE 08/05

☐☐ PICA   PICA ☐☐

1. MEDICARE ☐(Medicare #)   MEDICAID ☐(Medicaid #)   TRICARE CHAMPUS ☐(Sponsor's SSN)   CHAMPVA ☐(Member ID#)   GROUP HEALTH PLAN ☐(SSN or ID)   FECA BLK LUNG ☐(SSN)   OTHER ☐(ID)   1a. INSURED'S I.D. NUMBER   (For Program in Item 1)

2. PATIENT'S NAME (Last Name, First Name, Middle Initial)   3. PATIENT'S BIRTH DATE MM ¦ DD ¦ YY   SEX M☐ F☐   4. INSURED'S NAME (Last Name, First Name, Middle Initial)

5. PATIENT'S ADDRESS (No., Street)   6. PATIENT RELATIONSHIP TO INSURED   Self☐ Spouse☐ Child☐ Other☐   7. INSURED'S ADDRESS (No., Street)

CITY   STATE   8. PATIENT STATUS   Single☐ Married☐ Other☐   CITY   STATE

ZIP CODE   TELEPHONE (Include Area Code) ( )   Employed☐ Full-Time Student☐ Part-Time Student☐   ZIP CODE   TELEPHONE (Include Area Code) ( )

9. OTHER INSURED'S NAME (Last Name, First Name, Middle Initial)   10. IS PATIENT'S CONDITION RELATED TO: 11. INSURED'S POLICY GROUP OR FECA NUMBER

a. OTHER INSURED'S POLICY OR GROUP NUMBER   a. EMPLOYMENT? (Current or Previous) ☐YES ☐NO   a. INSURED'S DATE OF BIRTH MM ¦ DD ¦ YY   SEX M☐ F☐

b. OTHER INSURED'S DATE OF BIRTH MM ¦ DD ¦ YY   SEX M☐ F☐   b. AUTO ACCIDENT? ☐YES ☐NO   PLACE (State) ___   b. EMPLOYER'S NAME OR SCHOOL NAME

c. EMPLOYER'S NAME OR SCHOOL NAME   c. OTHER ACCIDENT? ☐YES ☐NO   c. INSURANCE PLAN NAME OR PROGRAM NAME

d. INSURANCE PLAN NAME OR PROGRAM NAME   10d. RESERVED FOR LOCAL USE   d. IS THERE ANOTHER HEALTH BENEFIT PLAN? ☐YES ☐NO   If yes, return to and complete item 9 a-d.

READ BACK OF FORM BEFORE COMPLETING & SIGNING THIS FORM.
12. PATIENT'S OR AUTHORIZED PERSON'S SIGNATURE I authorize the release of any medical or other information necessary to process this claim. I also request payment of government benefits either to myself or to the party who accepts assignment below.

SIGNED_____ DATE_____

13. INSURED'S OR AUTHORIZED PERSON'S SIGNATURE I authorize payment of medical benefits to the undersigned physician or supplier for services described below.

SIGNED_____

14. DATE OF CURRENT: MM ¦ DD ¦ YY ◄ ILLNESS (First symptom) OR INJURY (Accident) OR PREGNANCY(LMP)   15. IF PATIENT HAS HAD SAME OR SIMILAR ILLNESS. GIVE FIRST DATE MM ¦ DD ¦ YY   16. DATES PATIENT UNABLE TO WORK IN CURRENT OCCUPATION MM ¦ DD ¦ YY FROM   TO MM ¦ DD ¦ YY

17. NAME OF REFERRING PROVIDER OR OTHER SOURCE   17a.   17b. NPI   18. HOSPITALIZATION DATES RELATED TO CURRENT SERVICES MM ¦ DD ¦ YY FROM   TO MM ¦ DD ¦ YY

19. RESERVED FOR LOCAL USE   20. OUTSIDE LAB? ☐YES ☐NO $ CHARGES

21. DIAGNOSIS OR NATURE OF ILLNESS OR INJURY (Relate Items 1, 2, 9 or 4 to Item 24E by Line)

1. |___.___   3. |___.___

2. |___.___   4. |___.___

22. MEDICAID RESUBMISSION CODE   ORIGINAL REF. NO.

23. PRIOR AUTHORIZATION NUMBER

24. A. DATE(S) OF SERVICE From			To			B. PLACE OF SERVICE	C. EMG	D. PROCEDURES, SERVICES, OR SUPPLIES (Explain Unusual Circumstances) CPT/HCPCS	MODIFIER	E. DIAGNOSIS POINTER	F. $ CHARGES	G. DAYS OR UNITS	H. EPSDT Family Plan	I. ID. QUAL.	J. RENDERING PROVIDER ID. #
MM	DD	YY	MM	DD	YY										
1														NPI	
2														NPI	
3														NPI	
4														NPI	
5														NPI	
6														NPI	

25. FEDERAL TAX I.D. NUMBER   SSN☐ EIN☐   26. PATIENT'S ACCOUNT NO.   27. ACCEPT ASSIGNMENT? (For govt. claims, see back) ☐YES ☐NO   28. TOTAL CHARGE $ 29. AMOUNT PAID $ 30. BALANCE DUE $

31. SIGNATURE OF PHYSICIAN OR SUPPLIER INCLUDING DEGREES OR CREDENTIALS (I certify that the statements on the reverse apply to this bill and are made a part thereof.)   32. SERVICE FACILITY LOCATION INFORMATION   33. BILLING PROVIDER INFO & PH # ( )

PATIENT AND INSURED INFORMATION   PHYSICIAN OR SUPPLIER INFORMATION

*Name:*_____

*Class/Section:*_____

*Date:*_____

EXERCISE 11.15

Manuel Labor comes to your facility for 45 minutes of massage treatment to his neck. The therapist treats Manuel under the doctor's supervision.

Before You Begin:
Read Chapter 11 in cpTeach® on "Medicine." Follow along in CPT® with the points illustrated in cpTeach®.

Purpose of this Lesson:
To help the student practice the concepts learned thus far and, in particular, to concentrate on those learned in the Medicine section.

Instructions:
1. Read each of the case studies below.

2. Select the correct codes needed for each. NOTE: Some of the cases may require more than one code.

3. Complete the CPT® portion of the CMS-1500 form located on the back of each exercise.

Notes: _____

_____

_____

_____

_____

_____

_____

EXERCISE 11.15

1500

HEALTH INSURANCE CLAIM FORM

APPROVED BY NATIONAL UNIFORM CLAIM COMMITTEE 08/05

| | PICA | | | | | | | | PICA | |

CARRIER

1. MEDICARE	MEDICAID	TRICARE CHAMPUS	CHAMPVA	GROUP HEALTH PLAN	FECA BLK LUNG	OTHER	1a. INSURED'S I.D. NUMBER	(For Program in Item 1)
(Medicare #)	(Medicaid #)	(Sponsor's SSN)	(Member ID#)	(SSN or ID)	(SSN)	(ID)		

2. PATIENT'S NAME (Last Name, First Name, Middle Initial)

3. PATIENT'S BIRTH DATE MM DD YY SEX M☐ F☐

4. INSURED'S NAME (Last Name, First Name, Middle Initial)

5. PATIENT'S ADDRESS (No., Street)

6. PATIENT RELATIONSHIP TO INSURED Self☐ Spouse☐ Child☐ Other☐

7. INSURED'S ADDRESS (No., Street)

CITY   STATE

8. PATIENT STATUS Single☐ Married☐ Other☐

CITY   STATE

ZIP CODE   TELEPHONE (Include Area Code) ( )

Employed☐ Full-Time Student☐ Part-Time Student☐

ZIP CODE   TELEPHONE (Include Area Code) ( )

9. OTHER INSURED'S NAME (Last Name, First Name, Middle Initial)

10. IS PATIENT'S CONDITION RELATED TO:

11. INSURED'S POLICY GROUP OR FECA NUMBER

a. OTHER INSURED'S POLICY OR GROUP NUMBER

a. EMPLOYMENT? (Current or Previous) ☐YES ☐NO

a. INSURED'S DATE OF BIRTH MM DD YY SEX M☐ F☐

b. OTHER INSURED'S DATE OF BIRTH MM DD YY SEX M☐ F☐

b. AUTO ACCIDENT? ☐YES ☐NO PLACE (State)

b. EMPLOYER'S NAME OR SCHOOL NAME

c. EMPLOYER'S NAME OR SCHOOL NAME

c. OTHER ACCIDENT? ☐YES ☐NO

c. INSURANCE PLAN NAME OR PROGRAM NAME

d. INSURANCE PLAN NAME OR PROGRAM NAME

10d. RESERVED FOR LOCAL USE

d. IS THERE ANOTHER HEALTH BENEFIT PLAN? ☐YES ☐NO If yes, return to and complete item 9 a-d.

PATIENT AND INSURED INFORMATION

READ BACK OF FORM BEFORE COMPLETING & SIGNING THIS FORM.

12. PATIENT'S OR AUTHORIZED PERSON'S SIGNATURE I authorize the release of any medical or other information necessary to process this claim. I also request payment of government benefits either to myself or to the party who accepts assignment below.

SIGNED_____ DATE_____

13. INSURED'S OR AUTHORIZED PERSON'S SIGNATURE I authorize payment of medical benefits to the undersigned physician or supplier for services described below.

SIGNED_____

14. DATE OF CURRENT: MM DD YY ILLNESS (First symptom) OR INJURY (Accident) OR PREGNANCY(LMP)

15. IF PATIENT HAS HAD SAME OR SIMILAR ILLNESS. GIVE FIRST DATE MM DD YY

16. DATES PATIENT UNABLE TO WORK IN CURRENT OCCUPATION MM DD YY MM DD YY FROM TO

17. NAME OF REFERRING PROVIDER OR OTHER SOURCE

17a.
17b. NPI

18. HOSPITALIZATION DATES RELATED TO CURRENT SERVICES MM DD YY MM DD YY FROM TO

19. RESERVED FOR LOCAL USE

20. OUTSIDE LAB? ☐YES ☐NO $ CHARGES

21. DIAGNOSIS OR NATURE OF ILLNESS OR INJURY (Relate Items 1, 2, 3 or 4 to Item 24E by Line)

1. _____ . _____
2. _____ . _____
3. _____ . _____
4. _____ . _____

22. MEDICAID RESUBMISSION CODE   ORIGINAL REF. NO.

23. PRIOR AUTHORIZATION NUMBER

24. A. DATE(S) OF SERVICE From MM DD YY To MM DD YY	B. PLACE OF SERVICE	C. EMG	D. PROCEDURES, SERVICES, OR SUPPLIES (Explain Unusual Circumstances) CPT/HCPCS MODIFIER	E. DIAGNOSIS POINTER	F. $ CHARGES	G. DAYS OR UNITS	H. EPSDT Family Plan	I. ID. QUAL.	J. RENDERING PROVIDER ID. #
1								NPI	
2								NPI	
3								NPI	
4								NPI	
5								NPI	
6								NPI	

PHYSICIAN OR SUPPLIER INFORMATION

25. FEDERAL TAX I.D. NUMBER   SSN EIN ☐☐

26. PATIENT'S ACCOUNT NO.

27. ACCEPT ASSIGNMENT? (For govt. claims, see back) ☐YES ☐NO

28. TOTAL CHARGE $

29. AMOUNT PAID $

30. BALANCE DUE $

31. SIGNATURE OF PHYSICIAN OR SUPPLIER INCLUDING DEGREES OR CREDENTIALS (I certify that the statements on the reverse apply to this bill and are made a part thereof.)

32. SERVICE FACILITY LOCATION INFORMATION

33. BILLING PROVIDER INFO & PH # ( )

McGUFFEY

*Name:*_____

*Class/Section:*_____

cpTeach *Date:*_____

2012

EXERCISE 11.16

Ms. Bea Worldy, a patient of Dr. Jones for years, comes to obtain a plague vaccine so that she can go on an expedition to South America. Dr. Jones' assistant administers the vaccine, and Bea promptly suffers a myocardial infarction. Dr. Jones sends for an ambulance and administers CPR for 10 minutes until the ambulance arrives.

Before You Begin:
Read Chapter 11 in cpTeach® on "Medicine." Follow along in CPT® with the points illustrated in cpTeach®.

Purpose of this Lesson:
To help the student practice the concepts learned thus far and, in particular, to concentrate on those learned in the Medicine section.

Instructions:
1. Read each of the case studies below.

2. Select the correct codes needed for each. NOTE: Some of the cases may require more than one code.

3. Complete the CPT® portion of the CMS-1500 form located on the back of each exercise.

Notes: _____
_____
_____
_____
_____
_____
_____

EXERCISE 11.16

1500

HEALTH INSURANCE CLAIM FORM

APPROVED BY NATIONAL UNIFORM CLAIM COMMITTEE 08/05

CARRIER

| | PICA | | | | | | PICA | | |

1. MEDICARE   MEDICAID   TRICARE CHAMPUS   CHAMPVA   GROUP HEALTH PLAN   FECA BLK LUNG   OTHER
(Medicare #)   (Medicaid #)   (Sponsor's SSN)   (Member ID#)   (SSN or ID)   (SSN)   (ID)

1a. INSURED'S I.D. NUMBER   (For Program in Item 1)

2. PATIENT'S NAME (Last Name, First Name, Middle Initial)

3. PATIENT'S BIRTH DATE   SEX
MM   DD   YY   M   F

4. INSURED'S NAME (Last Name, First Name, Middle Initial)

5. PATIENT'S ADDRESS (No., Street)

6. PATIENT RELATIONSHIP TO INSURED
Self   Spouse   Child   Other

7. INSURED'S ADDRESS (No., Street)

CITY   STATE

8. PATIENT STATUS
Single   Married   Other

CITY   STATE

ZIP CODE   TELEPHONE (Include Area Code)
( )

Employed   Full-Time Student   Part-Time Student

ZIP CODE   TELEPHONE (Include Area Code)
( )

9. OTHER INSURED'S NAME (Last Name, First Name, Middle Initial)

10. IS PATIENT'S CONDITION RELATED TO:

11. INSURED'S POLICY GROUP OR FECA NUMBER

a. OTHER INSURED'S POLICY OR GROUP NUMBER

a. EMPLOYMENT? (Current or Previous)
YES   NO

a. INSURED'S DATE OF BIRTH   SEX
MM   DD   YY   M   F

b. OTHER INSURED'S DATE OF BIRTH   SEX
MM   DD   YY   M   F

b. AUTO ACCIDENT?   PLACE (State)
YES   NO

b. EMPLOYER'S NAME OR SCHOOL NAME

c. EMPLOYER'S NAME OR SCHOOL NAME

c. OTHER ACCIDENT?
YES   NO

c. INSURANCE PLAN NAME OR PROGRAM NAME

d. INSURANCE PLAN NAME OR PROGRAM NAME

10d. RESERVED FOR LOCAL USE

d. IS THERE ANOTHER HEALTH BENEFIT PLAN?
YES   NO   If yes, return to and complete item 9 a-d.

READ BACK OF FORM BEFORE COMPLETING & SIGNING THIS FORM.
12. PATIENT'S OR AUTHORIZED PERSON'S SIGNATURE I authorize the release of any medical or other information necessary to process this claim. I also request payment of government benefits either to myself or to the party who accepts assignment below.

SIGNED_____ DATE_____

13. INSURED'S OR AUTHORIZED PERSON'S SIGNATURE I authorize payment of medical benefits to the undersigned physician or supplier for services described below.

SIGNED_____

PATIENT AND INSURED INFORMATION

14. DATE OF CURRENT: ILLNESS (First symptom) OR INJURY (Accident) OR PREGNANCY(LMP)
MM   DD   YY

15. IF PATIENT HAS HAD SAME OR SIMILAR ILLNESS. GIVE FIRST DATE   MM   DD   YY

16. DATES PATIENT UNABLE TO WORK IN CURRENT OCCUPATION
FROM   MM   DD   YY   TO   MM   DD   YY

17. NAME OF REFERRING PROVIDER OR OTHER SOURCE

17a.
17b. NPI

18. HOSPITALIZATION DATES RELATED TO CURRENT SERVICES
FROM   MM   DD   YY   TO   MM   DD   YY

19. RESERVED FOR LOCAL USE

20. OUTSIDE LAB? $ CHARGES
YES   NO

21. DIAGNOSIS OR NATURE OF ILLNESS OR INJURY (Relate Items 1, 2, 9 or 4 to Item 24E by Line)

1. |___.___
2. |___.___
3. |___.___
4. |___.___

22. MEDICAID RESUBMISSION CODE   ORIGINAL REF. NO.

23. PRIOR AUTHORIZATION NUMBER

24. A. DATE(S) OF SERVICE						B. PLACE OF SERVICE	C. EMG	D. PROCEDURES, SERVICES, OR SUPPLIES (Explain Unusual Circumstances)		E. DIAGNOSIS POINTER	F. $ CHARGES	G. DAYS OR UNITS	H. EPSDT Family Plan	I. ID. QUAL.	J. RENDERING PROVIDER ID. #
From			To					CPT/HCPCS	MODIFIER						
MM	DD	YY	MM	DD	YY										
1														NPI	
2														NPI	
3														NPI	
4														NPI	
5														NPI	
6														NPI	

25. FEDERAL TAX I.D. NUMBER   SSN EIN

26. PATIENT'S ACCOUNT NO.

27. ACCEPT ASSIGNMENT? (For govt. claims, see back)
YES   NO

28. TOTAL CHARGE
$

29. AMOUNT PAID
$

30. BALANCE DUE
$

31. SIGNATURE OF PHYSICIAN OR SUPPLIER INCLUDING DEGREES OR CREDENTIALS
(I certify that the statements on the reverse apply to this bill and are made a part thereof.)

32. SERVICE FACILITY LOCATION INFORMATION

33. BILLING PROVIDER INFO & PH # ( )

PHYSICIAN OR SUPPLIER INFORMATION

EXERCISE 11.17

Dr. I. M. Waiting is called to a 24-hour emergency room one Sunday at 11 p.m. to see Mr. Ura Gass. He races down there to examine Mr. Gass who is complaining of lower right abdominal pain. Dr. Waiting performs an expanded problem focused history and expanded problem focused exam, orders some blood tests and concludes, with a decision of low complexity (upon completion of the physical exam and review of the lab work), that Mr. Gass is having gas pains. Dr. Waiting has been Mr. Gass' family doctor for 20 years. Dr. Waiting was not on call.

Before You Begin:
Read Chapter 11 in cpTeach® on "Medicine." Follow along in CPT® with the points illustrated in cpTeach®.

Purpose of this Lesson:
To help the student practice the concepts learned thus far and, in particular, to concentrate on those learned in the Medicine section.

Instructions:
1. Read each of the case studies below.

2. Select the correct codes needed for each. NOTE: Some of the cases may require more than one code.

3. Complete the CPT® portion of the CMS-1500 form located on the back of each exercise.

Notes: _____
_____
_____
_____
_____
_____
_____

Name: _____

Class/Section: _____

Date: _____

2012

EXERCISE 11.17

[1500]

HEALTH INSURANCE CLAIM FORM

APPROVED BY NATIONAL UNIFORM CLAIM COMMITTEE 08/05

	PICA						PICA	

1. MEDICARE (Medicare #)   **MEDICAID** (Medicaid #)   **TRICARE CHAMPUS** (Sponsor's SSN)   **CHAMPVA** (Member ID#)   **GROUP HEALTH PLAN** (SSN or ID)   **FECA BLK LUNG** (SSN)   **OTHER** (ID)

1a. INSURED'S I.D. NUMBER (For Program in Item 1)

2. PATIENT'S NAME (Last Name, First Name, Middle Initial)

3. PATIENT'S BIRTH DATE MM DD YY   **SEX** M ☐ F ☐

4. INSURED'S NAME (Last Name, First Name, Middle Initial)

5. PATIENT'S ADDRESS (No., Street)

6. PATIENT RELATIONSHIP TO INSURED Self ☐ Spouse ☐ Child ☐ Other ☐

7. INSURED'S ADDRESS (No., Street)

CITY   STATE

8. PATIENT STATUS Single ☐ Married ☐ Other ☐

CITY   STATE

ZIP CODE   TELEPHONE (Include Area Code) ( )

Employed ☐ Full-Time Student ☐ Part-Time Student ☐

ZIP CODE   TELEPHONE (Include Area Code) ( )

9. OTHER INSURED'S NAME (Last Name, First Name, Middle Initial)

10. IS PATIENT'S CONDITION RELATED TO:

11. INSURED'S POLICY GROUP OR FECA NUMBER

a. OTHER INSURED'S POLICY OR GROUP NUMBER

a. EMPLOYMENT? (Current or Previous) ☐ YES ☐ NO

a. INSURED'S DATE OF BIRTH MM DD YY   **SEX** M ☐ F ☐

b. OTHER INSURED'S DATE OF BIRTH MM DD YY   **SEX** M ☐ F ☐

b. AUTO ACCIDENT? ☐ YES ☐ NO   PLACE (State)

b. EMPLOYER'S NAME OR SCHOOL NAME

c. EMPLOYER'S NAME OR SCHOOL NAME

c. OTHER ACCIDENT? ☐ YES ☐ NO

c. INSURANCE PLAN NAME OR PROGRAM NAME

d. INSURANCE PLAN NAME OR PROGRAM NAME

10d. RESERVED FOR LOCAL USE

d. IS THERE ANOTHER HEALTH BENEFIT PLAN? ☐ YES ☐ NO If yes, return to and complete item 9 a-d.

READ BACK OF FORM BEFORE COMPLETING & SIGNING THIS FORM.

12. PATIENT'S OR AUTHORIZED PERSON'S SIGNATURE I authorize the release of any medical or other information necessary to process this claim. I also request payment of government benefits either to myself or to the party who accepts assignment below.

SIGNED _____ DATE _____

13. INSURED'S OR AUTHORIZED PERSON'S SIGNATURE I authorize payment of medical benefits to the undersigned physician or supplier for services described below.

SIGNED _____

14. DATE OF CURRENT: MM DD YY ILLNESS (First symptom) OR INJURY (Accident) OR PREGNANCY(LMP)

15. IF PATIENT HAS HAD SAME OR SIMILAR ILLNESS. GIVE FIRST DATE MM DD YY

16. DATES PATIENT UNABLE TO WORK IN CURRENT OCCUPATION FROM MM DD YY TO MM DD YY

17. NAME OF REFERRING PROVIDER OR OTHER SOURCE

17a.   17b. NPI

18. HOSPITALIZATION DATES RELATED TO CURRENT SERVICES FROM MM DD YY TO MM DD YY

19. RESERVED FOR LOCAL USE

20. OUTSIDE LAB? ☐ YES ☐ NO $ CHARGES

21. DIAGNOSIS OR NATURE OF ILLNESS OR INJURY (Relate Items 1, 2, 3 or 4 to Item 24E by Line)

1. |___.___   3. |___.___

2. |___.___   4. |___.___

22. MEDICAID RESUBMISSION CODE   ORIGINAL REF. NO.

23. PRIOR AUTHORIZATION NUMBER

24. A. DATE(S) OF SERVICE			B. PLACE OF SERVICE	C. EMG	D. PROCEDURES, SERVICES, OR SUPPLIES (Explain Unusual Circumstances)		E. DIAGNOSIS POINTER	F. $ CHARGES	G. DAYS OR UNITS	H. EPSDT Family Plan	I. ID. QUAL.	J. RENDERING PROVIDER ID. #
From MM DD YY	To MM DD YY				CPT/HCPCS	MODIFIER						
1											NPI	
2											NPI	
3											NPI	
4											NPI	
5											NPI	
6											NPI	

25. FEDERAL TAX I.D. NUMBER SSN ☐ EIN ☐

26. PATIENT'S ACCOUNT NO.

27. ACCEPT ASSIGNMENT? (For govt. claims, see back) ☐ YES ☐ NO

28. TOTAL CHARGE $

29. AMOUNT PAID $

30. BALANCE DUE $

31. SIGNATURE OF PHYSICIAN OR SUPPLIER INCLUDING DEGREES OR CREDENTIALS (I certify that the statements on the reverse apply to this bill and are made a part thereof.)

32. SERVICE FACILITY LOCATION INFORMATION

33. BILLING PROVIDER INFO & PH # ( )

CARRIER   PATIENT AND INSURED INFORMATION   PHYSICIAN OR SUPPLIER INFORMATION

WORKBOOK

cpTeach
2012

*Name:*_____

*Class/Section:*_____

*Date:*_____

EXERCISE 11.18

Mr. M.T. Plate returns to your office for his intramuscular injection of testosterone, 100 mg. Your nurse administers the injection, under the physician's supervision, and sends Mr. Plate home.

Before You Begin:
Read Chapter 11 in cpTeach® on "Medicine." Follow along in CPT® with the points illustrated in cpTeach®.

Purpose of this Lesson:
To help the student practice the concepts learned thus far and, in particular, to concentrate on those learned in the Medicine section.

Instructions:
1. Read each of the case studies below.

2. Select the correct codes needed for each. NOTE: Some of the cases may require more than one code.

3. Complete the CPT® portion of the CMS-1500 form located on the back of each exercise.

Notes: _____

_____

_____

_____

_____

_____

_____

EXERCISE 11.18

WORKBOOK

Name:_____

Class/Section:_____

cpTeach

Date:_____

2012

1500

HEALTH INSURANCE CLAIM FORM

APPROVED BY NATIONAL UNIFORM CLAIM COMMITTEE 08/05

CARRIER

PICA		PICA

1. MEDICARE   MEDICAID   TRICARE CHAMPUS   CHAMPVA   GROUP HEALTH PLAN   FECA BLK LUNG   OTHER   1a. INSURED'S I.D. NUMBER   (For Program in Item 1)
(Medicare #)   (Medicaid #)   (Sponsor's SSN)   (Member ID#)   (SSN or ID)   (SSN)   (ID)

2. PATIENT'S NAME (Last Name, First Name, Middle Initial)   3. PATIENT'S BIRTH DATE   MM   DD   YY   SEX   M   F   4. INSURED'S NAME (Last Name, First Name, Middle Initial)

5. PATIENT'S ADDRESS (No., Street)   6. PATIENT RELATIONSHIP TO INSURED   Self   Spouse   Child   Other   7. INSURED'S ADDRESS (No., Street)

CITY   STATE   8. PATIENT STATUS   Single   Married   Other   CITY   STATE

ZIP CODE   TELEPHONE (Include Area Code)   ( )   Employed   Full-Time Student   Part-Time Student   ZIP CODE   TELEPHONE (Include Area Code)   ( )

9. OTHER INSURED'S NAME (Last Name, First Name, Middle Initial)   10. IS PATIENT'S CONDITION RELATED TO: 11. INSURED'S POLICY GROUP OR FECA NUMBER

a. OTHER INSURED'S POLICY OR GROUP NUMBER   a. EMPLOYMENT? (Current or Previous)   YES   NO   a. INSURED'S DATE OF BIRTH   MM   DD   YY   SEX   M   F

b. OTHER INSURED'S DATE OF BIRTH   MM   DD   YY   SEX   M   F   b. AUTO ACCIDENT?   PLACE (State)   YES   NO   b. EMPLOYER'S NAME OR SCHOOL NAME

c. EMPLOYER'S NAME OR SCHOOL NAME   c. OTHER ACCIDENT?   YES   NO   c. INSURANCE PLAN NAME OR PROGRAM NAME

d. INSURANCE PLAN NAME OR PROGRAM NAME   10d. RESERVED FOR LOCAL USE   d. IS THERE ANOTHER HEALTH BENEFIT PLAN?   YES   NO   If yes, return to and complete Item 9 a-d.

READ BACK OF FORM BEFORE COMPLETING & SIGNING THIS FORM.
12. PATIENT'S OR AUTHORIZED PERSON'S SIGNATURE I authorize the release of any medical or other information necessary to process this claim. I also request payment of government benefits either to myself or to the party who accepts assignment below.

SIGNED_____ DATE_____

13. INSURED'S OR AUTHORIZED PERSON'S SIGNATURE I authorize payment of medical benefits to the undersigned physician or supplier for services described below.

SIGNED_____

PATIENT AND INSURED INFORMATION

14. DATE OF CURRENT: MM DD YY   ILLNESS (First symptom) OR INJURY (Accident) OR PREGNANCY (LMP)   15. IF PATIENT HAS HAD SAME OR SIMILAR ILLNESS. GIVE FIRST DATE MM DD YY   16. DATES PATIENT UNABLE TO WORK IN CURRENT OCCUPATION   MM DD YY   FROM   TO   MM DD YY

17. NAME OF REFERRING PROVIDER OR OTHER SOURCE   17a.   17b. NPI   18. HOSPITALIZATION DATES RELATED TO CURRENT SERVICES   MM DD YY   FROM   TO   MM DD YY

19. RESERVED FOR LOCAL USE   20. OUTSIDE LAB?   YES   NO $ CHARGES

21. DIAGNOSIS OR NATURE OF ILLNESS OR INJURY (Relate Items 1, 2, 9 or 4 to Item 24E by Line)
1. |___.___   3. |___.___
2. |___.___   4. |___.___

22. MEDICAID RESUBMISSION CODE   ORIGINAL REF. NO.

23. PRIOR AUTHORIZATION NUMBER

24. A. DATE(S) OF SERVICE						B. PLACE OF SERVICE	C. EMG	D. PROCEDURES, SERVICES, OR SUPPLIES (Explain Unusual Circumstances) CPT/HCPCS | MODIFIER	E. DIAGNOSIS POINTER	F. $ CHARGES	G. DAYS OR UNITS	H. EPSDT Family Plan	I. ID. QUAL.	J. RENDERING PROVIDER ID. #
From MM	DD	YY	To MM	DD	YY									
1													NPI	
2													NPI	
3													NPI	
4													NPI	
5													NPI	
6													NPI	

25. FEDERAL TAX I.D. NUMBER   SSN   EIN   26. PATIENT'S ACCOUNT NO.   27. ACCEPT ASSIGNMENT? (For govt. claims, see back)   YES   NO   28. TOTAL CHARGE $ 29. AMOUNT PAID $ 30. BALANCE DUE $

31. SIGNATURE OF PHYSICIAN OR SUPPLIER INCLUDING DEGREES OR CREDENTIALS (I certify that the statements on the reverse apply to this bill and are made a part thereof.)   32. SERVICE FACILITY LOCATION INFORMATION   33. BILLING PROVIDER INFO & PH # ( )

PHYSICIAN OR SUPPLIER INFORMATION

Name:_____

Class/Section:_____

cpTeach
2012
Date:_____

EXERCISE 11.19

Ms. Anne S. Thesia returns to your office for a postoperative follow-up check after her surgery 2 days ago. Your physician, Dr. I.M. Reddy, reevaluates Ms. Thesia and concludes that the surgery went well and that Ms. Thesia is progressing as expected.

Before You Begin:
Read Chapter 11 in cpTeach® on "Medicine." Follow along in CPT® with the points illustrated in cpTeach®.

Purpose of this Lesson:
To help the student practice the concepts learned thus far and, in particular, to concentrate on those learned in the Medicine section.

Instructions:
1. Read each of the case studies below.

2. Select the correct codes needed for each. NOTE: Some of the cases may require more than one code.

3. Complete the CPT® portion of the CMS-1500 form located on the back of each exercise.

Notes: _____

_____

_____

_____

_____

_____

_____

EXERCISE 11.19

1500

HEALTH INSURANCE CLAIM FORM

APPROVED BY NATIONAL UNIFORM CLAIM COMMITTEE 08/05

	PICA							PICA	

CARRIER

1. MEDICARE	MEDICAID	TRICARE CHAMPUS	CHAMPVA	GROUP HEALTH PLAN	FECA BLK LUNG	OTHER	1a. INSURED'S I.D. NUMBER	(For Program in Item 1)
(Medicare #)	(Medicaid #)	(Sponsor's SSN)	(Member ID#)	(SSN or ID)	(SSN)	(ID)		

2. PATIENT'S NAME (Last Name, First Name, Middle Initial)	3. PATIENT'S BIRTH DATE MM DD YY SEX M F	4. INSURED'S NAME (Last Name, First Name, Middle Initial)

5. PATIENT'S ADDRESS (No., Street)	6. PATIENT RELATIONSHIP TO INSURED Self Spouse Child Other	7. INSURED'S ADDRESS (No., Street)

CITY	STATE	9. PATIENT STATUS Single Married Other	CITY	STATE

ZIP CODE	TELEPHONE (Include Area Code) ( )	Employed Full-Time Student Part-Time Student	ZIP CODE	TELEPHONE (Include Area Code) ( )

PATIENT AND INSURED INFORMATION

9. OTHER INSURED'S NAME (Last Name, First Name, Middle Initial)	10. IS PATIENT'S CONDITION RELATED TO:	11. INSURED'S POLICY GROUP OR FECA NUMBER

a. OTHER INSURED'S POLICY OR GROUP NUMBER	a. EMPLOYMENT? (Current or Previous) YES NO	a. INSURED'S DATE OF BIRTH MM DD YY SEX M F

b. OTHER INSURED'S DATE OF BIRTH MM DD YY SEX M F	b. AUTO ACCIDENT? YES NO PLACE (State)	b. EMPLOYER'S NAME OR SCHOOL NAME

c. EMPLOYER'S NAME OR SCHOOL NAME	c. OTHER ACCIDENT? YES NO	c. INSURANCE PLAN NAME OR PROGRAM NAME

d. INSURANCE PLAN NAME OR PROGRAM NAME	10d. RESERVED FOR LOCAL USE	d. IS THERE ANOTHER HEALTH BENEFIT PLAN? YES NO If yes, return to and complete item 9 a-d.

READ BACK OF FORM BEFORE COMPLETING & SIGNING THIS FORM.

12. PATIENT'S OR AUTHORIZED PERSON'S SIGNATURE I authorize the release of any medical or other information necessary to process this claim. I also request payment of government benefits either to myself or to the party who accepts assignment below. SIGNED_____ DATE_____	13. INSURED'S OR AUTHORIZED PERSON'S SIGNATURE I authorize payment of medical benefits to the undersigned physician or supplier for services described below. SIGNED_____

14. DATE OF CURRENT: MM DD YY ILLNESS (First symptom) OR INJURY (Accident) OR PREGNANCY(LMP)	15. IF PATIENT HAS HAD SAME OR SIMILAR ILLNESS. GIVE FIRST DATE MM DD YY	16. DATES PATIENT UNABLE TO WORK IN CURRENT OCCUPATION MM DD YY MM DD YY FROM TO

17. NAME OF REFERRING PROVIDER OR OTHER SOURCE	17a. 17b. NPI	18. HOSPITALIZATION DATES RELATED TO CURRENT SERVICES MM DD YY MM DD YY FROM TO

19. RESERVED FOR LOCAL USE	20. OUTSIDE LAB? YES NO $ CHARGES

21. DIAGNOSIS OR NATURE OF ILLNESS OR INJURY (Relate Items 1, 2, 9 or 4 to Item 24E by Line) 1.⌊___.___ 3.⌊___.___ 2.⌊___.___ 4.⌊___.___	22. MEDICAID RESUBMISSION CODE ORIGINAL REF. NO. 23. PRIOR AUTHORIZATION NUMBER

24. A. DATE(S) OF SERVICE						B. PLACE OF SERVICE	C. EMG	D. PROCEDURES, SERVICES, OR SUPPLIES (Explain Unusual Circumstances)		E. DIAGNOSIS POINTER	F. $ CHARGES	G. DAYS OR UNITS	H. EPSDT Family Plan	I. ID. QUAL.	J. RENDERING PROVIDER ID. #
From MM DD YY			To MM DD YY					CPT/HCPCS	MODIFIER						
1														NPI	
2														NPI	
3														NPI	
4														NPI	
5														NPI	
6														NPI	

PHYSICIAN OR SUPPLIER INFORMATION

25. FEDERAL TAX I.D. NUMBER SSN EIN	26. PATIENT'S ACCOUNT NO.	27. ACCEPT ASSIGNMENT? (For govt. claims, see back) YES NO	28. TOTAL CHARGE $	29. AMOUNT PAID $	30. BALANCE DUE $

31. SIGNATURE OF PHYSICIAN OR SUPPLIER INCLUDING DEGREES OR CREDENTIALS (I certify that the statements on the reverse apply to this bill and are made a part thereof.)	32. SERVICE FACILITY LOCATION INFORMATION	33. BILLING PROVIDER INFO & PH # ( )

Name:_____

Class/Section:_____

Date:_____

2012

Exercise 11.20

1. _____ Destruction of localized lesion of choroid (e.g., choroidal neovascularization), transpupillary thermo-therapy.

2. _____ Extracorporeal shock wave involving the musculo-skeletal system, not otherwise specified, low energy.

3. _____ Destruction of macular drusen, photocoagulation.

4. _____ Insertion of a temporary prostatic urethral stent.

5. _____ Cryopreservation; reproductive tissue, ovarian

Before You Begin:
Make sure you look at the Category III codes found toward the end of your CPT codebook.

Purpose of this Lesson:
To familiarize you with the usage of Category III codes in place of Unlisted Procedure codes.

Instructions:
1. Read the question or exercise below.

2. Choose the correct Category III, Unlisted Procedure code, or correct CPT® for each service.

Modifiers

Modifiers are adjectives. They further describe or limit the procedure to which they are appended.

Modifiers can be written in one of two ways. These are:

a. Procedure code + dash (-) + modifier

      i.e., 19366-22

b. Procedure code + modifier

      i.e., 1936622

MODIFIERS

There are 32 modifiers in CPT® that are applicable to physicians' procedures. The following is a brief list of these. You should check in Appendix A in your CPT® codebook for a complete description of all CPT® modifiers available to you.

- *-22*   *Increased Procedural Services*
- *-23*   *Unusual Anesthesia*
- *-24*   *Unrelated Evaluation and Management Service by the Same Physician During a Postoperative Period*
- *-25*   *Significant, Separately Identifiable Evaluation and Management Service by the Same Physician on the Same Day of the Procedure or Other Service*
- *-26*   *Professional Component*
- *-32*   *Mandated Services*
- *-33*   *Preventive Services*
- *-47*   *Anesthesia by Surgeon*

Overuse of the -22 is kind of like the boy who cried wolf...

Tip

Note that modifier -51 goes at the end of all secondary procedures and that the major procedure is reported without the addition of the modifier -51.

Key

Use of the modifier -53 shows the computer that you were unable to complete the service and that you may come back at another time to try the service.

Modifiers should be used accurately. Trying to look on the rosy side will distort the facts and will cause you trouble.

-50	*Bilateral Procedure*
-51	*Multiple Procedures*
-52	*Reduced Services*
-53	*Discontinued Procedure*
-54	*Surgical Care Only*
-55	*Postoperative Management Only*
-56	*Preoperative Management Only*
-57	*Decision for Surgery*
-58	*Staged or Related Procedure or Service by the Same Physician During the Postoperative Period*
-59	*Distinct Procedural Service*
-62	*Two Surgeons*
-63	*Procedure Performed on Infants less than 4 kg*
-66	*Surgical Team*
-76	*Repeat Procedure or Service by Same Physician*
-77	*Repeat Procedure by Another Physician*
-78	*Unplanned Return to the Operating/Procedure Room by the Same Physician Following Initial Procedure for a Related Procedure During the Postoperative Period*
-79	*Unrelated Procedure or Service by the Same Physician During the Postoperative Period*
-80	*Assistant Surgeon*
-81	*Minimum Assistant Surgeon*
-82	*Assistant Surgeon (when qualified resident surgeon is not available)*
-90	*Reference (Outside) Laboratory*
-91	*Repeat Clinical Diagnostic Laboratory Test*
-92	*Alternative Laboratory Platform Testing*
-99	*Multiple Modifiers*

MODIFIERS APPROVED FOR AMBULATORY SURGERY CENTER (ASC) HOSPITAL OUTPATIENT USE

As you can see by looking at the CPT® codebook, there is a listing of HCPCS National modifiers as well as for ambulatory surgery center/hospital outpatient facility modifiers. We will take each of the modifiers that are applicable to the ASC and that are not obvious to the average coder and provide a brief explanation for each.

-25	*Significant, Separately Identifiable Evaluation and Management Service by the Same Physician on the Same Day of the Procedure or Other Service*

This modifier indicates that the physician provided an E/M service on the same day that he or she also provided a non-E/M service. An example may be the use of the ER on the same day that the radiology department was also used, or another would be the use of the ER to provide an E/M service while the patient was also sutured to repair a laceration he received as a result of a dog bite.

-27   Multiple Outpatient Hospital E/M Encounters on the Same Date

Probably the best way to describe the modifier -27 is by giving an example. Let's say that a patient comes into the hospital emergency room complaining of stomach pains. The patient appears to be relatively normal and healthy. She is placed in an examination room of the ER and is examined by the on call physician who discovers, after completing a thorough history and exam, that the patient is a 35-year-old married female (newlywed as of about 8 months) who has been feeling sick for the past 3 weeks on and off. Today's episode was brought on when she went to work and almost threw up at the morning coffee break, as one of her coworkers was making a new pot of coffee. Since she had not been feeling well for some time, one of the coworkers suggested that she be seen. This patient recently moved to your town and has just recently established her primary care physician, but did not call to see if there was any availability at his office.

The ER physician orders some blood work, completes some tests, and determines that this patient is 5-months pregnant. During the time it takes for the tests to be completed, the patient begins to complain of some heavy cramping and vaginal bleeding. The ER doctor administers some turbutaline and calls the on call OB/GYN who suggests that the patient be moved to the observation unit once she seems stable enough and reports to the ER physician that she will be right in after completing a delivery that she is part of right this second. The patient is moved to the observation unit where the OB/GYN visits her, diagnoses the patient to be in pre-term labor, and decides to admit her to the hospital.

As you can see from this example, there are several places (locations) of the hospital that were used for this patient when she was still in an ambulatory or outpatient mode. These included the emergency room and the hospital observation area. In order for the hospital to be able to effectively report the use of these facilities, it can employ the correct codes for the emergency room and the hospital observation area and append the modifier –27 to each of these to indicate that there was more than one hospital E/M encounter that occurred on the same date. The book makes a special point of telling the coder that this modifier is not to be used by the physician to report multiple E/M services on the same date. This makes sense when you recall that when a physician provides multiple E/M services on the same date, the smaller services (e.g., office visit) can be grouped with the larger one (e.g., hospital admission) and only the one service that includes the history, exam and medical decision making is reported.

-50   Bilateral Procedure

Used by the ASC to denote that two sides of the same service were performed (e.g., bilateral breast reconstructions = 19366 for the right side and 19366-50 for the left).

Key

Remember: An adjective, in order to make sense, must refer back to the noun. If we were to say "pretty" without saying <u>what</u> was pretty, it would not make sense to the person with whom we were speaking. Referring back to the procedure, therefore, is important to the modifier. A modifier by itself makes no sense unless it refers back to the procedure that it is supposed to be describing or limiting.

Tip

Remember: ASCs are paid for the use of their facilities. It is important, therefore, to list all the services provided by the physician, and to use the appropriate modifiers so that the facility can properly show the amount of time it was occupied.

-52   *Reduced Services*

Shows that the time frame needed on the surgical or ER space was reduced because the service was reduced.

-58   *Staged or Related Procedure or Service by the Same Physician During the Postoperative Period*

Signifies that when placed on the end of a code that the service was part of a staged or related procedure that has already occurred for the purpose of the ASC, indicates to the carrier that the suite at the ASC will be used on an additional occasion because the procedure was staged or related, or that was more extensive than the original service, or that the service described was some sort of therapy for the original service.

-59   *Distinct Procedural Service*

Used by the ASC to report that two or more services were done on the same day that may appear to be related, but that in reality are distinct and separate services and that the use of the facility was for these purposes.

-73   *Discontinued Out-Patient Hospital/Ambulatory Surgery Center (ASC) Procedure Prior to the Administration of Anesthesia*

This modifier is unique to the ASC modifiers in that it clearly shows that the procedure had to be aborted before the anesthesia was actually administered. Keep in mind that it would be okay to use this modifier even if the patient had already been sedated…just as long as the patient had not actually received the anesthesia. The use of this modifier on the end of the CPT code lets the insurance company know that all of the work to set up the ASC and prep had been done; the patient had been brought in, but the full-blown procedure had never been done on the patient due to the discontinuation of the service on the part of the physician. If the patient decides to back out of the service, you would not use this modifier, as an insurance company would not pay for this anyway.

-74   *Discontinued Out-Patient Hospital/Ambulatory Surgery Center (ASC) Procedure After the Administration of Anesthesia*

This modifier is another one that is unique to the ASC modifier section and is similar in concept to the one described before (i.e., modifier –73). The difference between these two modifiers is that the –74 modifier lets someone know that the anesthesia had already been administered when the procedure was discontinued.

Tip

CPT suggests that if there is another available modifier that can be used in place of modifier -59, it should be used instead.

-76　　Repeat Procedure or Service by Same Physician
-77　　Repeat Procedure by Another Physician

Both of these modifiers, when used on a claim for the ASC, will indicate that a service is being repeated subsequent to an original service. The −76 cautions the carrier to look at the fact that the service was already done by the same physician, and the −77 cautions the carrier that the service being repeated was already done by someone else other than who is performing the service today.

-78　　Unplanned Return to the Operating/Procedure Room by the Same Physician Following Initial Procedure for a Related Procedure During the Postoperative Period

As we have already discussed, this modifier is somewhat similar to the repeat procedure modifiers in that we are coming back to do another surgery. The difference here lies in the fact that with the use of this modifier we want to express two things. The first is that the service being done may or may not be the same as the original service, and the second is that the patient is returning to the operating room during the postoperative period. This postoperative period notation is important to the carrier as it indicates that there may have been a complication or that there may be another injury that the patient has sustained that required the return to the operating room.

-79　　Unrelated Procedure or Service by the Same Physician During the Postoperative Period

Modifier −79 is used to indicate that another procedure or service (i.e., a procedure that has nothing to do with the first service you did) was done during the postoperative time of another service (like a laceration repair done during the postoperative period of a total hip replacement). It is these postoperative time frames and the global fee periods that surround them that get the carriers confused on whether or not they should pay for some services done within the postoperative time frames. Use of the modifiers indicates that the services were legitimate and unrelated to other procedures that have already been done.

-91　　Repeat Clinical Diagnostic Laboratory Test

Used to describe situations in which the test was repeated to make sure that the progress of the patient was proceeding as expected (or not). It is not used when you want to confirm initial results, or if you have had problems with the equipment, or for any other reason when you just want to redo the test. There must be a legitimate reason that the test is being re-done to warrant the use of this modifier.

Modifiers -76 and -77 are used when something happens that requires a service to be repeated.

Key

Note that modifier -79 is conceptually the same as the -24. Both are services that occur during the postoperative period. The difference is that the -24 is an unrelated E/M service that occurs during the post-op, and the -79 is any other "procedure" that is unrelated and occurs during the post-op.

LEVEL II (HCPCS/NATIONAL) MODIFIERS

There are 33 Level II (or National Code) modifiers that are available in the CPT® codebook. There are many others available to you in HCPCS. Here in **cpT**each® we will not take these modifiers in the order in which they appear in the CPT® codebook, because it will make more sense to you if we keep fingers and toes together as opposed to keeping the modifiers alphabetically.

The modifiers start off with modifiers for the eyes. You will note that these "eye" modifiers start with an "E." There are four eye modifiers; two for the left eye and two for the right, each of which indicates either an upper or lower lid. The modifiers are self-explanatory and you would use them on any procedure that had to do with eyes to describe where the service occurred (i.e., upper or lower lid, left or right eye). It is interesting to note that upper lids are mentioned with odd numbers and lower lids are mentioned with even numbers, followed in concept with the fact that the left side comes before right.

These modifiers are appended to the end of the procedure code in the same way that regular CPT modifiers are added on.

- **-E1**   *Upper left, eyelid*
- **-E2**   *Lower left, eyelid*
- **-E3**   *Upper right, eyelid*
- **-E4**   *Lower right, eyelid*

The modifiers continue with the fingers (hand) and, as you might guess, start off with the letter "F" for fingers. Once again, the left hand precedes the right hand for the most part with the exception of the left thumb which is the only modifier for hand that has two alpha characters. The reason for the two alpha characters is that modifiers contain only two digits. Since there are 10 fingers, you could not exactly say –F10 as that would make the modifier three digits instead of two.

- **-F1**   *Left hand, second digit*
- **-F2**   *Left hand, third digit*
- **-F3**   *Left hand, fourth digit*
- **-F4**   *Left hand, fifth digit*
- **-F5**   *Right hand, thumb*
- **-F6**   *Right hand, second digit*
- **-F7**   *Right hand, third digit*
- **-F8**   *Right hand, fourth digit*
- **-F9**   *Right hand, fifth digit*
- **-FA**   *Left hand, thumb*

Key

For ophthalmology codes and "ear" codes in the Medicine section, *the bilateral nature of the codes is assumed* (i.e., it is understood that when you examine one eye, you will also examine the other). Therefore, use of the bilateral -50 modifier is not required.

The third set of Level II modifiers, which is pretty easy to understand, has to do with the digits of the feet. As you might guess, they start off with the letter "T" for toes. These modifiers follow the same format as those for the hands.

-T1	*Left foot, second digit*
-T2	*Left foot, third digit*
-T3	*Left foot, fourth digit*
-T4	*Left foot, fifth digit*
-T5	*Right foot, great toe*
-T6	*Right foot, second digit*
-T7	*Right foot, third digit*
-T8	*Right foot, fourth digit*
-T9	*Right foot, fifth digit*
-TA	*Left foot, great toe*

The next two modifiers talk about on which side of the patient the service took place. That could either be the left or the right side. As might be expected, using the modifier –LT modifies the left side, and using the modifier –RT indicates the right side.

-LT	*left side*
-RT	*right side*

The next group of modifiers has to do with the heart. These modifiers describe the left circumflex, left anterior descending and right coronary arteries. The left circumflex artery is logically indicated by the two alpha digits LC for left circumflex coronary artery. The left anterior descending artery is indicated by the two letters that most closely match its description (the l and the D), hence, modifier –LD. Finally, the modifier for the right coronary artery is –RC as the description implies it should be.

-LC	*Left circumflex coronary artery (Hospitals use with codes 92980-92984, 92995, 92996)*
-LD	*Left anterior descending coronary artery (Hospitals use with codes 92980-92984, 92995, 92996)*
-RC	*Right coronary artery (Hospitals use with codes 92980-92984, 92995, 92996)*

Finally, we end our discussion of the Level II modifiers with two modifiers that have to do with ambulances. Unlike all the others in this entire group, there is neither rhyme nor reason as to how they chose these. They both start off with the letter "Q" which I suppose you could use to mean "Quick," but what the "M" or the "N" could mean is beyond me. You will use them as described below.

> *-QM*   *Ambulance service provided under arrangement by a provider of*
>   *services*
>
> *-QN*   *Ambulance service furnished directly by a provider of services*

The –QM means that if a nursing home were providing the services to a patient and the patient needed an ambulance, the employees of the nursing home, being the "provider," would call and request an ambulance. The –QN means that the provider of services (in our example, the nursing home) provided the ambulance services themselves.

> *-GG*   *Performance and payment of a screening mammogram and diagnos-*
>   *tic mammogram on the same patient, same day*

You will note that in looking at this modifier, there is a difference between a screening mammogram (when we see if the patient has any lesions that may look suspicious) and a diagnostic one in which we look to see exactly what is wrong with the patient. You would use this modifier to explain to Medicare that these two services happened on the same day.

> *-GH*   *Diagnostic mammogram converted from screening mammogram on*
>   *same day*

In this case, you started providing the screening mammogram and then it turned into a diagnostic one.

This concludes our discussion of modifiers. Keep reading them over and over again until you feel comfortable with what each one means and how they can help you further explain to your carrier what happened during each patient encounter.

Name:_____

Class/Section:_____

Date:_____

WORKBOOK

cpTeach
2012

EXERCISE 12.1

1.   Sally is an unusual girl. _____

2.   That is a reduced procedure. _____

3.   This was an unusual surgery. _____

4.   Dr. Bailey performed a bilateral reconstruction. _____

5.   Dr. M. Houston performed multiple surgeries. _____

6.   Dr. Jones is the assistant surgeon. _____

7.   We performed a repeat x-ray. _____

8.   The consultation required by the insurance carrier was a mandated
      service. _____

9.   The service performed was a discontinued procedure. _____

10.   Our doctor provided the preoperative management. _____

Before You Begin:
Read Chapter 12 in cpTeach® on "Modifiers." Follow along in CPT® with the points illustrated in cpTeach®.

Purpose of this Lesson:
To familiarize the student with the different CPT® modifiers and their corresponding unique descriptions as well as with their proper use.

Instructions:
1.   Identify the adjectives in each of the sentences below by circling the word.

2.   Write a modifier that describes each adjective.

Before You Begin:

Read chapter 12 in cpTeach® on "Modifiers." Follow along in CPT® with the points illustrated in cpTeach®.

Purpose of this Lesson:

To familiarize the student with the different CPT® modifiers and the two correct ways to write modifiers.

Instructions:

1. Attach each of the modifiers below to both the "fictitious" and real codes listed.

2. Write each one in two different ways.

3. Identify the meaning of each modifier.

EXERCISE 12.2

1. 88888 using modifier -26

   _____

   _____

2. 33333 using modifier -66

   _____

   _____

3. 33333 and 22222 using modifier -51. NOTE: 33333 is the major service.

   _____

   _____

4. 33333 using modifier -50. Show both the right and left sides.

   _____

   _____

5. 33333 using modifier -54

   _____

   _____

6. 33333 using modifier -55

   _____

   _____

7. 33333 using modifier -56

   _____

   _____

Name:_____

Class/Section:_____

Date:_____

2012

8.   33333 using modifier -80.   Also show how the primary surgeon's bill
would look.

PRIMARY SURGEON   ASSISTANT SURGEON

_____   _____

_____   _____

_____   _____

_____

9.   77777 using modifier -76.   Also show how the first claim would
have looked.

FIRST CLAIM   SECOND CLAIM

_____   _____

_____   _____

_____   _____

_____

10.   99252 using modifier -32. (This code is not fictitious)

_____

_____

11.   99243 using modifier -25. (This code is not fictitious)

_____

_____

Before You Begin:
Make sure you look at the
Category III codes found
toward the end of your CPT
codebook.

Purpose of this Lesson:
To familiarize you with
the usage of Category III
codes in place of Unlisted
Procedure codes.

Instructions:
1. Read the question or
exercise below.

2. Choose the correct
Category III, Unlisted
Procedure code, or
correct CPT® for each
service.

WORKBOOK

cpTeach
Expert Medical Coding Made Easy
2012

Name:_____

Class/Section:_____

Date:_____

Before You Begin:
Read Chapter 12 in cpTeach® on "Modifiers." Follow along in your CPT® with the points illustrated in cpTeach®.

Purpose of this Lesson:
To familiarize the student with the different CPT® modifiers and their corresponding unique descriptions as well as with their proper use.

Instructions:
1. Match the following CPT® modifiers to their corresponding descriptions.

EXERCISE 12.3

1. -47 _____
2. -22 _____
3. -57 _____
4. -32 _____
5. -50 _____
6. -51 _____
7. -52 _____
8. -59 _____
9. -54 _____
10. -55 _____
11. -56 _____
12. -25 _____
13. -76 _____
14. -58 _____
15. -80 _____
16. -99 _____
17. -79 _____
18. -53 _____

A. Repeat Procedure or Service by Same Physician

B. Significant, Separately Identifiable E/M Service by Same Physician on Same Day of Procedure or Other Service

C. Preoperative Management Only

D. Staged or Related Procedure or Service by Same Physician During Post-Op Period

E. Surgical Care Only

F. Assistant Surgeon

G. Postoperative Management Only

H. Distinct Procedural Service

I. Multiple Modifiers

J. Bilateral Procedure

K. Mandated Services

L. Decision for Surgery

M. Increased Procedural Services

N. Anesthesia by Surgeon

O. Reduced Services

P. Unrelated Procedure/Service/Same MD during post-op

Q. Multiple Procedures

R. Discontinued Procedure

Name:_____

Class/Section:_____

cpTeach
2012   Date:_____

EXERCISE 12.4

1.   List five modifiers that describe services that may have occurred more than once.

_____   _____   _____

_____   _____   _____

2.   List two modifiers that describe the concept of more than one doctor working with other doctors in an *equal* capacity.

_____   _____   _____

3.   List three modifiers that describe one doctor helping (not as a primary physician) another in surgery.

_____   _____   _____

4.   List five modifiers that break up the surgical package.

_____   _____   _____

_____   _____   _____

5.   List two modifiers that describe anesthesia services.

_____   _____   _____

6.   List five modifiers that can be appended to evaluation and management services.

_____   _____   _____

_____   _____

Before You Begin:
Read Chapter 12 in cpTeach® on "Modifiers." Follow along in your CPT® with the points illustrated in cpTeach®.

Purpose of this Lesson:
To familiarize the student with the different CPT® modifiers and their corresponding unique descriptions as well as with their proper use.

Instructions:
1.   For each of the following descriptions or adjectives listed below, name the modifiers that may describe them.

WORKBOOK

Name:_____

Class/Section:_____

cpTeach

Date:_____

2012

Before You Begin:

Read Chapter 12 in cpTeach® on "Modifiers." Follow along in your CPT® with the points illustrated in cpTeach®.

Purpose of this Lesson:

To familiarize the student with the different CPT® modifiers for physicians (as opposed to modifiers for the ASC's) and their corresponding unique descriptions as well as with their proper use.

Instructions:

1. For each of the modifiers below give the meaning and write an example of how it may be used

EXERCISE 12.5

-24   _____

_____

Example: _____

-26   _____

_____

Example: _____

-79   _____

_____

Example: _____

-53   _____

_____

Example: _____

Name:_____

Class/Section:_____

cpTeach   Date:_____
2012

EXERCISE 12.6

Before You Begin:
Read Chapter 12 in cpTeach® on "Modifiers." Follow along in your CPT® with the points illustrated in cpTeach®.

Purpose of this Lesson:
To familiarize the student with the different CPT® modifiers for physicians and their corresponding unique descriptions as well as with their proper use

Instructions:
1. Read the following true and false statements.

2. Mark the statement true if the conditions apply or false if the conditions do not apply.

1. _____   The modifier -51 for Multiple Procedures can be used in the Radiology section.

2. _____   The modifier -56 can be used to describe postoperative services.

3. _____   The modifier -50 for Bilateral Procedures can be used to describe bilateral views (x-rays) taken of two knees (see 73560).

4. _____   The modifier -55 can be used to describe postoperative office visits.

5. _____   The modifier -51 can be used in the Medicine section for services other than E/M to describe multiple services which occurred on the same day.

6. _____   The modifier -91 can be used to describe doing the same lab test on different days.

7. _____   The modifier -59 for Distinct Procedural Service can be used when the physician wants to report that a service was provided on the same day as another service and it was unique and distinct from the other.

8. _____   The modifier -62 for Two Surgeons can be used when one physician performs the surgery and another does the anesthesia.

9. _____   Modifier -57 (Decision for Surgery) is used on the E/M code when the E/M code was the one during which the physician decided to operate.

10. _____   Modifier -53 (Discontinued Service) + Modifier -52 (Reduced Service) both mean that the entire procedure, as described in the CPT codebook was not completed.

EXERCISE 12.7

Dee O. Eigh comes to your office complaining of pain on the right foot particularly in the area of the great toe and the second and third toes. You examine the entire foot, take extensive x-rays and conclude that the toes require surgery to remove bony processes that are bothering the patient. You complete the ostectomy on first, second and third metatarsal heads. Code the surgery, keeping in mind that you want to point out to Medicare which toes were operated on.

Before You Begin:

Read Chapter 12 in cpTeach® on "Modifiers." Follow along in CPT® with the points illustrated in cpTeach®.

Purpose of this Lesson:

To familiarize the student with the different modifiers and how to use them, and to give the student practice in coding real operative reports. For additional practice exercises, please contact MedBooks for our Advanced Case Study Workbook.

Instructions:

1. Using the CMS-1500 claim form, decide which modifiers to use for each patient in the following case studies. Complete the CPT® coding portion of the CMS-1500 claim form on the back of each page.

Notes: _____

_____

_____

_____

_____

_____

_____

EXERCISE 12.7

1500

HEALTH INSURANCE CLAIM FORM

APPROVED BY NATIONAL UNIFORM CLAIM COMMITTEE 08/05

CARRIER

☐☐ PICA   PICA ☐☐

1. MEDICARE MEDICAID TRICARE CHAMPUS CHAMPVA GROUP HEALTH PLAN FECA BLK LUNG OTHER	1a. INSURED'S I.D. NUMBER (For Program in Item 1)
☐ (Medicare #) ☐ (Medicaid #) ☐ (Sponsor's SSN) ☐ (Member ID#) ☐ (SSN or ID) ☐ (SSN) ☐ (ID)	

2. PATIENT'S NAME (Last Name, First Name, Middle Initial)	3. PATIENT'S BIRTH DATE MM DD YY SEX M☐ F☐	4. INSURED'S NAME (Last Name, First Name, Middle Initial)

5. PATIENT'S ADDRESS (No., Street)	6. PATIENT RELATIONSHIP TO INSURED Self☐ Spouse☐ Child☐ Other☐	7. INSURED'S ADDRESS (No., Street)

CITY STATE	8. PATIENT STATUS Single☐ Married☐ Other☐	CITY STATE
ZIP CODE TELEPHONE (Include Area Code) ( )	Employed☐ Full-Time Student☐ Part-Time Student☐	ZIP CODE TELEPHONE (Include Area Code) ( )

9. OTHER INSURED'S NAME (Last Name, First Name, Middle Initial)	10. IS PATIENT'S CONDITION RELATED TO:	11. INSURED'S POLICY GROUP OR FECA NUMBER
a. OTHER INSURED'S POLICY OR GROUP NUMBER	a. EMPLOYMENT? (Current or Previous) ☐ YES ☐ NO	a. INSURED'S DATE OF BIRTH MM DD YY SEX M☐ F☐
b. OTHER INSURED'S DATE OF BIRTH MM DD YY SEX M☐ F☐	b. AUTO ACCIDENT? PLACE (State) ☐ YES ☐ NO	b. EMPLOYER'S NAME OR SCHOOL NAME
c. EMPLOYER'S NAME OR SCHOOL NAME	c. OTHER ACCIDENT? ☐ YES ☐ NO	c. INSURANCE PLAN NAME OR PROGRAM NAME
d. INSURANCE PLAN NAME OR PROGRAM NAME	10d. RESERVED FOR LOCAL USE	d. IS THERE ANOTHER HEALTH BENEFIT PLAN? ☐ YES ☐ NO If yes, return to and complete item 9 a-d.

READ BACK OF FORM BEFORE COMPLETING & SIGNING THIS FORM.

12. PATIENT'S OR AUTHORIZED PERSON'S SIGNATURE I authorize the release of any medical or other information necessary to process this claim. I also request payment of government benefits either to myself or to the party who accepts assignment below. SIGNED_____ DATE_____	13. INSURED'S OR AUTHORIZED PERSON'S SIGNATURE I authorize payment of medical benefits to the undersigned physician or supplier for services described below. SIGNED_____

PATIENT AND INSURED INFORMATION

14. DATE OF CURRENT: MM DD YY ILLNESS (First symptom) OR INJURY (Accident) OR PREGNANCY (LMP)	15. IF PATIENT HAS HAD SAME OR SIMILAR ILLNESS. GIVE FIRST DATE MM DD YY	16. DATES PATIENT UNABLE TO WORK IN CURRENT OCCUPATION FROM MM DD YY TO MM DD YY
17. NAME OF REFERRING PROVIDER OR OTHER SOURCE	17a. 17b. NPI	18. HOSPITALIZATION DATES RELATED TO CURRENT SERVICES FROM MM DD YY TO MM DD YY
19. RESERVED FOR LOCAL USE		20. OUTSIDE LAB? ☐ YES ☐ NO $ CHARGES

21. DIAGNOSIS OR NATURE OF ILLNESS OR INJURY (Relate Items 1, 2, 9 or 4 to Item 24E by Line)	22. MEDICAID RESUBMISSION CODE ORIGINAL REF. NO.
1. |____|.|____| 3. |____|.|____|	23. PRIOR AUTHORIZATION NUMBER
2. |____|.|____| 4. |____|.|____|	

24. A. DATE(S) OF SERVICE From MM DD YY To MM DD YY	B. PLACE OF SERVICE	C. EMG	D. PROCEDURES, SERVICES, OR SUPPLIES (Explain Unusual Circumstances) CPT/HCPCS	MODIFIER	E. DIAGNOSIS POINTER	F. $ CHARGES	G. DAYS OR UNITS	H. EPSDT Family Plan	I. ID. QUAL.	J. RENDERING PROVIDER ID. #
1										NPI
2										NPI
3										NPI
4										NPI
5										NPI
6										NPI

25. FEDERAL TAX I.D. NUMBER SSN☐ EIN☐	26. PATIENT'S ACCOUNT NO.	27. ACCEPT ASSIGNMENT? (For govt. claims, see back) ☐ YES ☐ NO	28. TOTAL CHARGE $	29. AMOUNT PAID $	30. BALANCE DUE $
31. SIGNATURE OF PHYSICIAN OR SUPPLIER INCLUDING DEGREES OR CREDENTIALS (I certify that the statements on the reverse apply to this bill and are made a part thereof.)	32. SERVICE FACILITY LOCATION INFORMATION		33. BILLING PROVIDER INFO & PH # ( )		

PHYSICIAN OR SUPPLIER INFORMATION

Name:_____

Class/Section:_____

Date:_____

2012

Exercise 12.8

A patient named Meg A. Watt comes to your office with a chalazion (small lump) on her right eyelid that has been bothering her for quite some time. You examine the lesion and decide that the patient should have it removed. You remove the chalazion, and the patient tolerates the surgery quite well. Code only for the surgery indicating to Medicare that you have removed the chalazion from the right upper lid.

Before You Begin:
Read Chapter 12 in cpTeach® on "Modifiers." Follow along in CPT® with the points illustrated in cpTeach®.

Purpose of this Lesson:
To familiarize the student with the different modifiers and how to use them, and to give the student practice in coding real operative reports. For additional practice exercises, please contact MedBooks for our Advanced Case Study Workbook.

Instructions:
1. Using the CMS-1500 claim form, decide which modifiers to use for each patient in the following case studies. Complete the CPT® coding portion of the CMS-1500 claim form on the back of each page.

Notes: _____

_____

_____

_____

_____

_____

_____

Name: _____

Class/Section: _____

cpTeach

Date: _____

WORKBOOK

2012

EXERCISE 12.8

1500

HEALTH INSURANCE CLAIM FORM

APPROVED BY NATIONAL UNIFORM CLAIM COMMITTEE 08/05

CARRIER

| | PICA | | | | | | | | | PICA | | |

| 1. MEDICARE | MEDICAID | TRICARE CHAMPUS | CHAMPVA | GROUP HEALTH PLAN | FECA BLK LUNG | OTHER | 1a. INSURED'S I.D. NUMBER | (For Program in Item 1) |
| (Medicare #) | (Medicaid #) | (Sponsor's SSN) | (Member ID#) | (SSN or ID) | (SSN) | (ID) | | |

2. PATIENT'S NAME (Last Name, First Name, Middle Initial)

3. PATIENT'S BIRTH DATE MM DD YY   SEX   M   F

4. INSURED'S NAME (Last Name, First Name, Middle Initial)

5. PATIENT'S ADDRESS (No., Street)

6. PATIENT RELATIONSHIP TO INSURED   Self   Spouse   Child   Other

7. INSURED'S ADDRESS (No., Street)

CITY   STATE

8. PATIENT STATUS   Single   Married   Other

CITY   STATE

ZIP CODE   TELEPHONE (Include Area Code) (   )

Employed   Full-Time Student   Part-Time Student

ZIP CODE   TELEPHONE (Include Area Code) (   )

9. OTHER INSURED'S NAME (Last Name, First Name, Middle Initial)

10. IS PATIENT'S CONDITION RELATED TO:

11. INSURED'S POLICY GROUP OR FECA NUMBER

a. OTHER INSURED'S POLICY OR GROUP NUMBER

a. EMPLOYMENT? (Current or Previous)   YES   NO

a. INSURED'S DATE OF BIRTH MM DD YY   SEX   M   F

b. OTHER INSURED'S DATE OF BIRTH MM DD YY   SEX   M   F

b. AUTO ACCIDENT?   PLACE (State)   YES   NO

b. EMPLOYER'S NAME OR SCHOOL NAME

c. EMPLOYER'S NAME OR SCHOOL NAME

c. OTHER ACCIDENT?   YES   NO

c. INSURANCE PLAN NAME OR PROGRAM NAME

d. INSURANCE PLAN NAME OR PROGRAM NAME

10d. RESERVED FOR LOCAL USE

d. IS THERE ANOTHER HEALTH BENEFIT PLAN?   YES   NO   If yes, return to and complete item 9 a-d.

READ BACK OF FORM BEFORE COMPLETING & SIGNING THIS FORM.

12. PATIENT'S OR AUTHORIZED PERSON'S SIGNATURE I authorize the release of any medical or other information necessary to process this claim. I also request payment of government benefits either to myself or to the party who accepts assignment below.

SIGNED _____   DATE _____

13. INSURED'S OR AUTHORIZED PERSON'S SIGNATURE I authorize payment of medical benefits to the undersigned physician or supplier for services described below.

SIGNED _____

14. DATE OF CURRENT: MM DD YY   ILLNESS (First symptom) OR INJURY (Accident) OR PREGNANCY(LMP)

15. IF PATIENT HAS HAD SAME OR SIMILAR ILLNESS. GIVE FIRST DATE MM DD YY

16. DATES PATIENT UNABLE TO WORK IN CURRENT OCCUPATION MM DD YY   FROM   TO   MM DD YY

17. NAME OF REFERRING PROVIDER OR OTHER SOURCE

17a.
17b. NPI

18. HOSPITALIZATION DATES RELATED TO CURRENT SERVICES MM DD YY   FROM   TO   MM DD YY

19. RESERVED FOR LOCAL USE

20. OUTSIDE LAB?   YES   NO $ CHARGES

21. DIAGNOSIS OR NATURE OF ILLNESS OR INJURY (Relate Items 1, 2, 9 or 4 to Item 24E by Line)

1. |___.___   3. |___.___
2. |___.___   4. |___.___

22. MEDICAID RESUBMISSION CODE   ORIGINAL REF. NO.

23. PRIOR AUTHORIZATION NUMBER

24. A. DATE(S) OF SERVICE						B. PLACE OF SERVICE	C. EMG	D. PROCEDURES, SERVICES, OR SUPPLIES (Explain Unusual Circumstances)		E. DIAGNOSIS POINTER	F. $ CHARGES	G. DAYS OR UNITS	H. EPSDT Family Plan	I. ID. QUAL.	J. RENDERING PROVIDER ID. #
From			To					CPT/HCPCS	MODIFIER						
MM	DD	YY	MM	DD	YY										
1															NPI
2															NPI
3															NPI
4															NPI
5															NPI
6															NPI

25. FEDERAL TAX I.D. NUMBER   SSN   EIN

26. PATIENT'S ACCOUNT NO.

27. ACCEPT ASSIGNMENT? (For govt. claims, see back)   YES   NO

28. TOTAL CHARGE $

29. AMOUNT PAID $

30. BALANCE DUE $

31. SIGNATURE OF PHYSICIAN OR SUPPLIER INCLUDING DEGREES OR CREDENTIALS (I certify that the statements on the reverse apply to this bill and are made a part thereof.)

32. SERVICE FACILITY LOCATION INFORMATION

33. BILLING PROVIDER INFO & PH # (   )

PHYSICIAN OR SUPPLIER INFORMATION

PATIENT AND INSURED INFORMATION

*Name:*_____

*Class/Section:*_____

*Date:*_____

EXERCISE 12.9

A patient comes into your office complaining of pain in the left hand and the inability to completely open the hand to a flat state (i.e., he is not able to lay his hand flat on the table). Upon examination, you decide that the patient could use a fasciectomy with a release of each of the five digits of the hand. You complete the surgery successfully. Code for the surgery only.

Before You Begin:
Read Chapter 12 in cpTeach® on "Modifiers." Follow along in CPT® with the points illustrated in cpTeach®.

Purpose of this Lesson:
To familiarize the student with the different modifiers and how to use them, and to give the student practice in coding real operative reports. For additional practice exercises, please contact MedBooks for our Advanced Case Study Workbook.

Instructions:
1. Using the CMS-1500 claim form, decide which modifiers to use for each patient in the following case studies. Complete the CPT® coding portion of the CMS-1500 claim form on the back of each page.

*Notes:*_____

_____

_____

_____

_____

_____

_____

EXERCISE **12.9**

1500

HEALTH INSURANCE CLAIM FORM

APPROVED BY NATIONAL UNIFORM CLAIM COMMITTEE 08/05

	PICA								PICA	

1. MEDICARE	MEDICAID	TRICARE CHAMPUS	CHAMPVA	GROUP HEALTH PLAN	FECA BLK LUNG	OTHER	1a. INSURED'S I.D. NUMBER	(For Program in Item 1)
(Medicare #)	(Medicaid #)	(Sponsor's SSN)	(Member ID#)	(SSN or ID)	(SSN)	(ID)		

2. PATIENT'S NAME (Last Name, First Name, Middle Initial)

3. PATIENT'S BIRTH DATE MM DD YY   SEX M F

4. INSURED'S NAME (Last Name, First Name, Middle Initial)

5. PATIENT'S ADDRESS (No., Street)

6. PATIENT RELATIONSHIP TO INSURED Self Spouse Child Other

7. INSURED'S ADDRESS (No., Street)

CITY   STATE

8. PATIENT STATUS Single Married Other

CITY   STATE

ZIP CODE   TELEPHONE (Include Area Code) ( )

Employed Full-Time Student Part-Time Student

ZIP CODE   TELEPHONE (Include Area Code) ( )

9. OTHER INSURED'S NAME (Last Name, First Name, Middle Initial)

10. IS PATIENT'S CONDITION RELATED TO:

11. INSURED'S POLICY GROUP OR FECA NUMBER

a. OTHER INSURED'S POLICY OR GROUP NUMBER

a. EMPLOYMENT? (Current or Previous) YES NO

a. INSURED'S DATE OF BIRTH MM DD YY   SEX M F

b. OTHER INSURED'S DATE OF BIRTH MM DD YY   SEX M F

b. AUTO ACCIDENT? YES NO   PLACE (State)

b. EMPLOYER'S NAME OR SCHOOL NAME

c. EMPLOYER'S NAME OR SCHOOL NAME

c. OTHER ACCIDENT? YES NO

c. INSURANCE PLAN NAME OR PROGRAM NAME

d. INSURANCE PLAN NAME OR PROGRAM NAME

10d. RESERVED FOR LOCAL USE

d. IS THERE ANOTHER HEALTH BENEFIT PLAN? YES NO If yes, return to and complete item 9 a-d.

READ BACK OF FORM BEFORE COMPLETING & SIGNING THIS FORM.

12. PATIENT'S OR AUTHORIZED PERSON'S SIGNATURE I authorize the release of any medical or other information necessary to process this claim. I also request payment of government benefits either to myself or to the party who accepts assignment below.

SIGNED_____   DATE_____

13. INSURED'S OR AUTHORIZED PERSON'S SIGNATURE I authorize payment of medical benefits to the undersigned physician or supplier for services described below.

SIGNED _____

14. DATE OF CURRENT: MM DD YY   ILLNESS (First symptom) OR INJURY (Accident) OR PREGNANCY(LMP)

15. IF PATIENT HAS HAD SAME OR SIMILAR ILLNESS. GIVE FIRST DATE MM DD YY

16. DATES PATIENT UNABLE TO WORK IN CURRENT OCCUPATION MM DD YY FROM TO MM DD YY

17. NAME OF REFERRING PROVIDER OR OTHER SOURCE

17a.

17b. NPI

18. HOSPITALIZATION DATES RELATED TO CURRENT SERVICES MM DD YY FROM TO MM DD YY

19. RESERVED FOR LOCAL USE

20. OUTSIDE LAB? YES NO $ CHARGES

21. DIAGNOSIS OR NATURE OF ILLNESS OR INJURY (Relate Items 1, 2, 9 or 4 to Item 24E by Line)

1. |____.____   3. |____.____

2. |____.____   4. |____.____

22. MEDICAID RESUBMISSION CODE   ORIGINAL REF. NO.

23. PRIOR AUTHORIZATION NUMBER

24. A. DATE(S) OF SERVICE		B. PLACE OF SERVICE	C. EMG	D. PROCEDURES, SERVICES, OR SUPPLIES (Explain Unusual Circumstances)		E. DIAGNOSIS POINTER	F. $ CHARGES	G. DAYS OR UNITS	H. EPSDT Family Plan	I. ID. QUAL.	J. RENDERING PROVIDER ID. #
From MM DD YY	To MM DD YY			CPT/HCPCS	MODIFIER						
1										NPI	
2										NPI	
3										NPI	
4										NPI	
5										NPI	
6										NPI	

25. FEDERAL TAX I.D. NUMBER   SSN EIN

26. PATIENT'S ACCOUNT NO.

27. ACCEPT ASSIGNMENT? (For govt. claims, see back) YES NO

28. TOTAL CHARGE $

29. AMOUNT PAID $

30. BALANCE DUE $

31. SIGNATURE OF PHYSICIAN OR SUPPLIER INCLUDING DEGREES OR CREDENTIALS (I certify that the statements on the reverse apply to the bill and are made a part thereof.)

32. SERVICE FACILITY LOCATION INFORMATION

33. BILLING PROVIDER INFO & PH # ( )

Name:_____

Class/Section:_____

Date:_____

2012

EXERCISE 12.10

You are the coder for an outpatient facility, and you are trying to describe a service of a diagnostic proctosigmoidoscopy that could not be completed due to the fact that the patient experienced some arrhythmias after she was sedated, but before the anesthesiologist administered any anesthesia. Code for the service as you would if you were the ASC.

Before You Begin:
Read Chapter 12 in cpTeach® on "Modifiers." Follow along in CPT® with the points illustrated in cpTeach®.

Purpose of this Lesson:
To familiarize the student with the different modifiers and how to use them, and to give the student practice in coding real operative reports. For additional practice exercises, please contact MedBooks for our Advanced Case Study Workbook.

Instructions:
1. Using the CMS-1500 claim form, decide which modifiers to use for each patient in the following case studies. Complete the CPT® coding portion of the CMS-1500 claim form on the back of each page.

Notes: _____

_____

_____

_____

_____

_____

_____

EXERCISE 12.10

Name:_____

Class/Section:_____

Date:_____

cpTeach 2012

1500
HEALTH INSURANCE CLAIM FORM
APPROVED BY NATIONAL UNIFORM CLAIM COMMITTEE 08/05

☐☐ PICA

PICA ☐☐

| 1. MEDICARE (Medicare #) | MEDICAID (Medicaid #) | TRICARE CHAMPUS (Sponsor's SSN) | CHAMPVA (Member ID#) | GROUP HEALTH PLAN (SSN or ID) | FECA BLK LUNG (SSN) | OTHER (ID) | 1a. INSURED'S I.D. NUMBER (For Program in Item 1) |

2. PATIENT'S NAME (Last Name, First Name, Middle Initial)

3. PATIENT'S BIRTH DATE MM DD YY   SEX M ☐ F ☐

4. INSURED'S NAME (Last Name, First Name, Middle Initial)

5. PATIENT'S ADDRESS (No., Street)

6. PATIENT RELATIONSHIP TO INSURED Self ☐ Spouse ☐ Child ☐ Other ☐

7. INSURED'S ADDRESS (No., Street)

CITY   STATE

8. PATIENT STATUS Single ☐ Married ☐ Other ☐

CITY   STATE

ZIP CODE   TELEPHONE (Include Area Code) ( )

Employed ☐ Full-Time Student ☐ Part-Time Student ☐

ZIP CODE   TELEPHONE (Include Area Code) ( )

9. OTHER INSURED'S NAME (Last Name, First Name, Middle Initial)

10. IS PATIENT'S CONDITION RELATED TO:

11. INSURED'S POLICY GROUP OR FECA NUMBER

a. OTHER INSURED'S POLICY OR GROUP NUMBER

a. EMPLOYMENT? (Current or Previous) YES ☐ NO ☐

a. INSURED'S DATE OF BIRTH MM DD YY   SEX M ☐ F ☐

b. OTHER INSURED'S DATE OF BIRTH MM DD YY   SEX M ☐ F ☐

b. AUTO ACCIDENT? YES ☐ NO ☐ PLACE (State)

b. EMPLOYER'S NAME OR SCHOOL NAME

c. EMPLOYER'S NAME OR SCHOOL NAME

c. OTHER ACCIDENT? YES ☐ NO ☐

c. INSURANCE PLAN NAME OR PROGRAM NAME

d. INSURANCE PLAN NAME OR PROGRAM NAME

10d. RESERVED FOR LOCAL USE

d. IS THERE ANOTHER HEALTH BENEFIT PLAN? YES ☐ NO ☐ If yes, return to and complete item 9 a-d.

READ BACK OF FORM BEFORE COMPLETING & SIGNING THIS FORM.
12. PATIENT'S OR AUTHORIZED PERSON'S SIGNATURE I authorize the release of any medical or other information necessary to process this claim. I also request payment of government benefits either to myself or to the party who accepts assignment below.

SIGNED_____ DATE_____

13. INSURED'S OR AUTHORIZED PERSON'S SIGNATURE I authorize payment of medical benefits to the undersigned physician or supplier for services described below.

SIGNED_____

14. DATE OF CURRENT: MM DD YY ◄ ILLNESS (First symptom) OR INJURY (Accident) OR PREGNANCY(LMP)

15. IF PATIENT HAS HAD SAME OR SIMILAR ILLNESS. GIVE FIRST DATE MM DD YY

16. DATES PATIENT UNABLE TO WORK IN CURRENT OCCUPATION MM DD YY FROM TO MM DD YY

17. NAME OF REFERRING PROVIDER OR OTHER SOURCE

17a.
17b. NPI

18. HOSPITALIZATION DATES RELATED TO CURRENT SERVICES MM DD YY FROM TO MM DD YY

19. RESERVED FOR LOCAL USE

20. OUTSIDE LAB? YES ☐ NO ☐ $ CHARGES

21. DIAGNOSIS OR NATURE OF ILLNESS OR INJURY (Relate Items 1, 2, 9 or 4 to Item 24E by Line)

1. |___.___   3. |___.___
2. |___.___   4. |___.___

22. MEDICAID RESUBMISSION CODE   ORIGINAL REF. NO.

23. PRIOR AUTHORIZATION NUMBER

24. A. DATE(S) OF SERVICE From MM DD YY To MM DD YY	B. PLACE OF SERVICE	C. EMG	D. PROCEDURES, SERVICES, OR SUPPLIES (Explain Unusual Circumstances) CPT/HCPCS MODIFIER	E. DIAGNOSIS POINTER	F. $ CHARGES	G. DAYS OR UNITS	H. EPSDT Family Plan	I. ID QUAL.	J. RENDERING PROVIDER ID. #
1									NPI
2									NPI
3									NPI
4									NPI
5									NPI
6									NPI

25. FEDERAL TAX I.D. NUMBER SSN ☐ EIN ☐

26. PATIENT'S ACCOUNT NO.

27. ACCEPT ASSIGNMENT? (For govt. claims, see back) YES ☐ NO ☐

28. TOTAL CHARGE $

29. AMOUNT PAID $

30. BALANCE DUE $

31. SIGNATURE OF PHYSICIAN OR SUPPLIER INCLUDING DEGREES OR CREDENTIALS (I certify that the statements on the reverse apply to this bill and are made a part thereof.)

32. SERVICE FACILITY LOCATION INFORMATION

33. BILLING PROVIDER INFO & PH # ( )

CARRIER

PATIENT AND INSURED INFORMATION

PHYSICIAN OR SUPPLIER INFORMATION

Name:_____

Class/Section:_____

Date:_____

WORKBOOK

cpTeach

2012

EXERCISE 12.11

Code for the same scenario, only this time pretend that the anesthesia had been administered. How would this change your coding?

Before You Begin:
Read Chapter 12 in cpTeach® on "Modifiers." Follow along in CPT® with the points illustrated in cpTeach®.

Purpose of this Lesson:
To familiarize the student with the different modifiers and how to use them, and to give the student practice in coding real operative reports. For additional practice exercises, please contact MedBooks for our Advanced Case Study Workbook.

Instructions:
1. Using the CMS-1500 claim form, decide which modifiers to use for each patient in the following case studies. Complete the CPT® coding portion of the CMS-1500 claim form on the back of each page.

Notes: _____
_____
_____
_____
_____
_____
_____
_____

EXERCISE 12.11

Name:_____

Class/Section:_____

Date:_____

2012

1500
HEALTH INSURANCE CLAIM FORM

APPROVED BY NATIONAL UNIFORM CLAIM COMMITTEE 08/05

| | PICA | | | | | | | PICA | |

1. MEDICARE (Medicare #) **MEDICAID** (Medicaid #) **TRICARE CHAMPUS** (Sponsor's SSN) **CHAMPVA** (Member ID#) **GROUP HEALTH PLAN** (SSN or ID) **FECA BLK LUNG** (SSN) **OTHER** (ID) | **1a. INSURED'S I.D. NUMBER** (For Program in Item 1)

2. PATIENT'S NAME (Last Name, First Name, Middle Initial) | **3. PATIENT'S BIRTH DATE** MM DD YY **SEX** M [ ] F [ ] | **4. INSURED'S NAME** (Last Name, First Name, Middle Initial)

5. PATIENT'S ADDRESS (No., Street) | **6. PATIENT RELATIONSHIP TO INSURED** Self [ ] Spouse [ ] Child [ ] Other [ ] | **7. INSURED'S ADDRESS** (No., Street)

CITY | STATE | **8. PATIENT STATUS** Single [ ] Married [ ] Other [ ] | CITY | STATE

ZIP CODE | TELEPHONE (Include Area Code) ( ) | Employed [ ] Full-Time Student [ ] Part-Time Student [ ] | ZIP CODE | TELEPHONE (Include Area Code) ( )

9. OTHER INSURED'S NAME (Last Name, First Name, Middle Initial) | **10. IS PATIENT'S CONDITION RELATED TO:** | **11. INSURED'S POLICY GROUP OR FECA NUMBER**

a. OTHER INSURED'S POLICY OR GROUP NUMBER | **a. EMPLOYMENT?** (Current or Previous) [ ] YES [ ] NO | **a. INSURED'S DATE OF BIRTH** MM DD YY **SEX** M [ ] F [ ]

b. OTHER INSURED'S DATE OF BIRTH MM DD YY **SEX** M [ ] F [ ] | **b. AUTO ACCIDENT?** PLACE (State) [ ] YES [ ] NO | **b. EMPLOYER'S NAME OR SCHOOL NAME**

c. EMPLOYER'S NAME OR SCHOOL NAME | **c. OTHER ACCIDENT?** [ ] YES [ ] NO | **c. INSURANCE PLAN NAME OR PROGRAM NAME**

d. INSURANCE PLAN NAME OR PROGRAM NAME | **10d. RESERVED FOR LOCAL USE** | **d. IS THERE ANOTHER HEALTH BENEFIT PLAN?** [ ] YES [ ] NO *If yes, return to and complete item 9 a-d.*

READ BACK OF FORM BEFORE COMPLETING & SIGNING THIS FORM.
12. PATIENT'S OR AUTHORIZED PERSON'S SIGNATURE I authorize the release of any medical or other information necessary to process this claim. I also request payment of government benefits either to myself or to the party who accepts assignment below.

SIGNED_____ DATE_____

13. INSURED'S OR AUTHORIZED PERSON'S SIGNATURE I authorize payment of medical benefits to the undersigned physician or supplier for services described below.

SIGNED_____

14. DATE OF CURRENT: MM DD YY **ILLNESS** (First symptom) OR **INJURY** (Accident) OR **PREGNANCY** (LMP) | **15. IF PATIENT HAS HAD SAME OR SIMILAR ILLNESS.** GIVE FIRST DATE MM DD YY | **16. DATES PATIENT UNABLE TO WORK IN CURRENT OCCUPATION** MM DD YY FROM TO MM DD YY

17. NAME OF REFERRING PROVIDER OR OTHER SOURCE | 17a. 17b. NPI | **18. HOSPITALIZATION DATES RELATED TO CURRENT SERVICES** MM DD YY FROM TO MM DD YY

19. RESERVED FOR LOCAL USE | **20. OUTSIDE LAB?** [ ] YES [ ] NO $ CHARGES

21. DIAGNOSIS OR NATURE OF ILLNESS OR INJURY (Relate Items 1, 2, 3 or 4 to Item 24E by Line)
1. |___.___| 3. |___.___|
2. |___.___| 4. |___.___| | **22. MEDICAID RESUBMISSION** CODE ORIGINAL REF. NO.

23. PRIOR AUTHORIZATION NUMBER

24. A. DATE(S) OF SERVICE		B. PLACE OF SERVICE	C. EMG	D. PROCEDURES, SERVICES, OR SUPPLIES (Explain Unusual Circumstances) CPT/HCPCS MODIFIER	E. DIAGNOSIS POINTER	F. $ CHARGES	G. DAYS OR UNITS	H. EPSDT Family Plan	I. ID. QUAL.	J. RENDERING PROVIDER ID. #
From MM DD YY	To MM DD YY									
1									NPI	
2									NPI	
3									NPI	
4									NPI	
5									NPI	
6									NPI	

25. FEDERAL TAX I.D. NUMBER SSN [ ] EIN [ ] | **26. PATIENT'S ACCOUNT NO.** | **27. ACCEPT ASSIGNMENT?** (For govt. claims, see back) [ ] YES [ ] NO | **28. TOTAL CHARGE** $ | **29. AMOUNT PAID** $ | **30. BALANCE DUE** $

31. SIGNATURE OF PHYSICIAN OR SUPPLIER INCLUDING DEGREES OR CREDENTIALS (I certify that the statements on the reverse apply to this bill and are made a part thereof.) | **32. SERVICE FACILITY LOCATION INFORMATION** | **33. BILLING PROVIDER INFO & PH #** ( )

CARRIER ← PATIENT AND INSURED INFORMATION ← PHYSICIAN OR SUPPLIER INFORMATION →

Practice Your Skills

Practice Your Skills:

The following lessons are real patient charts taken from doctors' records.

Try your hand at coding each one of these on the corresponding CMS-1500 claim form. There are chances that some information may be missing.

Remember:

This happens too many times in real life. Code what you see.

Purpose of these Lesson:

To familiarize the student with real life experiences, including doctor's hand-writing, E/M, etc.

Instructions:

1. Review each patient's chart.

2. Fill out each CMS-1500 claim form correctly.

Exercise 13.1 - 13.10

EXERCISE 13.1

POOH, WINNIE MAE	RM: 509B
10-02-99/10	
DR. N. MORIN	
ADMITTED: 10-26-__	

HISTORY
ST. CATHERINE'S HOSPITAL
ANYTOWN, LOUISIANA

Information should
be recorded on all
POSITIVE
and also relevant
NEGATIVE
Findings.

ORDER OF
RECORDING

1. Chief Complaint

2. History of Present Illness

3. History of Past Illness
    (a) Childhood
    (b) Adult
    (c) Operations
    (d) Injuries

4. Family History

5. Social History

6. Review of Systems
    (a) Skeletal
    (b) Muscular
    (c) Circulatory
    (d) Respiratory
    (e) Digestive
    (f) Urinary
    (g) Endocrine
    (h) Reproductive
    (i) Nervous

Chief Complaint & Present Illness:

This fifty-nine year old white female is being admitted for release of a right trigger thumb which she attributes to excessive needlework some six months ago. Since then, she has tried the usual modalities to include heat, aspirin, etc.; however, in spite of same, the thumb has continued to lock with flexion. She consulted the undersigned on 9-25-__ and was told that she had a right thumb which was labelled a trigger thumb. She was advised that surgical intervention was the treatment of choice in view of persistence of signs and symptoms and lack of response to the usual modalties. She has consented to same.

Past History:

Some fourteen years ago, she underwent a complete hysterectomy prior to which she had a tube and one ovary excision for a tumor in the ovary. No history of other serious operations, illnesses or accidents.

Family History:

Her father died of some lung disease, etiology unknown. Her mother had diabetes. There is also a history of cancer of the liver in the family. She has quit smoking as of 2 1/2 years ago. There are no known allergies except to Darvon.

Physical Examination:

GENERAL:	A somewhat obese white female of about stated age in no gross distress.
HEAD:	No abnormalities noted.
CHEST:	Clear to percussion and auscultation.
HEART:	No enlargements, no murmurs.
	BP: 150/84. Regular rate and rhythm.
ABDOMEN:	No masses felt. No tenderness on palpation. Liver and spleen negative.
GENITOURINARY:	Normal female.
RECTAL:	Deferred.
NEUROLOGICAL:	Normal.

Exercise 13.1

POOH, WINNIE MAE	
10-02-__/01	RM: 509B
DR. N. MORIN	
ADMITTED: 10-26-__	

HISTORY
ST. CATHERINE'S HOSPITAL
ANYTOWN, LOUISIANA

<table>
<tr><td valign="top" width="30%">

Information should
be recorded on all
POSITIVE
and also relevant
NEGATIVE
Findings.

**ORDER OF
RECORDING**

1. Chief Complaint

2. History of Present Illness

3. History of Past Illness
   (a) Childhood
   (b) Adult
   (c) Operations
   (d) Injuries

4. Family History

5. Social History

6. Review of Systems
   (a) Skeletal
   (b) Muscular
   (c) Circulatory
   (d) Respiratory
   (e) Digestive
   (f) Urinary
   (g) Endocrine
   (h) Reproductive
   (i) Nervous

</td><td valign="top">

--page 2--

CONTINUATION OF HISTORY & PHYSICAL

EXTREMITIES: Normal except for the right thumb where a triggering mechanism with locking with full flexion of the thumb is demonstrated by the patient and experienced by the examiner. There is also tenderness on palpation of the IP joint and MP joint.

IMPRESSION: **RIGHT TRIGGER THUMB**

SIGNATURE:_____

DR. N. MORIN/js
cc:
dict: 10-26-__
tran: 10-27-__

</td></tr>
</table>

EXERCISE 13.1

Name:_____

Class/Section:_____

Date:_____

cpTeach 2012

1500

HEALTH INSURANCE CLAIM FORM

APPROVED BY NATIONAL UNIFORM CLAIM COMMITTEE 08/05

[ ][ ] PICA

1. MEDICARE	MEDICAID	TRICARE CHAMPUS	CHAMPVA	GROUP HEALTH PLAN	FECA BLK LUNG	OTHER	1a. INSURED'S I.D. NUMBER	(For Program in Item 1)
(Medicare #)	(Medicaid #)	(Sponsor's SSN)	(Member ID#)	(SSN or ID)	(SSN)	(ID)		

2. PATIENT'S NAME (Last Name, First Name, Middle Initial)

3. PATIENT'S BIRTH DATE MM DD YY   SEX   M [ ] F [ ]

4. INSURED'S NAME (Last Name, First Name, Middle Initial)

5. PATIENT'S ADDRESS (No., Street)

6. PATIENT RELATIONSHIP TO INSURED Self [ ] Spouse [ ] Child [ ] Other [ ]

7. INSURED'S ADDRESS (No., Street)

CITY   STATE

8. PATIENT STATUS Single [ ] Married [ ] Other [ ]

CITY   STATE

ZIP CODE   TELEPHONE (Include Area Code) (   )

Employed [ ] Full-Time Student [ ] Part-Time Student [ ]

ZIP CODE   TELEPHONE (Include Area Code) (   )

9. OTHER INSURED'S NAME (Last Name, First Name, Middle Initial)

10. IS PATIENT'S CONDITION RELATED TO:

11. INSURED'S POLICY GROUP OR FECA NUMBER

a. OTHER INSURED'S POLICY OR GROUP NUMBER

a. EMPLOYMENT? (Current or Previous) [ ] YES [ ] NO

a. INSURED'S DATE OF BIRTH MM DD YY   SEX M [ ] F [ ]

b. OTHER INSURED'S DATE OF BIRTH MM DD YY   SEX M [ ] F [ ]

b. AUTO ACCIDENT?   PLACE (State) [ ] YES [ ] NO

b. EMPLOYER'S NAME OR SCHOOL NAME

c. EMPLOYER'S NAME OR SCHOOL NAME

c. OTHER ACCIDENT? [ ] YES [ ] NO

c. INSURANCE PLAN NAME OR PROGRAM NAME

d. INSURANCE PLAN NAME OR PROGRAM NAME

10d. RESERVED FOR LOCAL USE

d. IS THERE ANOTHER HEALTH BENEFIT PLAN? [ ] YES [ ] NO   If yes, return to and complete item 9 a-d.

READ BACK OF FORM BEFORE COMPLETING & SIGNING THIS FORM.

12. PATIENT'S OR AUTHORIZED PERSON'S SIGNATURE I authorize the release of any medical or other information necessary to process this claim. I also request payment of government benefits either to myself or to the party who accepts assignment below.

SIGNED_____   DATE_____

13. INSURED'S OR AUTHORIZED PERSON'S SIGNATURE I authorize payment of medical benefits to the undersigned physician or supplier for services described below.

SIGNED_____

14. DATE OF CURRENT: MM DD YY   ILLNESS (First symptom) OR INJURY (Accident) OR PREGNANCY(LMP)

15. IF PATIENT HAS HAD SAME OR SIMILAR ILLNESS. GIVE FIRST DATE MM DD YY

16. DATES PATIENT UNABLE TO WORK IN CURRENT OCCUPATION MM DD YY FROM   TO   MM DD YY

17. NAME OF REFERRING PROVIDER OR OTHER SOURCE

17a.

17b. NPI

18. HOSPITALIZATION DATES RELATED TO CURRENT SERVICES MM DD YY FROM   TO   MM DD YY

19. RESERVED FOR LOCAL USE

20. OUTSIDE LAB? [ ] YES [ ] NO $ CHARGES

21. DIAGNOSIS OR NATURE OF ILLNESS OR INJURY (Relate Items 1, 2, 3 or 4 to Item 24E by Line)

1. |___.___| 3. |___.___|

2. |___.___| 4. |___.___|

22. MEDICAID RESUBMISSION CODE   ORIGINAL REF. NO.

23. PRIOR AUTHORIZATION NUMBER

24. A. DATE(S) OF SERVICE						B. PLACE OF SERVICE	C. EMG	D. PROCEDURES, SERVICES, OR SUPPLIES (Explain Unusual Circumstances)		E. DIAGNOSIS POINTER	F. $ CHARGES	G. DAYS OR UNITS	H. EPSDT Family Plan	I. ID. QUAL.	J. RENDERING PROVIDER ID. #
From MM	DD	YY	To MM	DD	YY			CPT/HCPCS	MODIFIER						
1														NPI	
2														NPI	
3														NPI	
4														NPI	
5														NPI	
6														NPI	

25. FEDERAL TAX I.D. NUMBER   SSN [ ] EIN [ ]

26. PATIENT'S ACCOUNT NO.

27. ACCEPT ASSIGNMENT? (For govt. claims, see back) [ ] YES [ ] NO

28. TOTAL CHARGE $

29. AMOUNT PAID $

30. BALANCE DUE $

31. SIGNATURE OF PHYSICIAN OR SUPPLIER INCLUDING DEGREES OR CREDENTIALS (I certify that the statements on the reverse apply to this bill and are made a part thereof.)

32. SERVICE FACILITY LOCATION INFORMATION

33. BILLING PROVIDER INFO & PH # (   )

CARRIER

PATIENT AND INSURED INFORMATION

PHYSICIAN OR SUPPLIER INFORMATION

EXERCISE 13.2

REPORT OF OPERATION
ST. CATHERINE'S HOSPITAL
ANYTOWN, LOUISIANA

CASE #   10-02- /01 _____   ROOM # 509B _____

NAME: POOH, WINNIE MAE _____   DATE: _____

SURGEON: NORMAN MORIN _____   ASSISTANT: _____

ANESTHETIST: _____   STARTED: _____ ENDED:_____

PREOPERATIVE DIAGNOSIS: Right trigger thumb.
POSTOPERATIVE DIAGNOSIS: Release of right trigger thumb.

PROCEDURE: With the patient under general anesthesia tourniquet control and cardiac monitoring the right hand and forearm were thoroughly prepped with Betadine and thereafter draped as to leave the palmar aspect of the hand exposed. A transverse incision was made parallel to the flexion crease of the MP joint of the thumb with the subcutaneous tissue incised by blunt dissection down to the tendon sheath of the long flexor to the thumb. This revealed the tendon sheath to be markedly thickened at the pulley. Marked restriction of the tendon just proximal to this tendon was so restricted at the pulley that the tendon tissue proximal to it had become bulbous. It also became extremely difficult to incise this tendon sheath without damaging the tendon. Nevertheless over a mosquito hemostat this was accomplished along its full length following which a full range of flexion of the thumb was obtained without restriction or triggering mechanism. The area was then thoroughly syringed out and antibiotic solution consisting of 2 grams of Kantrex, 15000 units Bacitracin, 1 liter of normal Saline following which was closed with a single subcuticular #3-0 Proler suture, following closure approximately 1/2 cc of Celestrosoluspan was instilled above the tendon, to be followed by the application of a pressure dressing and a release of the tourniquet. Immediate blood supply was noted to the thumb following release of the tourniquet. The patient withstood the procedure well and was given 2 grams of AncefIV during the procedure. She was thereafter taken to recovery.

DR. N. MORIN/js
cc:
dict: 10-27-__
tran: 10-27-__

EXERCISE 13.2

Name:_____

Class/Section:_____

Date:_____

2012

1500
HEALTH INSURANCE CLAIM FORM
APPROVED BY NATIONAL UNIFORM CLAIM COMMITTEE 08/05

| | PICA | | | | | | | | PICA | |

1. MEDICARE (Medicare #) **MEDICAID** (Medicaid #) **TRICARE CHAMPUS** (Sponsor's SSN) **CHAMPVA** (Member ID#) **GROUP HEALTH PLAN** (SSN or ID) **FECA BLK LUNG** (SSN) **OTHER** (ID)   **1a. INSURED'S I.D. NUMBER** (For Program in Item 1)

2. PATIENT'S NAME (Last Name, First Name, Middle Initial)   **3. PATIENT'S BIRTH DATE** MM DD YY **SEX** M F   **4. INSURED'S NAME (Last Name, First Name, Middle Initial)**

5. PATIENT'S ADDRESS (No., Street)   **6. PATIENT RELATIONSHIP TO INSURED** Self Spouse Child Other   **7. INSURED'S ADDRESS (No., Street)**

CITY   **STATE**   **8. PATIENT STATUS** Single Married Other   **CITY**   **STATE**

ZIP CODE   **TELEPHONE (Include Area Code)** ( )   Employed Full-Time Student Part-Time Student   **ZIP CODE**   **TELEPHONE (Include Area Code)** ( )

9. OTHER INSURED'S NAME (Last Name, First Name, Middle Initial)   **10. IS PATIENT'S CONDITION RELATED TO:**   **11. INSURED'S POLICY GROUP OR FECA NUMBER**

a. OTHER INSURED'S POLICY OR GROUP NUMBER   **a. EMPLOYMENT? (Current or Previous)** YES NO   **a. INSURED'S DATE OF BIRTH** MM DD YY **SEX** M F

b. OTHER INSURED'S DATE OF BIRTH MM DD YY **SEX** M F   **b. AUTO ACCIDENT?** YES NO **PLACE (State)**   **b. EMPLOYER'S NAME OR SCHOOL NAME**

c. EMPLOYER'S NAME OR SCHOOL NAME   **c. OTHER ACCIDENT?** YES NO   **c. INSURANCE PLAN NAME OR PROGRAM NAME**

d. INSURANCE PLAN NAME OR PROGRAM NAME   **10d. RESERVED FOR LOCAL USE**   **d. IS THERE ANOTHER HEALTH BENEFIT PLAN?** YES NO If yes, return to and complete item 9 a-d.

READ BACK OF FORM BEFORE COMPLETING & SIGNING THIS FORM.
12. PATIENT'S OR AUTHORIZED PERSON'S SIGNATURE I authorize the release of any medical or other information necessary to process this claim. I also request payment of government benefits either to myself or to the party who accepts assignment below.

SIGNED_____   DATE_____

13. INSURED'S OR AUTHORIZED PERSON'S SIGNATURE I authorize payment of medical benefits to the undersigned physician or supplier for services described below.

SIGNED_____

14. DATE OF CURRENT: MM DD YY ILLNESS (First symptom) OR INJURY (Accident) OR PREGNANCY(LMP)   **15. IF PATIENT HAS HAD SAME OR SIMILAR ILLNESS.** GIVE FIRST DATE MM DD YY   **16. DATES PATIENT UNABLE TO WORK IN CURRENT OCCUPATION** FROM MM DD YY TO MM DD YY

17. NAME OF REFERRING PROVIDER OR OTHER SOURCE   17a. 17b. NPI   **18. HOSPITALIZATION DATES RELATED TO CURRENT SERVICES** FROM MM DD YY TO MM DD YY

19. RESERVED FOR LOCAL USE   **20. OUTSIDE LAB?** YES NO **$ CHARGES**

21. DIAGNOSIS OR NATURE OF ILLNESS OR INJURY (Relate Items 1, 2, 9 or 4 to Item 24E by Line)   **22. MEDICAID RESUBMISSION CODE** ORIGINAL REF. NO.

1. |____.____   3. |____.____

2. |____.____   4. |____.____   **23. PRIOR AUTHORIZATION NUMBER**

24. A. DATE(S) OF SERVICE						B. PLACE OF SERVICE	C. EMG	D. PROCEDURES, SERVICES, OR SUPPLIES (Explain Unusual Circumstances)		E. DIAGNOSIS POINTER	F. $ CHARGES	G. DAYS OR UNITS	H. EPSDT Family Plan	I. ID. QUAL.	J. RENDERING PROVIDER ID. #
From			To					CPT/HCPCS	MODIFIER						
MM	DD	YY	MM	DD	YY										
1														NPI	
2														NPI	
3														NPI	
4														NPI	
5														NPI	
6														NPI	

25. FEDERAL TAX I.D. NUMBER SSN EIN   **26. PATIENT'S ACCOUNT NO.**   **27. ACCEPT ASSIGNMENT?** (For govt. claims, see back) YES NO   **28. TOTAL CHARGE** $ **29. AMOUNT PAID** $ **30. BALANCE DUE** $

31. SIGNATURE OF PHYSICIAN OR SUPPLIER INCLUDING DEGREES OR CREDENTIALS (I certify that the statements on the reverse apply to this bill and are made a part thereof.)   **32. SERVICE FACILITY LOCATION INFORMATION**   **33. BILLING PROVIDER INFO & PH # ( )**

Exercise 13.3

SHOESTRING, HELEN 10-02-99/10 DR. N. MORIN ADMITTED: 02-12-__	RM: 509B

HISTORY
ST. CATHERINE'S HOSPITAL
ANYTOWN, LOUISIANA

Information should
be recorded on all
POSITIVE
and also relevant
NEGATIVE
Findings.

ORDER OF RECORDING

1. Chief Complaint

2. History of Present Illness

3. History of Past Illness
   (a) Childhood
   (b) Adult
   (c) Operations
   (d) Injuries

4. Family History

5. Social History

6. Review of Systems
   (a) Skeletal
   (b) Muscular
   (c) Circulatory
   (d) Respiratory
   (e) Digestive
   (f) Urinary
   (g) Endocrine
   (h) Reproductive
   (i) Nervous

History:
This 53 year old white female is being admitted for a left foot bunionectomy as treatment for a disabling hallux valgus deformity with bunion formation involving this foot. She was seen by the undersigned the early part of January at which time she requested something be done. She has consequently been scheduled for a simple bunionectomy with no associated osteotomy of the first metatarsal.

Past History:
At age 22, patient had a tonsillectomy and in 1999, she had a tumor apparently secondary to the endometriosis. In 2001, she had a hemorrhoidectomy and has otherwise been well with no other surgeries. No illnesses or accidents.

Family History:
No history of cancer. Father and paternal grandfather had diabetes. Her mother has high blood pressure. No other familial diseases.

Systemic Review:
Within normal limits except for allergies to plant pollens. No drug allergies. Patient does not smoke or drink.

Physical Examination:

GENERAL:	A well developed, well nourished, white female of about stated age.
HEAD:	No abnormalities.
CHEST:	Clear to percussion and ausculation.
HEART:	No enlargements. No murmurs. Blood pressure 160/90. Regular rate & rhythm.
ABDOMEN:	No masses felt. no tenderness to palpation. Liver and spleen negative.
GU:	Normal female.
RECTAL:	Deferred.
NEUROLOGICAL:	Normal
EXTREMITIES:	Normal except for left foot where there is a mild hallux valgus deformity with bunion formation with tenderness on palpation of the bunion which is somewhat inflamed.
IMPRESSION:	(1) Hallux valgus deformity

Name: _____

Class/Section: _____

cpTeach 2012

Date: _____

EXERCISE 13.3

1500

HEALTH INSURANCE CLAIM FORM

APPROVED BY NATIONAL UNIFORM CLAIM COMMITTEE 08/05

	PICA						PICA	

1. MEDICARE (Medicare #)   MEDICAID (Medicaid #)   TRICARE CHAMPUS (Sponsor's SSN)   CHAMPVA (Member ID#)   GROUP HEALTH PLAN (SSN or ID)   FECA BLK LUNG (SSN)   OTHER (ID)   **1a.** INSURED'S I.D. NUMBER   (For Program in Item 1)

2. PATIENT'S NAME (Last Name, First Name, Middle Initial)   **3.** PATIENT'S BIRTH DATE MM DD YY   SEX   M   F   **4.** INSURED'S NAME (Last Name, First Name, Middle Initial)

5. PATIENT'S ADDRESS (No., Street)   **6.** PATIENT RELATIONSHIP TO INSURED   Self   Spouse   Child   Other   **7.** INSURED'S ADDRESS (No., Street)

CITY   STATE   **8.** PATIENT STATUS   Single   Married   Other   CITY   STATE

ZIP CODE   TELEPHONE (Include Area Code) ( )   Employed   Full-Time Student   Part-Time Student   ZIP CODE   TELEPHONE (Include Area Code) ( )

9. OTHER INSURED'S NAME (Last Name, First Name, Middle Initial)   **10.** IS PATIENT'S CONDITION RELATED TO: **11.** INSURED'S POLICY GROUP OR FECA NUMBER

a. OTHER INSURED'S POLICY OR GROUP NUMBER   **a.** EMPLOYMENT? (Current or Previous)   YES   NO   **a.** INSURED'S DATE OF BIRTH MM DD YY   SEX   M   F

b. OTHER INSURED'S DATE OF BIRTH MM DD YY   SEX   M   F   **b.** AUTO ACCIDENT?   YES   NO   PLACE (State)   **b.** EMPLOYER'S NAME OR SCHOOL NAME

c. EMPLOYER'S NAME OR SCHOOL NAME   **c.** OTHER ACCIDENT?   YES   NO   **c.** INSURANCE PLAN NAME OR PROGRAM NAME

d. INSURANCE PLAN NAME OR PROGRAM NAME   **10d.** RESERVED FOR LOCAL USE   **d.** IS THERE ANOTHER HEALTH BENEFIT PLAN?   YES   NO   If yes, return to and complete item 9 a-d.

READ BACK OF FORM BEFORE COMPLETING & SIGNING THIS FORM.

12. PATIENT'S OR AUTHORIZED PERSON'S SIGNATURE I authorize the release of any medical or other information necessary to process this claim. I also request payment of government benefits either to myself or to the party who accepts assignment below.

SIGNED _____ DATE _____

13. INSURED'S OR AUTHORIZED PERSON'S SIGNATURE I authorize payment of medical benefits to the undersigned physician or supplier for services described below.

SIGNED _____

14. DATE OF CURRENT: MM DD YY ILLNESS (First symptom) OR INJURY (Accident) OR PREGNANCY (LMP)   **15.** IF PATIENT HAS HAD SAME OR SIMILAR ILLNESS. GIVE FIRST DATE MM DD YY   **16.** DATES PATIENT UNABLE TO WORK IN CURRENT OCCUPATION MM DD YY FROM TO MM DD YY

17. NAME OF REFERRING PROVIDER OR OTHER SOURCE   **17a.**   **17b.** NPI   **18.** HOSPITALIZATION DATES RELATED TO CURRENT SERVICES MM DD YY FROM TO MM DD YY

19. RESERVED FOR LOCAL USE   **20.** OUTSIDE LAB?   YES   NO $ CHARGES

21. DIAGNOSIS OR NATURE OF ILLNESS OR INJURY (Relate Items 1, 2, 9 or 4 to Item 24E by Line)

1. |___.___   3. |___.___

2. |___.___   4. |___.___

22. MEDICAID RESUBMISSION CODE   ORIGINAL REF. NO.

23. PRIOR AUTHORIZATION NUMBER

24. A. DATE(S) OF SERVICE			B. PLACE OF SERVICE	C. EMG	D. PROCEDURES, SERVICES, OR SUPPLIES (Explain Unusual Circumstances)		E. DIAGNOSIS POINTER	F. $ CHARGES	G. DAYS OR UNITS	H. EPSDT Family Plan	I. ID. QUAL.	J. RENDERING PROVIDER ID. #
From MM DD YY	To MM DD YY				CPT/HCPCS	MODIFIER						
1											NPI	
2											NPI	
3											NPI	
4											NPI	
5											NPI	
6											NPI	

25. FEDERAL TAX I.D. NUMBER   SSN EIN   **26.** PATIENT'S ACCOUNT NO.   **27.** ACCEPT ASSIGNMENT? (For govt. claims, see back) YES NO   **28.** TOTAL CHARGE $ **29.** AMOUNT PAID $ **30.** BALANCE DUE $

31. SIGNATURE OF PHYSICIAN OR SUPPLIER INCLUDING DEGREES OR CREDENTIALS (I certify that the statements on the reverse apply to this bill and are made a part thereof.)   **32.** SERVICE FACILITY LOCATION INFORMATION   **33.** BILLING PROVIDER INFO & PH # ( )

CARRIER

PATIENT AND INSURED INFORMATION

PHYSICIAN OR SUPPLIER INFORMATION

EXERCISE 13.4

REPORT OF OPERATION
ST. CATHERINE'S HOSPITAL
ANYTOWN, LOUISIANA

CASE #   08-47- /01   ROOM # 507

NAME: SHOESTRING, HELEN   DATE: _____

SURGEON: NORMAN MORIN   ASSISTANT: _____

ANESTHETIST: _____   STARTED: _____ ENDED: _____

PREOPERATIVE DIAGNOSIS: Hallux Valgus deformity with bunion formation,
                                       left large toe.

POSTOPERATIVE DIAGNOSIS: Same.

PROCEDURE: With the patient under general anesthesia and cardiac monitoring, the tourniquet was applied to the left lower extremity following of which the leg was exsanguinated and prepped with Betadine with the prep extending from the tip of the toes to the mid-calf, to be followed by proper draping, leaving the foot exposed. A longitudinal incision was then made along the medial aspect of the proximal phalanx of the medial border for approximatelly 1 1/2 inch in length. The subcutaneous tissue was then incised in line with the skin incision, care being taken to control all possible bleeders. Thereafter, a flap was developed with that base proximally, overlying the prominent first metatarsal head. This flap was reflected proximally, following of which a bunionectomy was carried out, after which an osteotomy of the prominent portion of the first metatarsal head was done. Using the Hall drill bur, this area was made smooth, following of which it was thoroughly syringed out with normal Saline and thereafter, sealed with bone wax. The abductor hallucis was then shortened by approximately one-quarter inch, as was the flap. The toe was held in neutral position and the area was repaired with interrupted #3-0 Dexon surtures. This corrected the hallux valgus deformity to a large degree. The subcutaneous tissues were also approximated with #3-0 interrupted dexon sutures and the skin closed with a #4-0 subcuticular steel suture. A pressure dressing was applied, maintaining the large toe in the corrected position. Following release of the tourniquet, good blood flow was noted in all toes. The patient withstood the procedure well and was given 2 grams of Keflin intravenously during the surgery.

DR. N. MORIN/js
cc:
dict: 2-13-__
tran: 2-13-__

Name:_____

Class/Section:_____

Date:_____

WORKBOOK · cpTeach 2012

EXERCISE 13.4

1500

HEALTH INSURANCE CLAIM FORM

APPROVED BY NATIONAL UNIFORM CLAIM COMMITTEE 08/05

| | PICA | | | | | | | | PICA | | |

1. MEDICARE MEDICAID TRICARE CHAMPUS CHAMPVA GROUP HEALTH PLAN FECA BLK LUNG OTHER   **1a.** INSURED'S I.D. NUMBER   (For Program in Item 1)

(Medicare #) (Medicaid #) (Sponsor's SSN) (Member ID#) (SSN or ID) (SSN) (ID)

2. PATIENT'S NAME (Last Name, First Name, Middle Initial)   **3.** PATIENT'S BIRTH DATE MM DD YY SEX M F   **4.** INSURED'S NAME (Last Name, First Name, Middle Initial)

5. PATIENT'S ADDRESS (No., Street)   **6.** PATIENT RELATIONSHIP TO INSURED Self Spouse Child Other   **7.** INSURED'S ADDRESS (No., Street)

CITY STATE   **8.** PATIENT STATUS Single Married Other   CITY STATE

ZIP CODE TELEPHONE (Include Area Code) ( )   Employed Full-Time Student Part-Time Student   ZIP CODE TELEPHONE (Include Area Code) ( )

9. OTHER INSURED'S NAME (Last Name, First Name, Middle Initial)   **10.** IS PATIENT'S CONDITION RELATED TO: **11.** INSURED'S POLICY GROUP OR FECA NUMBER

a. OTHER INSURED'S POLICY OR GROUP NUMBER   **a.** EMPLOYMENT? (Current or Previous) YES NO   **a.** INSURED'S DATE OF BIRTH MM DD YY SEX M F

b. OTHER INSURED'S DATE OF BIRTH MM DD YY SEX M F   **b.** AUTO ACCIDENT? PLACE (State) YES NO   **b.** EMPLOYER'S NAME OR SCHOOL NAME

c. EMPLOYER'S NAME OR SCHOOL NAME   **c.** OTHER ACCIDENT? YES NO   **c.** INSURANCE PLAN NAME OR PROGRAM NAME

d. INSURANCE PLAN NAME OR PROGRAM NAME   **10d.** RESERVED FOR LOCAL USE   **d.** IS THERE ANOTHER HEALTH BENEFIT PLAN? YES NO If yes, return to and complete item 9 a-d.

READ BACK OF FORM BEFORE COMPLETING & SIGNING THIS FORM.

12. PATIENT'S OR AUTHORIZED PERSON'S SIGNATURE I authorize the release of any medical or other information necessary to process this claim. I also request payment of government benefits either to myself or to the party who accepts assignment below.

SIGNED_____ DATE_____

13. INSURED'S OR AUTHORIZED PERSON'S SIGNATURE I authorize payment of medical benefits to the undersigned physician or supplier for services described below.

SIGNED_____

14. DATE OF CURRENT: MM DD YY ILLNESS (First symptom) OR INJURY (Accident) OR PREGNANCY (LMP)   **15.** IF PATIENT HAS HAD SAME OR SIMILAR ILLNESS. GIVE FIRST DATE MM DD YY   **16.** DATES PATIENT UNABLE TO WORK IN CURRENT OCCUPATION MM DD YY FROM TO MM DD YY

17. NAME OF REFERRING PROVIDER OR OTHER SOURCE   **17a.**   **17b.** NPI   **18.** HOSPITALIZATION DATES RELATED TO CURRENT SERVICES MM DD YY FROM TO MM DD YY

19. RESERVED FOR LOCAL USE   **20.** OUTSIDE LAB? YES NO $ CHARGES

21. DIAGNOSIS OR NATURE OF ILLNESS OR INJURY (Relate Items 1, 2, 9 or 4 to Item 24E by Line)

1. |___.___   3. |___.___   2. |___.___   4. |___.___

22. MEDICAID RESUBMISSION CODE ORIGINAL REF. NO.

23. PRIOR AUTHORIZATION NUMBER

24. A. DATE(S) OF SERVICE						**B.**	**C.**	**D.** PROCEDURES, SERVICES, OR SUPPLIES		**E.**	**F.**	**G.**	**H.**	**I.**	**J.**
From			To			PLACE OF		(Explain Unusual Circumstances)		DIAGNOSIS		DAYS OR	EPSDT Family	ID.	RENDERING
MM	DD	YY	MM	DD	YY	SERVICE	EMG	CPT/HCPCS	MODIFIER	POINTER	$ CHARGES	UNITS	Plan	QUAL.	PROVIDER ID. #
1														NPI	
2														NPI	
3														NPI	
4														NPI	
5														NPI	
6														NPI	

25. FEDERAL TAX I.D. NUMBER SSN EIN   **26.** PATIENT'S ACCOUNT NO.   **27.** ACCEPT ASSIGNMENT? (For govt. claims, see back) YES NO   **28.** TOTAL CHARGE $ **29.** AMOUNT PAID $ **30.** BALANCE DUE $

31. SIGNATURE OF PHYSICIAN OR SUPPLIER INCLUDING DEGREES OR CREDENTIALS (I certify that the statements on the reverse apply to this bill and are made a part thereof.)   **32.** SERVICE FACILITY LOCATION INFORMATION   **33.** BILLING PROVIDER INFO & PH # ( )

CARRIER PATIENT AND INSURED INFORMATION PHYSICIAN OR SUPPLIER INFORMATION

EXERCISE 13.5

SHOESTRING, HELEN

CASE #: 08-47- /01

DR. N. MORIN

DISCHARGED: 02-16-__

DISCHARGE SUMMARY
ST. CATHERINE'S HOSPITAL
ANYTOWN, LOUISIANA

Information should
be recorded on all
POSITIVE
and also relevant
NEGATIVE
Findings.

ORDER OF RECORDING

1. Chief Complaint

2. History of Present Illness

3. History of Past Illness
   (a) Childhood
   (b) Adult
   (c) Operations
   (d) Injuries

4. Family History

5. Social History

6. Review of Systems
   (a) Skeletal
   (b) Muscular
   (c) Circulatory
   (d) Respiratory
   (e) Digestive
   (f) Urinary
   (g) Endocrine
   (h) Reproductive
   (i) Nervous

A 53 year old white female admitted on 2-12-__, for left foot surgery in the form of a bunionectomy with first metatarsal osteotomy as treatment for a hallux valgus deformity with bunion formation about the left foot. This was carried out on 2-13-__, following which the patient had for all practical purposes, an uneventful immediate postoperative recovery, allowing for ambulation with crutches with no weight bearing on the day post surgery. Her temperature, pulse, and respiration have reverted to normal. The patient has little pain. She has good toe circulation and motion and is ambulating without difficulty. She is consequently being discharged to her home on this date, 2-16-__, to continue on no weight bearing regime. She has been asked to return to the underwriter's office within two weeks for removal of sutures. She has been provided with 20 Tylenol #4 to be taken 1 q. 4h. p.r.n. pain.

DR. N. MORIN/js
cc:
dict: 2-16-__
tran: 2-16-__

EXERCISE 13.5

Name:_____

Class/Section:_____

Date:_____

2012

| 1500 |

HEALTH INSURANCE CLAIM FORM

APPROVED BY NATIONAL UNIFORM CLAIM COMMITTEE 08/05

CARRIER

| PICA | | | | | | | | PICA |

| 1. MEDICARE | MEDICAID | TRICARE CHAMPUS | CHAMPVA | GROUP HEALTH PLAN | FECA BLK LUNG | OTHER | 1a. INSURED'S I.D. NUMBER | (For Program in Item 1) |
| *(Medicare #)* | *(Medicaid #)* | *(Sponsor's SSN)* | *(Member ID#)* | *(SSN or ID)* | *(SSN)* | *(ID)* | | |

2. PATIENT'S NAME (Last Name, First Name, Middle Initial)

3. PATIENT'S BIRTH DATE MM DD YY   SEX   M □   F □

4. INSURED'S NAME (Last Name, First Name, Middle Initial)

5. PATIENT'S ADDRESS (No., Street)

6. PATIENT RELATIONSHIP TO INSURED   Self □   Spouse □   Child □   Other □

7. INSURED'S ADDRESS (No., Street)

CITY   STATE

8. PATIENT STATUS   Single □   Married □   Other □

CITY   STATE

ZIP CODE   TELEPHONE (Include Area Code)   (   )

Employed □   Full-Time Student □   Part-Time Student □

ZIP CODE   TELEPHONE (Include Area Code)   (   )

9. OTHER INSURED'S NAME (Last Name, First Name, Middle Initial)

10. IS PATIENT'S CONDITION RELATED TO:

11. INSURED'S POLICY GROUP OR FECA NUMBER

a. OTHER INSURED'S POLICY OR GROUP NUMBER

a. EMPLOYMENT? (Current or Previous)   YES □   NO □

a. INSURED'S DATE OF BIRTH MM DD YY   SEX   M □   F □

b. OTHER INSURED'S DATE OF BIRTH MM DD YY   SEX   M □   F □

b. AUTO ACCIDENT?   PLACE (State)   YES □   NO □

b. EMPLOYER'S NAME OR SCHOOL NAME

c. EMPLOYER'S NAME OR SCHOOL NAME

c. OTHER ACCIDENT?   YES □   NO □

c. INSURANCE PLAN NAME OR PROGRAM NAME

d. INSURANCE PLAN NAME OR PROGRAM NAME

10d. RESERVED FOR LOCAL USE

d. IS THERE ANOTHER HEALTH BENEFIT PLAN?   YES □   NO □   *If yes, return to and complete item 9 a-d.*

READ BACK OF FORM BEFORE COMPLETING & SIGNING THIS FORM.

12. PATIENT'S OR AUTHORIZED PERSON'S SIGNATURE I authorize the release of any medical or other information necessary to process this claim. I also request payment of government benefits either to myself or to the party who accepts assignment below.

SIGNED_____   DATE_____

13. INSURED'S OR AUTHORIZED PERSON'S SIGNATURE I authorize payment of medical benefits to the undersigned physician or supplier for services described below.

SIGNED_____

PATIENT AND INSURED INFORMATION

14. DATE OF CURRENT: MM DD YY   ILLNESS (First symptom) OR INJURY (Accident) OR PREGNANCY(LMP)

15. IF PATIENT HAS HAD SAME OR SIMILAR ILLNESS. GIVE FIRST DATE MM DD YY

16. DATES PATIENT UNABLE TO WORK IN CURRENT OCCUPATION MM DD YY   FROM   TO   MM DD YY

17. NAME OF REFERRING PROVIDER OR OTHER SOURCE

17a.

17b. NPI

18. HOSPITALIZATION DATES RELATED TO CURRENT SERVICES MM DD YY   FROM   TO   MM DD YY

19. RESERVED FOR LOCAL USE

20. OUTSIDE LAB?   YES □   NO □ $ CHARGES

21. DIAGNOSIS OR NATURE OF ILLNESS OR INJURY (Relate Items 1, 2, 3 or 4 to Item 24E by Line)

1. |___.___   3. |___.___

2. |___.___   4. |___.___

22. MEDICAID RESUBMISSION CODE   ORIGINAL REF. NO.

23. PRIOR AUTHORIZATION NUMBER

24. A. DATE(S) OF SERVICE						B. PLACE OF SERVICE	C. EMG	D. PROCEDURES, SERVICES, OR SUPPLIES (Explain Unusual Circumstances)		E. DIAGNOSIS POINTER	F. $ CHARGES	G. DAYS OR UNITS	H. EPSDT Family Plan	I. ID QUAL.	J. RENDERING PROVIDER ID. #
From			To					CPT/HCPCS	MODIFIER						
MM	DD	YY	MM	DD	YY										
1														NPI	
2														NPI	
3														NPI	
4														NPI	
5														NPI	
6														NPI	

25. FEDERAL TAX I.D. NUMBER   SSN □ EIN □

26. PATIENT'S ACCOUNT NO.

27. ACCEPT ASSIGNMENT? (For govt. claims, see back)   YES □   NO □

28. TOTAL CHARGE $

29. AMOUNT PAID $

30. BALANCE DUE $

31. SIGNATURE OF PHYSICIAN OR SUPPLIER INCLUDING DEGREES OR CREDENTIALS (I certify that the statements on the reverse apply to this bill and are made a part thereof.)

32. SERVICE FACILITY LOCATION INFORMATION

33. BILLING PROVIDER INFO & PH # (   )

PHYSICIAN OR SUPPLIER INFORMATION

EXERCISE 13.6

REPORT OF OPERATION
ST. CATHERINE'S HOSPITAL
ANYTOWN, LOUISIANA

CASE #   <u>Out Patient</u>   ROOM # _____

NAME: <u>MADELINE, LAURA</u>   DATE: _____5-26_____

SURGEON: <u>NORMAN MORIN</u>   ASSISTANT: _____

ANESTHETIST: _____   STARTED: _____ ENDED:_____

PREOPERATIVE DIAGNOSIS: Laceration, right index, long and small fingers
with involvement of extensor expansion of the
index and small fingers.

POSTOPERATIVE DIAGNOSIS: Same.

PROCEDURE: Under local anesthesia, 50 mg of Demerol and 2 grams of Ancef were give intravenously approximately one hour prior the procedure. The hand was thoroughly cleansed with Betadine and 10cc of 1% Xlyocaine was used to block the digital nerves to the index, long and small fingers of the right hand. The patient was then taken to surgery where a thorough Betadine prep was again carried out, following which the hand was draped in the usual manner, leaving the hand exposed. The extensor expansion of the index finger of the right hand had been lacerated longitudinally through its med-section. This laceration was over the dorsum of the index, proximal interphalangeal joint. Similarly, the right ring and small fingers also had a V-shaped laceration of the proximal interphalangeal joint of these respective fingers with the base lying laterally. The extensor expansion of the ring finger was intact. However, the extensor expansion to the small finger was, for all practical purposes, thoroughly avulsed from the ring finger side and destroyed through its thumb lateral side. Following a debridement of all fingers to include the skin, subcutaneous tissue and damaged extensor expansion, the extensor expansion to the index finger was repaired with #3-0 interrupted Dexon sutures, following which a repair was attempted of the small finger extensor expansion. This was done with some difficulty because of a lack of tissue. Nevertheless, some of the attachment was obtained, leaving the tendon incontinuity, but lacking a lateral thumb site expansion attachment. The skin was also closed over all of these fingers with a through and through suture of the skin and subcutaneous tissue, using interrupted Dexon #3-0 sutures. During the procedure, the hand was frequently washed with an antibiotic solution, consisting of 2 grams of Dantrex and 50,000 units of Bacitracin, and 500cc of normal Saline. Following the procedure, the fingers were wrapped individually with Telfa, gauze and tube-gauze dressing and the patient's hand was placed in a sling with the hand higher than the elbow. She was provided with 14 Ultaracef 500 mg size to be taken one every 12 hours and with 20 Tylenol #4 to be taken 1 q4h prn pain. She was also advised to return to the Emergency Room on 6-2-__ at 6:15 a.m. for change of dressing.

DR. N. MORIN/
em
cc:

EXERCISE 13.6

Name:_____

Class/Section:_____

Date:_____

2012

1500

HEALTH INSURANCE CLAIM FORM

APPROVED BY NATIONAL UNIFORM CLAIM COMMITTEE 08/05

PICA		PICA

1. MEDICARE MEDICAID TRICARE CHAMPVA GROUP FECA OTHER	1a. INSURED'S I.D. NUMBER (For Program in Item 1)
(Medicare #) (Medicaid #) CHAMPUS (Member ID#) HEALTH PLAN BLK LUNG (ID) (Sponsor's SSN) (SSN or ID) (SSN)	

2. PATIENT'S NAME (Last Name, First Name, Middle Initial)	3. PATIENT'S BIRTH DATE MM DD YY SEX M F	4. INSURED'S NAME (Last Name, First Name, Middle Initial)

5. PATIENT'S ADDRESS (No., Street)	6. PATIENT RELATIONSHIP TO INSURED Self Spouse Child Other	7. INSURED'S ADDRESS (No., Street)
CITY STATE	8. PATIENT STATUS Single Married Other	CITY STATE
ZIP CODE TELEPHONE (Include Area Code) ( )	Employed Full-Time Student Part-Time Student	ZIP CODE TELEPHONE (Include Area Code) ( )

9. OTHER INSURED'S NAME (Last Name, First Name, Middle Initial)	10. IS PATIENT'S CONDITION RELATED TO:	11. INSURED'S POLICY GROUP OR FECA NUMBER
a. OTHER INSURED'S POLICY OR GROUP NUMBER	a. EMPLOYMENT? (Current or Previous) YES NO	a. INSURED'S DATE OF BIRTH MM DD YY SEX M F
b. OTHER INSURED'S DATE OF BIRTH MM DD YY SEX M F	b. AUTO ACCIDENT? PLACE (State) YES NO	b. EMPLOYER'S NAME OR SCHOOL NAME
c. EMPLOYER'S NAME OR SCHOOL NAME	c. OTHER ACCIDENT? YES NO	c. INSURANCE PLAN NAME OR PROGRAM NAME
d. INSURANCE PLAN NAME OR PROGRAM NAME	10d. RESERVED FOR LOCAL USE	d. IS THERE ANOTHER HEALTH BENEFIT PLAN? YES NO If yes, return to and complete item 9 a-d.

READ BACK OF FORM BEFORE COMPLETING & SIGNING THIS FORM.

12. PATIENT'S OR AUTHORIZED PERSON'S SIGNATURE I authorize the release of any medical or other information necessary to process this claim. I also request payment of government benefits either to myself or to the party who accepts assignment below.

SIGNED_____ DATE_____

19. INSURED'S OR AUTHORIZED PERSON'S SIGNATURE I authorize payment of medical benefits to the undersigned physician or supplier for services described below.

SIGNED_____

14. DATE OF CURRENT: ILLNESS (First symptom) OR MM DD YY INJURY (Accident) OR PREGNANCY(LMP)	15. IF PATIENT HAS HAD SAME OR SIMILAR ILLNESS. GIVE FIRST DATE MM DD YY	16. DATES PATIENT UNABLE TO WORK IN CURRENT OCCUPATION MM DD YY MM DD YY FROM TO
17. NAME OF REFERRING PROVIDER OR OTHER SOURCE	17a. 17b. NPI	18. HOSPITALIZATION DATES RELATED TO CURRENT SERVICES MM DD YY MM DD YY FROM TO
19. RESERVED FOR LOCAL USE		20. OUTSIDE LAB? $ CHARGES YES NO

21. DIAGNOSIS OR NATURE OF ILLNESS OR INJURY (Relate Items 1, 2, 9 or 4 to Item 24E by Line)

1. |___.___   3. |___.___

2. |___.___   4. |___.___

22. MEDICAID RESUBMISSION CODE ORIGINAL REF. NO.

23. PRIOR AUTHORIZATION NUMBER

24. A. DATE(S) OF SERVICE		B. PLACE OF SERVICE	C. EMG	D. PROCEDURES, SERVICES, OR SUPPLIES (Explain Unusual Circumstances)		E. DIAGNOSIS POINTER	F. $ CHARGES	G. DAYS OR UNITS	H. EPSDT Family Plan	I. ID. QUAL.	J. RENDERING PROVIDER ID. #
From MM DD YY	To MM DD YY			CPT/HCPCS	MODIFIER						
1											NPI
2											NPI
3											NPI
4											NPI
5											NPI
6											NPI

25. FEDERAL TAX I.D. NUMBER SSN EIN	26. PATIENT'S ACCOUNT NO.	27. ACCEPT ASSIGNMENT? (For govt. claims, see back) YES NO	28. TOTAL CHARGE $	29. AMOUNT PAID $	30. BALANCE DUE $
31. SIGNATURE OF PHYSICIAN OR SUPPLIER INCLUDING DEGREES OR CREDENTIALS (I certify that the statements on the reverse apply to this bill and are made a part thereof.)	32. SERVICE FACILITY LOCATION INFORMATION		33. BILLING PROVIDER INFO & PH # ( )		

CARRIER

PATIENT AND INSURED INFORMATION

PHYSICIAN OR SUPPLIER INFORMATION

<u>**EXERCISE 13.7**</u>

REPORT OF OPERATION
ST. CATHERINE'S HOSPITAL
ANYTOWN, LOUISIANA

CASE #   <u>OP</u>   ROOM # _____

NAME: <u>MADELINE, LAURA</u>   DATE: <u>6-2</u>_____

SURGEON: <u>NORMAN MORIN</u>   ASSISTANT: _____

ANESTHETIST: _____   STARTED: _____ ENDED:_____

PREOPERATIVE DIAGNOSIS: Healing laceration, right index, long and small fingers.

POSTOPERATIVE DIAGNOSIS: Same.

OPERATION: **Dressing change.**

<u>**PROCEDURE:**</u> The old dressing was removed after which the operative and injury sites were inspected. The index, long and small finger lacerations were found to be healing nicely with no evidence of infection. Consequently, they were thoroughly cleansed with Betadine and thereafter a band-aid was applied to the index and long finger while the small finger was also covered with a band-aid but immobilized in a volar splint. The patient was advised to remove the band-aid from the index and long fingers within a few days and to mobilize these fingers as much as possible. She is to be rechecked by the undersigned in approximately one week.

DR. N. MORIN/nm
cc:
dict: 6-02-__
tran: 6-02-__

EXERCISE 13.7

Name: _____

Class/Section: _____

cpTeach

Date: _____

2012

1500

HEALTH INSURANCE CLAIM FORM

APPROVED BY NATIONAL UNIFORM CLAIM COMMITTEE 08/05

☐☐ PICA PICA ☐☐

| 1. MEDICARE ☐ (Medicare #) MEDICAID ☐ (Medicaid #) TRICARE CHAMPUS ☐ (Sponsor's SSN) CHAMPVA ☐ (Member ID#) GROUP HEALTH PLAN ☐ (SSN or ID) FECA BLK LUNG ☐ (SSN) OTHER ☐ (ID) | 1a. INSURED'S I.D. NUMBER (For Program in Item 1) |

2. PATIENT'S NAME (Last Name, First Name, Middle Initial)

3. PATIENT'S BIRTH DATE MM DD YY SEX M ☐ F ☐

4. INSURED'S NAME (Last Name, First Name, Middle Initial)

5. PATIENT'S ADDRESS (No., Street)

6. PATIENT RELATIONSHIP TO INSURED Self ☐ Spouse ☐ Child ☐ Other ☐

7. INSURED'S ADDRESS (No., Street)

CITY STATE

9. PATIENT STATUS Single ☐ Married ☐ Other ☐

Employed ☐ Full-Time Student ☐ Part-Time Student ☐

CITY STATE

ZIP CODE TELEPHONE (Include Area Code) ( )

ZIP CODE TELEPHONE (Include Area Code) ( )

9. OTHER INSURED'S NAME (Last Name, First Name, Middle Initial)

10. IS PATIENT'S CONDITION RELATED TO:

11. INSURED'S POLICY GROUP OR FECA NUMBER

a. OTHER INSURED'S POLICY OR GROUP NUMBER

a. EMPLOYMENT? (Current or Previous) ☐ YES ☐ NO

a. INSURED'S DATE OF BIRTH MM DD YY SEX M ☐ F ☐

b. OTHER INSURED'S DATE OF BIRTH MM DD YY SEX M ☐ F ☐

b. AUTO ACCIDENT? ☐ YES ☐ NO PLACE (State)

b. EMPLOYER'S NAME OR SCHOOL NAME

c. EMPLOYER'S NAME OR SCHOOL NAME

c. OTHER ACCIDENT? ☐ YES ☐ NO

c. INSURANCE PLAN NAME OR PROGRAM NAME

d. INSURANCE PLAN NAME OR PROGRAM NAME

10d. RESERVED FOR LOCAL USE

d. IS THERE ANOTHER HEALTH BENEFIT PLAN? ☐ YES ☐ NO If yes, return to and complete item 9 a-d.

READ BACK OF FORM BEFORE COMPLETING & SIGNING THIS FORM.

12. PATIENT'S OR AUTHORIZED PERSON'S SIGNATURE I authorize the release of any medical or other information necessary to process this claim. I also request payment of government benefits either to myself or to the party who accepts assignment below.

SIGNED_____ DATE_____

13. INSURED'S OR AUTHORIZED PERSON'S SIGNATURE I authorize payment of medical benefits to the undersigned physician or supplier for services described below.

SIGNED _____

14. DATE OF CURRENT: MM DD YY ILLNESS (First symptom) OR INJURY (Accident) OR PREGNANCY (LMP)

15. IF PATIENT HAS HAD SAME OR SIMILAR ILLNESS. GIVE FIRST DATE MM DD YY

16. DATES PATIENT UNABLE TO WORK IN CURRENT OCCUPATION MM DD YY MM DD YY FROM TO

17. NAME OF REFERRING PROVIDER OR OTHER SOURCE

17a. 17b. NPI

18. HOSPITALIZATION DATES RELATED TO CURRENT SERVICES MM DD YY MM DD YY FROM TO

19. RESERVED FOR LOCAL USE

20. OUTSIDE LAB? ☐ YES ☐ NO $ CHARGES

21. DIAGNOSIS OR NATURE OF ILLNESS OR INJURY (Relate Items 1, 2, 3 or 4 to Item 24E by Line)

1. |___.___ 3. |___.___

2. |___.___ 4. |___.___

22. MEDICAID RESUBMISSION CODE ORIGINAL REF. NO.

23. PRIOR AUTHORIZATION NUMBER

24. A. DATE(S) OF SERVICE		B. PLACE OF SERVICE	C. EMG	D. PROCEDURES, SERVICES, OR SUPPLIES (Explain Unusual Circumstances)		E. DIAGNOSIS POINTER	F. $ CHARGES	G. DAYS OR UNITS	H. EPSDT Family Plan	I. ID. QUAL.	J. RENDERING PROVIDER ID. #
From MM DD YY	To MM DD YY			CPT/HCPCS	MODIFIER						
1											NPI
2											NPI
3											NPI
4											NPI
5											NPI
6											NPI

25. FEDERAL TAX I.D. NUMBER SSN ☐ EIN ☐

26. PATIENT'S ACCOUNT NO.

27. ACCEPT ASSIGNMENT? (For govt. claims, see back) ☐ YES ☐ NO

28. TOTAL CHARGE $

29. AMOUNT PAID $

30. BALANCE DUE $

31. SIGNATURE OF PHYSICIAN OR SUPPLIER INCLUDING DEGREES OR CREDENTIALS (I certify that the statements on the reverse apply to this bill and are made a part thereof.)

32. SERVICE FACILITY LOCATION INFORMATION

33. BILLING PROVIDER INFO & PH # ( )

CARRIER

PATIENT AND INSURED INFORMATION

PHYSICIAN OR SUPPLIER INFORMATION

EXERCISE 13.8

DATE: 10 December 20____

ORTHOPEDIC CONSULTATION REPORT ON KARA S. MYERSON
ST. CATHERINE'S HOSPITAL
ANYTOWN, LOUISIANA

HISTORY:

This 25-year-old white female had been perfectly well until November 30, 20__ at which time while working as a bartender at Morrison's Grill in Anytown, she sustained an injury to her right index finger. The patient states that while washing glasses, she lacerated this finger on a broken glass. She was taken soon thereafter to St. Catherine's Hospital where she was examined by Dr. Alexander and taken to surgery for repair of this laceration. Following discharge from the hospital some six days later, she was routinely rechecked by Dr. Alexander who in due time referred her to The Rehabilitation Center for approximately six months of treatment, initially on a daily basis and thereafter on an every other day basis. Approximately six months post-injury, she was rehospitalized for a revision in the hope of obtaining a better range of motion of this finger. Following this surgery, she was again referred to physiotherapy for three months of treatments. About that time Dr. Alexander left town. Since then she has consulted Drs. Miller and Wood, but no treatment has been given. She has received no other type of treatment, nor has she been seen by any other physician.

When seen by the writer on September 10, 20__, she stated that on September 2, 20__, she returned to work as a salesperson at Ray's Stereo and remained at work until August 28, 20__, when she was laid off. She has not worked since.

She further stated that with cold weather changes, the thumb, index and long fingers of her right hand become numb. She also finds that with prolonged use of this hand, these fingers do not work as well as they used to. She had no other complaints referable to this hand or to any other portion of her body.

PAST HISTORY:

She denied previous injury to/or pain in this hand prior to the injury of November 30, 20__. She also denied re-injury since.

EXERCISE 13.8

DATE: 10 December 20____

ORTHOPEDIC CONSULTATION REPORT ON KARA S. MYERSON - Page 2
ST. CATHERINE'S HOSPITAL
ANYTOWN, LOUISIANA

PHYSICAL EXAMINATION - Right Hand

There is a 2-3/4" long, laxy No. 3 incisional-type scar extending from just proximal to the proximal interphalangeal joint flexion crease of the right index finger crossing the flexion crease of the base of this finger and ending over the mid portion of the palm of the hand. There is also a 1-1/4" long by 1/4" wide scar over the supine aspect of the distal forearm just proximal to the flexion crease of the wrist proximalto which lies there 1/4" long, transversely placed, puncture-type scars scattered over the mid supine aspect of the mid forearm 1" to 1-1/2" from one another.

The index finger is held in mid flexion attitude at the proximal interphalangeal joint.

There is no other external evidence of injury or of gross deformity.

There is no swelling, increased heat, rubor, or masses felt.

There is no tenderness on palpation.

There is questionable residual atrophy of the right forearm and intrinsic hand muscles together with minimal relative weakness of the right grip as compared to the left.

There is a full range of painless and equal wrist motion.

Active finger motion is full, equal, and painless bilaterally except for the right index finger which is limited in flexion to 146 degrees at the distal interphalangeal joint as compared to 111 degrees on the left; the proximal interphalangeal joint motion is limited to 112 degrees on the right as compared to 70 degrees on the left, while metacarpophalangeal joint motion is to 87 degrees bilaterally.

Extension is full and equal in the metacarpal and distal interphalangeal joints, while proximal inter-phalangeal joint motion is limited to 165 degrees on the right as compared to 197 degrees on the left.

The "pinch" motion is full and equal bilaterally, but somewhat weaker on the right.

The above range of motion is painless.

There are no sensory or circulatory changes.

<u>EXERCISE 13.8</u>

DATE: 10 December 20____

ORTHOPEDIC CONSULTATION REPORT ON KARA S. MYERSON - Page 3
ST. CATHERINE'S HOSPITAL
ANYTOWN, LOUISIANA

<u>Dynamometer Readings:</u> Right - 120, 100; Left - 205, 185.
The patient is left-handed but uses the right hand for everything except writing and feeding herself.

<u>Circumferential Measurements:</u>   6 inches above olecranon:

Right: 9-1/2 inches.

Left: 9-5/8 inches.

6 inches below olecranon:

Right: 7-1/2 inches.

Left: 7-5/8 inches.

X-RAYS

Right Hand: AP, lateral, and oblique views reveal no evidence of bone or joint abnormality.

OPINION

It is the writer's opinion that the November 30, 20__ right hand laceration and superimposed surgeries have resulted in a twenty percent partial permanent disability of the right index and a seven percent partial permanent disability of the right hand. This, however, is felt to be a mild functional disability which should not prevent this patient from returning to her previous occupation as a bartender.

Norman P. Morin, M.D.

wh
Original: Baggett, McCall, Singleton & Ranier

EXERCISE **13.8**

1500

HEALTH INSURANCE CLAIM FORM

APPROVED BY NATIONAL UNIFORM CLAIM COMMITTEE 08/05

| | PICA | | | | | | | | PICA | |

1. MEDICARE	MEDICAID	TRICARE CHAMPUS	CHAMPVA	GROUP HEALTH PLAN	FECA BLK LUNG	OTHER	1a. INSURED'S I.D. NUMBER (For Program in Item 1)
(Medicare #)	(Medicaid #)	(Sponsor's SSN)	(Member ID#)	(SSN or ID)	(SSN)	(ID)	

2. PATIENT'S NAME (Last Name, First Name, Middle Initial)

3. PATIENT'S BIRTH DATE MM DD YY   SEX M☐ F☐

4. INSURED'S NAME (Last Name, First Name, Middle Initial)

5. PATIENT'S ADDRESS (No., Street)

6. PATIENT RELATIONSHIP TO INSURED   Self☐ Spouse☐ Child☐ Other☐

7. INSURED'S ADDRESS (No., Street)

CITY   STATE

8. PATIENT STATUS   Single☐ Married☐ Other☐

CITY   STATE

ZIP CODE   TELEPHONE (Include Area Code) ( )

Employed☐ Full-Time Student☐ Part-Time Student☐

ZIP CODE   TELEPHONE (Include Area Code) ( )

9. OTHER INSURED'S NAME (Last Name, First Name, Middle Initial)

10. IS PATIENT'S CONDITION RELATED TO:

11. INSURED'S POLICY GROUP OR FECA NUMBER

a. OTHER INSURED'S POLICY OR GROUP NUMBER

a. EMPLOYMENT? (Current or Previous)   YES☐ NO☐

a. INSURED'S DATE OF BIRTH MM DD YY   SEX M☐ F☐

b. OTHER INSURED'S DATE OF BIRTH MM DD YY   SEX M☐ F☐

b. AUTO ACCIDENT?   PLACE (State)   YES☐ NO☐

b. EMPLOYER'S NAME OR SCHOOL NAME

c. EMPLOYER'S NAME OR SCHOOL NAME

c. OTHER ACCIDENT?   YES☐ NO☐

c. INSURANCE PLAN NAME OR PROGRAM NAME

d. INSURANCE PLAN NAME OR PROGRAM NAME

10d. RESERVED FOR LOCAL USE

d. IS THERE ANOTHER HEALTH BENEFIT PLAN?   YES☐ NO☐ If yes, return to and complete item 9 a-d.

READ BACK OF FORM BEFORE COMPLETING & SIGNING THIS FORM.

12. PATIENT'S OR AUTHORIZED PERSON'S SIGNATURE I authorize the release of any medical or other information necessary to process this claim. I also request payment of government benefits either to myself or to the party who accepts assignment below.

SIGNED_____   DATE_____

13. INSURED'S OR AUTHORIZED PERSON'S SIGNATURE I authorize payment of medical benefits to the undersigned physician or supplier for services described below.

SIGNED_____

14. DATE OF CURRENT: MM DD YY ◄ ILLNESS (First symptom) OR INJURY (Accident) OR PREGNANCY(LMP)

15. IF PATIENT HAS HAD SAME OR SIMILAR ILLNESS. GIVE FIRST DATE MM DD YY

16. DATES PATIENT UNABLE TO WORK IN CURRENT OCCUPATION MM DD YY   MM DD YY FROM   TO

17. NAME OF REFERRING PROVIDER OR OTHER SOURCE

17a.

17b. NPI

18. HOSPITALIZATION DATES RELATED TO CURRENT SERVICES MM DD YY   MM DD YY FROM   TO

19. RESERVED FOR LOCAL USE

20. OUTSIDE LAB? $ CHARGES   YES☐ NO☐

21. DIAGNOSIS OR NATURE OF ILLNESS OR INJURY (Relate Items 1, 2, 9 or 4 to Item 24E by Line)

1. |___.___   3. |___.___

2. |___.___   4. |___.___

22. MEDICAID RESUBMISSION CODE   ORIGINAL REF. NO.

23. PRIOR AUTHORIZATION NUMBER

24. A. DATE(S) OF SERVICE		B.	C.	D. PROCEDURES, SERVICES, OR SUPPLIES	E.	F.	G.	H.	I.	J.
From To MM DD YY MM DD YY		PLACE OF SERVICE	EMG	(Explain Unusual Circumstances) CPT/HCPCS MODIFIER	DIAGNOSIS POINTER	$ CHARGES	DAYS OR UNITS	EPSDT Family Plan	ID. QUAL.	RENDERING PROVIDER ID. #
1									NPI	
2									NPI	
3									NPI	
4									NPI	
5									NPI	
6									NPI	

25. FEDERAL TAX I.D. NUMBER   SSN EIN ☐☐

26. PATIENT'S ACCOUNT NO.

27. ACCEPT ASSIGNMENT? (For govt. claims, see back) YES☐ NO☐

28. TOTAL CHARGE $

29. AMOUNT PAID $

30. BALANCE DUE $

31. SIGNATURE OF PHYSICIAN OR SUPPLIER INCLUDING DEGREES OR CREDENTIALS (I certify that the statements on the reverse apply to this bill and are made a part thereof.)

32. SERVICE FACILITY LOCATION INFORMATION

33. BILLING PROVIDER INFO & PH # ( )

CARRIER

PATIENT AND INSURED INFORMATION

PHYSICIAN OR SUPPLIER INFORMATION

EXERCISE **13.9**

REPORT OF OPERATION
MAGEN DAVID HOSPITAL
HIGHWATERS, FLORIDA

CASE #   15A-16- /01   ROOM # 213 East

NAME: HUFF, SARAH C.   DATE: 7/14/

SURGEON: ANDREW HINKLE, M.D.   ASSISTANT: _____

ANESTHETIST: _____   STARTED: _____   ENDED: _____

PREOPERATIVE DIAGNOSIS: Bilateral tubal occlusion.
POSTOPERATIVE DIAGNOSIS: Same plus pelvic peritoneal adhesions.

TITLE OF OPERATION: 1. Laparoscopy. 2. Laparotomy. 3. Lysis and excision of pelvic perito-neal adhesions with microlaser. 4. Bilateral tubal reanastomosis with microlaser. 5. Chromopertubation.

OPERATIVE PROCEDURE AND FINDINGS: On inspection of the pelvis there were filmy adhesions in the anterior cul-de-sac. Following vaporization of these adhesions the anterior cul-de-sac appeared normal. The round ligament appeared grossly normal. The uterine fundus was unre-markable. The proximal portion of the right Fallopian tube extended approximately 5 cm from the coronal portion of the tube. There was a segmental interruption of the right tube. The distal segment of the right tube was 6 cm in length and had fine appearing fimbria with an easily identifiable os-teum. There were dense adhesions from the proximal stump of the distal segment to the right pelvic sidewall and to the right ovary. The right ovary appeared bilobed consistent with a previous wedge resection. In the area of the wedge resection the distal segment of the Fallopian tube, the cecum, omentum, and sigmoid were densely adherent to the ovary. Following vaporization of these adhe-sion attachments, the above noted structures were found to be normal. An isthmic-isthmic anasto-mosis was performed on the right side. Following anastomosis chromopertubation demonstrated prompt fill and spill from the distal end of the right tube. The cul-de-sac was free of disease. The left ovary appeared grossly normal. The left Fallopian tube had a proximal segment which was ap-proximately 4 cm in length and a distal segment which was approximately 5 cm in length. On the left, the fimbria appeared grossly normal with an easily identifiable osteum. An isthmic-ampullary anastomosis was performed on the left side.

<u>**EXERCISE 13.9**</u>

DATE: **July 17, 20___**

REPORT OF OPERATION ON SARAH HUFF - Page 2
MAGEN DAVID HOSPITAL
HIGHWATERS, FLORIDA

<u>**OPERATIVE PROCEDURE AND FINDINGS:**</u> **continued**   Following anastomisis chromopertubation demonstrated prompt fill and spill from the distal end of the left tube. Inspection of the upper abdomen revealed the right kidney to be approximately 1/2 size to the left consistent with her previous intravenous pyelogram. No other abnormalities were noted.

The anterior lip of the cervix was grasped with a tenaculum and a Cohen Eder cannula inserted into the endocervical canal and secured to the tenaculum.

Through a subumbilical incision the Verres' needle was introduced into the abdominal cavity which was then distended with 2.5 liters of carbon dioxide under continuous low pressure flow. The Verres' needle was removed and the laparoscopic trocar and laparoscope introduced. Because of the above noted adhesions adequate visualization of the pelvis could not be obtained. The abdomen was transilluminated and an accessory forcep passed suprapubically in the midline. The findings were noted. Laparoscopic photographs were taken. It was elected to proceed with laparotomy. All laparoscopic instruments were removed and the subumbilical incision closed with a subcuticular suture of 3-0 Vicryl. The Cohen-Eder cannula was removed and a Hui intrauterine insufflation cannula was inserted. The tenaculum was removed. A Foley catheter was placed. A vaginal pack was placed in the vagina for elevation of the fundus.

The patient was reprepped and redraped in the usual sterile fashion in the supine position. The abdomen was opened through excision of her previous Pfannienstiel incision scar. The upper abdomen was B explored. A self-retaining retractor was placed and the intestines packed out of the field with lap tapes. Attention was directed to the right adnexa. Utilizing the microscopically controlled carbon dioxide laser with 11 watts average output in a superpulse mode with a 0.2 mm focused spotsize, adhesions from the distal right tube to the ovary, and adhesions from the ovary to the cecum, omentum, and sigmoid were vaporized along avascular lines. A peritoneal defect created on the sidewall was closed with interrupted sutures of 6-0 Vicryl. Attention was directed to the distal segment of the proximal stump. This was freed from adhesions to the mesosalpinx with microlaser. The laser was used to incise through the serosa and muscularis of the tube and the lumen cut sharply. Chromopertubation demonstrated prompt spill from a normal appearing lumen. A pediatric feeding tube was passed through the fimbriated end of the tube and the distal segment distended with descending chromopertubation. The proximal stump of the distal segment was incised with the laser and the lumen cross cut. Again, a normal lumen with free spill was noted. The mesosalpinx was closed with interrupted sutures of 6-0 Vicryl.

EXERCISE 13.9

DATE: July 17, 20___

REPORT OF OPERATION ON SARAH HUFF - Page 3

MAGEN DAVID HOSPITAL

HIGHWATERS, FLORIDA

OPERATIVE PROCEDURE AND FINDINGS: **continued**   Reanastomosis was performed using 4 radial sutures of 8-0 Vicryl. Chromopertubation now demonstrated prompt fill and spill from the distal end of the tube. The serosa was reapproximated with interrupted sutures of 8-0 Vicryl. Attention was directed to the left side where a similar procedure was performed with similar results. Several fine bands of adhesions from the proximal portion of the distal segment on the left to the left ovary required laser vaporization prior to reanastomosis.

At the termination of the procedure, a careful inspection was made for hemostasis and this being assured, all instruments were removed. The anterior peritoneum was closed with 2-0 Vicryl. Just prior to complete peritoneal closure 100 cc of Hyskon was instilled into the pelvis for prevention of postoperative adhesions. The fascia was closed with 0 Vicryl, subcutaneous tissue with 2-0 Vicryl and the skin with clips. A sterile dressing was placed over the incision. The vaginal pack and Hui catheter were removed. Estimated blood loss was less than 50 cc. Sponge and needle counts were correct times two. Estimated duration of procedure was 4 1/2 hours. The patient was sent to the recovery room in good condition having tolerated anesthesia and procedures well.

DR. A. HINKLE/sp
cc:
dict: 7-17-__
tran: 7-18-__

EXERCISE 13.9

WORKBOOK

McGUFFEY

cpTeach

2012

Name:_____

Class/Section:_____

Date:_____

1500

HEALTH INSURANCE CLAIM FORM

APPROVED BY NATIONAL UNIFORM CLAIM COMMITTEE 08/05

PICA

| | PICA |

1. MEDICARE | MEDICAID | TRICARE CHAMPUS | CHAMPVA | GROUP HEALTH PLAN | FECA BLK LUNG | OTHER | 1a. INSURED'S I.D. NUMBER (For Program in Item 1)

(Medicare #) | (Medicaid #) | (Sponsor's SSN) | (Member ID#) | (SSN or ID) | (SSN) | (ID)

2. PATIENT'S NAME (Last Name, First Name, Middle Initial) | 3. PATIENT'S BIRTH DATE MM DD YY SEX M F | 4. INSURED'S NAME (Last Name, First Name, Middle Initial)

5. PATIENT'S ADDRESS (No., Street) | 6. PATIENT RELATIONSHIP TO INSURED Self Spouse Child Other | 7. INSURED'S ADDRESS (No., Street)

CITY | STATE | 8. PATIENT STATUS Single Married Other | CITY | STATE

ZIP CODE | TELEPHONE (Include Area Code) ( ) | Employed Full-Time Student Part-Time Student | ZIP CODE | TELEPHONE (Include Area Code) ( )

9. OTHER INSURED'S NAME (Last Name, First Name, Middle Initial) | 10. IS PATIENT'S CONDITION RELATED TO: | 11. INSURED'S POLICY GROUP OR FECA NUMBER

a. OTHER INSURED'S POLICY OR GROUP NUMBER | a. EMPLOYMENT? (Current or Previous) YES NO | a. INSURED'S DATE OF BIRTH MM DD YY SEX M F

b. OTHER INSURED'S DATE OF BIRTH MM DD YY SEX M F | b. AUTO ACCIDENT? PLACE (State) YES NO | b. EMPLOYER'S NAME OR SCHOOL NAME

c. EMPLOYER'S NAME OR SCHOOL NAME | c. OTHER ACCIDENT? YES NO | c. INSURANCE PLAN NAME OR PROGRAM NAME

d. INSURANCE PLAN NAME OR PROGRAM NAME | 10d. RESERVED FOR LOCAL USE | d. IS THERE ANOTHER HEALTH BENEFIT PLAN? YES NO If yes, return to and complete item 9 a-d.

READ BACK OF FORM BEFORE COMPLETING & SIGNING THIS FORM.
12. PATIENT'S OR AUTHORIZED PERSON'S SIGNATURE I authorize the release of any medical or other information necessary to process this claim. I also request payment of government benefits either to myself or to the party who accepts assignment below.

SIGNED_____ DATE_____

13. INSURED'S OR AUTHORIZED PERSON'S SIGNATURE I authorize payment of medical benefits to the undersigned physician or supplier for services described below.

SIGNED_____

14. DATE OF CURRENT: MM DD YY ILLNESS (First symptom) OR INJURY (Accident) OR PREGNANCY(LMP) | 15. IF PATIENT HAS HAD SAME OR SIMILAR ILLNESS. GIVE FIRST DATE MM DD YY | 16. DATES PATIENT UNABLE TO WORK IN CURRENT OCCUPATION MM DD YY FROM TO MM DD YY

17. NAME OF REFERRING PROVIDER OR OTHER SOURCE | 17a. | 17b. NPI | 18. HOSPITALIZATION DATES RELATED TO CURRENT SERVICES MM DD YY FROM TO MM DD YY

19. RESERVED FOR LOCAL USE | 20. OUTSIDE LAB? YES NO $ CHARGES

21. DIAGNOSIS OR NATURE OF ILLNESS OR INJURY (Relate Items 1, 2, 9 or 4 to Item 24E by Line)

1. |___.___ | 3. |___.___
2. |___.___ | 4. |___.___

22. MEDICAID RESUBMISSION CODE ORIGINAL REF. NO.

23. PRIOR AUTHORIZATION NUMBER

24. A. DATE(S) OF SERVICE						B. PLACE OF SERVICE	C. EMG	D. PROCEDURES, SERVICES, OR SUPPLIES (Explain Unusual Circumstances) CPT/HCPCS MODIFIER	E. DIAGNOSIS POINTER	F. $ CHARGES	G. DAYS OR UNITS	H. EPSDT Family Plan	I. ID. QUAL.	J. RENDERING PROVIDER ID. #
From MM DD YY	To MM DD YY													
1													NPI	
2													NPI	
3													NPI	
4													NPI	
5													NPI	
6													NPI	

25. FEDERAL TAX I.D. NUMBER SSN EIN | 26. PATIENT'S ACCOUNT NO. | 27. ACCEPT ASSIGNMENT? (For govt. claims, see back) YES NO | 28. TOTAL CHARGE $ | 29. AMOUNT PAID $ | 30. BALANCE DUE $

31. SIGNATURE OF PHYSICIAN OR SUPPLIER INCLUDING DEGREES OR CREDENTIALS (I certify that the statements on the reverse apply to this bill and are made a part thereof.) | 32. SERVICE FACILITY LOCATION INFORMATION | 33. BILLING PROVIDER INFO & PH # ( )

CARRIER

PATIENT AND INSURED INFORMATION

PHYSICIAN OR SUPPLIER INFORMATION

EXERCISE 13.10

REPORT OF OPERATION

MAGEN DAVID HOSPITAL

HIGHWATERS, FLORIDA

CASE #   190069231   ROOM # 621 West

NAME: SPINOFF, BETH   DATE: 7/31/

SURGEON: ANDREW HINKLE, M.D.   ASSISTANT:

ANESTHETIST: STARTED: ENDED:

PREOPERATIVE DIAGNOSIS: Cystocele, enterocele, rectocele.
POSTOPERATIVE DIAGNOSIS: Same.

TITLE OF OPERATION: Examination under anesthesia, repair of cystocele, transvaginal repair of anterior enterocele and rectocele.

OPERATIVE FINDINGS: Prior to induction of anesthesia the patient was placed in lithotomy position. She was again examined. The previously noted defect of the tremendous bulge in the anterior vaginal wall with a thinning defect centrally was again noted. In addition, the moderate rectocele was noted. It was elected to proceed with a vaginal approach. The patient was prepped and shaved in a standard fashion and thereafter was draped. A weighted vaginal speculum was placed. The dissection was initiated near the vaginal cuff where a triangular portion of vaginal mucosa was excised extending the incision by sharp dissection to just below the urethral meatus. The upper portion of the bulge was found to be a cystocele. The perivesical fascia being extremely thin and attenuated along the bladder to herniate through. The more distal portion of the bulge was an enterocele which had dissected underneath the base of the bladder extending from the upper portion of the vaginal wall to immediately adjacent to the previous culdoplasty. The dissection was carried along the hernia sac and it was consequently entered identifying the previous sutures from the Halban culdoplasty and indeed indentifying the rectum immediately adjacent to the vaginal cuff. After firmly establishing the nature of the peritoneal sac a 2-0 Novofil permanent nylon suture was placed in pursestring fashion as high as could be placed securely and tied down totally obliterating the enterocele sac.

DATE: July 31, 20___

REPORT OF OPERATION ON BETH SPINOFF - Page 2
MAGEN DAVID HOSPITAL
HIGHWATERS, FLORIDA

OPERATIVE PROCEDURE AND FINDINGS: continued   The bladder cystocele was then corrected by doing a pursestring suture across the most dependent part tying this down and involuting a significant portion of the central cystocele defect in this fashion. The perivesical fascia was then dissected free and then plicated across the midline with interrupted 2-0 PDS sutures.   Approximately four separate sutures were placed. Additional supporting strength to the anterior vaginal wall was derived from going quite lateral and securing perivaginal fascia across the midline. Additional vaginal mucosa was trimmed away.

Following this, the vaginal mucosa on the anterior wall was closed with interrupted 2-0 Vicryl sutures. A very satisfactory anterior repair was accomplished with good support and total obliteration of the previously noted bulge and enterocele and cystocele. A standard posterior repair was then accomplished incising the peritoneum, excising a diamond wedge of tissue up to the most dominant part of the rectocele. The rectum and its perirectal fascia were dissected from the vaginal mucosa. The dissection was carried to the upper portion of the vaginal cuff. Imbrication of the rectocele with interrupted 2-0 Vicryl was then accomplished going through the anteroir vaginal wall, plicating the rectocele across the midline and creating satisfactory support in this fashion. The vaginal mucosa was closed with a running 3-0 Vicryl. Additional sutures, near the distal portion of the vagina obliterated the remaining rectocele and brought the levator muscles across the midline. The perineoplasty was closed and finished in standard fashion. At the conclusion, the patient had a very satisfactory support and all presenting defects had been corrected. The measured blood loss was 250 cc. Estimated blood loss was 300 cc. Sponge and needle counts were correct. The patient tolerated surgery without difficulty and was taken to the recovery room in good condition. The Foley catheter was placed and the urine was noted to be clear.

DR. A. HINKLE/sp
cc:
dict: 08-01-__
tran: 08-01-__

Name:_____

Class/Section:_____

Date:_____

cpTeach
2012

EXERCISE **13.10**

1500

HEALTH INSURANCE CLAIM FORM

APPROVED BY NATIONAL UNIFORM CLAIM COMMITTEE 08/05

PICA | | | | PICA | |

1. MEDICARE ☐ (Medicare #) MEDICAID ☐ (Medicaid #) TRICARE CHAMPUS ☐ (Sponsor's SSN) CHAMPVA ☐ (Member ID#) GROUP HEALTH PLAN ☐ (SSN or ID) FECA BLK LUNG ☐ (SSN) OTHER ☐ (ID) | 1a. INSURED'S I.D. NUMBER (For Program in Item 1)

2. PATIENT'S NAME (Last Name, First Name, Middle Initial) | 3. PATIENT'S BIRTH DATE MM DD YY SEX M☐ F☐ | 4. INSURED'S NAME (Last Name, First Name, Middle Initial)

5. PATIENT'S ADDRESS (No., Street) | 6. PATIENT RELATIONSHIP TO INSURED Self☐ Spouse☐ Child☐ Other☐ | 7. INSURED'S ADDRESS (No., Street)

CITY | STATE | 8. PATIENT STATUS Single☐ Married☐ Other☐ | CITY | STATE

ZIP CODE | TELEPHONE (Include Area Code) ( ) | Employed☐ Full-Time Student☐ Part-Time Student☐ | ZIP CODE | TELEPHONE (Include Area Code) ( )

9. OTHER INSURED'S NAME (Last Name, First Name, Middle Initial) | 10. IS PATIENT'S CONDITION RELATED TO: | 11. INSURED'S POLICY GROUP OR FECA NUMBER

a. OTHER INSURED'S POLICY OR GROUP NUMBER | a. EMPLOYMENT? (Current or Previous) ☐YES ☐NO | a. INSURED'S DATE OF BIRTH MM DD YY SEX M☐ F☐

b. OTHER INSURED'S DATE OF BIRTH MM DD YY SEX M☐ F☐ | b. AUTO ACCIDENT? PLACE (State) ☐YES ☐NO | b. EMPLOYER'S NAME OR SCHOOL NAME

c. EMPLOYER'S NAME OR SCHOOL NAME | c. OTHER ACCIDENT? ☐YES ☐NO | c. INSURANCE PLAN NAME OR PROGRAM NAME

d. INSURANCE PLAN NAME OR PROGRAM NAME | 10d. RESERVED FOR LOCAL USE | d. IS THERE ANOTHER HEALTH BENEFIT PLAN? ☐YES ☐NO If yes, return to and complete item 9 a-d.

READ BACK OF FORM BEFORE COMPLETING & SIGNING THIS FORM.
12. PATIENT'S OR AUTHORIZED PERSON'S SIGNATURE I authorize the release of any medical or other information necessary to process this claim. I also request payment of government benefits either to myself or to the party who accepts assignment below.

SIGNED_____ DATE_____ | 13. INSURED'S OR AUTHORIZED PERSON'S SIGNATURE I authorize payment of medical benefits to the undersigned physician or supplier for services described below.

SIGNED_____

14. DATE OF CURRENT: MM DD YY ILLNESS (First symptom) OR INJURY (Accident) OR PREGNANCY(LMP) | 15. IF PATIENT HAS HAD SAME OR SIMILAR ILLNESS. GIVE FIRST DATE MM DD YY | 16. DATES PATIENT UNABLE TO WORK IN CURRENT OCCUPATION MM DD YY MM DD YY FROM TO

17. NAME OF REFERRING PROVIDER OR OTHER SOURCE | 17a. 17b. NPI | 18. HOSPITALIZATION DATES RELATED TO CURRENT SERVICES MM DD YY MM DD YY FROM TO

19. RESERVED FOR LOCAL USE | 20. OUTSIDE LAB? ☐YES ☐NO $ CHARGES

21. DIAGNOSIS OR NATURE OF ILLNESS OR INJURY (Relate Items 1, 2, 9 or 4 to Item 24E by Line)
1. |____.____ 3. |____.____
2. |____.____ 4. |____.____ | 22. MEDICAID RESUBMISSION CODE ORIGINAL REF. NO.

23. PRIOR AUTHORIZATION NUMBER

24. A. DATE(S) OF SERVICE From MM DD YY To MM DD YY	B. PLACE OF SERVICE	C. EMG	D. PROCEDURES, SERVICES, OR SUPPLIES (Explain Unusual Circumstances) CPT/HCPCS MODIFIER	E. DIAGNOSIS POINTER	F. $ CHARGES	G. DAYS OR UNITS	H. EPSDT Family Plan	I. ID. QUAL.	J. RENDERING PROVIDER ID. #
1								NPI	
2								NPI	
3								NPI	
4								NPI	
5								NPI	
6								NPI	

25. FEDERAL TAX I.D. NUMBER ☐SSN ☐EIN | 26. PATIENT'S ACCOUNT NO. | 27. ACCEPT ASSIGNMENT? (For govt. claims, see back) ☐YES ☐NO | 28. TOTAL CHARGE $ | 29. AMOUNT PAID $ | 30. BALANCE DUE $

31. SIGNATURE OF PHYSICIAN OR SUPPLIER INCLUDING DEGREES OR CREDENTIALS (I certify that the statements on the reverse apply to this bill and are made a part thereof.) | 32. SERVICE FACILITY LOCATION INFORMATION | 33. BILLING PROVIDER INFO & PH # ( )

CARRIER
PATIENT AND INSURED INFORMATION
PHYSICIAN OR SUPPLIER INFORMATION

WHAT'S WRONG WITH THIS PICTURE?

The following CMS-1500 claim forms represent real cases that have been submitted to carriers in the recent past. Your job is to assess them and see what is wrong (or right) with each form by looking only at the diagnosis code section (see space 21 and space 24E) and the CPT® code section (see space 24D). Remember, some codes may no longer be valid.

You can also look at the dates of service (space 24A), the charges (space 24F), and the units column (space 24G). Note that the year was specifically kept out of the date area, and you should make the assumption that the claim is for the current year, or the past year, depending on the point in time you are completing these exercises. You are not to concern yourself with anything else (e.g., missing patient name, addresses, etc.) or missing federal tax I.D. number or physician name.

What you are trying to do is to pull everything together that you have learned in your course work and use of cpTeach®. Place your critique of each claim form in the space provided for you on each form.

Good luck!

EXERCISE 13.11

1500
HEALTH INSURANCE CLAIM FORM
APPROVED BY NATIONAL UNIFORM CLAIM COMMITTEE 08/05

13.11

1. MEDICARE	MEDICAID	TRICARE CHAMPUS (Sponsor's SSN)	CHAMPVA (Member ID#)	GROUP HEALTH PLAN (SSN or ID)	FECA BLK LUNG (SSN)	OTHER (ID)	1a. INSURED'S I.D. NUMBER (For Program in Item 1)

2. PATIENT'S NAME (Last

5. PATIENT'S ADDRESS

CITY   STATE

ZIP CODE

9. OTHER INSURED'S NA

a. OTHER INSURED'S PO

b. OTHER INSURED'S DA
   MM   DD   YY   SEX   F

c. EMPLOYER'S NAME O

d. INSURANCE PLAN NAME OR PROGRAM NAME   10d. RESERVED FOR LOCAL USE   d. IS THERE ANOTHER HEALTH BENEFIT PLAN?
   YES   NO   If yes, return to and complete Item 9 a-d.

READ BACK OF FORM BEFORE COMPLETING & SIGNING THIS FORM.
12. PATIENT'S OR AUTHORIZED PERSON'S SIGNATURE I authorize the release of any medical or other information necessary to process this claim. I also request payment of government benefits either to myself or to the party who accepts assignment below.

SIGNED _____   DATE _____

19. INSURED'S OR AUTHORIZED PERSON'S SIGNATURE I authorize payment of medical benefits to the undersigned physician or supplier for services described below.

SIGNED _____

14. DATE OF CURRENT: ◄ ILLNESS (First symptom) OR INJURY (Accident) OR PREGNANCY(LMP)
    MM   DD   YY

15. IF PATIENT HAS HAD SAME OR SIMILAR ILLNESS. GIVE FIRST DATE MM DD YY

16. DATES PATIENT UNABLE TO WORK IN CURRENT OCCUPATION
    FROM MM DD YY   TO MM DD YY

17. NAME OF REFERRING PROVIDER OR OTHER SOURCE   17a.
                                                 17b. NPI

18. HOSPITALIZATION DATES RELATED TO CURRENT SERVICES
    FROM MM DD YY   TO MM DD YY

19. RESERVED FOR LOCAL USE

20. OUTSIDE LAB? $ CHARGES
    YES   NO

21. DIAGNOSIS OR NATURE OF ILLNESS OR INJURY (Relate Items 1, 2, 9 or 4 to Item 24E by Line)

1. **Severe spinal stenosis, thoracic**   9. **Thoracic disc**

2. **Degenerative disk disease**   4.

22. MEDICAID RESUBMISSION CODE   ORIGINAL REF. NO.

23. PRIOR AUTHORIZATION NUMBER

24. A. DATE(S) OF SERVICE From MM DD YY To MM DD YY	B. PLACE OF SERVICE	C. EMG	D. PROCEDURES, SERVICES, OR SUPPLIES (Explain Unusual Circumstances) CPT/HCPCS | MODIFIER	E. DIAGNOSIS POINTER	F. $ CHARGES	G. DAYS OR UNITS	H. EPSDT Family Plan	I. ID. QUAL.	J. RENDERING PROVIDER ID. #
1	2 27	21		63045 99	50 51	1,2,3	4256 00			NPI
2	2 27	21		20250	51	1,2,3	650 00			NPI
3	2 27	21		63048	51	1,2,3	500 00			NPI
4	2 27	21		63048	51	1,2,3	500 00			NPI
5	2 27	21		63048	51	1,2,3	500 00			NPI
6										NPI

25. FEDERAL TAX I.D. NUMBER   SSN EIN   26. PATIENT'S ACCOUNT NO.   27. ACCEPT ASSIGNMENT? (For govt. claims, see back) YES NO   28. TOTAL CHARGE $ 29. AMOUNT PAID $ 30. BALANCE DUE $

31. SIGNATURE OF PHYSICIAN OR SUPPLIER INCLUDING DEGREES OR CREDENTIALS (I certify that the statements on the reverse apply to this bill and are made a part thereof.)

32. SERVICE FACILITY LOCATION INFORMATION

33. BILLING PROVIDER INFO & PH # (   )

EXERCISE 13.12

```
1500
```

HEALTH INSURANCE CLAIM FORM

APPROVED BY NATIONAL UNIFORM CLAIM COMMITTEE 08/05

| | PICA | | | | | | | PICA | |

| 1. MEDICARE | MEDICAID | TRICARE CHAMPUS | CHAMPVA | GROUP HEALTH PLAN | FECA BLK LUNG | OTHER | 1a. INSURED'S I.D. NUMBER | (For Program in Item 1) |
| (Medicare #) | (Medicaid #) | (Sponsor's SSN) | (Member ID#) | (SSN or ID) | (SSN) | (ID) | | |

13.12

_____

_____

_____

_____

_____

_____

_____

_____

2. PATIENT'S NAME (Last ... Initial)

5. PATIENT'S ADDRESS

CITY   STATE

ZIP CODE   (Include Area Code)

9. OTHER INSURED'S NAME

a. OTHER INSURED'S PO...   SEX F ☐

b. OTHER INSURED'S DATE   MM   DD   YY

c. EMPLOYER'S NAME O...

☐ YES   ☐ NO

d. INSURANCE PLAN NAME OR PROGRAM NAME | 10d. RESERVED FOR LOCAL USE | d. IS THERE ANOTHER HEALTH BENEFIT PLAN?
☐ YES   ☐ NO   If yes, return to and complete item 9 a-d.

READ BACK OF FORM BEFORE COMPLETING & SIGNING THIS FORM.

12. PATIENT'S OR AUTHORIZED PERSON'S SIGNATURE I authorize the release of any medical or other information necessary to process this claim. I also request payment of government benefits either to myself or to the party who accepts assignment below.

SIGNED_____   DATE_____

13. INSURED'S OR AUTHORIZED PERSON'S SIGNATURE I authorize payment of medical benefits to the undersigned physician or supplier for services described below.

SIGNED_____

| 14. DATE OF CURRENT: MM DD YY | ILLNESS (First symptom) OR INJURY (Accident) OR PREGNANCY(LMP) | 15. IF PATIENT HAS HAD SAME OR SIMILAR ILLNESS. GIVE FIRST DATE MM DD YY | 16. DATES PATIENT UNABLE TO WORK IN CURRENT OCCUPATION FROM MM DD YY TO MM DD YY |

| 17. NAME OF REFERRING PROVIDER OR OTHER SOURCE | 17a. | 18. HOSPITALIZATION DATES RELATED TO CURRENT SERVICES FROM MM DD YY TO MM DD YY |
| | 17b. NPI | |

| 19. RESERVED FOR LOCAL USE | 20. OUTSIDE LAB?   ☐ YES   ☐ NO $ CHARGES |

21. DIAGNOSIS OR NATURE OF ILLNESS OR INJURY (Relate Items 1, 2, 9 or 4 to Item 24E by Line)

1. | **873.50 Facial laceration complicated**   3. |____ , ____

2. | **873.52 Facial laceration complicated**   4. |____ , ____

22. MEDICAID RESUBMISSION CODE   ORIGINAL REF. NO.

23. PRIOR AUTHORIZATION NUMBER

24. A. DATE(S) OF SERVICE From MM DD YY To MM DD YY	B. PLACE OF SERVICE	C. EMG	D. PROCEDURES, SERVICES, OR SUPPLIES (Explain Unusual Circumstances) CPT/HCPCS MODIFIER	E. DIAGNOSIS POINTER	F. $ CHARGES	G. DAYS OR UNITS	H. EPSDT Family Plan	I. ID. QUAL.	J. RENDERING PROVIDER ID. #
1	5 16	22		12011		1	350 00			NPI	
2	5 16	22		12011		1	350 00			NPI	
3	5 16	22		12011		1	350 00			NPI	
4										NPI	
5										NPI	
6										NPI	

| 25. FEDERAL TAX I.D. NUMBER   SSN EIN | 26. PATIENT'S ACCOUNT NO. | 27. ACCEPT ASSIGNMENT? (For govt. claims, see back) ☐ YES ☐ NO | 28. TOTAL CHARGE $ | 29. AMOUNT PAID $ | 30. BALANCE DUE $ |

| 31. SIGNATURE OF PHYSICIAN OR SUPPLIER INCLUDING DEGREES OR CREDENTIALS (I certify that the statements on the reverse apply to this bill and are made a part thereof.) | 32. SERVICE FACILITY LOCATION INFORMATION | 33. BILLING PROVIDER INFO & PH # (   ) |

Name: _____

Class/Section: _____

Date: _____

2012

EXERCISE 13.13

1500

HEALTH INSURANCE CLAIM FORM

APPROVED BY NATIONAL UNIFORM CLAIM COMMITTEE 08/05

| | PICA | | | | | | | | | | PICA | |

1. MEDICARE	MEDICAID	TRICARE CHAMPUS	CHAMPVA	GROUP HEALTH PLAN	FECA BLK LUNG	OTHER	1a. INSURED'S I.D. NUMBER	(For Program in Item 1)
(Medicare #)	(Medicaid #)	(Sponsor's SSN)	(Member ID#)	(SSN or ID)	(SSN)	(ID)		

13.13

2. PATIENT'S NAME (Last ... Initial)

_____

5. PATIENT'S ADDRESS (

_____

CITY ... STATE

_____

ZIP CODE ... de Area Code)

_____

9. OTHER INSURED'S NA

_____

a. OTHER INSURED'S PO ... SEX / F ☐

_____

b. OTHER INSURED'S DA
MM DD YY

_____

c. EMPLOYER'S NAME O

_____

| | YES | | NO |

d. INSURANCE PLAN NAME OR PROGRAM NAME | 10d. RESERVED FOR LOCAL USE | d. IS THERE ANOTHER HEALTH BENEFIT PLAN?
☐ YES ☐ NO   If yes, return to and complete item 9 a-d.

READ BACK OF FORM BEFORE COMPLETING & SIGNING THIS FORM.

12. PATIENT'S OR AUTHORIZED PERSON'S SIGNATURE I authorize the release of any medical or other information necessary to process this claim. I also request payment of government benefits either to myself or to the party who accepts assignment below.

SIGNED _____ DATE _____

13. INSURED'S OR AUTHORIZED PERSON'S SIGNATURE I authorize payment of medical benefits to the undersigned physician or supplier for services described below.

SIGNED _____

| 14. DATE OF CURRENT: MM DD YY | ILLNESS (First symptom) OR INJURY (Accident) OR PREGNANCY(LMP) | 15. IF PATIENT HAS HAD SAME OR SIMILAR ILLNESS. GIVE FIRST DATE MM DD YY | 16. DATES PATIENT UNABLE TO WORK IN CURRENT OCCUPATION MM DD YY FROM TO MM DD YY |

| 17. NAME OF REFERRING PROVIDER OR OTHER SOURCE | 17a. | 18. HOSPITALIZATION DATES RELATED TO CURRENT SERVICES MM DD YY FROM TO MM DD YY |
| | 17b. NPI | |

| 19. RESERVED FOR LOCAL USE | 20. OUTSIDE LAB? $ CHARGES ☐ YES ☐ NO |

21. DIAGNOSIS OR NATURE OF ILLNESS OR INJURY (Relate Items 1, 2, 9 or 4 to Item 24E by Line)

22. MEDICAID RESUBMISSION CODE ORIGINAL REF. NO.

1. | **398.90**　　　　　　　3. | **396.30**

23. PRIOR AUTHORIZATION NUMBER

2. | **396.00**　　　　　　　4. |

24. A. DATE(S) OF SERVICE						B. PLACE OF SERVICE	C. EMG	D. PROCEDURES, SERVICES, OR SUPPLIES (Explain Unusual Circumstances) CPT/HCPCS	MODIFIER	E. DIAGNOSIS POINTER	F. $ CHARGES	G. DAYS OR UNITS	H. EPSDT Family Plan	I. ID. QUAL.	J. RENDERING PROVIDER ID. #
	From MM DD YY			To MM DD YY											
1	2	16			21			99223			135	00			NPI
2															NPI
3	2	18			21			99241			80	00			NPI
4															NPI
5															NPI
6															NPI

| 25. FEDERAL TAX I.D. NUMBER SSN EIN | 26. PATIENT'S ACCOUNT NO. | 27. ACCEPT ASSIGNMENT? (For govt. claims, see back) ☐ YES ☐ NO | 28. TOTAL CHARGE $ | 29. AMOUNT PAID $ | 30. BALANCE DUE $ |

| 31. SIGNATURE OF PHYSICIAN OR SUPPLIER INCLUDING DEGREES OR CREDENTIALS (I certify that the statements on the reverse apply to this bill and are made a part thereof.) | 32. SERVICE FACILITY LOCATION INFORMATION | 33. BILLING PROVIDER INFO & PH # (　　　) |

CARRIER

PATIENT AND INSURED INFORMATION

PHYSICIAN OR SUPPLIER INFORMATION

EXERCISE **13.4**

Name: _____

Class/Section: _____

Date: _____

2012

1500

HEALTH INSURANCE CLAIM FORM

APPROVED BY NATIONAL UNIFORM CLAIM COMMITTEE 08/05

| | PICA | | | | | | PICA | |

13.14

| 1. MEDICARE | MEDICAID | TRICARE CHAMPUS | CHAMPVA | GROUP HEALTH PLAN | FECA BLK LUNG | OTHER | 1a. INSURED'S I.D. NUMBER | (For Program in Item 1) |
| (Medicare #) | (Medicaid #) | (Sponsor's SSN) | (Member ID#) | (SSN or ID) | (SSN) | (ID) | | |

2. PATIENT'S NAME (Last

5. PATIENT'S ADDRESS (

CITY   STATE

ZIP CODE   de Area Code)

9. OTHER INSURED'S NA

a. OTHER INSURED'S PC   SEX

b. OTHER INSURED'S DA   MM   DD   YY   F

c. EMPLOYER'S NAME O

| | | YES | | NO | |

d. INSURANCE PLAN NAME OR PROGRAM NAME   10d. RESERVED FOR LOCAL USE   d. IS THERE ANOTHER HEALTH BENEFIT PLAN?

| | YES | | NO | | If yes, return to and complete item 9 a-d. |

READ BACK OF FORM BEFORE COMPLETING & SIGNING THIS FORM.

12. PATIENT'S OR AUTHORIZED PERSON'S SIGNATURE I authorize the release of any medical or other information necessary to process this claim. I also request payment of government benefits either to myself or to the party who accepts assignment below.

13. INSURED'S OR AUTHORIZED PERSON'S SIGNATURE I authorize payment of medical benefits to the undersigned physician or supplier for services described below.

SIGNED _____   DATE _____   SIGNED _____

| 14. DATE OF CURRENT: MM DD YY | ◄ ILLNESS (First symptom) OR INJURY (Accident) OR PREGNANCY(LMP) | 15. IF PATIENT HAS HAD SAME OR SIMILAR ILLNESS. GIVE FIRST DATE MM DD YY | 16. DATES PATIENT UNABLE TO WORK IN CURRENT OCCUPATION MM DD YY   MM DD YY FROM   TO |

17. NAME OF REFERRING PROVIDER OR OTHER SOURCE

17a.

17b. NPI

18. HOSPITALIZATION DATES RELATED TO CURRENT SERVICES
MM DD YY   MM DD YY
FROM   TO

19. RESERVED FOR LOCAL USE

20. OUTSIDE LAB? $ CHARGES
| | YES | | NO |

21. DIAGNOSIS OR NATURE OF ILLNESS OR INJURY (Relate Items 1, 2, 9 or 4 to Item 24E by Line)

1. | **425.50 Prim Cardiomyopathy; NEC**   3. |____.____

2. |____.____   4. |____.____

22. MEDICAID RESUBMISSION CODE   ORIGINAL REF. NO.

23. PRIOR AUTHORIZATION NUMBER

24. A. DATE(S) OF SERVICE				B. PLACE OF SERVICE	C. EMG	D. PROCEDURES, SERVICES, OR SUPPLIES (Explain Unusual Circumstances) CPT/HCPCS MODIFIER	E. DIAGNOSIS POINTER	F. $ CHARGES	G. DAYS OR UNITS	H. EPSDT Family Plan	I. ID. QUAL.	J. RENDERING PROVIDER ID. #
From MM DD YY	To MM DD YY											
1	3	14			11		99202			55	00			NPI
2													NPI
3													NPI
4													NPI
5													NPI
6													NPI

| 25. FEDERAL TAX I.D. NUMBER   SSN EIN | 26. PATIENT'S ACCOUNT NO. | 27. ACCEPT ASSIGNMENT? (For govt. claims, see back) YES   NO | 28. TOTAL CHARGE $ | 29. AMOUNT PAID $ | 30. BALANCE DUE $ |

31. SIGNATURE OF PHYSICIAN OR SUPPLIER INCLUDING DEGREES OR CREDENTIALS (I certify that the statements on the reverse apply to this bill and are made a part thereof.)

32. SERVICE FACILITY LOCATION INFORMATION

33. BILLING PROVIDER INFO & PH # (   )

Name: _____

Class/Section: _____

Date: _____

cpTeach
2012

EXERCISE 13.15

1500

HEALTH INSURANCE CLAIM FORM

APPROVED BY NATIONAL UNIFORM CLAIM COMMITTEE 08/05

PICA   PICA

13.15

| 1. MEDICARE | MEDICAID | TRICARE CHAMPUS | CHAMPVA | GROUP HEALTH PLAN | FECA BLK LUNG | OTHER | 1a. INSURED'S I.D. NUMBER | (For Program in Item 1) |

2. PATIENT'S NAME (Last...

5. PATIENT'S ADDRESS...

CITY   STATE

ZIP CODE   ...de Area Code)

9. OTHER INSURED'S NA...

a. OTHER INSURED'S PO...   SEX   F ☐

b. OTHER INSURED'S DA...
   MM   DD   YY

c. EMPLOYER'S NAME OR...

YES ☐   NO ☐

d. INSURANCE PLAN NAME OR PROGRAM NAME   10d. RESERVED FOR LOCAL USE   d. IS THERE ANOTHER HEALTH BENEFIT PLAN?
                                                                              ☐ YES   ☐ NO   If yes, return to and complete item 9 a-d.

READ BACK OF FORM BEFORE COMPLETING & SIGNING THIS FORM.

12. PATIENT'S OR AUTHORIZED PERSON'S SIGNATURE I authorize the release of any medical or other information necessary to process this claim. I also request payment of government benefits either to myself or to the party who accepts assignment below.

SIGNED_____ DATE_____

19. INSURED'S OR AUTHORIZED PERSON'S SIGNATURE I authorize payment of medical benefits to the undersigned physician or supplier for services described below.

SIGNED_____

| 14. DATE OF CURRENT: MM DD YY | ILLNESS (First symptom) OR INJURY (Accident) OR PREGNANCY(LMP) | 15. IF PATIENT HAS HAD SAME OR SIMILAR ILLNESS. GIVE FIRST DATE MM DD YY | 16. DATES PATIENT UNABLE TO WORK IN CURRENT OCCUPATION MM DD YY FROM   TO   MM DD YY |

17. NAME OF REFERRING PROVIDER OR OTHER SOURCE   17a.   17b. NPI   18. HOSPITALIZATION DATES RELATED TO CURRENT SERVICES MM DD YY FROM   TO   MM DD YY

19. RESERVED FOR LOCAL USE   20. OUTSIDE LAB? $ CHARGES
                              ☐ YES   ☐ NO

21. DIAGNOSIS OR NATURE OF ILLNESS OR INJURY (Relate Items 1, 2, 9 or 4 to Item 24E by Line)

1. | **425.50 Prim Cardiomyopathy; NEC**   3. |_____

2. |_____   4. |_____

22. MEDICAID RESUBMISSION CODE   ORIGINAL REF. NO.

23. PRIOR AUTHORIZATION NUMBER

24. A. DATE(S) OF SERVICE From / To MM DD YY MM DD YY	B. PLACE OF SERVICE	C. EMG	D. PROCEDURES, SERVICES, OR SUPPLIES (Explain Unusual Circumstances) CPT/HCPCS MODIFIER	E. DIAGNOSIS POINTER	F. $ CHARGES	G. DAYS OR UNITS	H. EPSDT Family Plan	I. ID. QUAL.	J. RENDERING PROVIDER ID. #
1	1 28	21		99223		175 00	1		NPI
2	1 31	21		93620		1800 00	1		NPI
3									NPI
4									NPI
5									NPI
6									NPI

25. FEDERAL TAX I.D. NUMBER   SSN ☐ EIN ☐   26. PATIENT'S ACCOUNT NO.   27. ACCEPT ASSIGNMENT? (For govt. claims, see back) ☐ YES ☐ NO   28. TOTAL CHARGE $ 29. AMOUNT PAID $ 30. BALANCE DUE $

31. SIGNATURE OF PHYSICIAN OR SUPPLIER INCLUDING DEGREES OR CREDENTIALS (I certify that the statements on the reverse apply to this bill and are made a part thereof.)   32. SERVICE FACILITY LOCATION INFORMATION   33. BILLING PROVIDER INFO & PH # (   )

CARRIER

PATIENT AND INSURED INFORMATION

PHYSICIAN OR SUPPLIER INFORMATION

EXERCISE 13.16

1500
HEALTH INSURANCE CLAIM FORM

APPROVED BY NATIONAL UNIFORM CLAIM COMMITTEE 08/05

13.16

PICA										PICA

1. MEDICARE   MEDICAID   TRICARE CHAMPUS   CHAMPVA   GROUP HEALTH PLAN   FECA BLK LUNG   OTHER   1a. INSURED'S I.D. NUMBER   (For Program in Item 1)

(Medicare #)   (Medicaid #)   (Sponsor's SSN)   (Member ID#)   (SSN or ID)   (SSN)   (ID)

2. PATIENT'S NAME (Last...   Initial)

5. PATIENT'S ADDRESS (...

CITY   STATE

ZIP CODE   (...de Area Code)

9. OTHER INSURED'S NA...

a. OTHER INSURED'S PO...   SEX F □

b. OTHER INSURED'S DA...
   MM   DD   YY

c. EMPLOYER'S NAME O...   YES □   NO □

d. INSURANCE PLAN NAME OR PROGRAM NAME   10d. RESERVED FOR LOCAL USE   d. IS THERE ANOTHER HEALTH BENEFIT PLAN? YES □ NO □ If yes, return to and complete item 9 a-d.

READ BACK OF FORM BEFORE COMPLETING & SIGNING THIS FORM.
12. PATIENT'S OR AUTHORIZED PERSON'S SIGNATURE I authorize the release of any medical or other information necessary to process this claim. I also request payment of government benefits either to myself or to the party who accepts assignment below.

SIGNED _____   DATE _____

19. INSURED'S OR AUTHORIZED PERSON'S SIGNATURE I authorize payment of medical benefits to the undersigned physician or supplier for services described below.

SIGNED _____

14. DATE OF CURRENT: ILLNESS (First symptom) OR INJURY (Accident) OR PREGNANCY(LMP)
    MM   DD   YY

15. IF PATIENT HAS HAD SAME OR SIMILAR ILLNESS. GIVE FIRST DATE MM DD YY

16. DATES PATIENT UNABLE TO WORK IN CURRENT OCCUPATION
    FROM MM DD YY   TO MM DD YY

17. NAME OF REFERRING PROVIDER OR OTHER SOURCE   17a.   17b. NPI

18. HOSPITALIZATION DATES RELATED TO CURRENT SERVICES
    FROM MM DD YY   TO MM DD YY

19. RESERVED FOR LOCAL USE

20. OUTSIDE LAB? $ CHARGES   YES □ NO □

21. DIAGNOSIS OR NATURE OF ILLNESS OR INJURY (Relate Items 1, 2, 9 or 4 to Item 24E by Line)

1. V42.1   3. |____

2. |____   4. |____

22. MEDICAID RESUBMISSION CODE   ORIGINAL REF. NO.

23. PRIOR AUTHORIZATION NUMBER

24. A. DATE(S) OF SERVICE From / To			B. PLACE OF SERVICE	C. EMG	D. PROCEDURES, SERVICES, OR SUPPLIES (Explain Unusual Circumstances) CPT/HCPCS	MODIFIER	E. DIAGNOSIS POINTER	F. $ CHARGES	G. DAYS OR UNITS	H. EPSDT Family Plan	I. ID. QUAL.	J. RENDERING PROVIDER ID. #
1	11 27		22		93505			350 00			NPI	
2											NPI	
3											NPI	
4											NPI	
5											NPI	
6											NPI	

25. FEDERAL TAX I.D. NUMBER   SSN □ EIN □

26. PATIENT'S ACCOUNT NO.

27. ACCEPT ASSIGNMENT? (For govt. claims, see back) YES □ NO □

28. TOTAL CHARGE $

29. AMOUNT PAID $

30. BALANCE DUE $

31. SIGNATURE OF PHYSICIAN OR SUPPLIER INCLUDING DEGREES OR CREDENTIALS (I certify that the statements on the reverse apply to this bill and are made a part thereof.)

32. SERVICE FACILITY LOCATION INFORMATION

33. BILLING PROVIDER INFO & PH # (   )

CARRIER

PATIENT AND INSURED INFORMATION

PHYSICIAN OR SUPPLIER INFORMATION

Name: _____

Class/Section: _____

Date: _____

WORKBOOK

cpTeach
2012

EXERCISE 13.17

1500

HEALTH INSURANCE CLAIM FORM

APPROVED BY NATIONAL UNIFORM CLAIM COMMITTEE 08/05

| | PICA | | | | | | | | PICA | |

13.17

_____

_____

_____

_____

_____

_____

_____

_____

| 1. MEDICARE | MEDICAID | TRICARE CHAMPUS | CHAMPVA | GROUP HEALTH PLAN | FECA BLK LUNG | OTHER | 1a. INSURED'S I.D. NUMBER | (For Program in Item 1) |
| (Medicare #) | (Medicaid #) | (Sponsor's SSN) | (Member ID#) | (SSN or ID) | (SSN) | (ID) | | |

2. PATIENT'S NAME (Last ... Initial)

5. PATIENT'S ADDRESS

CITY   STATE

ZIP CODE   (...de Area Code)

9. OTHER INSURED'S NA...

a. OTHER INSURED'S PO...

SEX F ☐

b. OTHER INSURED'S DA... MM DD YY

c. EMPLOYER'S NAME O...

| | | YES | NO | | | |

d. INSURANCE PLAN NAME OR PROGRAM NAME   10d. RESERVED FOR LOCAL USE   d. IS THERE ANOTHER HEALTH BENEFIT PLAN?
☐ YES ☐ NO   If yes, return to and complete item 9 a-d.

READ BACK OF FORM BEFORE COMPLETING & SIGNING THIS FORM.

12. PATIENT'S OR AUTHORIZED PERSON'S SIGNATURE I authorize the release of any medical or other information necessary to process this claim. I also request payment of government benefits either to myself or to the party who accepts assignment below.

SIGNED_____ DATE _____

13. INSURED'S OR AUTHORIZED PERSON'S SIGNATURE I authorize payment of medical benefits to the undersigned physician or supplier for services described below.

SIGNED _____

| 14. DATE OF CURRENT: MM DD YY | ILLNESS (First symptom) OR INJURY (Accident) OR PREGNANCY(LMP) | 15. IF PATIENT HAS HAD SAME OR SIMILAR ILLNESS. GIVE FIRST DATE MM DD YY | 16. DATES PATIENT UNABLE TO WORK IN CURRENT OCCUPATION MM DD YY FROM TO MM DD YY |

17. NAME OF REFERRING PROVIDER OR OTHER SOURCE   17a.   17b. NPI   18. HOSPITALIZATION DATES RELATED TO CURRENT SERVICES MM DD YY FROM TO MM DD YY

19. RESERVED FOR LOCAL USE   20. OUTSIDE LAB? $ CHARGES   ☐ YES ☐ NO

21. DIAGNOSIS OR NATURE OF ILLNESS OR INJURY (Relate Items 1, 2, 9 or 4 to Item 24E by Line)   22. MEDICAID RESUBMISSION CODE   ORIGINAL REF. NO.

1. |__**447.1 Stricture of artery**__   9. |____.____

2. |__**401.9 Hypertension NOS**__   4. |____.____

23. PRIOR AUTHORIZATION NUMBER

24. A. DATE(S) OF SERVICE From MM DD YY To MM DD YY	B. PLACE OF SERVICE	C. EMG	D. PROCEDURES, SERVICES, OR SUPPLIES (Explain Unusual Circumstances) CPT/HCPCS	MODIFIER	E. DIAGNOSIS POINTER	F. $ CHARGES	G. DAYS OR UNITS	H. EPSDT Family Plan	I. ID. QUAL.	J. RENDERING PROVIDER ID. #
1	9 19	21	99223			175 00			NPI	
2	9 20	21	99238			60 00			NPI	
3									NPI	
4									NPI	
5									NPI	
6									NPI	

| 25. FEDERAL TAX I.D. NUMBER | SSN EIN | 26. PATIENT'S ACCOUNT NO. | 27. ACCEPT ASSIGNMENT? (For govt. claims, see back) ☐ YES ☐ NO | 28. TOTAL CHARGE $ | 29. AMOUNT PAID $ | 30. BALANCE DUE $ |

31. SIGNATURE OF PHYSICIAN OR SUPPLIER INCLUDING DEGREES OR CREDENTIALS (I certify that the statements on the reverse apply to this bill and are made a part thereof.)   32. SERVICE FACILITY LOCATION INFORMATION   33. BILLING PROVIDER INFO & PH # ( )

CARRIER   PATIENT AND INSURED INFORMATION   PHYSICIAN OR SUPPLIER INFORMATION

EXERCISE **13.18**

Name: _____

Class/Section: _____

Date: _____

2012

1500

HEALTH INSURANCE CLAIM FORM

APPROVED BY NATIONAL UNIFORM CLAIM COMMITTEE 08/05

		PICA										PICA		

1. MEDICARE	MEDICAID	TRICARE CHAMPUS	CHAMPVA	GROUP HEALTH PLAN	FECA BLK LUNG	OTHER	1a. INSURED'S I.D. NUMBER	(For Program in Item 1)
(Medicare #)	(Medicaid #)	(Sponsor's SSN)	(Member ID#)	(SSN or ID)	(SSN)	(ID)		

13.18

_____
_____
_____
_____
_____
_____
_____
_____

2. PATIENT'S NAME (Last... initial)

5. PATIENT'S ADDRESS (

CITY   STATE

ZIP CODE   de Area Code)

9. OTHER INSURED'S NA

a. OTHER INSURED'S PO   SEX   F

b. OTHER INSURED'S DA
   MM   DD   YY

c. EMPLOYER'S NAME O

	YES		NO

d. INSURANCE PLAN NAME OR PROGRAM NAME | 10d. RESERVED FOR LOCAL USE | d. IS THERE ANOTHER HEALTH BENEFIT PLAN?
| | YES | NO | If yes, return to and complete item 9 a-d. |

READ BACK OF FORM BEFORE COMPLETING & SIGNING THIS FORM.

12. PATIENT'S OR AUTHORIZED PERSON'S SIGNATURE I authorize the release of any medical or other information necessary to process this claim. I also request payment of government benefits either to myself or to the party who accepts assignment below.

SIGNED_____ DATE_____

13. INSURED'S OR AUTHORIZED PERSON'S SIGNATURE I authorize payment of medical benefits to the undersigned physician or supplier for services described below.

SIGNED _____

14. DATE OF CURRENT: ILLNESS (First symptom) OR INJURY (Accident) OR PREGNANCY(LMP) MM DD YY	15. IF PATIENT HAS HAD SAME OR SIMILAR ILLNESS. GIVE FIRST DATE MM DD YY	16. DATES PATIENT UNABLE TO WORK IN CURRENT OCCUPATION MM DD YY MM DD YY FROM TO

17. NAME OF REFERRING PROVIDER OR OTHER SOURCE	17a.	18. HOSPITALIZATION DATES RELATED TO CURRENT SERVICES MM DD YY MM DD YY FROM TO
	17b. NPI	

19. RESERVED FOR LOCAL USE	20. OUTSIDE LAB? $ CHARGES YES NO

21. DIAGNOSIS OR NATURE OF ILLNESS OR INJURY (Relate Items 1, 2, 9 or 4 to Item 24E by Line)

1. **722.10 Herniated lumbar disk**   9. |___|___

2. |___|___   4. |___|___

22. MEDICAID RESUBMISSION CODE	ORIGINAL REF. NO.

23. PRIOR AUTHORIZATION NUMBER

24. A. DATE(S) OF SERVICE From MM DD YY To MM DD YY	B. PLACE OF SERVICE	C. EMG	D. PROCEDURES, SERVICES, OR SUPPLIES (Explain Unusual Circumstances) CPT/HCPCS MODIFIER	E. DIAGNOSIS POINTER	F. $ CHARGES	G. DAYS OR UNITS	H. EPSDT Family Plan	I. ID. QUAL.	J. RENDERING PROVIDER ID. #
1	3 08	21	63030 20	1	4401 00				NPI
2	3 08	21	63030 81	1	880 20				NPI
3	3 07	21	72265 20	1	572 00				NPI
4									NPI
5									NPI
6									NPI

25. FEDERAL TAX I.D. NUMBER SSN EIN	26. PATIENT'S ACCOUNT NO.	27. ACCEPT ASSIGNMENT? (For govt. claims, see back) YES NO	28. TOTAL CHARGE $	29. AMOUNT PAID $	30. BALANCE DUE $

31. SIGNATURE OF PHYSICIAN OR SUPPLIER INCLUDING DEGREES OR CREDENTIALS (I certify that the statements on the reverse apply to this bill and are made a part thereof.)	32. SERVICE FACILITY LOCATION INFORMATION	33. BILLING PROVIDER INFO & PH # ( )

EXERCISE 13.19

Name: _____

Class/Section: _____

Date: _____

cpTeach 2012

1500

HEALTH INSURANCE CLAIM FORM

APPROVED BY NATIONAL UNIFORM CLAIM COMMITTEE 08/05

| | PICA | | | | | | | | | PICA | |

| 1. MEDICARE | MEDICAID | TRICARE CHAMPUS (Sponsor's SSN) | CHAMPVA (Member ID#) | GROUP HEALTH PLAN (SSN or ID) | FECA BLK LUNG (SSN) | OTHER (ID) | 1a. INSURED'S I.D. NUMBER | (For Program in Item 1) |
| (Medicare #) | (Medicaid #) | | | | | | | |

13.19

_____

_____

_____

_____

_____

_____

_____

_____

2. PATIENT'S NAME (Last ... Initial)

5. PATIENT'S ADDRESS (

CITY   STATE

ZIP CODE   (...de Area Code)

9. OTHER INSURED'S NA...

a. OTHER INSURED'S PO...   SEX   F

b. OTHER INSURED'S DA... MM DD YY

c. EMPLOYER'S NAME OR...

YES   NO

d. INSURANCE PLAN NAME OR PROGRAM NAME   10d. RESERVED FOR LOCAL USE   d. IS THERE ANOTHER HEALTH BENEFIT PLAN?

YES   NO   If yes, return to and complete Item 9 a-d.

READ BACK OF FORM BEFORE COMPLETING & SIGNING THIS FORM.

12. PATIENT'S OR AUTHORIZED PERSON'S SIGNATURE I authorize the release of any medical or other information necessary to process this claim. I also request payment of government benefits either to myself or to the party who accepts assignment below.

SIGNED _____ DATE _____

19. INSURED'S OR AUTHORIZED PERSON'S SIGNATURE I authorize payment of medical benefits to the undersigned physician or supplier for services described below.

SIGNED _____

| 14. DATE OF CURRENT: MM DD YY | ILLNESS (First symptom) OR INJURY (Accident) OR PREGNANCY(LMP) | 15. IF PATIENT HAS HAD SAME OR SIMILAR ILLNESS. GIVE FIRST DATE MM DD YY | 16. DATES PATIENT UNABLE TO WORK IN CURRENT OCCUPATION MM DD YY FROM   TO MM DD YY |

| 17. NAME OF REFERRING PROVIDER OR OTHER SOURCE | 17a. | 18. HOSPITALIZATION DATES RELATED TO CURRENT SERVICES MM DD YY FROM   TO MM DD YY |
| | 17b. NPI | |

| 19. RESERVED FOR LOCAL USE | | 20. OUTSIDE LAB? $ CHARGES |
| | | YES   NO |

21. DIAGNOSIS OR NATURE OF ILLNESS OR INJURY (Relate Items 1, 2, 9 or 4 to Item 24E by Line)

1. 038.9   3. 276.5

2. 185   4.

22. MEDICAID RESUBMISSION CODE   ORIGINAL REF. NO.

23. PRIOR AUTHORIZATION NUMBER

24. A. DATE(S) OF SERVICE From MM DD YY	To MM DD YY	B. PLACE OF SERVICE	C. EMG	D. PROCEDURES, SERVICES, OR SUPPLIES (Explain Unusual Circumstances) CPT/HCPCS	MODIFIER	E. DIAGNOSIS POINTER	F. $ CHARGES	G. DAYS OR UNITS	H. EPSDT Family Plan	I. ID. QUAL.	J. RENDERING PROVIDER ID. #
1	6 09		21		99222		1,2,3	175 00	1		NPI
2	6 10		21		99232		1,2,3	60 00	1		NPI
3											NPI
4											NPI
5											NPI
6											NPI

| 25. FEDERAL TAX I.D. NUMBER   SSN EIN | 26. PATIENT'S ACCOUNT NO. | 27. ACCEPT ASSIGNMENT? (For govt. claims, see back) YES NO | 28. TOTAL CHARGE $ | 29. AMOUNT PAID $ | 30. BALANCE DUE $ |

31. SIGNATURE OF PHYSICIAN OR SUPPLIER INCLUDING DEGREES OR CREDENTIALS (I certify that the statements on the reverse apply to this bill and are made a part thereof.)

32. SERVICE FACILITY LOCATION INFORMATION

33. BILLING PROVIDER INFO & PH # ( )

EXERCISE 13.20

Name: _____

Class/Section: _____

Date: _____

Workbook cpTeach 2012

1500
HEALTH INSURANCE CLAIM FORM

APPROVED BY NATIONAL UNIFORM CLAIM COMMITTEE 08/05

| | PICA | | | | | | | | | | PICA | |

13.20

_____

_____

_____

_____

_____

_____

_____

_____

_____

_____

21. DIAGNOSIS OR NATURE OF ILLNESS OR INJURY (Relate Items 1, 2, 9 or 4 to Item 24E by Line)

1. **Headache 784.0**   3. **Severe right leg pain 729.5**

2. **Cardiovascular disease 437.9**   4.

	DATE(S) OF SERVICE From MM DD YY	To MM DD YY	B. PLACE OF SERVICE	C. EMG	D. PROCEDURES, SERVICES, OR SUPPLIES (Explain Unusual Circumstances) CPT/HCPCS	MODIFIER	E. DIAGNOSIS POINTER	F. $ CHARGES	G. DAYS OR UNITS	H. EPSDT Family Plan	I. ID QUAL.	J. RENDERING PROVIDER ID. #
1	2 28		23		62270		1	163 00			NPI	
2	2 27		23		99243		1	155 00			NPI	
3	2 27		23		99050	22	1	150 00			NPI	
4	2 28		21		99231		1	50 00			NPI	
5	3 01		21		99231		1	50 00			NPI	
6											NPI	

25. FEDERAL TAX I.D. NUMBER   SSN EIN   **26. PATIENT'S ACCOUNT NO.**   **27. ACCEPT ASSIGNMENT?** (For govt. claims, see back) YES NO   **28. TOTAL CHARGE** $ **29. AMOUNT PAID** $ **30. BALANCE DUE** $

31. SIGNATURE OF PHYSICIAN OR SUPPLIER INCLUDING DEGREES OR CREDENTIALS (I certify that the statements on the reverse apply to this bill and are made a part thereof.)   **32. SERVICE FACILITY LOCATION INFORMATION**   **33. BILLING PROVIDER INFO & PH # (   )**

EXERCISE 13.21

Name:_____

Class/Section:_____

Date:_____

1500

HEALTH INSURANCE CLAIM FORM

APPROVED BY NATIONAL UNIFORM CLAIM COMMITTEE 08/05

| | PICA | | | | | | | | 1a. INSURED'S I.D. NUMBER | (For Program in Item 1) | PICA | |

1. MEDICARE	MEDICAID	TRICARE CHAMPUS	CHAMPVA	GROUP HEALTH PLAN	FECA BLK LUNG	OTHER	1a. INSURED'S I.D. NUMBER		(For Program in Item 1)
(Medicare #)	(Medicaid #)	(Sponsor's SSN)	(Member ID#)	(SSN or ID)	(SSN)	(ID)			

2. PATIENT'S NAME (Last

13.21

5. PATIENT'S ADDRESS (

CITY   STATE

ZIP CODE   de Area Code)

9. OTHER INSURED'S NA

a. OTHER INSURED'S PO   SEX   F

b. OTHER INSURED'S DA MM DD YY

c. EMPLOYER'S NAME OF

| | YES | | NO | |

d. INSURANCE PLAN NAME OR PROGRAM NAME | 10d. RESERVED FOR LOCAL USE | d. IS THERE ANOTHER HEALTH BENEFIT PLAN?
| | YES | | NO | If yes, return to and complete item 9 a-d.

READ BACK OF FORM BEFORE COMPLETING & SIGNING THIS FORM.

12. PATIENT'S OR AUTHORIZED PERSON'S SIGNATURE I authorize the release of any medical or other information necessary to process this claim. I also request payment of government benefits either to myself or to the party who accepts assignment below.

SIGNED_____ DATE_____

13. INSURED'S OR AUTHORIZED PERSON'S SIGNATURE I authorize payment of medical benefits to the undersigned physician or supplier for services described below.

SIGNED_____

| 14. DATE OF CURRENT: MM DD YY | ILLNESS (First symptom) OR INJURY (Accident) OR PREGNANCY(LMP) | 15. IF PATIENT HAS HAD SAME OR SIMILAR ILLNESS. GIVE FIRST DATE MM DD YY | 16. DATES PATIENT UNABLE TO WORK IN CURRENT OCCUPATION MM DD YY MM DD YY FROM TO |

| 17. NAME OF REFERRING PROVIDER OR OTHER SOURCE | 17a. | 18. HOSPITALIZATION DATES RELATED TO CURRENT SERVICES MM DD YY MM DD YY |
| | 17b. NPI | FROM TO |

19. RESERVED FOR LOCAL USE | 20. OUTSIDE LAB? $ CHARGES | | YES | | NO

21. DIAGNOSIS OR NATURE OF ILLNESS OR INJURY (Relate Items 1, 2, 9 or 4 to Item 24E by Line)

1. | **238.7**   3. |

2. | **436**   4. |

22. MEDICAID RESUBMISSION CODE   ORIGINAL REF. NO.

23. PRIOR AUTHORIZATION NUMBER

24. A. DATE(S) OF SERVICE						B. PLACE OF SERVICE	C. EMG	D. PROCEDURES, SERVICES, OR SUPPLIES (Explain Unusual Circumstances) CPT/HCPCS MODIFIER	E. DIAGNOSIS POINTER	F. $ CHARGES	G. DAYS OR UNITS	H. EPSDT Family Plan	I. ID. QUAL.	J. RENDERING PROVIDER ID. #
From MM	DD	YY	To MM	DD	YY									
1 6	09					21		99245	1,2	200 00	1		NPI	
2 6	08					21		99232	1,2	50 00	1		NPI	
3 6	08					21		85055	1,2	100 00	1		NPI	
4													NPI	
5													NPI	
6													NPI	

25. FEDERAL TAX I.D. NUMBER	SSN EIN	26. PATIENT'S ACCOUNT NO.	27. ACCEPT ASSIGNMENT? (For govt. claims, see back)	28. TOTAL CHARGE	29. AMOUNT PAID	30. BALANCE DUE
			YES NO	$	$	$

31. SIGNATURE OF PHYSICIAN OR SUPPLIER INCLUDING DEGREES OR CREDENTIALS (I certify that the statements on the reverse apply to this bill and are made a part thereof.)

32. SERVICE FACILITY LOCATION INFORMATION

33. BILLING PROVIDER INFO & PH # ( )

CARRIER

PATIENT AND INSURED INFORMATION

PHYSICIAN OR SUPPLIER INFORMATION

EXERCISE **13.22**

Name:_____

Class/Section:_____

Date:_____

2012

1500

HEALTH INSURANCE CLAIM FORM

APPROVED BY NATIONAL UNIFORM CLAIM COMMITTEE 08/05

PICA

1. MEDICARE   MEDICAID   TRICARE CHAMPUS   CHAMPVA   GROUP HEALTH PLAN   FECA BLK LUNG   OTHER   1a. INSURED'S I.D. NUMBER   (For Program in Item 1)

(Medicare #)   (Medicaid #)   (Sponsor's SSN)   (Member ID#)   (SSN or ID)   (SSN)   (ID)

2. PATIENT'S NAME (Last

13.22

_____

_____

_____

_____

_____

_____

_____

_____

_____

5. PATIENT'S ADDRESS (

CITY   STATE

ZIP CODE

9. OTHER INSURED'S NA

a. OTHER INSURED'S PO   SEX
                                                                                               F

b. OTHER INSURED'S DA
   MM   DD   YY

c. EMPLOYER'S NAME O

YES   NO

d. INSURANCE PLAN NAME OR PROGRAM NAME   10d. RESERVED FOR LOCAL USE   d. IS THERE ANOTHER HEALTH BENEFIT PLAN?

YES   NO   If yes, return to and complete item 9 a-d.

READ BACK OF FORM BEFORE COMPLETING & SIGNING THIS FORM.

12. PATIENT'S OR AUTHORIZED PERSON'S SIGNATURE I authorize the release of any medical or other information necessary to process this claim. I also request payment of government benefits either to myself or to the party who accepts assignment below.

SIGNED_____   DATE_____

13. INSURED'S OR AUTHORIZED PERSON'S SIGNATURE I authorize payment of medical benefits to the undersigned physician or supplier for services described below.

SIGNED_____

14. DATE OF CURRENT: ILLNESS (First symptom) OR   15. IF PATIENT HAS HAD SAME OR SIMILAR ILLNESS.   16. DATES PATIENT UNABLE TO WORK IN CURRENT OCCUPATION
    MM   DD   YY   INJURY (Accident) OR   GIVE FIRST DATE MM   DD   YY   MM   DD   YY   MM   DD   YY
                       PREGNANCY(LMP)   FROM   TO

17. NAME OF REFERRING PROVIDER OR OTHER SOURCE   17a.   18. HOSPITALIZATION DATES RELATED TO CURRENT SERVICES
                                                                     MM   DD   YY   MM   DD   YY
                                                   17b. NPI   FROM   TO

19. RESERVED FOR LOCAL USE   20. OUTSIDE LAB? $ CHARGES
                                                                  YES   NO

21. DIAGNOSIS OR NATURE OF ILLNESS OR INJURY (Relate Items 1, 2, 9 or 4 to Item 24E by Line)   22. MEDICAID RESUBMISSION
                                                                                                 CODE   ORIGINAL REF. NO.

1. |760.8   3. |_____ .

                                                                 23. PRIOR AUTHORIZATION NUMBER

2. |_____ .   4. |_____ .

24. A. DATE(S) OF SERVICE					B. PLACE OF SERVICE	C. EMG	D. PROCEDURES, SERVICES, OR SUPPLIES (Explain Unusual Circumstances) CPT/HCPCS MODIFIER	E. DIAGNOSIS POINTER	F. $ CHARGES	G. DAYS OR UNITS	H. EPSDT Family Plan	I. ID. QUAL.	J. RENDERING PROVIDER ID. #
From MM	DD	YY	To MM	DD	YY									
1	01		1	01	11			J1070	1	15 00			NPI	
1	01		1	01	11			99212	1	150 00			NPI	
													NPI	
													NPI	
													NPI	
													NPI	

25. FEDERAL TAX I.D. NUMBER   SSN EIN   26. PATIENT'S ACCOUNT NO.   27. ACCEPT ASSIGNMENT? (For govt. claims, see back)   28. TOTAL CHARGE   29. AMOUNT PAID   30. BALANCE DUE

                                                                           YES   NO $ 165 00 $ 0 00 $ 165 00

31. SIGNATURE OF PHYSICIAN OR SUPPLIER INCLUDING DEGREES OR CREDENTIALS (I certify that the statements on the reverse apply to this bill and are made a part thereof.)   32. SERVICE FACILITY LOCATION INFORMATION   33. BILLING PROVIDER INFO & PH # (   )

EXERCISE 13.23

1500

HEALTH INSURANCE CLAIM FORM

APPROVED BY NATIONAL UNIFORM CLAIM COMMITTEE 08/05

| | | PICA | | | | | | | | | | PICA | | |

13.23

1. MEDICARE	MEDICAID	TRICARE CHAMPUS	CHAMPVA	GROUP HEALTH PLAN	FECA BLK LUNG	OTHER	1a. INSURED'S I.D. NUMBER	(For Program in Item 1)
(Medicare #)	(Medicaid #)	(Sponsor's SSN)	(Member ID#)	(SSN or ID)	(SSN)	(ID)		

2. PATIENT'S NAME (Last ... Initial)

5. PATIENT'S ADDRESS

CITY   STATE

ZIP CODE   (Include Area Code)

9. OTHER INSURED'S NAME

a. OTHER INSURED'S PO...   SEX   F

b. OTHER INSURED'S DATE
MM DD YY

c. EMPLOYER'S NAME OR

    YES   NO

d. INSURANCE PLAN NAME OR PROGRAM NAME   10d. RESERVED FOR LOCAL USE   d. IS THERE ANOTHER HEALTH BENEFIT PLAN?

    YES   NO   If yes, return to and complete Item 9 a-d.

READ BACK OF FORM BEFORE COMPLETING & SIGNING THIS FORM.

12. PATIENT'S OR AUTHORIZED PERSON'S SIGNATURE I authorize the release of any medical or other information necessary to process this claim. I also request payment of government benefits either to myself or to the party who accepts assignment below.

SIGNED _____ DATE _____

13. INSURED'S OR AUTHORIZED PERSON'S SIGNATURE I authorize payment of medical benefits to the undersigned physician or supplier for services described below.

SIGNED _____

14. DATE OF CURRENT: ILLNESS (First symptom) OR INJURY (Accident) OR PREGNANCY(LMP)	15. IF PATIENT HAS HAD SAME OR SIMILAR ILLNESS. GIVE FIRST DATE	16. DATES PATIENT UNABLE TO WORK IN CURRENT OCCUPATION
MM DD YY	MM DD YY	FROM MM DD YY TO MM DD YY

17. NAME OF REFERRING PROVIDER OR OTHER SOURCE   17a.   17b. NPI

18. HOSPITALIZATION DATES RELATED TO CURRENT SERVICES
FROM MM DD YY TO MM DD YY

19. RESERVED FOR LOCAL USE   20. OUTSIDE LAB?   YES   NO $ CHARGES

21. DIAGNOSIS OR NATURE OF ILLNESS OR INJURY (Relate Items 1, 2, 9 or 4 to Item 24E by Line)

1. | 826.00   3. |

2. | 4. |

22. MEDICAID RESUBMISSION CODE   ORIGINAL REF. NO.

23. PRIOR AUTHORIZATION NUMBER

24. A. DATE(S) OF SERVICE From MM DD YY	To MM DD YY	B. PLACE OF SERVICE	C. EMG	D. PROCEDURES, SERVICES, OR SUPPLIES (Explain Unusual Circumstances) CPT/HCPCS	MODIFIER	E. DIAGNOSIS POINTER	F. $ CHARGES	G. DAYS OR UNITS	H. EPSDT Family Plan	I. ID. QUAL.	J. RENDERING PROVIDER ID. #
1	1 01	1 01	22	29355		1	150 00			NPI	
2										NPI	
3	1 01	1 01	11	27500		1	475 00			NPI	
4										NPI	
5										NPI	
6										NPI	

25. FEDERAL TAX I.D. NUMBER	SSN EIN	26. PATIENT'S ACCOUNT NO.	27. ACCEPT ASSIGNMENT? (For govt. claims, see back) YES NO	28. TOTAL CHARGE $ 625 00	29. AMOUNT PAID $ 0 00	30. BALANCE DUE $ 625 00

31. SIGNATURE OF PHYSICIAN OR SUPPLIER INCLUDING DEGREES OR CREDENTIALS (I certify that the statements on the reverse apply to this bill and are made a part thereof.)

32. SERVICE FACILITY LOCATION INFORMATION

33. BILLING PROVIDER INFO & PH # ( )

WORKBOOK

cpTeach
2012

Name:_____

Class/Section:_____

Date:_____

CARRIER

EXERCISE 13.24

1500
HEALTH INSURANCE CLAIM FORM
APPROVED BY NATIONAL UNIFORM CLAIM COMMITTEE 08/05

| | PICA | | | | | | | | PICA | | |

13.24

_____

_____

_____

_____

_____

_____

_____

_____

_____

1. MEDICARE	MEDICAID	TRICARE CHAMPUS	CHAMPVA	GROUP HEALTH PLAN	FECA BLK LUNG	OTHER	1a. INSURED'S I.D. NUMBER	(For Program in Item 1)
(Medicare #)	(Medicaid #)	(Sponsor's SSN)	(Member ID#)	(SSN or ID)	(SSN)	(ID)		

2. PATIENT'S NAME (Last ... Initial)

5. PATIENT'S ADDRESS (...)

CITY ... STATE

ZIP CODE ... (...de Area Code)

9. OTHER INSURED'S NA...

a. OTHER INSURED'S PO... SEX F

b. OTHER INSURED'S DA... MM DD YY

c. EMPLOYER'S NAME O...

YES NO

d. INSURANCE PLAN NAME OR PROGRAM NAME

10d. RESERVED FOR LOCAL USE

d. IS THERE ANOTHER HEALTH BENEFIT PLAN?
YES NO If yes, return to and complete item 9 a-d.

READ BACK OF FORM BEFORE COMPLETING & SIGNING THIS FORM.
12. PATIENT'S OR AUTHORIZED PERSON'S SIGNATURE I authorize the release of any medical or other information necessary to process this claim. I also request payment of government benefits either to myself or to the party who accepts assignment below.

SIGNED _____ DATE _____

13. INSURED'S OR AUTHORIZED PERSON'S SIGNATURE I authorize payment of medical benefits to the undersigned physician or supplier for services described below.

SIGNED _____

14. DATE OF CURRENT: MM DD YY	ILLNESS (First symptom) OR INJURY (Accident) OR PREGNANCY(LMP)	15. IF PATIENT HAS HAD SAME OR SIMILAR ILLNESS. GIVE FIRST DATE MM DD YY	16. DATES PATIENT UNABLE TO WORK IN CURRENT OCCUPATION MM DD YY TO MM DD YY

| 17. NAME OF REFERRING PROVIDER OR OTHER SOURCE | 17a. | 18. HOSPITALIZATION DATES RELATED TO CURRENT SERVICES MM DD YY TO MM DD YY |
| | 17b. NPI | FROM TO |

19. RESERVED FOR LOCAL USE

20. OUTSIDE LAB? $ CHARGES
YES NO

21. DIAGNOSIS OR NATURE OF ILLNESS OR INJURY (Relate Items 1, 2, 9 or 4 to Item 24E by Line)
1. **171.4** .
2. .
3. .
4. .

22. MEDICAID RESUBMISSION CODE ORIGINAL REF. NO.

23. PRIOR AUTHORIZATION NUMBER

24. A. DATE(S) OF SERVICE From MM DD YY	To MM DD YY	B. PLACE OF SERVICE	C. EMG	D. PROCEDURES, SERVICES, OR SUPPLIES (Explain Unusual Circumstances) CPT/HCPCS	MODIFIER	E. DIAGNOSIS POINTER	F. $ CHARGES	G. DAYS OR UNITS	H. EPSDT Family Plan	I. ID. QUAL.	J. RENDERING PROVIDER ID. #
1	01 02	01 02	22	11600		1	160 00			NPI	
2	01 02	01 02	22	12001		1	190 00			NPI	
3										NPI	
4										NPI	
5										NPI	
6										NPI	

25. FEDERAL TAX I.D. NUMBER	SSN EIN	26. PATIENT'S ACCOUNT NO.	27. ACCEPT ASSIGNMENT? (For govt. claims, see back) YES NO	28. TOTAL CHARGE $ 320 00	29. AMOUNT PAID $ 0 00	30. BALANCE DUE $ 320 00

31. SIGNATURE OF PHYSICIAN OR SUPPLIER INCLUDING DEGREES OR CREDENTIALS (I certify that the statements on the reverse apply to this bill and are made a part thereof.)

32. SERVICE FACILITY LOCATION INFORMATION

33. BILLING PROVIDER INFO & PH # ( )

PATIENT AND INSURED INFORMATION

PHYSICIAN OR SUPPLIER INFORMATION

WORKBOOK

cpTeach
24th Edition

2012

Name:_____

Class/Section:_____

Date:_____

EXERCISE 13.25

1500

HEALTH INSURANCE CLAIM FORM

APPROVED BY NATIONAL UNIFORM CLAIM COMMITTEE 08/05

| | PICA | | | | | | | | PICA | | |

13.25

1. MEDICARE	MEDICAID	TRICARE CHAMPUS	CHAMPVA	GROUP HEALTH PLAN	FECA BLK LUNG	OTHER	1a. INSURED'S I.D. NUMBER	(For Program in Item 1)
(Medicare #)	(Medicaid #)	(Sponsor's SSN)	(Member ID#)	(SSN or ID)	(SSN)	(ID)		

2. PATIENT'S NAME (Last ... Initial)

5. PATIENT'S ADDRESS

CITY   STATE

ZIP CODE   (...de Area Code)

9. OTHER INSURED'S NA...

a. OTHER INSURED'S PO...   SEX   F ☐

b. OTHER INSURED'S DA...
MM   DD   YY

c. EMPLOYER'S NAME O...

        ☐ YES   ☐ NO

d. INSURANCE PLAN NAME OR PROGRAM NAME | 10d. RESERVED FOR LOCAL USE | d. IS THERE ANOTHER HEALTH BENEFIT PLAN?
     ☐ YES   ☐ NO   *If yes, return to and complete item 9 a-d.*

READ BACK OF FORM BEFORE COMPLETING & SIGNING THIS FORM.

12. PATIENT'S OR AUTHORIZED PERSON'S SIGNATURE I authorize the release of any medical or other information necessary to process this claim. I also request payment of government benefits either to myself or to the party who accepts assignment below.

SIGNED_____ DATE_____

13. INSURED'S OR AUTHORIZED PERSON'S SIGNATURE I authorize payment of medical benefits to the undersigned physician or supplier for services described below.

SIGNED_____

| 14. DATE OF CURRENT:
MM DD YY | ILLNESS (First symptom) OR INJURY (Accident) OR PREGNANCY (LMP) | 15. IF PATIENT HAS HAD SAME OR SIMILAR ILLNESS. GIVE FIRST DATE MM DD YY | 16. DATES PATIENT UNABLE TO WORK IN CURRENT OCCUPATION
MM DD YY   MM DD YY
FROM   TO |

17. NAME OF REFERRING PROVIDER OR OTHER SOURCE | 17a. | 18. HOSPITALIZATION DATES RELATED TO CURRENT SERVICES
MM DD YY   MM DD YY
     | 17b. NPI | FROM   TO

19. RESERVED FOR LOCAL USE | 20. OUTSIDE LAB? $ CHARGES
     ☐ YES   ☐ NO

21. DIAGNOSIS OR NATURE OF ILLNESS OR INJURY (Relate Items 1, 2, 9 or 4 to Item 24E by Line)

1. | 821.00   3. |_____

2. |_____   4. |_____

22. MEDICAID RESUBMISSION CODE   ORIGINAL REF. NO.

23. PRIOR AUTHORIZATION NUMBER

24. A. DATE(S) OF SERVICE						B. PLACE OF SERVICE	C. EMG	D. PROCEDURES, SERVICES, OR SUPPLIES (Explain Unusual Circumstances) CPT/HCPCS MODIFIER	E. DIAGNOSIS POINTER	F. $ CHARGES	G. DAYS OR UNITS	H. EPSDT Family Plan	I. ID. QUAL.	J. RENDERING PROVIDER ID. #
	From MM	DD	YY	To MM	DD	YY									
1	04	21		04	21		11		99024	1	50 00			NPI	
2														NPI	
3														NPI	
4														NPI	
5														NPI	
6														NPI	

| 25. FEDERAL TAX I.D. NUMBER   SSN EIN | 26. PATIENT'S ACCOUNT NO. | 27. ACCEPT ASSIGNMENT?
(For govt. claims, see back)
☐ YES   ☐ NO | 28. TOTAL CHARGE
$ 50 00 | 29. AMOUNT PAID
$ 0 00 | 30. BALANCE DUE
$ 50 00 |

31. SIGNATURE OF PHYSICIAN OR SUPPLIER INCLUDING DEGREES OR CREDENTIALS (I certify that the statements on the reverse apply to this bill and are made a part thereof.)

32. SERVICE FACILITY LOCATION INFORMATION

33. BILLING PROVIDER INFO & PH # ( )

Name: _____

Class/Section: _____

cpTeach
2012

Date: _____

EXERCISE 13.26

1500

HEALTH INSURANCE CLAIM FORM

APPROVED BY NATIONAL UNIFORM CLAIM COMMITTEE 08/05

| | PICA | | | | | | | | PICA | |

1. MEDICARE	MEDICAID	TRICARE CHAMPUS	CHAMPVA	GROUP HEALTH PLAN	FECA BLK LUNG	OTHER	1a. INSURED'S I.D. NUMBER	(For Program in Item 1)
(Medicare #)	(Medicaid #)	(Sponsor's SSN)	(Member ID#)	(SSN or ID)	(SSN)	(ID)		

13.26

_____

_____

_____

_____

_____

_____

_____

_____

_____

2. PATIENT'S NAME (Last ... initial)

5. PATIENT'S ADDRESS

CITY   STATE

ZIP CODE   de Area Code)

9. OTHER INSURED'S NA

a. OTHER INSURED'S PO   SEX   F

b. OTHER INSURED'S DA
   MM   DD   YY

c. EMPLOYER'S NAME O

                                          YES   NO

d. INSURANCE PLAN NAME OR PROGRAM NAME | 10d. RESERVED FOR LOCAL USE | d. IS THERE ANOTHER HEALTH BENEFIT PLAN?
                                                                           YES   NO   If yes, return to and complete item 9 a-d.

READ BACK OF FORM BEFORE COMPLETING & SIGNING THIS FORM.

12. PATIENT'S OR AUTHORIZED PERSON'S SIGNATURE I authorize the release of any medical or other information necessary to process this claim. I also request payment of government benefits either to myself or to the party who accepts assignment below.

SIGNED_____   DATE_____

13. INSURED'S OR AUTHORIZED PERSON'S SIGNATURE I authorize payment of medical benefits to the undersigned physician or supplier for services described below.

SIGNED _____

14. DATE OF CURRENT: ILLNESS (First symptom) OR | 15. IF PATIENT HAS HAD SAME OR SIMILAR ILLNESS. | 16. DATES PATIENT UNABLE TO WORK IN CURRENT OCCUPATION
    MM   DD   YY   INJURY (Accident) OR   GIVE FIRST DATE   MM   DD   YY   MM   DD   YY   MM   DD   YY
                   PREGNANCY (LMP)   FROM   TO

17. NAME OF REFERRING PROVIDER OR OTHER SOURCE | 17a. | 18. HOSPITALIZATION DATES RELATED TO CURRENT SERVICES
                                                17b. NPI   MM   DD   YY   MM   DD   YY
                                                            FROM   TO

19. RESERVED FOR LOCAL USE | 20. OUTSIDE LAB? $ CHARGES
                              YES   NO

21. DIAGNOSIS OR NATURE OF ILLNESS OR INJURY (Relate Items 1, 2, 9 or 4 to Item 24E by Line)

1. **255.0** ____   3. ____ . ____

2. **791.9** ____   4. ____ . ____

22. MEDICAID RESUBMISSION CODE   ORIGINAL REF. NO.

23. PRIOR AUTHORIZATION NUMBER

24. A. DATE(S) OF SERVICE From		To			B. PLACE OF SERVICE	C. EMG	D. PROCEDURES, SERVICES, OR SUPPLIES (Explain Unusual Circumstances) CPT/HCPCS	MODIFIER	E. DIAGNOSIS POINTER	F. $ CHARGES	G. DAYS OR UNITS	H. EPSDT Family Plan	I. ID. QUAL.	J. RENDERING PROVIDER ID. #
MM DD YY	MM DD YY													
1	01 01	01 01	21			99233		1,2	60 00			NPI	
2	01 02	01 02	21			99252		1,2	75 00			NPI	
3												NPI	
4												NPI	
5												NPI	
6												NPI	

25. FEDERAL TAX I.D. NUMBER   SSN EIN | 26. PATIENT'S ACCOUNT NO. | 27. ACCEPT ASSIGNMENT? (For govt. claims, see back)   YES   NO | 28. TOTAL CHARGE $ **135** 00 | 29. AMOUNT PAID $ **0** 00 | 30. BALANCE DUE $ **135** 00

31. SIGNATURE OF PHYSICIAN OR SUPPLIER INCLUDING DEGREES OR CREDENTIALS (I certify that the statements on the reverse apply to this bill and are made a part thereof.) | 32. SERVICE FACILITY LOCATION INFORMATION | 33. BILLING PROVIDER INFO & PH # ( )

CARRIER

PATIENT AND INSURED INFORMATION

PHYSICIAN OR SUPPLIER INFORMATION

Name: _____

Class/Section: _____

Date: _____

EXERCISE 13.27

WORKBOOK cpTeach 2012

1500

HEALTH INSURANCE CLAIM FORM
APPROVED BY NATIONAL UNIFORM CLAIM COMMITTEE 08/05

PICA

13.27

1. MEDICARE	MEDICAID	TRICARE CHAMPUS	CHAMPVA	GROUP HEALTH PLAN	FECA BLK LUNG	OTHER	1a. INSURED'S I.D. NUMBER	(For Program in Item 1)
(Medicare #)	(Medicaid #)	(Sponsor's SSN)	(Member ID#)	(SSN or ID)	(SSN)	(ID)		

2. PATIENT'S NAME (Last

5. PATIENT'S ADDRESS

CITY ... STATE

ZIP CODE ... (de Area Code)

9. OTHER INSURED'S NA

a. OTHER INSURED'S PO

b. OTHER INSURED'S DA   MM   DD   YY   SEX   F

c. EMPLOYER'S NAME OR

YES   NO

d. INSURANCE PLAN NAME OR PROGRAM NAME

10d. RESERVED FOR LOCAL USE

d. IS THERE ANOTHER HEALTH BENEFIT PLAN?   YES   NO   If yes, return to and complete Item 9 a-d.

READ BACK OF FORM BEFORE COMPLETING & SIGNING THIS FORM.

12. PATIENT'S OR AUTHORIZED PERSON'S SIGNATURE I authorize the release of any medical or other information necessary to process this claim. I also request payment of government benefits either to myself or to the party who accepts assignment below.

SIGNED_____   DATE_____

19. INSURED'S OR AUTHORIZED PERSON'S SIGNATURE I authorize payment of medical benefits to the undersigned physician or supplier for services described below.

SIGNED_____

14. DATE OF CURRENT:	ILLNESS (First symptom) OR INJURY (Accident) OR PREGNANCY (LMP)	15. IF PATIENT HAS HAD SAME OR SIMILAR ILLNESS. GIVE FIRST DATE MM DD YY	16. DATES PATIENT UNABLE TO WORK IN CURRENT OCCUPATION FROM TO

17. NAME OF REFERRING PROVIDER OR OTHER SOURCE   17a.   17b. NPI

18. HOSPITALIZATION DATES RELATED TO CURRENT SERVICES   FROM   TO

19. RESERVED FOR LOCAL USE

20. OUTSIDE LAB?   YES   NO $ CHARGES

21. DIAGNOSIS OR NATURE OF ILLNESS OR INJURY (Relate Items 1, 2, 9 or 4 to Item 24E by Line)

1. **958.3**   9.

2.   4.

22. MEDICAID RESUBMISSION CODE   ORIGINAL REF. NO.

23. PRIOR AUTHORIZATION NUMBER

24. A. DATE(S) OF SERVICE From MM DD YY To MM DD YY	B. PLACE OF SERVICE	C. EMG	D. PROCEDURES, SERVICES, OR SUPPLIES (Explain Unusual Circumstances) CPT/HCPCS MODIFIER	E. DIAGNOSIS POINTER	F. $ CHARGES	G. DAYS OR UNITS	H. EPSDT Family Plan	I. ID. QUAL.	J. RENDERING PROVIDER ID. #
1	11 09 11 09	11	96372	958.3	15 00				NPI
2									NPI
3									NPI
4									NPI
5									NPI
6									NPI

25. FEDERAL TAX I.D. NUMBER SSN EIN	26. PATIENT'S ACCOUNT NO.	27. ACCEPT ASSIGNMENT? (For govt. claims, see back) YES NO	28. TOTAL CHARGE $ 15 00	29. AMOUNT PAID $ 0 00	30. BALANCE DUE $ 15 00

31. SIGNATURE OF PHYSICIAN OR SUPPLIER INCLUDING DEGREES OR CREDENTIALS (I certify that the statements on the reverse apply to this bill and are made a part thereof.)

32. SERVICE FACILITY LOCATION INFORMATION

33. BILLING PROVIDER INFO & PH # (   )

EXERCISE 13.28

1500

HEALTH INSURANCE CLAIM FORM

APPROVED BY NATIONAL UNIFORM CLAIM COMMITTEE 08/05

PICA							PICA

1. MEDICARE	MEDICAID	TRICARE CHAMPUS	CHAMPVA	GROUP HEALTH PLAN	FECA BLK LUNG	OTHER	1a. INSURED'S I.D. NUMBER	(For Program in Item 1)
(Medicare #)	(Medicaid #)	(Sponsor's SSN)	(Member ID#)	(SSN or ID)	(SSN)	(ID)		

2. PATIENT'S NAME (Last ... Initial)

13.28

5. PATIENT'S ADDRESS (

CITY   STATE

ZIP CODE   (Include Area Code)

9. OTHER INSURED'S NA

a. OTHER INSURED'S PO   SEX   F

b. OTHER INSURED'S DATE   MM   DD   YY

c. EMPLOYER'S NAME O

d. INSURANCE PLAN NAME OR PROGRAM NAME   10d. RESERVED FOR LOCAL USE   d. IS THERE ANOTHER HEALTH BENEFIT PLAN?   YES   NO   If yes, return to and complete item 9 a-d.

READ BACK OF FORM BEFORE COMPLETING & SIGNING THIS FORM.

12. PATIENT'S OR AUTHORIZED PERSON'S SIGNATURE I authorize the release of any medical or other information necessary to process this claim. I also request payment of government benefits either to myself or to the party who accepts assignment below.

SIGNED_____   DATE_____

13. INSURED'S OR AUTHORIZED PERSON'S SIGNATURE I authorize payment of medical benefits to the undersigned physician or supplier for services described below.

SIGNED_____

14. DATE OF CURRENT: MM DD YY ILLNESS (First symptom) OR INJURY (Accident) OR PREGNANCY(LMP)	15. IF PATIENT HAS HAD SAME OR SIMILAR ILLNESS. GIVE FIRST DATE MM DD YY	16. DATES PATIENT UNABLE TO WORK IN CURRENT OCCUPATION MM DD YY FROM TO MM DD YY

17. NAME OF REFERRING PROVIDER OR OTHER SOURCE	17a.	18. HOSPITALIZATION DATES RELATED TO CURRENT SERVICES MM DD YY FROM TO MM DD YY
	17b. NPI	

19. RESERVED FOR LOCAL USE	20. OUTSIDE LAB? YES NO $ CHARGES

21. DIAGNOSIS OR NATURE OF ILLNESS OR INJURY (Relate Items 1, 2, 9 or 4 to Item 24E by Line)

1. 180.9   3.

2.   4.

22. MEDICAID RESUBMISSION CODE   ORIGINAL REF. NO.

23. PRIOR AUTHORIZATION NUMBER

24. A DATE(S) OF SERVICE From MM DD YY To MM DD YY	B. PLACE OF SERVICE	C. EMG	D. PROCEDURES, SERVICES, OR SUPPLIES (Explain Unusual Circumstances) CPT/HCPCS MODIFIER	E. DIAGNOSIS POINTER	F. $ CHARGES	G. DAYS OR UNITS	H. EPSDT Family Plan	I. ID. QUAL.	J. RENDERING PROVIDER ID. #
1	02 07	02 07	11		3000F		1	250 00			NPI	
2	02 07	02 07	11		99213		1	95 00			NPI	
3										NPI	
4										NPI	
5										NPI	
6										NPI	

25. FEDERAL TAX I.D. NUMBER SSN EIN	26. PATIENT'S ACCOUNT NO.	27. ACCEPT ASSIGNMENT? (For govt. claims, see back) YES NO	28. TOTAL CHARGE $ 340 00	29. AMOUNT PAID $ 0 00	30. BALANCE DUE $ 340 00

31. SIGNATURE OF PHYSICIAN OR SUPPLIER INCLUDING DEGREES OR CREDENTIALS (I certify that the statements on the reverse apply to this bill and are made a part thereof.)

32. SERVICE FACILITY LOCATION INFORMATION

33. BILLING PROVIDER INFO & PH # (   )

WORKBOOK

cpTeach
28th Edition

2012

Name:_____

Class/Section:_____

Date:_____

EXERCISE 13.29

1500

HEALTH INSURANCE CLAIM FORM

APPROVED BY NATIONAL UNIFORM CLAIM COMMITTEE 08/05

CARRIER

| | PICA | | | | | | | | | PICA | |

13.29

1. MEDICARE	MEDICAID	TRICARE CHAMPUS (Sponsor's SSN)	CHAMPVA (Member ID#)	GROUP HEALTH PLAN (SSN or ID)	FECA BLK LUNG (SSN)	OTHER (ID)	1a. INSURED'S I.D. NUMBER	(For Program In Item 1)

PATIENT AND INSURED INFORMATION

2. PATIENT'S NAME (Last

5. PATIENT'S ADDRESS (

CITY   STATE

ZIP CODE   de Area Code)

9. OTHER INSURED'S NA

a. OTHER INSURED'S PO   SEX
                                         F

b. OTHER INSURED'S DA
   MM   DD   YY

c. EMPLOYER'S NAME O

| YES | NO |

d. INSURANCE PLAN NAME OR PROGRAM NAME   10d. RESERVED FOR LOCAL USE   d. IS THERE ANOTHER HEALTH BENEFIT PLAN?

| YES | NO | If yes, return to and complete Item 9 a-d.

READ BACK OF FORM BEFORE COMPLETING & SIGNING THIS FORM.

12. PATIENT'S OR AUTHORIZED PERSON'S SIGNATURE I authorize the release of any medical or other information necessary to process this claim. I also request payment of government benefits either to myself or to the party who accepts assignment below.

SIGNED_____   DATE_____

19. INSURED'S OR AUTHORIZED PERSON'S SIGNATURE I authorize payment of medical benefits to the undersigned physician or supplier for services described below.

SIGNED_____

| 14. DATE OF CURRENT: MM DD YY | ILLNESS (First symptom) OR INJURY (Accident) OR PREGNANCY(LMP) | 15. IF PATIENT HAS HAD SAME OR SIMILAR ILLNESS. GIVE FIRST DATE MM DD YY | 16. DATES PATIENT UNABLE TO WORK IN CURRENT OCCUPATION MM DD YY MM DD YY FROM TO |

| 17. NAME OF REFERRING PROVIDER OR OTHER SOURCE | 17a. | 18. HOSPITALIZATION DATES RELATED TO CURRENT SERVICES MM DD YY MM DD YY |
| | 17b. NPI | FROM TO |

19. RESERVED FOR LOCAL USE

20. OUTSIDE LAB? $ CHARGES
| YES | NO |

21. DIAGNOSIS OR NATURE OF ILLNESS OR INJURY (Relate Items 1, 2, 9 or 4 to Item 24E by Line)

1. | **V23.81**   3. |

2. | **763.5**   4. |

22. MEDICAID RESUBMISSION CODE   ORIGINAL REF. NO.

23. PRIOR AUTHORIZATION NUMBER

PHYSICIAN OR SUPPLIER INFORMATION

24. A. DATE(S) OF SERVICE						B. PLACE OF SERVICE	C. EMG	D. PROCEDURES, SERVICES, OR SUPPLIES (Explain Unusual Circumstances) CPT/HCPCS MODIFIER	E. DIAGNOSIS POINTER	F. $ CHARGES	G. DAYS OR UNITS	H. EPSDT Family Plan	I. ID. QUAL.	J. RENDERING PROVIDER ID. #
	From MM	DD	YY	To MM	DD	YY									
1	01	01		01	01		21		99234	1	150 00			NPI	
2	01	01		01	01		21		99239	2	100 00			NPI	
3														NPI	
4														NPI	
5														NPI	
6														NPI	

| 25. FEDERAL TAX I.D. NUMBER | SSN EIN | 26. PATIENT'S ACCOUNT NO. | 27. ACCEPT ASSIGNMENT? (For govt. claims, see back) YES NO | 28. TOTAL CHARGE $ 250 00 | 29. AMOUNT PAID $ 0 00 | 30. BALANCE DUE $ 250 00 |

31. SIGNATURE OF PHYSICIAN OR SUPPLIER INCLUDING DEGREES OR CREDENTIALS (I certify that the statements on the reverse apply to this bill and are made a part thereof.)

32. SERVICE FACILITY LOCATION INFORMATION

33. BILLING PROVIDER INFO & PH # (   )

EXERCISE 13.30

Name:_____

Class/Section:_____

Date:_____

2012

1500

HEALTH INSURANCE CLAIM FORM

APPROVED BY NATIONAL UNIFORM CLAIM COMMITTEE 08/05

| | PICA | | | | | | | | PICA | |

| 1. MEDICARE | MEDICAID | TRICARE CHAMPUS | CHAMPVA | GROUP HEALTH PLAN | FECA BLK LUNG | OTHER | 1a. INSURED'S I.D. NUMBER | (For Program in Item 1) |

(Medicare #) (Medicaid #) (Sponsor's SSN) (Member ID#) (SSN or ID) (SSN) (ID)

13.30

_____

_____

_____

_____

_____

_____

_____

_____

2. PATIENT'S NAME (Last...   Initial)

5. PATIENT'S ADDRESS (STATE

CITY

ZIP CODE   de Area Code)

9. OTHER INSURED'S NA

a. OTHER INSURED'S PO   SEX F

b. OTHER INSURED'S DA
   MM   DD   YY

c. EMPLOYER'S NAME O

| | YES | NO |

d. INSURANCE PLAN NAME OR PROGRAM NAME | 10d. RESERVED FOR LOCAL USE | d. IS THERE ANOTHER HEALTH BENEFIT PLAN?

YES   NO   If yes, return to and complete item 9 a-d.

READ BACK OF FORM BEFORE COMPLETING & SIGNING THIS FORM.

12. PATIENT'S OR AUTHORIZED PERSON'S SIGNATURE I authorize the release of any medical or other information necessary to process this claim. I also request payment of government benefits either to myself or to the party who accepts assignment below.

SIGNED_____   DATE_____

13. INSURED'S OR AUTHORIZED PERSON'S SIGNATURE I authorize payment of medical benefits to the undersigned physician or supplier for services described below.

SIGNED_____

| 14. DATE OF CURRENT: | ILLNESS (First symptom) OR INJURY (Accident) OR PREGNANCY(LMP) | 15. IF PATIENT HAS HAD SAME OR SIMILAR ILLNESS. GIVE FIRST DATE   MM   DD   YY | 16. DATES PATIENT UNABLE TO WORK IN CURRENT OCCUPATION |
MM   DD   YY ◄ | FROM   MM   DD   YY   TO   MM   DD   YY

17. NAME OF REFERRING PROVIDER OR OTHER SOURCE | 17a. | 18. HOSPITALIZATION DATES RELATED TO CURRENT SERVICES
| 17b. NPI | FROM   MM   DD   YY   TO   MM   DD   YY

19. RESERVED FOR LOCAL USE | 20. OUTSIDE LAB? $ CHARGES
| YES   NO

21. DIAGNOSIS OR NATURE OF ILLNESS OR INJURY (Relate Items 1, 2, 3 or 4 to Item 24E by Line)

1. | 763.5 | 3. |___.___|

2. |___.___| 4. |___.___|

22. MEDICAID RESUBMISSION CODE   ORIGINAL REF. NO.

23. PRIOR AUTHORIZATION NUMBER

| 24. A. DATE(S) OF SERVICE From   To | | B. PLACE OF | C. | D. PROCEDURES, SERVICES, OR SUPPLIES (Explain Unusual Circumstances) | | E. DIAGNOSIS | F. | G. DAYS OR | H. EPSDT Family | I. ID. | J. RENDERING |
MM DD YY MM DD YY	SERVICE	EMG	CPT/HCPCS	MODIFIER	POINTER	$ CHARGES	UNITS	Plan	QUAL.	PROVIDER ID. #
1	11 01 11 01	21		99235		763.5	185 00			NPI	
2	11 01 11 01	21		99217		763.5	100 00			NPI	
3										NPI	
4										NPI	
5										NPI	
6										NPI	

| 25. FEDERAL TAX I.D. NUMBER   SSN EIN | 26. PATIENT'S ACCOUNT NO. | 27. ACCEPT ASSIGNMENT? (For govt. claims, see back)   YES   NO | 28. TOTAL CHARGE $ 285 00 | 29. AMOUNT PAID $ 0 00 | 30. BALANCE DUE $ 285 00 |

31. SIGNATURE OF PHYSICIAN OR SUPPLIER INCLUDING DEGREES OR CREDENTIALS (I certify that the statements on the reverse apply to this bill and are made a part thereof.) | 32. SERVICE FACILITY LOCATION INFORMATION | 33. BILLING PROVIDER INFO & PH # (   )

WORKBOOK

Burt

2012

cpTeach
Expert Medical Coding Made Easy!

"I've reviewed and used many textbooks designed for entry-level CPT® coding. Unfortunately, most were not. cpTeach® is different. I'm so impressed with the methodology and techniques used in this winner of a guide! The cartoons enhance the book's content, which makes reading and learning fun. Thank you for such an invaluable textbook!"

SHARON F. TURNER, CMC, CMIS, CMAA, CHI, CBCS
DIRECTOR OF EDUCATION
MEDICAL BILLING COMPUTER TRAINING INSTITUTE

"Students are continuing to understand CPT coding with more clarity by using your books. The numbers are increasing regarding them successfully passing the certification exam. I can't thank you enough."

MADELINE SHORTER-HALL, B.B.A., AS, CPC
HIT PROGRAM DIRECTOR
MEDICAL ASSISTING

"Highly recommended reading. cpTeach® offers you and your physician clients a highly accessible way to learn the ins and outs of CPT® coding."

JERRY S. HUSS, CPA
EDITOR-IN-CHIEF
CPA HEALTH NICHE ADVISOR

Cover Designed by Mark Lerner

MedBooks, Inc.
101 West Buckingham Rd. Richardson, Tx. 75081
(800) 443 - 7397 (972) 994 - 0215 fax
www.medbooks.com

ISBN 978-1-937816-04-9
53995
9 781937 816049

24th Edition

WORKBOOK

MedBooks

(Left panel)

...fidence!

...PCS, Anatomy & Physiology, Health ...om this former American Medical As- ...a pro. Whether you are learning in the ...ow in its 24th annual edition, is—as ...er, in mind!

...MPREHENSIVE

...NG AVAILABLE

...tomy, Physiology, Medical Terminology.

...wealth of content, helpful hints, dia- ...ons and other innovative learning tools ...

...m section to section of the CPT®, ICD, ...so *cpTeach®* packs each chapter with ...ike a pro in each area of service.

...l one of the few guides to be updated

...d points needed to conquer most por-

...reds of graphs, cartoons
...nts
...ine
...ogy & Laboratory
...logy
...leting the CMS Claim

...king Tips

...ced by the AMA. She ...decades of experience ...eminars, to give CPT® ...and on the job. Her ...*h*® the most used text ...personally taught more

...g a career of more than ...al manuals and review- ...oute to cpTeach, a text ...les of medical coding.

CPSIA information can be obtained at www.ICGtesting.com
Printed in the USA
BVOW050458030512

288914BV00001B/1/P